BOOKS BY THOMAS B. COSTAIN

THE LAST LOVE

A HISTORY OF THE PLANTAGENETS

- The Last Plantagenets
- The Three Edwards
- The Magnificent Century
- The Conquering Family

THE CHORD OF STEEL

THE DARKNESS AND THE DAWN

BELOW THE SALT

THE TONTINE

THE MISSISSIPPI BUBBLE

THE WHITE AND THE GOLD: The French Regime in Canada

THE SILVER CHALICE

SON OF A HUNDRED KINGS

HIGH TOWERS

THE MONEYMAN

THE BLACK ROSE

RIDE WITH ME

JOSHUA: A Biography (with Rogers MacVeagh)

FOR MY GREAT FOLLY

Anthologies

TWELVE SHORT NOVELS

STORIES TO REMEMBER (with John Beecroft)

MORE STORIES TO REMEMBER (with John Beecroft)

30 STORIES TO REMEMBER (with John Beecroft)

READ WITH ME

READ WITH ME

Selected by

THOMAS B. COSTAIN

Garden City, New York

DOUBLEDAY & COMPANY, INC.

1965

All of the characters in this book are fictitious, and any resemblance to actual persons, living or dead, is purely coincidental.

Grateful acknowledgment is made for permission to use the following copyrighted material:

Albee, George Sumner—"The Next Voice You Hear" by George Sumner Albee. Copyright 1948 by George Sumner Albee. Reprinted by permission of Harold Ober Associates Incorporated.

Allen, Hervey—"The City of Brotherly Love" from *Action at Aquila* by Hervey Allen. Copyright 1937, 1938 by Hervey Allen. Reprinted by permission of Holt, Rinehart and Winston, Inc.

Barrett, William E.—*The Lilies of the Field* by William E. Barrett. Copyright © 1962 by William E. Barrett. Reprinted by permission of Doubleday & Company, Inc.

Beer, Thomas—"Tact" from *Mrs. Egg and Other Barbarians* by Thomas Beer. Copyright 1947 by Alice Baldwin Beer. Reprinted by permission of Alfred A. Knopf, Inc.

Behan, Brendan—"The Confirmation Suit," reprinted by Bernard Geis Associates from *Brendan Behan's Island* by Brendan Behan. © Brendan Behan and Paul Hogarth, 1962.

Benét, Stephen Vincent—"The Ballad of Leif the Lucky" originally published in *American Cavalcade*. Copyright 1937 by Stephen Vincent Benét. Reprinted by permission of Brandt & Brandt; "Johnny Pye and The Fool-Killer" (from *Tales For Midnight*) from *Selected Works of Stephen Vincent Benét* (Holt, Rinehart and Winston, Inc.). Copyright 1938 by Stephen Vincent Benét. Reprinted by permission of Brandt & Brandt.

Bradshaw, George—"A Portrait Reversed." Copyright, 1949, by The Curtis Publishing. Reprinted from *Practise to Deceive* by George Bradshaw by permission of Harcourt, Brace & World, Inc.

Chesterton, Gilbert K.—"The Queer Feet." Reprinted by permission of Dodd, Mead & Company from *The Innocence of Father Brown* by G. K. Chesterton. Copyright 1911 by Dodd, Mead & Company, Inc. © 1910. R 1938 by permission of Miss D. E. Collins and Cassell & Co. Ltd.

Christie, Agatha—"Accident" by Agatha Christie. Reprinted by permission of Dodd, Mead & Company from *Witness for the Prosecution* by Agatha Christie. Copyright 1944 by Agatha Christie. Reprinted by permission of Dodd, Mead & Company, the author and Hugh Massie Limited.

Endore, Guy—Selected portions of "Epilogue" and "More Epilogue" from *King of Paris*. Copyright © 1956 by Guy Endore. Reprinted by permission of Simon and Schuster, Inc.

Fitzgerald, F. Scott—"Magnetism" is reprinted with permission of Charles Scribner's Sons from *The Stories of F. Scott Fitzgerald,* edited by Malcolm Cowley. Copyright 1951 Charles Scribner's Sons.

Library of Congress Catalog Card Number 65–16263

Printed in the United States of America
First Edition

Gallico, Paul—"The Snow Goose." Copyright, 1940 by Curtis Publishing Company. *The Snow Goose* by Paul Gallico is reprinted by permission of Alfred A. Knopf, Inc.

Godden, Rumer—"Mooltiki" from *Mooltiki: Stories and Poems from India* by Rumer Godden. Copyright © 1941, 1957 by Rumer Godden. Reprinted by permission of The Viking Press, Inc., the author and Macmillan & Co. Ltd.

Hecht, Ben—"Miracle of the Fifteen Murderers" from *The Collected Stories of Ben Hecht* by Ben Hecht. Copyright 1945 by Ben Hecht. Reprinted by permission of Crown Publishers, Inc.

Hemingway, Ernest—"In Another Country" (copyright 1927 Charles Scribner's Sons; renewal copyright © 1955) is reprinted with the permission of Charles Scribner's Sons from *Men Without Women.*

Household, Geoffrey—"Children's Crusade" from *The Brides of Solomon and Other Stories* by Geoffrey Household, copyright © 1958 by Geoffrey Household, reprinted by permission of Atlantic-Little, Brown and Company.

Kantor, MacKinlay—"Lobo." Copyright © 1957 by MacKinlay Kantor. Reprinted by permission of World Publishing Company.

Kipling, Rudyard—"The Man Who Was" from *Life's Handicap* by Rudyard Kipling by permission of Mrs. George Bambridge and the Macmillan Company of Canada Ltd. and Doubleday & Company, Inc.

Leacock, Stephen—"My Revelations as a Spy" from *Frenzied Fiction* by Stephen Leacock. Reprinted by permission of Dodd, Mead and Company from *Frenzied Fiction* by Stephen Leacock. Also reprinted by permission of McClelland and Stewart Limited from *Frenzied Fiction* by Stephen Leacock.

McCarthy, Mary—"Ask Me No Questions" by Mary McCarthy. Copyright © 1957 by Mary McCarthy. Reprinted from *Memories of a Catholic Girlhood* by Mary McCarthy by permission of Harcourt, Brace & World, Inc. First published in *The New Yorker.*

O'Hara, John—"Exactly Eight Thousand Dollars Exactly." © Copyright 1960 by John O'Hara; "The Sun-Dodgers." © Copyright 1962 by John O'Hara; from *49 Stories.* Reprinted by permission of Random House, Inc.

Parker, Dorothy—"Clothe the Naked" from *The Portable Dorothy Parker.* Copyright 1938 by Dorothy Parker. Reprinted by permission of The Viking Press, Inc.

Pickthall, Marjorie—"The Worker in Sandalwood" by Marjorie Pickthall from *Cavalcade of the North.* Reprinted by permission of McClelland & Stewart, Ltd.

Porter, Katherine Anne—"The Source," copyright, 1941 by Katherine Anne Porter; "The Witness," copyright, 1944 by Katherine Anne Porter; "The Old Order," copyright, 1936, © 1964, by Katherine Anne Porter; "The Last Leaf," copyright, 1944, by Katherine Anne Porter; from *The Leaning Tower and Other Stories.* Reprinted by permission of Harcourt, Brace & World, Inc.

Priestley, J. B.—"The Other Place" from *The Other Place and Other Stories of the Same Sort.* Copyright 1953 by J. B. Priestley. Reprinted by permission of A. D. Peters.

Runyon, Damon—"Johnny One-Eye" from *Runyon A La Carte by Damon*

Runyon. Copyright 1941 by the Chase National Bank, Executor of the Estate of Damon Runyon. Published by J. B. Lippincott.

Scoggins, C. E.–"The Proud Old Name" by C. E. Scoggins. Copyright 1924, by The Curtis Publishing Company. Reprinted by permission of Brandt & Brandt.

Sheean, Vincent–"Pieces of a Fan" from *Pieces of a Fan* by Vincent Sheean. Copyright 1937 by Vincent Sheean. Reprinted by permission of the author.

Wiesel, Elie–"Dawn." Reprinted by arrangement with Hill and Wang, Inc. © Editions du Seuel 1960. English translation © Elie Wiesel.

Wodehouse, P. G.–"The Clicking of Cuthbert" (Chapter I from *The Clicking of Cuthbert* by P. G. Wodehouse). Copyright 1922, 1955 by P. G. Wodehouse. Reprinted by permission of the author and the author's agents, Scott Meredith Literary Agency, Inc.

Woolf, Virginia–"The Legacy" from *A Haunted House and Other Stories* by Virginia Woolf, copyright, 1944, by Harcourt, Brace & World, Inc. and reprinted with their permission.

TABLE OF CONTENTS

ALBEE, GEORGE SUMNER	The Next Voice You Hear	3
ALLEN, HERVEY	The City of Brotherly Love	15
BARRETT, WILLIAM E.	The Lilies of the Field	37
BEER, THOMAS	Tact	81
BEHAN, BRENDAN	The Confirmation Suit	99
BENÉT, STEPHEN VINCENT	Johnny Pye and the Fool-Killer	109
	The Ballad of Leif the Lucky	129
BRADSHAW, GEORGE	A Portrait Reversed	133
CHESTERTON, G. K.	The Queer Feet	147
CHRISTIE, AGATHA	Accident	165
ENDORE, GUY	The King of Paris Dies	175
FITZGERALD, F. SCOTT	Magnetism	187
GALLICO, PAUL	The Snow Goose	209
GODDEN, RUMER	Mooltiki	227
HECHT, BEN	Miracle of the Fifteen Murderers	247
HEMINGWAY, ERNEST	In Another Country	265
HOUSEHOLD, GEOFFREY	Children's Crusade	273
KANTOR, MAC KINLAY	Lobo	289
KIPLING, RUDYARD	The Man Who Was	321
LEACOCK, STEPHEN	My Revelations as a Spy	335
MC CARTHY, MARY	Ask Me No Questions	345
O'HARA, JOHN	Exactly Eight Thousand Dollars Exactly	383
	The Sun-Dodgers	393
PARKER, DOROTHY	Clothe the Naked	405
PICKTHALL, MARJORIE	The Worker in Sandalwood	415
PORTER, KATHERINE ANNE	They Trample on Your Heart	423

PRIESTLEY, J. B.	The Other Place	447
RUNYON, DAMON	Johnny One-Eye	471
SCOGGINS, C. E.	The Proud Old Name	485
SHEEAN, VINCENT	The Pieces of a Fan	531
WIESEL, ELIE	Dawn	545
WODEHOUSE, P. G.	The Clicking of Cuthbert	599
WOOLF, VIRGINIA	The Legacy	615

READ WITH ME

A WORD OF EXPLANATION

There is a tendency today to watch stories in motion picture houses in preference to reading them or to sit at home in front of a television set (thereby subjecting oneself to the intense irritation of commercials). There is no denying that this easy way has some advantages but neither can a sense of regret be dismissed for the pleasant days when the public sought and found the best of entertainment in reading books and magazines, and so could retain for future perusal and reference anything which seemed particularly good.

Having spent the better part of a lifetime as a magazine editor, I find that I still carry in my mind vivid recollections of the stories I liked best out of the many thousands I read each year. Among the hundreds that I recall clearly are some that are old and many also that are quite new. It seems worthwhile to rescue the old ones from the obscurity of library shelves and to persuade readers (or people who should be readers) that these tales, old and new, are more worthy of their attention than most of what is being offered on television or at the movies. Accordingly, having some comparatively idle time on my hands, I have spent several pleasant months refreshing my memory of those which have been special favorites; and I have emerged with a list which I find as engaging as ever. All of them (or so it seems to me) either carry the delightful patina of age or display the vigor and gloss that distinguishes the best of modern fiction.

Looking them over again, I realize that all possess some qualities in common. They deal with active aspects of life. They are brilliant, imaginative, and different. As they are without exception the work of authors of distinction, it is hardly necessary to add that they are written with style and power. With such a rich supply to draw from, it has not been hard to assemble a list in which no two stories are alike in theme or treatment. Some are long and some are quite short. A few go back to the turn of the century but many were published during recent years.

It is my hope that readers will find in them some of the pleasure I enjoyed when I first encountered them.

Thomas B. Costain

The Next Voice You Hear **George Sumner Albee**

This is a story which undertakes to tell what might happen if the Divine Voice elected to reach the ears of unthinking people on earth through a medium created by human ingenuity, radio. People all over the world are thrown into a state of terror and bewilderment by the pronouncements which come over the air lanes and by the strange miracles which are brought to pass in order to induce belief. Can the lowering of a continent beneath the level of the sea for one minute be accepted as within the bounds of possibility? There are other happenings almost equally strange and bizarre. The results sought must be learned only by reading the story.

"The Next Voice You Hear" was published by *Cosmopolitan* in 1948 and later was made into a motion picture.

THE NEXT VOICE YOU HEAR

George Sumner Albee

It was exactly at nine thirty-eight P. M. on the first Monday in March that the strange, majestic voice was first heard on the radio.

Just why that day and hour were chosen nobody can say. Maybe they marked the centennial of something or other; say the Creation. In any event, whether by accident or design, they guaranteed a sizeable radio audience in the United States.

The immediate reaction was, of course, disbelief. People simply could not believe their own ears. Floyd Uffelman of 677 Tatnall Place, Doylestown, Pennsylvania, for instance, had taken his nightly bath to get rid of the dust he had collected at the cement plant, where he tended a kiln. He was down cellar playing with his son Lyman's electric train, the tracks of which were set up on pine planks on sawhorses. Lyman's portable radio, on the tool bench, was following the antics of Doctor I. Q. Suddenly Doctor I. Q. faded out and the voice, a deep, gentle one, benevolent but firm, said:

> *"This is God. I am sorry to say I must interrupt you. A plan of creation ought by rights to go forward under its own rules, but you, dear children of the Sun's third planet, are so near to destroying yourselves I must step in. I shall spend this week with you."*

Floyd switched off the electric train and stood for a moment gaping at the furnace, from which he half believed the words had come. After that, ignoring Doctor I. Q., Floyd went up the stairs to the kitchen. In the kitchen, Mrs. Uffelman, a wiry, freckled woman who had once been the best soft-ball pitcher in the country, was sprinkling clothes.

"Were you listening to the radio just now?" Floyd asked, as he closed the door to the cellar.

"Does it look like it? Anyhow," Jean Uffelman said, "it's not on, if you mean the radio in the living room."

"I'll bet it was Lyman," said Floyd. "I'll bet that kid's got a microphone or something rigged up in his room."

With Jean looking after him in bewilderment he climbed to his son's room but, when he got there, Lyman was sitting with one foot in his hand agonizing over compound fractions.

"Hi," said Lyman. "How's it running?"

"Fine," said his father. "What did you do to the radio?"

"Me? Nothing. Is it busted?" the boy asked. "If it is, you busted it. You took it down to the cellar. I wish I had it. How can I do my arithmetic without my radio?"

It had the aura of truth. Floyd went slowly down to the living room, deeply puzzled. His puzzlement took him out of the house, after a minute or two, to the front door of his neighbor, Gene Hukill, who drove a laundry truck.

"Gene," Floyd said, "this is a funny question to ask, but were you folks listening to Doctor I. Q. just now?"

"Nope," answered Gene. "Lux Radio Theater."

"Never mind, then," said Floyd disappointed. "I guess you wouldn't have heard it."

"Say, did you hear it too?" demanded Gene in astonishment. He shouted to his wife: "Martha, the Uffelmans heard it too! Isn't that the darndest thing? I wonder what it was."

"Sure was queer," agreed Floyd. "I wonder."

And Doylestown, in the United States, was not the only town that felt wonderment on that cool March evening. Even in Europe and Asia, where because of time differences the broadcast was heard in the morning and afternoon, its impact was fairly powerful, since there was not an active radio station large or small that did not transmit it. In each case the native language was used. Arabs heard the announcement in Arabic, South African tribesmen in Ba Ronga dialect; a little fifty-watter on a remote Polynesian atoll achieved the impossible by voicing it, at one and the same time, in fourteen dialects.

In the larger cities in the United States response was sharp and instantaneous. Almost before puzzled executives of broadcasting companies could call their chief engineers to ask who was playing tricks, the news commentators were on the air joking about the hoax. People left their bridge games to telephone to their friends and ask gaily, "Did you hear it?" The late editions of the newspapers gave the story a moderately good play. A New York Times editorial writer risked a guess. Probably a practical joker in the Long Lines Division of the Telephone Company, he surmised, had hooked all of the transcontinental circuits together for a few seconds, thus permitting his voice to be heard simultaneously over every radio network.

However, by morning the news reports from Europe, Asia, Africa, South America and Australia were in, and it was public knowledge that the broadcast had been world-wide and multilingual. There was not a shop, not an office in which it did not automatically become the topic of the day. Meeting at the water cooler or on the fire escape for a cigarette one man would ask another, "What do you think of it?" The answer, whether the city was Denver, Antwerp or Singapore, was almost invariably, "I don't know." It can be safely said that no day in history has heard the humble words "I don't know" spoken oftener than that first Tuesday in March, 1950. Urban and suburban wives phoned their husbands' offices all morning long. "Have you found out about it?" they demanded. "Well, call me back if you hear anything."

There was general relaxation when, shortly after lunch*, Dr. C. Rountree Petra, professor of electrical engineering at the Massachusetts Institute of Technology, issued a statement to the press. "The so-called heavenly broadcast of Monday evening," said Dr. Petra, with a sniff, "is easily explained. A single broadcasting station of high power, with multiple transmitters manned by linguists, could perpetrate such a hoax without difficulty. I have no doubt that something of this nature was done, although the motivation is obscure in view of the expense entailed."

Russia was at once suspected. The Kremlin indignantly denied complicity, upon which suspicion in many minds became certainty.

The sun went down. In the lavender dusk of early March, factories, stores and offices closed. Managers of movie theaters knew by seven o'clock that business was going to be bad. By eight the ammeters in the power stations were registering heavy loads. "Every radio in the city must be on," an Omaha supervisor scribbled on his Tuesday evening report. Nor were listeners disappointed. Exactly at nine thirty-eight, while Fibber McGee and his doctor friend were exchanging insults, they faded out and the serene, friendly voice spoke again. The second message was briefer than the first. It was:

> *"Do not be afraid. I only want to convince you that I really am God and that I am visiting you this week."*

This time, observers stood in the control rooms of all the broadcasting companies. Direction finders, including the extremely sensitive instrument of the Federal Communications Commission, took a hasty

* For the sake of simplicity all references to time are keyed to the Eastern seaboard of the U. S. A.–The Editors.

'fix' while the Voice was on the air. But no sign of trickery was discovered. The direction finders simply pointed towards whichever broadcasting station was nearest to them. Russia was absolved, at least tentatively. The Petra theory of a super-station was utterly discredited. Television receivers glowed with a golden light and showed what appeared to be a small section of a complex but very beautiful pattern.

On Wednesday the newspapers gave page after page to the Voice. Experts by the dozen were interviewed. The unanimous view of those scientists who could be reached for comment–some of them seemed to be hiding–was that the Voice was a man's. Here a teacher of diction in Hollywood went chemists and physicists one better. The man, he insisted, from his accent was Massachusetts-born, had attended Groton.

"If it were actually God speaking," pointed out a professor of logic, E. R. Matthias of the University of Idaho, "he would not find it necessary to use the radio. God, we may presume, is logical. It is illogical to neglect those millions of human beings who do not own radio sets. Therefore, this is not God speaking."

Ministers of the gospel were more reserved in their statements. Members of a little known sect in the Ozarks, the Turpentine Branch Immediate Personal Redemptionists, wrapped themselves in sheets and gathered on a hilltop to await the imminent end of the world, but their infantile antics were deplored. "Even if the voice be not the Lord's," said an Episcopal bishop who had been deeply moved by the broadcasts, "it reminds us of something too many of us forget. God is here with us."

Plain citizens, rather surprisingly, were less skeptical than their intellectual and spiritual leaders. A typical "Inquiring Reporter" column in the Des Moines Register, for instance, ran: The Question: What do you think of the Voice? The Answers: Sallie da Silva, housewife, 2213 Granger Street. "If it really is God, He has just the kind of voice I always thought He would have. It is a kind voice, and I am sure He means us no harm." Howard Ellsmere, 434 Dacoima Avenue. "Sure it could be God. I think this is just about what God would do, remind us He is here. Because that is all it would take, brother! If we know He is here we will all behave a heck of a lot better." The "heck" was the reporter's. Mr. Ellsmere had used a stronger word.

Wednesday evening prayer meetings across the nation were enthusiastically attended; most churches had installed radios. The third utterance was the briefest of all, intended evidently to answer some of the questions which had been raised. It consisted of only three words. To the indignation of those who believed God must be somber and funereal, the words were delivered with a fatherly chuckle. They were: *"It is I."*

Like the others the third message somehow crept into the coils and condensers of every radio transmitter in operation, including even those of ships at sea which were designed for code and did not have microphones. This last was a sort of absent-minded miracle which suggested a possible answer to the question why, if the Voice really belonged to God, He was using the radio. A pronouncement out of the empty sky would have been frightening and might easily have caused widespread panic. But people were used to hearing voices on the radio. The Lord was simply using the radio stations as a convenient means of introducing Himself gradually, without too great a shock. He was being considerate.

His knowledge of human psychology, beyond question, was superb. (This is not surprising, when one comes to think of it.) The very brevity of His, "It is I," message went far towards convincing those who had a liking for modesty and understatement. In England, for instance, a number of people of considerable authority now stated their belief that it was actually God speaking. In Maine, Vermont, New Hampshire and Massachusetts in the United States the same thing occurred. Lias Plum, a Nantucket cod fisherman, put it: "He a'n't talky. It's Him."

On Thursday another device was employed. It takes all kinds of people to make a world—and God, Who, of course, knew this as well as we do, put on a display of miracles on Thursday for the ignorant and the superstitious. Miracles occurred about fifty miles apart all around the globe; so many, indeed, that the newspapers filled whole editions with them, printing them in small type and numbering them like the Hundred Neediest Cases.

Most of the miracles were small, modest affairs. Oranges in the Hobart Street Market in Fond du Lac, Wisconsin, rolled up the wall and aligned themselves on the ceiling, where they spelt out the words, "Men are my sons and therefore brothers," in a pretty frame of parsley. A lion in the Copenhagen zoo got out of his cage, strolled into the countryside until he spied some sheep in a field and deliberately lay down with them. It was a bit too early in the year for him to find a lamb. In Pasadena, California, a nervous woman, whose husband gritted his teeth in bed, leaped from the Arroyo Seco bridge in an attempt to end it all. She remained suspended in mid-air over a eucalyptus tree for forty-five minutes until a fire engine thrust an extension ladder up to her—a lesson in patience.

There was no discernible pattern in these minor miracles unless it was that the queerer ones—those most likely to get themselves talked about—took place in remote, backward areas. Thus it was in an Irish seacoast village, Spiddal on Galway Bay, that a farm laborer known as "Banty" O'Shea, on the point of running over a little girl with a bicycle, went sprawling on the cobbles as his bicycle was turned into stone. Not only was the bicycle turned into stone, but it became a public fountain with both of its stone handle bars spouting pure spring water. Such a happening made more of an impression on the Irish than any number of full-page advertisements in the Dublin papers would have done. Visitors to Spiddal are permitted to sit on the bicycle. Fee, sixpence; Mr. B. O'Shea, Proprietor.

These earlier miracles, small though they were, had a wildly infuriating effect upon many persons who had been troubled but little by the deep, dynamic voice on the radio.

In the Chamber of Deputies in France there was a near-riot, with members hurling epithets like "Camel" back and forth and charging one another with a betrayal of rationalism and the spirit of the Revolution—all because a school of herring with tri-color fins swam up the Seine startling the drowsy fishermen.

A certain Bostwick B. Sinkle, vice-president of a garden-hose company of Urbana, Illinois, who had risen to his position by falsifying the books and getting another man fired for theft, and who boasted that his personal motto was, "To hell with everybody but me," threw a luncheon meeting of the Urbana Junior Chamber of Commerce into pandemonium. "I know somebody in this room is out to get me," he shouted, "and I know who it is. Well, let me tell you this! Anybody that pulls any fake miracles around my house is going to get both barrels of a shotgun!"

Consciences long buried were sending up tender green stalks like tulip bulbs.

Beyond doubt the angriest man in this country, however, was Walter P. Valerian of New York City, president of the Association for the Advancement of Iconoclasm and Atheism. Earlier in the week, Mr. Valerian, alarmed by the direction the wind was taking, had taken newspaper space and radio time to advertise: "There is no God and we can prove it!" But the miracles drove him to drastic measures. Sending out telegrams by the handful, he summoned members of his association in all parts of the country to hurry to New York by plane for a mass demonstration of protest.

The Lord's Thursday evening broadcast was quite lengthy and had a theological tone. It was:

"Every pebble beneath your feet, every drop of water is a miracle; but since you have lost your ability to feel awe I have had to

perform today these other miracles which are a suspension of natural law. My willingness to break the law should show you how deeply I love you, but the fact that I have done so will now lend encouragement to those very doubters who have the hardest shells. They will point out to you that an omniscient, omnipotent being would not need to break his own laws. Let me tell you something which has long bewildered men. Even an omnipotent deity must limit his own powers. Otherwise creation would be complete and perfect in the moment of its birth—a magic trick and not a genuine creation. God works; and there can be no work where there is no resistance. However, this will not convince the die-hards. Hence on the morrow, Friday, I shall perform several sizeable miracles during the forenoon. And promptly at noon I shall sink the continent of Australia beneath the sea for one minute."*

Sometimes, in March, the snowbanks look as solid as white marble. But the warmth of the lengthening days, although they do not show it, has weakened them. A day a little bit sunnier than the rest comes along, and all at once the solid snowbanks are gone and the brooks are roaring. . . . Much the same sort of thing happened after the Thursday evening broadcast. Disbelief melted away. Literally overnight, people by tens of millions became certain that the Voice was God's.

Around the shrines in India crowds of the devout stretched as far away as the eye could see. Virtually the entire Moslem world was trudging the roads towards Mecca. Endless parades of weeping, laughing suppliants, with religious images and lighted candles, thronged the streets of European cities. Firecrackers rattled day and night in the yellow dust of China.

The Australian radio stations took over the air, with all available networks rebroadcasting. God had chosen exactly the right continent for His final demonstration. People of another country might have put on a craven scramble for rowboats. Not the Australians! "There is no sign at all here of funk," came the calm, good-humored voice of the Melbourne announcer. "Nobody's got the wind up. The general attitude is that a minute under water can do nobody any harm and may do some of our citizens a lot of good. We feel concern for babies and the elderly, but we are sure that God—and if He brings this one off there will be no doubt about His being God!—will see to it that they come to no serious harm."

Arrangements were made for blimps to circle over Melbourne and Sydney and transmit eye-witness accounts of Great Flood II.

* The hour was stated in each listener's local time.

Extras were on the streets before breakfast Friday morning. God had promised "sizeable" miracles for the forenoon, and they were quite sizeable. In the United States every last ounce of metal owned by the Army, the Navy and the Air Force was gone from its accustomed place. The whole huge tonnage of it, from buckles to battleships, neatly cut up into scrap, lay piled ready for the furnaces around the steel mills of Pennsylvania and Ohio. Consternation was felt. Was this favoritism? True, the United States was one of two nations whose war potential was feared by other peoples of the world. But what about the other? Had nothing happened to Russia's military equipment?

Something had. It did not come out until midmorning. By then the outrage felt by the Kremlin was sufficient to blast aside its own censorship. All of the shining rows of Russian tanks, planes and siege-guns were gone. In their place stood rank upon rank of manure carts, each cart bearing a neat placard with a quotation from Lenin: "Peace, Bread and the Land."

Through the ambassador at Washington, the U.S.S.R. laid an anguished protest before the Council of the United Nations. "We charge," the pale, perspiring ambassador thundered, "an international conspiracy of capitalist encirclement!" This was too much for the delegate from Burma, Mr. Pa Ku. Mr. Pa Ku actually giggled. The giggle infuriated the Russian delegation so much that, as one man, it rose from its collective seat to stalk from the council chamber. At this juncture something still more humiliating took place. Unseen hands gripped each delegate by the seat of his trousers and returned him sternly to his chair.

As for the protest meeting of the atheists in New York, people merely smiled when they read what happened there. Barely had the group of demonstrators led by Mr. Valerian marched into Times Square when God turned every last one of them into an angel. Arched, sweeping wings, with feathers of purest white, grew abruptly out of their shoulder blades, and over their heads appeared halos of bright gold. They had a frightfully embarrassing time of it trying to sneak away in taxicabs; they could not get their overcoats on over their wings, and they could not get their hats on over their halos.

The announcer and reporters flying over Australia grew almost incoherent with tension as the second hands of their watches swept away eleven fifty-eight, eleven fifty-nine and, finally, the dot of noon. The BBC man, however, chatted along as coolly as if he were describing a cricket match. "As predicted," he said, "the continent is now sinking. The rate is quite rapid; about that of a modern passenger lift, I should say. There; the last church steeple has disappeared. The water is a-swirl with floating objects. Dear, dear, what a clutter people do keep about their houses! Now the hilltops are under. . . . Fifty seconds, fifty-five . . . yes, she's popping up again. Right-o! Up she comes, good old Australia, none the worse for her little drenching!"

Landing craft raced for the shore the instant there was a shore to race for. The first citizen to be reached by an announcer lugging a portable transmitter was a certain Col. Humphrey Arbuthnot, D.S.C., Retired. "Tell the radio audience, sir," panted the announcer, "did you really go under?"

"Don't be an ass," trumpeted the colonel. "I'm dripping, aren't I? Beastly ocean poured right into the room. Tons of it! Didn't break the windows. Had the foresight to open 'em. Good show, what? I say, you wouldn't have a dry towel about you, would you?"

God's broadcast of Friday evening was devoted to picking up loose ends.

> *"I urge the hysterical paraders and the fanatics bent on founding new religions to disband," He said. "We have too many religions as it is. . . . Must my visit mean that the world is coming to an end? Behave with dignity that I may be proud of you. And for heaven's sake stop committing suicide. I know this is difficult for you to believe, but we have problems here too, and one of them is housing. Anyhow suicide gets you nothing; I shall just have to send you back again, or send you on to make the same mistakes on another level. There is no final death; a soul has many dimensions; it dies in only three. . . . Now listen to your soul; do as it bids you. Good night."*

Saturday was a busy, busy day. The dictators of half a dozen Latin countries resigned and gave their handsome silk sashes to their daughters. An international banking cartel with headquarters in Portugal went out of business because its directors felt that their methods, never too admirable, had become unwelcome if not obsolete. Officers of the CIO and the AF of L met in Detroit. "Be it resolved," they proclaimed, "that labor and management have the single duty of supplying goods to consumers. We request that labor-management disputes from now on be arbitrated by a consumers' jury." Several large corporations in England, France, Holland and the United States discharged their paid lobbyists and announced new operating policies. Small businessmen by the hundreds of thousands experienced a similar change of heart. Typical of these latter was Jaime Diaz, a garage owner of Mexico City. Calling his mechanics together, Senor Diaz said, "From now on, amigos, when we charge a customer for a new distributor coil let us actually put in the coil."

It was the lesser malefactors who were the lucky ones, the men, women and children who spent Saturday returning stolen books to public libraries, repaying old loans, sending gifts to forgotten aunts in old ladies' homes, and so on. The real evildoers sat alone in darkened rooms with their memories and prospects. They enjoyed neither.

For ninety-nine percent of the human race, it was astounding what a happy, friendly, pleasant place the Earth had become by Saturday night. There were celebrations everywhere, from Bombay to Bermuda–some of them more colorful than wise. A bunch of Loop taxi drivers in a Chicago bar, for instance, sang "For He's a Jolly Good Fellow," with such emphasis on the 'He' as to make it perfectly obvious that they were singing about the Lord. This was bad taste, beyond question. Still, the Lord apparently took no offense. It is even possible that He was amused.

His Saturday evening broadcast was His farewell. Those who heard it will never forget His voice. It is impossible to describe it. Perhaps, though, it will not be irreverent to say that it had the gentleness, the fondness, the infinite patience of the voice of an older brother teaching a beloved younger brother to skate, or make a kite, or whittle.

All across the world the radios hummed. Then there came silence and the beautiful Voice. It said:

> *"Forgive me, dear friends, for my trespass in coming to you as I have. It was necessary. Now I shall take my leave. You will find that most of your problems remain with you. You still have pain and unhappiness; you still need to feed and clothe and govern yourselves. You still confront uranium. Need I tell you why? Surely it must be plain to you that, if God exists, He must from the very fact of His existence have a purpose. Surely you see what your part in that purpose is. A planet is a school. Live, dear children, and learn. And now–until we meet again, good-by."*

On the Seventh Day, we presume, He rested.

The City of Brotherly Love **Hervey Allen**

In the early thirties two novels were published which became great best sellers, *Gone With the Wind* and *Anthony Adverse.* Both were of most unusual length, both were highly dramatic and exciting, and both were written with extraordinary facility. For many years the book public waited impatiently to hear from the authors again. Margaret Mitchell's untimely death came before she could present another "GWTW"–if indeed she had it in mind to write another book. Hervey Allen's next book, a story of the American Civil War, was not published until five years after *Anthony Adverse.*

It is almost certainly true that comparatively few people now are familiar with *Action at Aquila* and it is fortunate that the first chapter of the book reads like a complete short story and so may be presented here. It is a richly dramatic tale, depicting scenes from Sherman's march to the sea and the devastation of southern homes, and at the same time showing the condition and the state of mind of the people on each side of the battle line.

THE CITY OF BROTHERLY LOVE

Hervey Allen

Southward, two mighty ranges of the Appalachians shouldered their way into the blue distance like tremendous caravans marching across eternity. Between those parallel ridges the Valley of the Shenandoah lay, apparently, as serene and beautiful as the interior of the Isle of Aves.

From a high shoulder of the Blue Ridge, where Colonel Nathaniel Franklin of the 6th Pennsylvania Cavalry had stopped for a moment to breathe his horse, he could see almost into North Carolina. "Rebel country," for the Confederates still held the upper part of the Valley and the horizons beyond.

Not that the colonel thought of it as rebel country, exactly. The sight of that magnificent landscape—despite its great beauty, perhaps because of it—brought to his eyes a mist of sorrow that threatened momentarily to overcast the countryside which rolled away southward before him. He brushed that mist indignantly away—and swore softly. He regarded all the country he was looking at as still a part of the United States, some of the inhabitants of which needed to be reconverted to the faith of their fathers—by apostolic blows and knocks if necessary. But there was nothing personal about the process to the colonel. The problem posed by the horizons rolling before him was, he liked to think, purely a military one. And in the old days he had had too many true friends on the yon side of the Potomac to lump them all under the one indignant epithet of "rebels," even now, after several years of desperate fighting.

There were not many Americans left, however, who still felt as the colonel did. He was naturally possessed of that state of being which in the eighteenth century would have been described as an amiable soul. There was nothing weak about his amiability, but it did make hate and blind bitterness about anything hard to bear. Now, in the early autumn of 1864, he sat looking down into the peaceful, because devastated, theatre of civil war with a dull ache about his heart.

He was too far up on the mountain for much of the particular devastation in the Valley to be noticeable. Here and there a gaunt chimney rising houseless and steeple-like amid the distant fields and woods showed where a farm or manor house had been burned. But the fields had not been out of cultivation long enough to make much difference in the general view. Over the enormous checkerboard of meadow and forest below him the drifting shadows of lofty cumulo-nimbus clouds conferred upon the Valley a kind of dream-life of its own, as though it mirrored the visions passing in some almighty brain. Five miles down and away he could see the white tents of his own command conspicuously dotted along the border of Aquila Creek.*

Nearer yet, from a great meadow laid like a green table-cloth in the midst of tiny hills, came the flash of weapons and accoutrements, a kind of sinister blink that followed small, black lines of mounted men manœuvring in a cavalry drill. Colson, his second in command, was putting the regiment through its paces down there. He watched the squadron flash into a charge. The sound of the mass yell, which was meant to be furious and to frighten an enemy, drifted up to him. At that height it sounded innocuous and childish, like the yells of boys playing Indians. Then the sudden voice of a bugle sounding recall died away into shivering echoes that lost themselves eventually in a thousand folds of the mountain walls.

Someone might have been sounding taps over the Valley, the colonel thought. The silence that followed was ominous.

It was accentuated rather than broken by the rushing lament of a mountain stream only a short distance down the road at the ford below. For a while the man on the black horse sat like a statue at gaze over the Valley, unable to rouse himself from a melancholy–perhaps an unsoldierly–but under the circumstances a natural enough reverie.

Thought is swifter than lightning. Perhaps its fluid nature is essentially the same. In a flash, as it were, while he sat breathing his horse and looking down from that giant height at his men manœuvring below in the Valley, the scenes of the past few weeks–the faces and places, the houses, the roads, and the very sound of voices–flowed through his mind . . .

In half an hour the colonel would be back with his men again. What that implied he knew only too well; relentless vigilance, and the constant anxiety of commanding in the face of the enemy. He was just re-

* Pronounced: *Ah-wy'-la.*

turning from a long leave of absence. This pause on the crest of the ridge was not only a breathing space for his horse. It was also his last opportunity to let his mind range back freely over the memories of home and the immediate past. That is not to say he was being sentimental. To tell the truth he was troubled, even perplexed, by some of the happenings of the past few weeks. Home as found had not been home exactly as he had expected to find it. The sight of the camp below had brought the end of his leave forcibly to mind. It was only natural that his thoughts should flash back along the trail behind him to linger for a few moments upon what had been for him a memorable experience.

It had been his first leave since 1861. He had been looking forward to it for years, he remembered. Twice it had been revoked just on the eve of a great battle. Finally, he had given up any hope of getting home at all. War and the life of the army had at last eclipsed the memory and even the desire for another kind of existence. He had learned to live with the past and future cancelled. And in three unforgettable years he had seen a deal of active service and rapid promotion.

He had been shot off his horse at Antietam and had a horse shot under him at Gettysburg. A sharpshooter had drilled a hole through the top of his campaign hat during a skirmish at Winchester only two months before. The graves of his friends and those of his men were scattered all over eastern Virginia, clear up into Pennsylvania. Even the infantry admitted that Colonel Nat Franklin was one cavalryman who was a genuine fighting man.

For its fine service in the Valley of Virginia his regiment had lately been nicknamed "Sheridan's Eyes." It was composed largely of woodsmen and scouts and was in almost constant touch with the enemy whenever any movement was afoot. It was during a lull in the fighting at the end of the summer of 1864, while his regiment was camping in the Valley, for once peacefully, that he had again applied for a furlough. He had hardly hoped that it would be granted. He had simply taken a chance. And then, quite unexpectedly, the furlough had come back promptly, approved by General Sheridan himself.

Three days later Colonel Franklin was back home again, not far from Philadelphia, in the old Pennsylvania village of Kennett Square.

His was the quietest home-coming possible. He could not even expect a family welcome. He was a bachelor. Most of his relatives lived elsewhere, and he had been an only child. Both father and mother had died some years before; his mother when he was still a boy, and his father while the colonel had been prospecting in the Far West and doing some unavoidable Indian fighting on the side. There had been six years of that before he had returned to take over the old place at Kennett Square and tried to drop back into the quiet ways of profitable Pennsylvania farming in a large and gentlemanly way. Then the call to arms had come when Sumter was fired on. He had been among the first to go.

So he was prepared to find the big stone farmhouse at Kennett Square lonely. It was inevitable that it should be. He still looked forward to changing that as soon as the war was over. Circumstances, he reflected, had prevented him thus far. His life had been too adventurous, too full of shifting incident to undertake the greatest adventure of all. But he was young yet. The prime of life still lay before him, he felt. And there might be several who would be glad to share in what, at worst, could be considered a prosperous life partnership. He hated to think of it in just that way. There had been Alice Cary, for instance. He might have been happy with her. He had almost reached an understanding with her just before Sumter was fired on.

Then the war had gone on and on. Alice had finally married a well-to-do neighbour, a very respectable fellow. He couldn't blame her. After all, what the colonel hadn't been able to do was simply to make a good bargain out of life, even the best of bargains. That was why he had hesitated. And yet it might come to that yet. Here he was in the fourth year of conflict returning to his regiment, and the war still seemed interminable.

That was one reason why the old house had seemed even lonelier than he had expected. There was no longer much to look forward to there. Its future did appear doubtful. Only the past had drawn him back to it. He knew that now. And yet that was not sufficient to explain why he had actually been glad to leave home again after only a week's stay.

What he hadn't expected to find, what had caused him to leave Kennett Square so soon, was a certain covert hostility on the part of some of his neighbours. Probably it was partly political. His father had been a great Democrat, a close friend and staunch supporter of President Buchanan. He had constantly opposed and deprecated the agitation of abolition, regarding it as the cause of inevitable conflict. In the Quaker community about Kennett Square that might still be remembered against his father's son. That there was nothing immediately personal about this "hostility," the colonel felt morally certain. People generally liked him. He had a warm heart combined with a decided strength of character. He was genially social. That made for popularity. Nevertheless, somehow, somewhere the colonel felt a gulf had opened between him and his neighbours.

Perhaps he had been out West and in the army too long to drop back into a settled way of civil life, with all of its emphasis upon property and petty local prejudices, without feeling a certain lack of air. At any rate, he soon had the sensation of being stifled. He tended to regard men now for what they were rather than for what they had. Probably some of his fellow townsmen resented it. War, battle, is a very special experience, and like a good many other soldiers back on leave, the colonel found that he was no longer quite able to explain himself even to old family friends. Above all he missed the easy tolerance of the spacious days before the war. Everybody seemed to have made up his mind now about everything–and to have closed it.

But if his Quaker acquaintances were inclined to look at his politics and even his army service somewhat askance, he was even less prepared for the virulent and white-hot hatred of the enemy made vocal by the sacred patriots and angry taxpayers of his once kindly native community. Frequent ferocious proposals for the disposal of Southern leaders, the grim personal hatred expressed for all rebels, for example, both surprised and annoyed him.

"I've only been fighting them," he would say in a half-deprecatory way when his lack of enthusiasm over a proposal "to hang the rebel cabinet in chains," or some similar suggestion, caused a lifting of fervent eyebrows to which he did not respond. "Come help us catch them," finally became his favourite rejoinder when too hard pressed. Few of his friends seemed to relish the twinkle in his eye at such times.

"Sir," said one of them, a particularly pompous and healthy merchant of his own town, when this invitation was extended to him, "I am already represented in the army by three bounty men and I feel I have more than done my duty. I might have bought government bonds, you know, instead of just sending out the last two men."

"Why, so you might," said the colonel, "so you might! And think of the interest you're losing. Why, Carter, it's damned noble of you! Let me shake you by the hand. No, no, the other one–the one that's losing the interest. I don't suppose you let the right hand know what the left hand is doing under such circumstances. Do you, Mr. Carter?" And he had left that respectable gentleman not a little confused, with both hands sticking out–and unshaken.

Suddenly all this had become quite intolerable to the colonel.

He had intended to spend most of his leave at home, but he could no longer, under the circumstances, think of wasting the precious month of it that still remained trying to explain himself to sullen neighbours and doubtful friends. What he needed above all was change and relaxation. To tell the truth, a little conviviality. So quite suddenly he wound up his affairs at Kennett Square, rented the farm, sold some of the animals—and without saying anything or good-bye to anybody, he had the bays hitched to the trap before sunrise one morning and set out for Philadelphia.

It was then nearly the end of September and for the first time that autumn there was the hint of frost to come in the early morning air. Also, for the first time since the colonel had been home on leave, he felt happy and carefree, almost boyish. He would even have liked to sing. But he knew too many sedate people along the Philadelphia road to permit himself to break out into a rich baritone at that hour of the morning—and just on the outskirts of Media! It might cause comment. He was in uniform and conspicuous enough already. A striking figure, in fact, in his campaign hat with its tarnished gold cord and acorns, with his large humorous mouth, sun-puckered eyes to match, and full black burnsides carefully cultivated to conceal a youthful expression that might not be quite impressive enough for a colonel of cavalry. It would never do for the colonel of the 6th Pennsylvania to look as young as he felt. Just as it would never do to break into song at that hour of the morning. Someone would certainly look out of the window and say, "There goes Nathaniel Franklin, and he's been drinking." "Drinking again," is the way they would say it. He knew them, those noses flattened against the pane, sniffing. Well, he would soon be shut of them all and fighting in the open again. Just then, however, he compromised by whistling instead of singing—and driving like the devil.

The morning road over the hills led from one cheerful vista to another. The brisk dawn air in the vicinity of Sharon Hill was exhilarating. He let the team have their heads and tore down the old Pike in the direction of Philadelphia with the sunrise glittering on the spokes of his wheels. As the roofs and flashing windows of the city came in sight—with Kennett Square and all that miles behind him—he felt relieved, convinced he was doing wisely, at home in the once-familiar, civilian world again. In short, his own old self, as he put it.

He didn't know exactly how or where he was going to spend the rest of his leave. He was just going to let it happen. First he intended to dispose of the team of bays. They had been eating their heads off at home. Then he had some errands to do. He wanted to get himself the finest saddle horse available, for he had been riding nothing but sorry nags since his old horse had been shot under him at Gettysburg. Also, for a quite important but purely private reason, he wanted to get a haversackful of toys.

That reason was a pleasant secret, one which caused him to smile as he watched the servant-girls flooding the sidewalks from hydrants and scrubbing the white marble steps while he rattled over the cobbles along Chestnut Street. It was still early. He ought to have plenty of time to get things done before the heat of the day began.

He soon disposed of his team and the trap for a fair price at a livery stable, and light-heartedly set out to get the toys and look up his old friends.

In the City of Brotherly Love, among other things he hoped to find that the patriotic rhetoric, with which nearly everyone now seemed to address a veteran on furlough, would at least be a little less bloodthirsty than in his own formerly peaceful neighbourhood. But in this mild hope he was disappointed. For whom should he encounter at the corner of Broad and Chestnut streets but his father's friend, old General John Fithian, a hearty veteran of the late Mexican War, and as fire-eating a commander of home-guard militia as ever ruined a white marble doorstep with broad yellow stains.

"A sight for sore eyes," roared the general, shifting his quid and bushy eyebrows in genuine and cordial excitement. "Why, what brings you back from the front, you young Hector? We've been hearing great things about you. What can I do for you? Where are you bound for?"

"I'm looking for a toy-store," said the colonel almost inadvertently, and somewhat annoyed. For the old general was a picturesque figure; the colonel was in uniform himself, and a crowd of idlers sensing the unusual had begun to surround them.

"Toy-store?" bellowed the older man, looking shocked. "Oh!" said he, suddenly grinning, "I see. Congratulations! I hadn't heard."

"No, no," replied the colonel hastily, "not that! Just for a young relative of mine–nice little girl." He felt it unnecessary to lie any further and turned rather red.

"Well, then, toy-store nothin'!" rumbled the general. "Come into the club and have a drink. The whole town will be there to give you a welcome. Why, man, you haven't seen any of your old friends for years." With that he linked his arm in the colonel's, and scattering the idlers before him with a broad fan of amber liquid, led his half-willing victim along Chestnut Street into the old Union League Club.

Now I'm in for it, reflected the colonel somewhat ruefully–and he was.

"Here's Nat Franklin back from the front," roared General Fithian, preceding him as herald and ringing a cuspidor like a gong after each glad announcement. "Here's Nat Franklin," *bong!* . . .

The devil! thought the colonel, but he was too human not to enjoy the cheery and cordial triumph they gave him. His own and his family friends surrounded him. Others joined rapidly, for the general was not to be denied—and it was by more than an average-sized crowd that he was finally swept into the bar. They drank up his news, and other things, and they continued to do so all afternoon.

Perhaps that was partly the trouble. Perhaps the afternoon and the other things had been a little too long. About four o'clock the colonel began to feel weary and to remember things which those about him could not see. He began to feel aloof from them, a bit irritable. He began to answer their innumerable questions honestly, even literally. Many of them, he could see, were shocked at this and didn't like it. Ferocious proposals no longer seemed funny even to those who made them. The room became slightly hushed. He began to tell them what he really thought of the war.

"A victory for any side is a defeat for every side now," the colonel heard himself saying. "It has all gone on so long . . ." His voice trailed away.

Above the eagles on his shoulders his face looked out not a little haggard after so many campaigns. To several there seemed to be a strange contradiction there. Again there was an awkward silence.

"Copperhead!" said someone suddenly.

A young fellow by the name of Moltan, who had just received a commission from Governor Curtin in the lately reorganized State Fencibles, put his hand to his mouth and turned a brick-red. He had not really meant to insult the colonel. He was proud of his new uniform. The epithet had slipped out because he felt and wanted to be conspicuous. But the colonel had not seen his gesture of embarrassment. He looked about him, bewildered. He mistook the embarrassment he saw in the other faces for hostility.

"No, no," he cried in indignant denial. "No, I'm a strong Union man. Why, that's all I've been fighting for! Can't you see that?"

It was now that young Moltan surpassed himself. "I can't say that I do, sir," he said.

The colonel stepped forward, his eyes blazing.

"Gentlemen, gentlemen," cried Mr. Arthur Biddle, hurrying to them across the room. "This must go no further!"

"Young man, you're an ass," rumbled old General Fithian indignantly. "You've insulted a brave warrior and your superior officer in a club where you're not a member. You'll apologize to him now."

"Or get out," added Mr. Biddle.

But to do him justice, young Moltan did apologize, and quite contritely, while the colonel tried to be as decent about it as he could. Nevertheless, he was greatly shaken. That anybody—that even a tipsy young fool should have called him a Copperhead seemed incredible.

The crowd finally broke up uneasily, trying to make the best of the matter. Most of them shook hands and departed. But some of them didn't. There would be considerable talk about the incident, the colonel was sure. Feeling distinctly miserable, he went into a corner with General Fithian and old Dr. David Craig and sat down.

"I can't understand it," he said.

"Well, it's natural enough," rumbled the general, who was always willing to precede the angels. "You see, the trouble with you, my boy, is that you haven't been home for years and you think people still feel the same as they did when you left us in 'sixty-one. Why, as a matter of fact, you talk more like the summer of 'fifty-nine!"

"Yes," agreed the doctor, "Fithian is right. The feeling now is more intense than you can imagine, after just serving in the army. If you think the men are bitter, you ought to hear the women. You're not a married man, you know, so you don't catch what's really going on. What the feeling is. Thousands of people have lost husbands, brothers, or sons. There's Andersonville and Libby. This city is full of wounded and crippled from a hundred battles. Our ships are destroyed. If anybody in Pennsylvania cherished a secret warmth for old Virginia friends, believe me, after Lee's invasion and Gettysburg they were cured of it. The feeling is more intense now in this state than it is in New England. To put it mildly, Nathaniel, you can't expect folks here to understand your sympathy for the suffering of the Southern people. They are too much preoccupied and exasperated by their own terrible losses and anxiety not to hurrah for the sternest kind of suggestions for reprisal. It's natural. It's human nature. Can't you see?"

"That's right," said the old general, nodding vigorously.

"But I still maintain we're all *one* people," replied the colonel quietly after a moment's silence. "That's the reason I'm a Union man."

"It's too fine a point to be understood now, I'm afraid," said the doctor sadly. "Cherish your idea, Nat. I rather admire you for it. But don't 'maintain' it, as you say."

"No, no," chimed in the general, "don't think of maintaining it. Just let your military record speak for you. Nobody can argue about that."

"Well, then," said the colonel, "I suppose the rest is silence, and I'll try to shift by your advice. But let me tell you both something before we leave. I want you to understand how *I* feel about this matter. You know we're not just fighting one war. We're fighting many. That is, the war is different to everyone who takes part in it. There's a general feeling, but there's a particular feeling too. Let me try to give you mine."

Unconsciously the colonel had lowered his voice as though what he was about to impart was of secret import—and in fact it was. He was going to reveal some things that haunted him. The heads of the three drew a little closer, where they sat alone in a corner of the Union League Club. The big room was deserted. It was about five o'clock of a desperately hot afternoon. Outside on Chestnut Street an occasional dray rumbled home somnolently over the cobbles. Voices passing on the sidewalk below the deep windows sounded tired and subdued.

"Let me tell you some of the things I've seen," continued the colonel even more confidentially than before. "It's all very well to speak of reprisals and punishment and military necessity, but it's quite another thing to have to carry them out personally. You know Sheridan has been destroying the Valley–everything–and the Pennsylvania cavalry has had quite a lot of house burnings on its hands. Did you ever burn a house while the family watched? You feel brave and noble, of course. Well, near a little cross-corners called Aquila–there's nothing left there but a stone springhouse now–there was a fellow named Crittendon had a nice big house. White pillars and all that. Nothing fancy either. Just a fine, comfortable American home. Now, I got specific orders to burn it and clean out the whole plantation. Crittendon, it seems, was a major in the rebel army on Early's staff and a damned troublesome fellow to the United States government. So we started off on a swift ride one night, hoping to catch him at home. We got there an hour after dawn, thanks to a burned bridge, and he'd gone. But Mrs. Crittendon was there. She was sitting on the front porch in a long white bedgown. She's an Englishwoman. She looked like a Greek statue when she stood up to meet us, and she said, 'Good morning, gentlemen!' "

"That was sort of taking advantage of you, wasn't it?" mused the doctor almost inaudibly.

"Exactly," said the colonel. "If she had screamed or gone into hysterics like most of 'em do, you know, or cursed us out lock, stock, and barrel! But she didn't. She just trembled a little like a fine straight tree—and looked down at us squirrels."

"Well, what did *you* say?" demanded old General Fithian, shifting his cud intensely.

"What does a gentleman say when he comes to burn a lady's house down? I distinguished myself, of course. I began by saying it was very early."

"Splendid!" said the doctor. "That must have made everything all right."

"–And that I was under the unfortunate necessity of burning the house down," continued the colonel. He lit a cigar the doctor offered him, and went on.

"She didn't try to argue. 'I presume you will first permit me to remove the people within, colonel,–and our clothes?' was all she asked. I gave her half an hour. She thanked me, without being sarcastic, and went in. I heard her give a dry sob at the door.

"My, there were a lot of people in that house! Some of them started to scream and carry on, but I could hear Mrs. Crittendon put an end to that. The first person that came out was an old lady, Major Crittendon's mother. She was carried on a mattress by some of the servants. It seems she's paralysed from the waist down. But she isn't paralysed from the chin up, let me say. She simply curled my hair. The troop was lined up before the porch, just as we'd ridden in, and they all heard her."

"What'd *she* say?" demanded the irrepressible general.

"She introduced herself. She began by saying she was a great-grandniece of Madam Washington, and that even Yankee pedlars might understand that. Then she saw or heard we were Pennsylvanians and she apologized for having called us Yankees. 'But you're only one peg up from the mud sills at that,' she said, and mentioned that the Pennsylvania farmers had let General Washington and his men starve at Valley Forge because the British gave them better prices for supplies at Philadelphia in 'seventy-eight. And that we hadn't changed any since, because she knew that when Robert Lee had gone into Pennsylvania the same farmers sold well water on hot days to his men. 'But, sir,' said she, 'they charged their own men more even on cool days. Honesty is the best policy, Colonel Franklin. You remember? Policy is all you know of honesty. How much are you going to charge us for burning the house down?' The rest was just pure, amber-coloured invective straight from the soul with a few old-fashioned oaths embedded in it like extinct flies. At last she had herself carried off to a knoll where she could watch the house burn down.

"By that time the babies were coming out crying, with their broken dolls, and toy horses, and things–which, of course, made us all feel like big, brave soldiers. Mrs. Crittendon lined them up some way back on the lawn with the blacks, who were trying to start hymns that she kept hushing. Finally they all seemed to be out. In fact, she nodded to me. So I took a couple of non-coms into the house with me and we got out our locofocos. We set fire to the curtains in the parlour. They were of some heavy English stuff. Mrs. Crittendon's wedding gifts, I imagine. Anyway, they flared up suddenly and then smouldered on with a kind of blinding smudge. It looked as though the whole house were on fire, although really nothing else had caught, when I heard Mrs. Crittendon calling frantically:

" 'Margaret, Margaret, where's Margaret?'

"We ran out, of course. Mrs. Crittendon wasn't calm any longer. 'It's my daughter,' she said. 'She must have stayed in the house. I thought we were all out.' She tried to go back herself, but just then Margaret ran out of the smoking doorway and stood on the porch. She must have delayed to put on her best things to save them, for she was dressed in the most elegant finery I ever saw: hoop-skirt, bonnet, lace dress, and ruffled pantalettes; she even had a little parasol. Another bright silk dress was thrown over one arm. She's about fifteen and one of the loveliest little girls you can well imagine. She took in everything at a glance and threw her extra dress out on the lawn for one of the blacks to pick up. Then she stamped her foot like a little empress and just yelled at us:

" 'If there's one gentleman left in the Old Army he'll come in and help me put that fire out.' And with that she dived back into the smoke and started to pull down the burning curtains.

"Her mother screamed at her that she'd catch afire in her lace dress. And she certainly would have. But half the troop was out of the saddle and we were all stamping out the fire and carrying the girl out to her mother before Mrs. Crittendon could get to her. The young minx had the gall to thank us, too. Afterwards, out on the lawn.

"It's very difficult for me to tell you in so many words just how intense the excitement was on the lawn after young Margaret's rescue. The slaves burst out singing. You know how darkies can put into song what we only feel. And they were certainly doing it that morning. Mrs. Crittendon couldn't stop them. She tried at first to hush that dirgelike singing. But I think it's to her credit to say that she finally broke down herself, and coming over to me, put her hands on my saddle and begged me as a Christian and a gentleman not to set fire to the house again. Now can you really imagine what it actually is like to have a charming and noble woman looking up into your face with tears in her eyes, asking you please not to make her and the children homeless, when you know she is helpless? Orders are orders, of course, but there was Mrs. Crittendon!" The colonel paused a moment as if the memory of that morning were overpowering.

"Oh, yes," said Dr. Craig, "I can imagine it all right!" The general cleared his throat uncomfortably. The colonel plunged on.

"It was perfectly plain the men were sick of that kind of soldiering too," he said. "They kept watching me and Mrs. Crittendon. By that time Margaret had come over to help her mother. The tension grew until even the horses got restless. The men let them have their heads, I suppose. Everyone wanted to be up and away and done with the mess. I couldn't blame them. Well, the lady begged me, and so did the young girl, and . . ."

"And so, of course, as a gallant man, you went right in and set the house afire again," suggested the doctor in a low tone.

There was a pause.

"Yes," said the colonel, looking miserable, "I did."

"What! what! Do you mean to tell me, Nat Franklin, you had the devilish crust to? The devil you did! Your father would never–no, sir," said the old general, pounding the floor with his cane, "never, sir!"

"Oh, it wasn't quite so bad as you think," continued the colonel. "No, we didn't just go in and start the fire up again. You know I couldn't! I advised Mrs. Crittendon to clear out as soon as she could with her stuff and her people, 'because,' said I, 'the next time, you know.'

"'Yes,' said she, 'I know,' and she broke down again.

"Then one of the babies with nothing on but a short night-shirt toddled up with a rag doll. He wanted to give it to 'the nice man.' That was me!

"'Come on, sergeant, we're licked,' was all I could say. 'Ride 'em off.'

"So we just rode away without looking back and went into camp a few miles higher up the Valley near a village called Aquila. We burned Aquila out. There wasn't anybody there. Everything went but a springhouse a little detached from the town. Springhouses don't catch well, you know."

"It's the dampness, I suppose," suggested the doctor dryly. "But look here, Franklin, murder will out. What happened to the Crittendons?"

"Well, we were just settled for supper, vedettes out up the Valley, and the rest of us gathered about the fires. The boys were frying their hardtack in bacon grease, which is against medical orders, of course–when in rides General Phil Sheridan and his hard-bitten staff.

"There'd been a devil of a ruction over at Cross Keys that day. A couple of wagon trains had been cut out and looted and burned by Early, and the general was tearing mad. It meant some weeks' delay in operations in the upper Valley. He didn't say much, which is a bad sign. He's usually good enough company. But he did order the men to dump their greasy bread on the fires and turn in on dry tack and water. There was a good deal of muffled swearing under the blankets as a consequence. And I think the general felt quite uncomfortable about that. Anyway, he borrowed some of my whisky and finished it all off himself, looking into a fire as moody as you please. Then he ordered me to turn out ten troopers and to accompany him and his staff. He was riding back to Winchester that night, he said. It looked as though he might be relieving me of command. We started. After a few miles the word was passed for me to join the general. We rode in the darkness for some time.

" 'Look here, Colonel Nat,' said he suddenly, 'didn't you get orders to burn out the Crittendon people today?'

" 'I did, general!' I had to say that, of course. 'I set fire to the Crittendon house at six-fifteen o'clock this morning.'

" 'And put it out at six-twenty-five same date.'

"I couldn't deny it.

" 'Now look here, Franklin,' he went on after a little, 'I'm an Irishman, even if I was born in old York State, and I never borrow whisky from an officer I'm goin' to court-martial. But orders are orders. I know this is a specially hard case: fine people! You've made it even harder now. But we can't go into that kind of thing. As a matter of fact, I've been easy on you. We both saw some Indian fighting in the West, so I've put you on reconnaissance almost entirely and relieved you so far of most of the dirty work. I've used your regiment for scouting and turned the harrying, and horse and house thieving over to Reinohlfennig and his bummers. Those Pennsylvania Dutch can only ride farm horses anyway. They're locusts; you're cavalry. When you get an order after this, no flinching. Begad, man, do you think I like it any better than you do?

" 'Burn the house tonight without touching anything,' he finally said. 'Without touching anything,' he repeated. 'Is that plain? That's all.'

"I saluted and fell back with my own men. To tell the truth I was pretty angry myself. He might have court-martialled me for disobedience of orders that morning, but to bring me back to burn the house and insinuate that we weren't to carry anything away! Just like saying, 'Don't carry off any cuckoo clocks or jewellery,' you know. That had me boiling, even if he is half an Irishman.

"When we got to the Crittendon house again there was a squadron of regulars bivouacked on the lawn, and the lamps in the house were lit. Sheridan gave a brief order and the squadron broke camp instantly and assembled mounted and at attention before the veranda.

" 'Colonel, send your own men to the woodpiles. Have them get pine knots, light them, and fall in by the porch here.'

"Then he had the officers assemble, and all of us, with his staff, went into the house.

"I was terribly relieved to find that no one was there. Mrs. Crittendon must have taken my advice and left that morning with her people. We went into the big parlour, where there was a portrait of a Continental officer over the fireplace, and a lot of candles burning. It was some moments before I noticed that on a couch in one of the alcoves there was a body covered by a tattered Confederate battle-flag.

" 'Gentlemen,' said General Sheridan, 'I am asking your assistance here in a personal matter.'

"He took a candlestick, went into the dark alcove, and pulled the flag down from the face of the form lying there. The strong, bearded countenance of a handsome man, whose hair was prematurely grey, was revealed in the yellow candlelight. He looked peculiarly waxen. His eyes were wide open and the collar of his grey uniform with tarnished gold leaves on it supported his chin.

" 'This was Major Douglas Charles Crittendon of the Confederate Army,' said General Sheridan. 'He was killed in the attack at Cross Keys this afternoon. Before he died I had time for a too-brief talk with him. He was an intimate classmate of mine at West Point. For many years he was an officer in the Old Army. He once commanded the squadron of U. S. Cavalry now lined up before his door. What I'm doing here is by his own dying request made this afternoon. He was most particular, and I gave him my word "to bury him in the ashes of his home." I realize now that he must have thought this house had already been burned. If there is anything in this proceeding which offends the principles of anyone present he is at liberty to withdraw.'

"No one made a move. In fact, we all stood completely awe-struck; some of us were overcome. General Sheridan paused for a moment, then laid the flag back on his friend's face.

" 'Will the new officers of the major's old regiment lend me a hand?' he said.

"The general and some of the young lieutenants from the troop outside then lifted the couch, upon which the major lay, out into the middle of the room, under the eyes of the portrait. They piled fire-wood about it. We all helped in that.

" 'I would like to have the guidon of the troop,' said the general.

"After a moment it was brought in to him.

" 'This is my own idea,' he said. 'I think Douglas . . . er—Major Crittendon will approve.' His voice was a little husky. He put the silk guidon on the breast of the flag-draped man on the couch. Upon that he laid the major's sword.

" 'I am sorry there is no priest here,' he said. 'Major Crittendon was the soul of honour, a true friend. A *very* gallant gentleman lies here . . .' He was unable to go on. 'God receive his stricken soul,' he managed to add finally. We said 'Amen' and trooped out of the room awkwardly enough. The empty house echoed with our heavy boots and the jingle of spurs.

"Outside the glare of the pine torches beat the darkness back for a space, wavering over the men and horses before the door.

"Sheridan stopped me for a moment on the porch and said, 'Franklin, you will be in charge in this neighbourhood for some time. Mrs. Crittendon must be in hiding hereabouts. We heard she left early this morning with her family and some wagons. Find her if you can. Do what you can for her. And give her this.' He gave me a small sealed package. 'And,' he said as he laid his hand on my arm, 'tell her that Phil Sheridan burned her house by a special order from Washington signed by the Secretary of War. If you can't find Mrs. Crittendon, see that the package is returned to me. These are bad times to live through. It's hard even for a soldier to tell what his duty is. Don't you find it so sometimes?' He smiled sadly and extended his hand.

"'Yes, sir, I do,' I said, and we shook hands warmly. That was all.

"He mounted his horse in the glare of the torches and brought the troop to present.

"'Colonel,' he said, 'carry out your orders.' Then they moved off at a rapid trot down the drive.

"That was a great burning. For miles the whole Valley leaped with light. The house was of pitch pine a century old. It made a great column of golden fire. Behind it the gloomy wall of the Blue Ridge towered up into heaven, watching the sparks drift out among the stars."

The spell of the colonel's deep but pleasant voice seemed to his rapt listeners to have been withdrawn too abruptly. Outside the street window, by which they sat, the head and shoulders of a lamplighter appeared suddenly and with startling clearness on his ladder as he cupped the white spurt of a match in his glowing hands.

"Lord," said the colonel, "is it as late as that? I apologize profoundly. Keeping you fellows from supper! It's not to be forgiven."

"Nonsense, nobody's going to be late for supper," said Dr. Craig, jumping up and brushing the cigar ashes off his vest and long coat; "you're coming home with me. I'm a widower, and I have meals when I want them. I keep a cook from the Eastern Shore. There'll be pepper pot and reed birds in butter. A very famous patient of mine has sent me some of the port that he's famous for. Nat, I'll bet you haven't had a meal like that in months."

"Not for years," said the colonel. "It sounds like—like eighteen-fifty-nine."

General Fithian groaned, however, and began to roll his eyes. "Craig," said he, "this is a damned outrage." He pounded his cane on the floor. "Ten days ago you put me on a diet of vegetables and milk toast. Am I supposed to go and just watch you two eat reed birds and things?"

"Tonight," said the doctor, "I'll permit you to relapse. You can take an extra five grains of calomel before going to bed."

"By God, I'm going to that homœopath in Camden," bumbled the general.

They went out and caught an accommodation stage for Spring Garden Street. On the way up Dr. Craig kept his two military friends and the much-amused civilian passengers, all gentlemen in plug hats and paper collars, in a constant gale of laughter by dictating to an imaginary druggist prescriptions in dog Latin for the cure of delicate complaints.

The memory of that evening's dinner at Dr. Craig's "perfect little residence" remained long in the colonel's mind as the outstanding evening of his furlough. It was a return in spirit to the urbanity and security of the time before the war. For, once ensconced in the doctor's old wainscoted dining-room under the new gas chandelier, with cool airs drifting in through the wide casement,—breezes from the doctor's back garden and the valley of the Wissahickon, laden with the remote odour of new-mown hay-fields and the domestic scent of house geraniums,—once ensconced there, with the present walled out, as it were, the clock on the stairs seemed by some magic of reversal to be ticking its way again through the serene hours of its grandfather past.

Gone were the high-keyed expectancy, the waiting for news, the nervous talk, and the taut, secret apprehensions of wartime. Out of the ken of the colonel's consciousness, into a kind oblivion, drifted involuntary visions of three years of angry battles; glimpses of red cannon lighting the clouds of midnight; half-heard cries of nervous sentinels and eerie night-birds along the dark shores of the embattled Potomac; the sinister glow in the sky of rebel camp-fires beyond the mountains, and the scene at twilight of the huddled wave of dead splashed along the stone wall of Marye's Heights.

Instead, there was the doctor, leaning back in his chair with one thumb easing the tension of his vest, and talking—relating wise, kindly, and humorous anecdotes of nearly half a century of practice. The healing quality of his healing personality seemed to pervade the room with a kind of merciful ribaldry of comment and his irrepressible hope and amusement at the vagaries of man.

And there, too, was General Jack Fithian, the best purveyor of self-appreciative laughter in Philadelphia, ruddy with port and good-nature; delighted to have an audience for his tales of the Mexican War.

It was curious how *that* war no longer seemed to be a war at all. No one had died in it. The very names of its battles were now a simple poetry without bloodshed: Palo Alto, Buena Vista, Cerro Gordo, and Chapultepec; from the wine-red lips of the old general they fell like single notes chimed on a carillon of romance. It was as though he had just taken his silver knife and struck lightly the half-filled glasses before him.

Was it possible, mused the colonel, was it possible that the grim annals of the battles in Virginia, along the Potomac, and in the Shenandoah could also become by future telling a mere mellifluous tale like that?

Yes, it was possible.

Perhaps it was a quality of prophetic insight imbibed with the doctor's port that murmured to him, "That, too, shall come to pass": Manassas, Malvern Hill, Antietam, and Fredericksburg–New Market, Winchester, and Monocacy–how they would sound, tinkling in the pages of history, after the necessary scar-tissue of forgetfulness had closed the wounds of time.

Suddenly the sullen and angry face of the boy who had called him Copperhead that afternoon seemed to be looking at the colonel again. He watched the passionate young features fade slowly into the cigar smoke.

How men felt–that was what would be forgotten!

He stirred uneasily; the room and its pleasant atmosphere resumed again. But he was no longer lost in the past. While Dr. Craig and the general talked, he had come to a sudden decision. It was something so impulsive that it seemed to have been decided for him. Now he knew how he was going to spend the remaining weeks of his leave. And it was because of that decision that he turned the talk to horses.

He wanted a new horse. The finest horse there was to be had in Philadelphia. His pockets were bursting with greenbacks from his unspent back pay–and good horses in Philadelphia were still to be had. Weren't they?

"Yes, indeed." Dr. Craig knew of a wonderful horse that belonged to a patient of his who had just died.

"He's probably had his eye on that horse all along," suggested Fithian. "Now, I have a fine animal myself. Do you know, Craig, I think I'll omit that extra calomel tonight. Listening to you and Nat horse-trading in your deceased patient's chattels makes me nervous. There, there, I'm sure you can get that horse cheap, colonel, as the doctor says. And he ought to know. He's probably taking it for his bill for the man's death. But I'd look at that horse's teeth closely."

"Confound you!" roared the doctor. "It's a magnificent animal, I say! And it's time for you to go to bed–and take your calomel."

"I won't," said the general, but he did.

The old-fashioned host saw both his guests to the doors of their bedrooms, with a candle. He struggled with the general over his calomel, and he lingered for some moments at the colonel's door in a kind of benevolent good-night chat.

". . . I didn't want to remind you of it in the dining-room tonight," said he, "but if you don't mind I'm still curious about something you told us this afternoon. Did you by any chance ever deliver that package Sheridan gave you to Mrs. Crittendon?"

"No," said the colonel, who was seated on the bed trying to draw off his boots. "No, I didn't. We made a thorough search of all that part of the Valley, but Mrs. Crittendon and her family seemed to have vanished into thin air. I can't even pick up a rumour of where they went. I was going to return the package to Sheridan at headquarters. In fact, I had it with me when I left, but a curious thing happened on the way up. You remember that springhouse at Aquila that I said wouldn't burn?"

The doctor nodded.

"Well, I stopped in there to give the nag a good drink just after I left camp and the Crittendon children had evidently been playing in it. It was full of a few toys they'd saved and dolls made out of corncobs, some broken dishes on an old stone set for a sort of elfin feast with wild cherry seeds and chinquapins. You know how children, little girls, furnish a dolls' house–pretty pitiable, too. The war seemed to have lost most of their toys for them–and it was so furtive and secret in that half-dark place. It's a shame the infants can't even play house, you know!"

"Yes, but how did you know it was the Crittendons?"

"Oh," said the colonel, "I felt sure I recognized the rag doll the child brought me the morning we tried to burn the house–it had only one eye."

"Ah, I remember; 'nice man,' eh?" said the doctor, smiling. He paused a moment, peering at the colonel as though he liked to see him in the room. "Well, nice man, good-night to you," said Dr. Craig a little ironically, and went off down the hall with his candle, leaving the colonel with one boot on, still sitting on the bed.

In his room Dr. Craig undressed rapidly, from long habit laying his clothes out in a precise manner on an old green chair. He could find them in the dark that way and dress instantly if he were called. He put on a long, almost unearthly, night-shirt that fell from neck to heel, and, although it was a warm night, a stocking-shaped, flannel night-cap. Thus attired, he sat on the big bed looking somewhat like a dunce. After a while from under the pillow he drew a photograph and sat staring at it. It was the picture of a young man in his early twenties and first moustache, in the uniform of a surgeon of the Union Army. Beads of moisture stood out on the doctor's forehead. Probably it was the night-cap. Presently they coursed down the furrows of his wise and foolish old face. "Murdered," said he, "murdered," and drew his sleeve rapidly across his eyes. He put the picture of his only son back under the pillow and blew out the candle.

The Lilies of the Field **William E. Barrett**

Early in the autumn of 1963 the word began to circulate that a small and inexpensive motion picture, called *The Lilies of the Field,* was going to prove a "sleeper"–one which unexpectedly becomes a great success. This opinion was quickly proven correct. In a very few weeks this quiet little entry had skyrocketed to a place among the first ten in the whole field, on figures compiled by *Variety.* Here it had to contend against formidable and much advertised pictures, whose costs had run high in the millions, and some of which seemed more on the order of bad dreams than sleepers.

The Lilies of the Field was made from a quite short novel of that title by William E. Barrett, a writer for whom I have always had a high admiration. I lost no time in obtaining a copy.

And now a word of advice. Everyone should read this story which is presented herewith. I make the suggestion because I believe the book to be better than the picture–even though Hollywood has since voted Sidney Poitier the best actor of the year on the strength of his splendid performance as leading man in *The Lilies of the Field.*

THE LILIES OF THE FIELD

William E. Barrett

chapter one

There is a young legend developing on the west side of the mountains. It will, inevitably, grow with the years. Like all legends, it is composed of falsehood and fact. In this case, the truth is more compelling than the trappings of imagination with which it had been invested. The man who has become a legendary figure was, perhaps, of greater stature in simple reality than he ever will be in the oft-repeated, and expanded, tales which commemorate his deeds. Here, before the whole matter gets out of hand, is how it was. . . .

His name was Homer Smith. He was twenty-four. He stood six foot two and his skin was a deep, warm black. He had large, strong features and widely spaced eyes. A sculptor would have interpreted the features in terms of character, but Homer Smith's mother had once said of him that he was two parts amiable and one part plain devil. It was a verdict that he accepted, as he accepted the days that came to him. He lived his life one day at a time. There was laughter in him.

He was a buck sergeant when he received his Army discharge at Fort Lewis. The Army years had been good to him and he had accumulated a sum of money through some slight thrift, much moonlighting and occasional gambling luck. He bought a secondhand station wagon in Seattle, equipped it for sleeping, and started out to see the West. He had not believed much of what he heard in the Army and he did not believe the tales that Westerners told about their country; he was, however, a curious man.

On a morning in May, Homer Smith drove into a valley west of the Rocky Mountain Range. Spring, which had stood aloof from him on the higher levels, moved down the valley to meet him. Blue, yellow, and pink flowers twinkled in the tawny expanse of buffalo and grama grass. He had grown up in South Carolina, a far different land from this. On his left, as he drove south, blue- and purple-tinted mountains tipped with snow formed a seemingly unbroken barrier against the East, and everything that the East represented. In this country, he had discovered, there was no South; "south" was merely an adjective prefixed to the noun "west."

Where the road curved away from the mountains to parallel a narrow, sluggish stream, he saw the women. One of them was working in an area of cultivated land and three more were building a fence behind a dilapidated farmhouse. There were no men visible and that was curious. The women wore bulky-looking garments and they had white cloths tied, scarf fashion, around their heads. Homer appraised the house and the out-buildings with one glance.

"Place needs a lot of work," he said.

He hadn't worked for a week. It wasn't necessary that he work unless he felt the urge. In that fact lay a new concept of freedom. He was a man of many skills and when he became restless with idle traveling, he had no difficulty in finding work to do; when work became onerous, or the road called to him, he moved on. Impulse turned the wheel and he drove into the badly rutted road which led to the farmhouse.

The woman in the field paused briefly to look toward the station wagon and so did the three women who were building a fence; a mere turning of heads, a brief pause before resuming the tasks which occupied them. The short, squat older woman who walked into the sunlight from the direction of the chicken run stood and watched Homer as he braked to a stop and slid from under the wheel. He chuckled in recognition of a familiar type. This was the sergeant, the top, the boss of these other women. No doubt about it.

"If you need a day's work done," he said cheerfully, "I'm for hire."

The woman had a hard, weather-beaten look. There were many deep lines on the broad surface of her face. Her eyes were small and sharply intent. She measured Homer before she spoke. She had a deep, guttural voice.

"Gott ist gut," she said. "He hass sent to me a big, stronk man."

Homer was intrigued by the heavy German accent, the careful spacing of words. He was amused, too, at the idea which the words conveyed.

"I dunno," he said. "He didn't say anything to me about sending me some place. I was just passing by."

"Ja. You did not pass."

There was aggressiveness in this old woman, an air of certainty which is the mark of bosses. Homer felt antagonism stir in him, but it was a fine day and he was carrying the day in his spirit. He had no quarrel with anyone. He waved one hand.

"I can build that fence better than those girls you've got," he said.

All of the lines in the woman's face seemed to draw together. He could see the effort that she was making to translate what he said in her own mind. He smiled reassuringly and strode away from her.

The three women had their fence half built, a high fence enclosing an area behind the house. Someone had dug postholes and spotted the posts in place. The women had fresh, unpainted planks and their method was for one woman to brace herself against the post, another to steady the plank, and the third to drive nails. All things considered they were not doing badly. They stopped work, startled, when Homer's tall figure loomed over them. He gripped the post and shook it. It was a more solid job than he anticipated. The older woman was right behind him.

"Nein!" she said.

Her voice sputtered through three emphatic German sentences and he did not have to understand the words. She did not want him meddling with the fence. She had other work for him to do. He turned and the woman tapped herself on the chest. He caught the words, "Mutter Maria Marthe" which registered as a name. She indicated each of the three women in turn with a jabbing forefinger.

"Sister Elisabeth, Sister Gertrud, Sister Agnes."

"Religious folk," Homer thought. He nodded his head to each of them. "I'm real happy to meet you," he said. "I'm Homer Smith."

Mother Maria Marthe formed his name silently with her lips, then uttered it as it translated in her mind: "Homerus Schmidt."

"Oh, ja! Schmidt!"

Broad smiles broke across the faces of the three women. This was something that they could understand, a stranger named Schmidt. Their smiles made him welcome and Homer felt immediately at ease with them. They did not have any color line; he was just people to them. He made another attempt to do something about the fence but the harsh voice of the older woman stopped him at the first gesture.

"Nein, Schmidt," she said.

She pointed to the roof and delivered herself of another series of inexplicable sentences. Homer understood her without difficulty. This old woman was a natural boss and bosses always got their ideas across. She wanted the roof fixed.

"That's not something you do with Scotch tape and chewing gum," he said. "I'd need a good ladder and shingles, and the right kind of nails."

She made no effort to understand him; she merely anticipated him. With a purposeful stride, she led the way to the barn. There was a large room given over to tools and equipment. She had shingles, not enough to reshingle a roof but enough to repair one that was not too far gone. She had nails of several sizes, including 3d flatheads. She had roofing cement. She had a ladder. Homer looked at her with respect. Here was a woman who knew what had to be done and what was needed to do it.

"Okay," he said. "I'll fix it good."

He was happy when he climbed the ladder and looked out over the valley. There was a chill in the wind but the sun was warm. He could see the three women working doggedly on their fence and, from his point of vantage, he could see what the fence enclosed. There was nothing in that little patch except a small statue and a privy.

"How about that?" he said softly. "All that work for just privacy. Away out here where there's nobody."

There was another privy north of the barn behind the foundation which marked the site of a house that had, obviously, burned down. This, he decided, was where the hired man had lived once, in a smaller house. It was curious that a fire would burn a man's house down and leave his privy standing. It hardly seemed sensible.

He surveyed the roof carefully, aware from the markings that someone had surveyed it before him, indicating the places where it would have to be repaired. He was glad of that because a man couldn't tell from the outside where a wood shingle roof leaked, and he had not been invited inside. He wondered if the women would have done this job if he hadn't come along. Probably so. He looked down on the woman who was beating away at the fence planks with a hammer. It would be comical, he thought, to watch them on this roof beating on the shingles.

He worked while he amused himself thinking, rocking the broken and warped shingles to break them away from the hidden nails, sliding new shingles in place and nailing them, covering the nails with roofing cement. He worked swiftly, easily, finding the rhythm best suited to the job and maintaining it. He didn't count time and he was startled when a deep, heavy carrying voice called: "Schmidt!"

Mother Maria Marthe was gesturing him down. The other women had already entered the house. The sun was directly overhead. Lunchtime. He scrambled down the ladder and slowed his pace as he approached the door of the house. There was a crucifix above the door, not a rugged Protestant cross but a crucifix. The word, "Catholic" came into his mind and with it the strange, awesome word, "nun." It had not occurred to him that these women were nuns. He found the idea incredible. What were they doing out here building fences?

They were standing in their places at a rough pine rectangular table that lacked a tablecloth, two on each side, Mother Maria Marthe at the head and a place for him, facing her. When he stood in his place, the older woman made the sign of the cross and the others followed her example. There was no doubt now. This was a Catholic place and these were nuns. Homer didn't join in the prayer and couldn't have done so if his Baptist conscience had permitted it. They prayed in German. It was a long prayer and, at a certain point, the rhythm changed as though something new had been added, something that wasn't in the memorized pattern. Homer was sensitive to rhythm. He was sensitive, too, to attitudes toward himself, a sensitivity born of race and skin color that set a man apart. He had delicate, invisible antennae which told him when he was noticed or discussed. He knew at the change in the prayer that these women were praying about him. The knowledge made him vaguely uncomfortable. Nobody was going to pray about getting a roof fixed, particularly a roof that wasn't in very bad shape. There had to be more to it than that.

"Amen" was the signal to be seated. Lunch consisted of thick cheese slices and coarse bread from a homemade loaf that was like a big, swollen pancake but solid. There was a glass of milk at each place; no coffee. Nobody talked and Homer studied the faces without staring at anybody. These were not young women, but two of them had a young look in spite of weather-roughened skin and tight dishtowel turbans that concealed their hair; Sister Gertrud who was the shortest nun, the one with the longest nose, and Sister Albertine who was frail-looking with large eyes, very blue. The other two, Sister Elisabeth and Sister Agnes, were sturdier and had broad faces. The eyes of Sister Elisabeth were brown.

Mother Maria Marthe presided grimly and it was obvious that no one was going to dawdle over lunch. All hands were going to eat in a hurry and go back to work. The sisters, seemingly, paid no attention to Homer Smith but he was aware of occasional hurried glances in his direction, and, more important to him, he felt friendliness. When he went back to his roof he was humming, and the hum grew to full song as he fell into the rhythm of the work. This was an interesting experience. The pay probably wouldn't be much. He didn't care. Maybe he wouldn't take any pay. He didn't know. Come night, he'd roll again.

In the pink of the evening, as he was cleaning the roof gutters, he saw Sister Agnes bringing in a cow, one cow in a country of herds. A few minutes later, as he gathered up his tools, he saw Mother Maria Marthe emerge from the house, followed by Sisters Elisabeth and Gertrud who were carrying an Army cot. The older woman carried a bucket. He watched them, momentarily baffled, but when the toolroom in the barn became their obvious destination, he put all of the pieces of the puzzle together.

"They are doing that for me," he said. "Room and bath."

The idea touched him. A cot to sleep on and a bucket in which to wash! It was what they had. He swung down the ladder and followed them with long strides. They turned, startled, when they heard him. The two sisters held firmly to the cot. It was not Army, merely Army-type, the kind that are sold in surplus stores, collapsible and cheaply made.

"I didn't figure to stay," he said, "but I've got me a bed in the car."

Mother Maria Marthe did not understand him, so he gestured to the car and turned toward it. She followed him. The two sisters, after a moment of hesitation and lacking definite instructions, joined the procession, still carrying the cot. He opened the station wagon from the rear and showed them the bed on which he slept. He had equipped that vehicle for living. He had his own bucket, too, a foot locker, a tool chest, and a guitar. The older nun nodded, then spoke to the other two in rapid-fire German. They started back to the house with the cot.

"Das ist gut, Schmidt," she said. "For zupper I rink a bell."

She walked away and Homer filled his bucket at the well, hauling it behind the barn for his wash-up. Supper was preceded by an even longer prayer than the one at lunch, and was only slightly more substantial as a meal. Sister Albertine served omelet with the coarse bread and a glass of milk. This was it; a house full of people living on the efforts of one cow and a few chickens. When another prayer had been said, two of the nuns made deft work of clearing away the dishes. There was a general air of relaxation. Sister Albertine, with badly concealed excitement, departed on a mysterious errand. Mother Maria Marthe sat less stiffly in her chair.

"Ve are Cherman," she said, "mit two from Hungary. Ve learn der Englisch."

Sister Albertine returned with a small, tinny, wind-up model phonograph, the type that is bought for very young children. She placed a record on the turntable when the dishwashing nuns returned. A harsh, badly distorted voice squawked something in German from the speaker, followed by the English equivalent. The five voices repeated the English, including in the pronunciation all of the phonograph noises.

"Please send the valet up to my room," they said.

"I have something to be pressed."

"Do not starch the collars of the shirts."

"Here is my laundry list."

"Four shirts."

"Five pairs of socks."

"One blouse."

"Two pajamas."

Homer listened, fascinated and repelled. He had never been exposed to the problem of learning another language. He resented the voice on the record which wasted the time of these people by teaching them to say stupid things. These nuns weren't ever going to see a valet, and they weren't going to have anything pressed. He had an expressive face and Mother Maria Marthe read it when the pause at the end of the record occurred. She halted Sister Albertine who was about to turn the record over.

"Vait!" she said. "Schmidt! He spiks der Englisch."

Homer sat suspended in the sudden hush, aware of the eyes. He was, suddenly, elevated above his status as a big, strong man, above the disembodied voice on the record. Sister Albertine was so carried away that she spoke without waiting for permission. She pointed to the phonograph.

"Vot iss named this?" she said.

"A phonograph."

Homer's reply broke down discipline. If Sister Albertine could ask a question so could anyone else. Each nun was indicating some object in the room. He named them as rapidly as he could, trying to speak the words distinctly. He could tell from their delighted expressions that they already knew the words "table," "chair," "window," "door," and the words for the other familiar objects. His identification pleased them by confirming what they knew. Mother Maria Marthe put a stop to the obvious. She went through the pantomime of shaking hands with one of the nuns and he told her what she was doing, pointing out the "you" and the "her." He became self-conscious about the South Carolina in his voice.

"If you learn English from me," he said apologetically, "you're sure enough going to get yourselves segregated some places."

They looked at him uncomprehendingly and he let the subject drop. That was something that he could not explain even to himself. Sister Albertine was drawing a sketch on a piece of paper. She showed it to him. It was a very good sketch of his station wagon.

"Automobile? No?" she said. "Auto bus, no?"

She knew that it had a special name and she did better with English than did the others. They were all interested but when he told them that it was a station wagon, he drew blank looks. With a few deft strokes, the nun drew a depot, than a wagon. This was a station and this, a wagon. How could you put them together and obtain something that resembled an automobile?

He did not explain that very well, but he tried. He was sorry when Mother Maria Marthe clapped her hands as a signal that class was over. He walked to his home on wheels in the cool darkness, with a thousand stars swung low above him and his brain filled with strange rhythms; German words and English words flavored with German. He did not ask himself why he was spending the night; he was here and it happened.

He wondered which of the nuns would have slept on the floor and managed without a bucket if he hadn't had his own equipment.

These nuns are nice people, he thought, and that old lady's got a shrewd mind, loose and easy.

chapter two

One of the privileges of freedom was that a man slept until he felt like rising, with no bugles blowing. Homer Smith was not a late sleeper but he did not believe in stumbling around in half light, waking up birds. The morning was nicely lighted in the sky when he rose, filled his bucket at the well and hauled it beyond the barn. There was a hammer hammering and, from the corners of his eyes, he could see Mother Maria Marthe watching him while he was filling his bucket. She did not bother him until he came back to the station wagon; then she descended angrily.

"Schmidt!" Her words tumbled out and they were so German, or so German-English, that they were incomprehensible. She did not, however, need words to convey meaning; she needed only gestures and emphasis. The gist of the message was plain. He was a lazy loafer who had no business sacking out when there was work to be done. Homer drew himself up, looking at her from his commanding height, as angry as she was.

"Look!" he said. "I ain't no nun and I ain't no hired hand, neither. I get up when I feel like getting up. If I don't want to work, I don't work."

He did not awe her. She stamped her foot, pointing emphatically at the house. *"Geh!"* she said. *"Mach schnell!"*

Being commanded to go to the house meant that he was expected to eat breakfast. That was an idea that made sense. He turned away, still angry. Sister Albertine greeted him shyly in the communal dining room. She had, obviously, been forced to waste her time preparing a late breakfast for him and she was nervous about it. She set two fried eggs before him, following them with two slabs of coarse bread, toasted. There was no coffee, only the inevitable milk.

"Old Mother sure sets a poor table," Homer said. "How come she can afford all that lumber outside and no money for chow?"

Sister Albertine stared at him, her large eyes seeming larger still as she tried to understand him. Homer didn't expect her to understand him. It was a comfort to him to express his feelings in words with a human audience to listen to him; he did not require a response.

"There's a mean streak in that old woman," he said. "I don't know why you girls put up with her. People got to sleep. People got to eat.

People got to have a little joy in living. She don't go for that. All this milk all the time and no coffee! And no milk of human kindness, neither. That woman just hasn't got it."

Sister Albertine gestured helplessly. "I do not understand," she said. "Speak slowly please."

Her English sounded like English, or more like English than Mother Maria Marthe's, even if she did speak one word at a time.

"I'm going to give you some soup," he said. "Got some soup in the car. Emergency rations. Got a can of peaches, too. You wait right here! I'll bring them right in."

Sister Albertine looked frightened but there was one note in the human voice that she understood, the note of command. She nodded her head weakly and started clearing the dishes from the table. Homer strode out to the station wagon.

"I hope Old Mother tries to stop me," he said. "Just let her ask me what I'm doing."

He was in a high, exalted mood, flying the flags of rebellion against authority. No one attempted to stop him and he took five cans of soup out of his locker, a can of peaches, a can opener. He saw Mother Maria Marthe bearing down on him as he started back to the house and his flags drooped on the flagstaff. He pretended that he did not see her and lengthened his stride. He piled his cans on the table, resisting the impulse to look over his shoulder. He went through the pantomime of opening the cans for the benefit of Sister Albertine.

"Soup," he said.

"*Ja.* Thank you."

She looked interested, but she also looked fearful. She did not have the authority to accept gifts, but she lacked the vocabulary necessary to refuse acceptance or to explain her dilemma. Homer sensed it.

"Old Mother will like that soup," he said. "Save a little wear and tear on that cow and those chickens."

He went out to face the dragon and the dragon was waiting for him. "Schmidt," Mother Maria Marthe said, "Ve build a shapel. I show you."

She led the way with firm tread to the old foundation over which a house had burned. Coarse grasses had grown around it and the foundation itself was a pit into which ash and brick and partially consumed timbers had fallen. She reached into her pocket and produced a sketch on a piece of coarse wrapping paper. It was a good sketch of a small church, a frame church that looked like many Baptist churches in the South except that it did not have a steeple. There was a cross on the first roof truss above the door.

"Who builds it?" he said.

Her eyes drilled into him. She was patient and she could wait upon the perception of a dull-witted male. Homer looked from the unsightly foundation to the sketch and back again. There was a pile of new lumber behind the barn.

"If you think that I'm building that, you're out of your mind," he said. "I'm one man. I ain't no contractor with a crew. I don't need all that work, neither." He handed the sketch back to her. "No."

There was hard-eyed contempt in the old woman's face. She folded the sketch into a hidden pocket. "Ve are vimmen," she said. "Ve build it."

"All right. You build it."

Anger boiled and bubbled in Homer Smith. He could feel the steam from it rising into his brain. He looked away from Mother Maria Marthe and it helped to bring his anger down to a simmer, not looking at her. She was a mean-minded, overriding, unreasonable old woman. He was going to get in his station wagon and drive. The warmth of the day touched his skin and he was looking toward the debris in the foundation. He had had his breakfast. Breakfast sort of committed a man to the day. He felt strongly about people passing judgment on him and he did not want this woman justified in thinking ill of him.

"I'll clean that old foundation for you before I go," he said.

He walked away from her, tall in his pride. There was a scoop shovel in the toolhouse and, surprisingly, a crowbar. He had a spade in his car. He came back and surveyed the ruin of a house. The builder had put down a solid foundation of granite. Not many farmhouses in this section of country were built like this. It made sense. A man had to have a cool place for his perishable stuff. The big house where the nuns lived was probably built the same way. The chimney stood above the foundation, tall and built of brick, a lonely thing without a house to keep it company.

"Strange how it burned the man's house and left his privy."

Homer shook his head over the familiar thought as he surveyed the ruin. The years had fallen on the grave of that house; snows and rains and blowing sand. The debris was packed into the pit and it looked like a town dump set in cement. A bulldozer would churn it up fast. He knew how to handle a bulldozer, but this was a place of hungry labor where a man was lucky because he had a shovel and a crowbar. Resentment against Mother Maria Marthe moved hotly in him again. He paced off the dimensions of the foundation, confirming what his eye told him. It was 18×26.

He dropped down into the pit and started probing. It had been a hot fire and the house had probably gone fast. Some of the lumber had survived, charred but not burned through. Someone had started the cleaning-out process long ago and quit. It was impossible to tell how that fire had gone. It probably smothered out some way. Maybe it happened in the winter and the snow came. There weren't any clues left to show what had happened to the roof. He did not believe that it had been reduced to ash.

"Old farmer took him some salvage," he said. "Hauled away what would haul."

He was encouraged when he discovered that the burned lumber moved against his pry. It had partially roofed the excavation. This hole wasn't as solidly packed as it looked. Fire-eaten though they were, the lumbers were heavy and he strained his muscles against them, heaving them out. His body absorbed thought and emotion, condensing them into sweat. When he heard a bell ringing in the distance he did not immediately translate it into meaning.

"Old Mother going to feed the slaves," he said.

Resentment returned. He was filthy. Clouds of black ash rose from his work clothes when he slapped them. He went to the station wagon for his bucket and washed in cold water from the well, accepting the icy touch of it gratefully. The nuns were standing in their places at the table, waiting for him before starting their prayers. He didn't say Catholic prayers with them but he had to be there. It was some idea in Old Mother's mind. He bowed his head. He had a prayer in his own heart when he accepted food. Nobody took food for granted when he was a child. It wasn't always easy to get and a person learned to be thankful when it was there.

He sat down at the table and there were soup plates at each place. Sister Albertine came in with a pot and a ladle. She looked happy. All the nuns looked happy. Mother Maria Marthe didn't look exactly happy but she didn't look as stern as usual. Homer's mood lifted. They were serving his soup.

Nobody talked. That seemed to be the rule at lunchtime. Still, without talking, it was a pleasant meal. Nice atmosphere. These girls, Homer thought, need better food. He wished that he had more cans in his car. He didn't feel full-fed when he rose but his stomach was friendly to him. When a man felt welcome at a table the food tasted better.

He was whistling when he returned to the excavation. He stood with his hands in his pockets looking at it. Old Mother, he repeated to himself, was out of her mind. Nobody could build a church like her drawing unless he was a contractor with people working for him, people skilled in doing different things. Women weren't ever going to build it, especially not women that built a fence so clumsy. All of which made cleaning out all of this mess ridiculous. He had told her that he'd clean it out before he left, however, and he'd do it.

He was a strong man and the work went fast when he didn't think about it. He got all of the odds and ends of wood and metal out of the hole, then worked them into a trench about a dozen yards away. He cleaned the stone steps that had led into the cellar from the outside, but the cellar was deep. A man could walk around in it with the top of his head under ground. Getting out the ash and the sand was not mere shoveling; it was hauling. He did not want to use his own pail so he rummaged around in the barn until he found a bucket that had seen hard service. After that, monotony claimed him; shoveling, filling, carrying out, and dumping.

He created a refuse pile that would have to be leveled off some day but he had no alternative and it did not worry him. Blue dusk came down on an uncompleted job and his muscles ached. The distant bell rang again.

They were back to eggs for the evening meal. The eggs irritated him. He was tired and hungry and he'd spent his day doing a job that didn't add up to anything. There wasn't enough food to satisfy him and Mother Maria Marthe sat stiffly at the head of the table keeping everything on a low key. She never said a word of thanks to anybody for anything.

"I'm going to get me my pay and leave."

The resolve sustained him, even when he was swept into an English lesson after dinner. The nuns, he discovered, had been studying English, not merely trying to learn it from a phonograph record. They brought their books with them and they knew many English words. Their problem was that they never heard anyone speak those words and they had no practice in speaking them. Homer was not in a mood for teaching anybody anything and he gave their problem only half his mind. He could feel the disappointment of the nuns but he was concentrating on the boss nun and he couldn't give any thought to the others. When Mother Maria Marthe clapped her hands at the conclusion of the lesson, he braced himself.

"I want to talk to you," he said. "I've been doing work for you. Good work. I want pay for what I do."

She sat silent, with her hands clasped in front of her. Her small eyes looked at him out of the wrinkled mask of her face but there was no light in them. He did not know whether she understood him or not; if she did, she would not admit it. She could make a person feel wrong, like a miserable sinner, by just looking at him. If she refused to cross over into English, he couldn't talk to her. He looked past her to the little table under the statue of the Mother of Jesus in the corner of the room. There was a book on the table, a big book, and it talked to him. The Bible! He crossed the room and looked at it, turning a few pages. The type was outlandish and did not look like words, but no other book was organized like this one.

"You wait right here," he said. "I'm coming back."

He was afraid that she would not wait, that she would close the door on him; but she waited. He brought his own Bible from the station wagon. It was the one he got in the Army. He had a passage in his mind and he turned pages rapidly. He tore half of the wrapping from a package of cigarettes and wrote on the white side, *Luke 10:7*.

Mother Maria Marthe rose heavily and crossed the room to her big Bible. She turned the pages and he knew what she was reading when the page-turning stopped:

"And in the same house remain, eating and drinking such things as they give: for the labourer is worthy of his hire."

It wasn't exactly what he wanted to say, but he hoped that she would get the idea about the laborer. She walked slowly back and reached for his pencil. In bold letters, she wrote, *Proverbs 1:14*.

He spun his own pages and read: "Cast in thy lot among us: let us all have one purse."

"No," he said. "I'm a poor man. I have to work for wages."

Mother Maria Marthe did not change expression. Without returning to consult her Bible, she wrote again on the fragment of cigarette package, *Matthew 6:28, 29*.

"And why take ye thought for raiment? Consider the lilies of the field, how they grow; they toil not, neither do they spin."

"And yet I say unto you. That even Solomon in all his glory was not arrayed like one of these."

Homer read, baffled. This old woman had answers out of the Book, which surprised him. They did not come to grips with the situation, they did not deal directly with his right to be paid, but they slowed down a man in argument. Before he went into the Army, he had had a head filled with Bible words and figures but they would not march straight for him now as they did once. It wouldn't make any difference. This old woman wasn't going to pay him. She'd never had any intention of paying him. She sat straight with her unblinking eyes fixed on his face.

"Schmidt," she said. "Tomorrow Sunday ist. Der Mass in Piedras iss nine by der clock."

"I don't go to Mass."

"Ve do."

She sat immovable, letting the statement stand in all finality until his comprehension caught up with it. She expected him to drive the nuns to Mass.

"How did you get there before I came?" he said.

"Ve valked."

That, too, had finality in it, completeness. Piedras was a little town. Homer had driven through it before he stopped here. It was over two miles away. He thought about those nuns, working hard all day on thin rations, walking miles along the road on Sunday. He liked those nuns. It wasn't fair to them.

"I'll drive you in," he said.

He walked out, then; not expecting thanks and not wanting any. A man was free when he could say "yes" or say "no." Old Mother had her ways and she was a tricky woman but she hadn't asked him to take her to Mass. He had to be honest about it; she hadn't asked him that. That wasn't her way. She put a problem up to a man. She knew how to set a problem up for him so there wasn't anything he could do but take it from her.

chapter three

The morning was still, with no movement in the wide and lonely land. Homer Smith rose early. He dressed in a pair of Army slacks, a button-down gray shirt, a blue necktie, a gray jacket. A man had to look sharp on Sunday if no other time. He wandered around aimlessly, missing the sense of life, movement and activity that he associated with this strange place in which he found himself. As time passed, with no bell sounding, it became apparent that there would be no breakfast. He remembered vaguely from the Army that Catholics, or some Catholics, did not have breakfast before Mass. His own hunger was the captive of Catholic custom and he was uncomfortable. He removed his bed from the station wagon, providing space if not comfort for his passengers. At 8:30 they emerged.

Mother Maria Marthe and her four nuns wore long black robes with white starched bibs and white bands across their foreheads under black hoods. They looked now like his idea of nuns but he was astonished at them.

"You girls sure look nice," he said.

Whether they understood his English or not, they recognized a compliment by its tone. They looked pleased. Mother Maria Marthe wasted no time on looking pleased. She sized up the station wagon, ordered the nuns into the back and elected to ride with the driver. There were no seats in the back so the passengers sat on the floor. There was something pleasant and companionable about that and Homer had an impulse to sing as he drove out onto the road. He didn't sing. The stiff, no-nonsense woman beside him wouldn't put in with singing. He was certain of that.

Piedras was a shabby little town and the church was a flat-roofed structure of adobe. Homer let his passengers out and stood beside the station wagon, ignoring the hard stare of Old Mother. This close was as close as he intended to go to a Catholic Mass. He waited until the nuns entered the church, then crossed the street. There were signs in Spanish all over the windows of a small café and he did not have to understand Spanish to recognize a place that sold beer and miscellaneous food. He wasn't certain that it would be open, but it was. A thin man with sad brown eyes rose from a stool and moved behind the counter.

"I want a man's breakfast," Homer said. "Ham and eggs, with lots of ham, and pancakes, and anything else you've got, and coffee. I want lots of coffee and I start with it."

"Sí. I can do it. You are the man who does the work for those nuns?"

"They do a lot of work themselves."

"Sí. This I know. It is a great folly. They cannot make the living in this country. It is not possible."

A steaming cup of coffee appeared on the counter in front of Homer and he inhaled the fragrance of it. The sad man had a grill behind the counter and he broke eggs onto it. Ham sizzled and Homer's nostrils twitched. He hadn't ever thought about nuns making a living. New thoughts interested him.

"They are Germans. They speak the good Spanish but nobody listens. There is no reason for it."

The little man talked on. He knew all about the nuns, or claimed that he did. They were from the wrong Germany, "the one that is Communist," and they escaped, which was a great embarrassment to their Order. But yes. There was some politics about it which no one could understand. "It is Church politics and politics of Europe, and who can understand the politics even when it is of his own country?" The nuns could not stay in Germany and the Order owned this land. It came to them in the will of Gus Ritter. Did the customer know Gus Ritter?

Everybody in this place knew him; *todo el mundo*. He was a hard, mean man who worked his family night and day to make money for him. His son and his son's wife burned to death in the house next to him. A lamp of kerosene caused it. He was too mean, Gus Ritter, to have electricity although poor people in this country had it. After his son burned up, he did not live long. He left his land to this Order of nuns because his sister in Germany belonged to it. For a long time the land was idle. Gus Ritter made good money from it growing the potato. These nuns came and they had nothing. They knew nothing except to teach. There was no school and they did not know the English. How could they teach? They sold some land to buy tools and furniture and lumber. For what purpose? What could they do? Would the customer have some more of the eggs?

The customer wasn't interested in eggs but he would have more ham. Homer Smith was enjoying this experience. He was catching up on his victuals after two lean days. The steady flow of talk from behind the counter fascinated him. He had always had a weakness for good talkers. He liked the cadences which Spanish brought to English and the occasional Spanish words or phrases, meaning nothing, delighted him because they so obviously belonged to what the man was trying to say.

"The Mass is finish," the man said.

There were a few people coming out of the church across the street. Homer rose and stretched. It had been a noble breakfast. As he was paying for it, he thought about those hungry nuns. He hesitated. Working only occasionally and traveling much, he had learned thrift. He shrugged and purchased five slices of ham which he carried to the car in a paper sack.

The main body of worshipers moved slowly out of the church; Spanish, all of them. Poor people. Homer towered above them as he stood beside his station wagon and he was aware of his physical superiority as he was aware of the curious glances that he attracted. Nobody spoke to him.

The nuns did not come out until after everyone else had gone. The priest came with them, a short, thin man in a brown robe with a white cord around his waist. Mother Maria Marthe was talking to him in Spanish. Her Spanish did not have a lot of German in it like her English did. She introduced Homer to the priest and he did not understand what she said about him, but he caught his own name. She called him "Señor Schmidt." Señor means "mister" in Spanish. He knew that. She never called him mister in English. The priest was Father Gomez. These Catholics were a comical people. They called themselves "Father" and "Mother" when they weren't and when they didn't aim to be.

The priest shook hands with him. He was a quiet man, half sad like all these Spanish, with a low voice. He wouldn't be likely to get a call from a Baptist church. He wasn't an exhorting type. He said something nice about Homer being good to the nuns.

"Mother Superior tells me that you are going to build her a chapel," he said.

"That is just an idea she's got in her head. One man can't do that."

Homer felt embarrassed when he read disappointment in the priest's eyes. He had no reason to feel embarrassed but he did. He spoke hurriedly to cover what he felt.

"I been studying your church. Never saw one like it before. Not close up."

"It is not impressive but I would like to show it to you."

The priest brightened. He led Homer to the wall of the church and showed him where the outside coating of adobe had cracked. There were adobe bricks underneath. "They are simple bricks," he said. "They are made out of adobe clay and a little straw, sometimes the manure of the horse, then dried in the sun."

The door was of rough board. Homer hesitated when the priest opened it. He had never been inside a Catholic church. There were vague memories in his mind about tales he had heard of weird Catholic spells and of idol worship, but he was curious about the construction of the building so he followed the priest in. There was an altar and there were rows of rough benches, strange-looking images that wore clothes, murals of Biblical scenes painted on the walls. The walls were whitewashed adobe, concealing the brickwork. There was a poverty about it that attracted Homer Smith. He understood poverty.

The priest was telling him that he had three other churches like this one in which he said Mass on Sundays, that his home parish was in the larger town of North Fork. Homer nodded. This was a busy man, a circuit-riding preacher. He respected him.

"I'm glad I saw your church," he said.

"It is a poor church but God comes down to it." The priest's eyes were intent upon Homer's face. "Mother Superior says that she prayed for someone to help her and that you came. What do you think about that?"

Homer laughed. He did not mean to laugh but this was a disturbing subject. "I think that she figures that she owns me. She figures that the Lord gave me to her as a present because she did all that praying."

"Not that!" the priest said. "I am certain, not that. But she has a need and she trusted in prayer. It is not a fault in her if she believes that God sent you."

"He didn't send a black Baptist to a Catholic nun. He didn't do anything like that."

"It would be odd, wouldn't it?"

"I don't see much sense in what she's doing."

"She does what she must at the present. These nuns have to live. She wants a place here ultimately for poor boys from the city; Spanish-speaking boys who get into trouble. No one is interested in them. They could work and learn and be happier in the country than in the city. No one will believe that until she proves it. She knows what she wants to do and she is strong of will."

"Yes," Homer said. "I know that. She's a strong-minded woman. But God didn't give me to her and she doesn't own me. She's got to get that out of her head."

He was thoughtful driving home and he declined the breakfast invitation, abrupt in his presentation of the paper sack to Mother Maria Marthe. "Just a little ham," he said. "Maybe you girls might like it."

He gave her no opportunity to say thanks or not to say thanks. He turned away hurriedly and climbed into the station wagon. He drove to a parking place close to the excavation and changed into his working clothes. He had an innate respect for the Sabbath and a disinclination to profane it with servile work, but the Army had relaxed the rigid rules of his boyhood. In the Army a job that had to be done on Sunday was done on Sunday. It was like the ass or the ox falling into a pit and having to be hauled out. The nuns, however, seemed to be abiding by the old rules so he restrained his urge to plunge in and finish the clearing of the excavation.

He walked around the excavation and measured it again. He returned to the station wagon and obtained a small pad from his locker. He covered the pad with figures. He had worked for many people and he had done many things. He had varied skills. Always he had worked with someone telling him what to do. Nobody, in all of his life before this, had told him to build a church. Nobody had ever said to him: "Here is the ground and here I want a church and it is your job to build it." It was like a call. It elevated him. He was all alone, one man, with a hole in the ground and a church to be built, and no one to tell him how.

He took his black pipe from his locker and packed it. He smoked cigarettes during the week, but on Sunday he smoked a pipe. It was his father's habit. His father could not afford to smoke tobacco seven days a week, so he settled for Sunday. Homer had been smoking a black pipe like his father's on Sunday ever since his father died. In his mind it was sort of a memorial and he drew satisfaction from it.

He sat on the small pile of partly consumed lumber that he had stacked a few yards away from the foundation. He puffed on his pipe and there was a sheen over his eyes. He was seeing something before him that wasn't there and the world around him did not exist. He was unaware of Mother Maria Marthe until she spread the wide skirts of her black robe and sat beside him on the lumber. It was the most companionable thing that she had ever done.

"Schmidt," she said, "ve can do it?"

It wasn't a statement; it was a question. That, too, was unusual, but Homer's mind was away out where the unusual is usual and nothing ordinary matters.

"It would take a powerful lot of work," he said, "and a lot of those 'dobe bricks."

"How much?"

"About the work, I don't know. Nearly four thousand bricks."

They sat silent, contemplating the foundation where once a house had stood and where a man and woman had burned to death. Mother Maria Marthe rose.

"Tomorrow ve go to North Fork," she said.

Homer didn't answer. North Fork was the big town of this section. He hadn't seen it yet. If she wanted to go, he'd take her. She wouldn't do anything about the gasoline. Gasoline was like the lilies of the field to her; somehow it would be provided.

The noon heat pressed down and he moved into the shade of the station wagon. The land was big and there was loneliness all around him. He thought about going back to Piedras and listening to the Spanish man at the eating place, but that was too much trouble. The day, without work or travel, seemed as big and as empty as the country. He took his guitar out of the station wagon. He traveled with everything that he liked in that old vehicle because it was his home while he rambled. He had bought the guitar in a pawnshop in Tacoma, a better instrument than the one he had owned back in South Carolina. He tuned it and played softly, feeling his way into a mood. In a little while he was singing, keeping his voice down, not putting out anything, singing to his own soul.

He sang "Wade in the Water" and "Deep River," "Blind Barnabas" and "Old Time Religion." He let his voice swell out a little on "Shenandoah" because, suddenly, the mood was right and the song was saying what he felt inside of him. Mother Maria Marthe returned then and he felt her presence without seeing her. His mood was stronger than her presence and his voice made its last crossing of the wide Missouri before he looked up. The old face, with its deeply graven wrinkles, was forbidding but the small eyes seemed less hard than usual.

"Schmidt," she said. "Come! Brink der music."

He rose reluctantly to follow her. He had been doing all right alone. His resentment melted when he saw the four nuns waiting expectantly in the dining room. The table had been pushed back and his chair was placed so that he would face them. They were women without music in a great, flat, lonely place that was intolerable without it. He looked at them and his heart lifted. These were people who needed something that he had to give.

He started softly, offering religion to religious people; "Swing Low, Sweet Chariot" and "Didn't My Lord Deliver Daniel." He warmed to them, then, and worked to lift them, swinging into: "Ezekiel Saw the Wheel" and "Dry Bones." Their feet moved and their eyes were alive. Old Mother sitting stiffly, didn't seem to mind, so he did "Water Boy" and "John Henry." He had no particular awareness of his voice except as an instrument like his guitar. It was deep, a bass-baritone, and he could do with a song whatever he felt like doing at the moment, but he did not try to make his voice obey any rules. When he finished "John Henry," Mother Maria Marthe clapped her hands. It wasn't applause; it was the end of his solo.

"Ve sing," she said.

He nodded, accepting the role of accompanist. "Give me the key," he said, "and let us hear how it goes."

The old nun nodded to Sister Albertine who had a moment of shyness. She wet her lips and her thin fingers tightened, making fists out of her hands. Her large blue eyes met Homer's and she leaned forward. She sang and her voice was true, a sweet voice, not strong but perfectly pitched. A man could follow it. Homer watched her and listened to her, tuning the guitar. What she was doing was chant, a simple thing. He drew deep organ sounds from the guitar and it was right. Everything was right; the voice, the music, the accompaniment. Sister Albertine felt him with her and she signaled to the others. They came in and they knew what they were doing. None of the voices was as good as Sister Albertine's but this chant did not call for good voices. Sister Gertrud's voice was harsh. Sisters Agnes and Elisabeth sounded like just anybody out of a Baptist choir, and the old Mother's voice was cracked; but, together, they made a strange, solemn sense.

This was Latin. It was Homer's first experience with sung Latin and he approved the sound of it. It belonged to this music. As they changed from one hymn to another, Sister Albertine led him into the sense of the new chant and the others joined in as he picked it up. Loneliness had long since dropped away from him and he felt exultation. He wanted to mingle his voice with these others but the words eluded him so long as he regarded them as words; when he thought of them merely as sounds, they made a pattern in his mind. He signaled to Sister Albertine for a repeat at one point and when he heard the sounds a second time they clung to his mind. The voices of the nuns came in again and his voice joined them.

Ave maris stella
Dei mater alma
Atque semper virgo
Felix coeli porta.

It was that easy. They stopped when Mother Maria Marthe clapped her hands. It was suppertime but Homer paid no attention to his food. He ate it but it made no impression on him. When he walked to the station wagon, he was empty of thought but filled with throbbing sound, a happy feeling of reverence. He stood for a long time looking at the shadowed shape of the excavation.

chapter four

North Fork had a population of 7094 people, which made it the metropolis of the west slope where towns were small and widely spaced. It was a spread-out town and the Livingston Construction Company was on the northern outskirts. Mother Maria Marthe was accompanied by Sister Gertrud. The two nuns left Homer Smith beside the station wagon while they entered the Livingston office. Homer lighted a cigarette and looked at the construction company property with interest. He had no idea why old Mother was visiting this place but it had a prosperous look.

Politician, this man, Livingston, he decided.

There were several earth-moving machines standing in a row and spaces indicating that there were others out on a job. There were four good-sized buildings and an adjoining lumber yard. All of which, on this side of the mountains, added up to road-building contracts and government work. A man didn't employ such equipment out in the wide open spaces by merely hanging out a sign or putting an ad in the paper.

Rolling in it, Homer thought. This man is doing all right.

He was idly curious about Mother Maria Marthe's mission but speculation never engaged his mind for long. He either knew something or he didn't know, found out ultimately or never found out. He walked around, admiring the equipment. He had resumed his post beside the station wagon when a short, firm-jawed, gray-haired man exited briskly from the office door. The man seemed angry, either temporarily or permanently so. He looked at Homer challengingly, looked past him, then met his eyes.

"Are you Schmidt?" he said incredulously.

"That's a German idea," Homer said softly. "My folks figured that it was Smith. Named me Homer."

"You're the man who is going to build a chapel for those nuns?"

Homer was about to say that that was another German idea, one of old Mother's ideas, but he didn't like the man's attitude. The man didn't seek information in a polite and orderly way.

"Yes," he said.

"I expected a different type. Hell! You'll never do it."

Homer kept his eyes on the other man's face; not answering, merely waiting. This was an attitude that he understood although he had not encountered it lately. This man expected to meet somebody white; when he discovered that he was dealing with a Negro, he "knew" that the job wouldn't be done. A voice inside Homer said: "The man's right. You know he's right. You won't do it." He closed the voice out, refusing to listen.

"I'm Orville Livingston," the man said. "I don't know how you got mixed up in this, but I told this nun when she first came here that she'd better go back again. I was Gus Ritter's friend and the executor of his estate. I turned his property over to this religious Order, which was what he wanted. I sold land for those nuns after they came here, without taking a commission. I had a man plow for them when they insisted on working the land that they kept, and I paid him personally. Now they want bricks. I've got to stop somewhere. I'm a Methodist."

"I'm a Baptist myself."

"You are? Then why are you working for them? If you are?"

"I haven't figured that out yet."

"You'll figure it out. Then you'll quit. Those nuns will figure it out, too; figure out that what people told them was right. Then they'll quit. They must. Women can't work that land and if their Church was interested in them, it wouldn't leave them out here. They'll quit and anything that they start will fall to ruin."

"Old Mother has a strong idea in her mind," Homer said softly. "She's going to do what she feels she must."

"Certainly. If somebody else supplies the bricks! Well, I won't. I wanted to see you before I told her."

Orville Livingston did not seem to realize that he had made Homer Smith the last toppling weight in the scales of decision against the nuns, and that he was telling him so.

"You've got that right," Homer said. "I can't talk against you on that. I'm still doing that job for them. I'm going to need two days work a week to keep it going. I can handle a bulldozer, almost any machinery you've got. Learned how in the Army."

"All right. I can use you Thursday and Friday if you can only work two days. I'll pay the going rate on whatever job you're assigned. Seven Thursday morning. I'll try you out."

Orville Livingston turned away. "Another thing," Homer said, "I'll need two sacks of cement. For them I'll pay cash."

"Three dollars. I'll have a man wheel them out."

Homer lighted another cigarette. Something had happened to him. He didn't plan any part of it. He had taken a job that he didn't want under a man whom he didn't like and he'd told the man that he was going to build a church. It didn't make sense. He stared across the big lot of the Livingston Construction Company, seeing none of it, seeking in his mind for a way out of a worrisome situation. A sentence kept repeating itself like an outside voice speaking to him; *"I expected a different type."* Then, another sentence; *"I wanted to see you before I told her."* He'd let old Mother down merely by being black.

A man wheeled out two sacks of cement and Homer paid for them. They weighed 94 pounds a sack and he heaved them into the back of the station wagon. His muscles felt good doing it.

The two nuns emerged from the office and any sentimental feeling that he had developed for Mother Maria Marthe vanished immediately. She was in bad humor.

"Schmidt," she said curtly, "ve go back."

"No, we don't. I've got things to do."

His pride stood tall, contradicting her and not explaining anything. The two nuns were riding in the front with him because there was no sensible alternative. He could hear the old nun breathing heavily.

"Ve haff no time," she said.

He ignored her and drove downtown. North Fork had a variety of stores concentrated on two streets. He found the town interesting after a period of isolation. He bought a spirit level and a couple of good saws, a heavy hammer, a chisel, and a hoe with a ventilated blade. The expenditure dismayed him but he assured himself that he would pay the money back to his fund out of his pay on Friday. He couldn't afford a big investment in something that probably wasn't going to get done.

"Schmidt," Mother Maria Marthe said when they were halfway home, "ve haff no bricks."

"We'll get some."

He didn't know where or how, but that was a problem of the future and the future was never quite real to him. A man couldn't calculate on time that hadn't arrived, happenings that hadn't happened; he had all that he could do in coping with what was already here. The here and the now of this afternoon was the finishing of the foundation clean-out. It took his afternoon and part of the next day. He built a mortar box, got a level on the foundation, chiseled off the rough spots and mixed cement. He started on the task of smoothing the top of the foundation with cement and he worked carefully, missing the direction of a boss while savoring the joy of being his own man with a job that was his to plan and to execute. On Thursday and Friday he worked in one of the Livingston road gangs and on Friday night he drew his pay.

"I owe myself more money than I earned."

The flat statement admitted of no argument. It was a fact. He weighed the fact thoughtfully for as long as it took him to walk to the North Fork supermarket. That market had been beckoning to him since he first saw it. He entered and selected a wheeled basket, pushing it before him. He passed all of the products which needed refrigeration but he selected an accumulation of canned goods and two cans of coffee. He hesitated for a long two minutes before buying a whole ham.

"We've got to eat better than we've been eating," he said defensively.

When he presented the two sacks of groceries to Mother Maria Marthe her face tightened like one of her hands folding into a fist, more bone and skin than flesh, more contraction than expression. He had a startled impression that there were tears in her eyes but he could not be certain because she turned away so abruptly, the groceries in her arms.

"*Ach*, Schmidt!" she said.

The next day she was more annoying than ever, yelling "Schmidt!" at him when he was counseling with himself over his work, bothering his life with orders and suggestions and just plain interference. He decided that she was a natural henpecker and that he'd been foolish in his idea that she had softness in her.

"Hard as a hammer," he muttered. "Always beating on something."

He had, however, established a new pattern without thinking about it. Buying groceries seemed the natural thing to do when he had his second payday a week later and he engaged in no hesitations or arguments with himself.

"Mouths to feed," he said.

He rather liked the idea, liked the nuns and responded warmly to their obvious liking for himself. He enjoyed the English lessons and the Sunday music. Everything in his life seemed to fall into line, work and more work, music, a little visiting, a little pondering, regular things to do at regular hours and no time to think about doing anything else.

The nuns worked all day in the fields as the weather grew warmer. He neither tried to understand their work nor to interfere with it. They were irrigating the land from a stream which fed into another puny stream that Westerners called a river. All that he knew about the irrigating process was that it was hard work. He had grown up in Columbia, South Carolina, and he was strictly city.

The idea of building a church obsessed him. He had no bricks but he laid floor when he had the foundation topped with cement. He used common lumber for his sub-floor and the best of his planks from the lumber pile for the surface. Some day, he thought, we'll maybe have money for linoleum or something. These planks won't take no polish.

He studied the church in Piedras every Sunday. There was not much to learn from it, but one feature of his own dream church baffled him. The brick chimney which had survived the fire stood high against the sky, higher than his projected roof. The fireplace and part of the stone mantel had survived, too, and that fireplace would be halfway down the right-hand side aisle of his church. He had never seen a church with a fireplace nor one with a chimney; that is, not a big chimney that called attention to itself.

Old Mother will probably have someone lay a log and sit herself in that warm spot come cold weather, he thought.

He tried to take it lightly but the chimney wasn't right. The church in Piedras had only a small hole near the altar side where a stovepipe would fit in winter, and it was a larger structure than his church. He could wreck the chimney, of course, but that old German, Gus Ritter, had built things to last. It would be difficult to get that chimney out of there with the equipment that he had. He did not like destroying something that had survived a disaster. That didn't seem right, either.

On a Tuesday in late July, the sad-faced man who ran the café in Piedras drove a beer truck up the road and parked behind the station wagon. He had another man with him and neither man was friendly.

"The padre says to the people that you must have brick."

There were about five hundred adobe bricks in the truck and the two men made only a pretense of helping to unload it. Homer unloaded five bricks to their one.

"It is of no use," the sad-faced man said, "but we have brought it."

"Thanks."

Homer did not waste time talking to people who did not want to talk to him. He understood dimly the attitude of these people. It was the attitude of Orville Livingston. They saw no future for the nuns and they did not want to encourage what they did not approve. They did not want to be involved, or called upon for a succession of services, either.

Brick gave Homer a new impetus. He puddled adobe to use as mortar and he set his guide lines. He had done a little bricklaying but not much of it. This adobe brick was tricky. The bricks were uneven in size and crude. He had to socket his floor joists and he built a temporary wooden bracing for his wall. He experimented and he worked slowly but, with the brick, the thing that he was creating became a reality.

He was leading three lives; the life of work in North Fork, the communal life of eating and singing with the nuns, the highly personal life of building a church. Mother Maria Marthe was a grimly irritating figure with her eternal "Schmidt!" and her interference, but most of the time he could block her out of his mind. When she annoyed him to the point where he could not block her out, he had spells of dark brooding during which he wondered why he was working harder than he had ever worked in his life, and for no pay; why he was staying here on this sun-baked prairie with so much world yet to see. It was a dull wonder, requiring no answer from him. The answer was before him. He was building a church.

He ran out of brick and, on a Monday night of full moon, life caught up with him.

It had been blazing, relentlessly hot for days and there was no moisture. Everything that he touched was hot and his clothing clung to his skin; yet this was not a sweating heat like the heat of the South, it was a frying heat that skilleted a man, making his skin itch. There was a restlessness in his blood and in his nerves, a vague unhappiness clouding his thought. He sat with his back against the left-rear wheel of his station wagon and picked listlessly on his guitar. In the distance a coyote howled.

The cry was a high-pitched keening, a sound that climbed to a peak and broke. Homer lifted his head. The silver white of the moon lay over everything like snow. He felt along the strings for that coyote cry. He knew that he wouldn't find it, but he understood it.

He had heard coyotes before, almost every night. He was sensitive to animal tongue. He knew when a coyote was seeking a woman of his own kind. This coyote was not seeking that. He was finding the night unbearable because it was so big and so bright. He was lonely in it, feeling small and lost.

The cry rose again and another coyote answered. The other coyote was lonely, too, but the coyotes were not lonely for each other. It was bigger than that. Homer fingered the string on his guitar, then laid it down. He couldn't say what they were saying; he could only feel it. He straightened his body and stood, looking to the west where the coyotes were. There was nothing out there, nothing but wide, flat land and miserable little places like Piedras. He turned his body slowly so that he was facing east.

The mountains were a deep violet color slashed with silver. Everything was still. The hush had swallowed the last cry of the coyote and frightened him into joining the silence. Homer stretched his arms wide.

"Time to go," he said.

He returned his guitar to its case and climbed into the front seat of the station wagon. The noisy roar of the engine responding to the starter shattered the night, but there was an urgency in Homer Smith that ignored sound and silence now. He drove down the rutted road to the main highway and, as the car picked up speed, he relaxed under the wheel.

Over the pass, beyond the mountains, lay the big city of the state. It had been a long time, too long a time! He could not tolerate nights so vast as this; he needed a city where people huddled together and kept one another warm. He sang softly as he drove and his car was a spinning reel on which the road wound up.

chapter five

The city was traffic-choked and noisy, and its lights were bright. The heat of summer rested on it like a cloud without rain, but a man could wet his throat with cold beer in the daytime and mingle with his own kind at night, eating and drinking whatever he found. He could listen to loud, rhythmic sound from juke boxes and dance with women and laugh at jokes. He could look into the eyes of women and see himself there, feeling pride in his manhood. He could stand big in his body with gray fog in his mind and hear his own blood running in his veins. He could go to the Baptist church on Sunday and sing hymns that his mother and his father sang before he was born, weeping a little because he had been a sinner all week. He could leave the church with all the sin washed out of him, feeling clean.

Homer Smith loved all of it, the standing tall and the falling down. Most of all, he liked the speech of men and women like himself, and the humor of them. A man heard no funny stories from people of another language who could not speak English well, and he could tell no funny stories. Humor belonged to the language that a man knew. He liked companionship and his room in the boardinghouse, and the bathroom down the hall where he could bathe in a tub instead of showering himself from a bucket. He liked the hard feel of pavement under his feet, the odor of cooking food that floated out of strange windows and doorways, the children who were in constant motion around him. He liked the sirens of police, fire, and hospital vehicles, the bright exteriors of taverns and the twilight dimness within. This was the city.

The nuns and a town named Piedras and the Livingston Construction Company belonged to a hazy dream, as unreal as incidents in the life of another man. He never sat down deliberately to think about them and such stray memories as floated in and out of his mind did not disturb him. His life in the Army was gone, too, to be recalled only through conscious effort and not worth that. He lived in what he had, and with what he had, finding life good.

His money ran low in ten days and he went to work for a wrecking company. His first job was with a crew that was wrecking a carbarn no longer used by the tramway company. It was heavy, dirty, dangerous work, with much steel to handle and grime over everything. The next job, by comparison, was easy. A half-block of houses had to come down to create a blank which could be converted into a parking lot. They were small and old, low-rent houses, known in the South as row houses but in the West as terraces; houses all alike, built together wall to wall. Everything that could be stripped by hand was stripped, then a crane, with a big metal ball, knocked the walls down. The job took three days.

On the third day, Homer was sorting through the salvage, stacking the theoretically usable doors, window frames and fixtures. There were sinks, basins, eight bathtubs. He piled the bathtubs, then stood looking at them, hearing in his mind a high, clear call as compelling as a coyote's cry to the moon.

"Those girls need a bathtub," he said.

It was the first time he had consciously thought about the nuns and they were suddenly alive in his mind. He had seen them hauling buckets of water from the well in the evening, many buckets, and he had seen how crude everything was about the house. Gus Ritter, that old German farmer, had been a tight-fisted man. He didn't improve a place except where it paid him.

The foreman was a big man, almost as big as Homer was. Homer sought him out. "How's to buy one of those tubs?" he said.

"Sure enough? You want your own personal tub, boy?"

"How much?"

"You could steal it and nobody would care. That kind is no good. You got some way to haul it?"

"Yes."

"Okay. Give me two bucks to keep it honest."

Homer gave him the two dollars. He saw the bills go into the foreman's pocket and he knew that the company would never see those bills. That didn't matter. He'd bought what he wanted at the price asked. The bathtubs were high and narrow, standing on dragon feet. He picked the best one of them. It wouldn't go into the station wagon so he upended it on the top, the feet pointing skyward, lashing it in place with rope. The bathroom windows had been removed intact, small windows of red, yellow, and green glass in diamond pattern. He bought two of them from the foreman for a dollar each and, with the purchase, a vision returned, haunting him.

He drew his pay at the end of the day and headed for the hills.

It was afternoon on Friday when he drove into familiar territory. He stayed on the highway when it looped around North Fork. The crops were prospering under a bright sun; potatoes, wheat, barley, lettuce, cauliflower. The hazy blue mountains were on his right. Within a few miles the fields on his left became bleak, sage, and greasewood, sprinkled with a few indomitable flowers of blue, yellow, and pink. A hawk floated low, gliding on motionless wings, and a rabbit scurried across the road.

Homer drove over a small bridge and the stream below it was a thin trickle. He turned to his right on a rutted road and the nuns were in the field, working on their variegated crop, fighting for their growing stuff against weeds and voracious insects and the parched dryness of the soil. It was good to see them again, but he did not slow down nor look in their direction. He was not certain of his reception and he was willing to defer it. He parked in his accustomed spot and sat looking at his unfinished church.

Nobody had disturbed it and no one had brought bricks with which to complete it. It had a desolate look; one wall built as high as a man's shoulder, the others low; the chimney pointing upward like the skeleton finger of a giant. There was an untidy scattering of rubble on the ground. Homer got the scoop shovel from the barn toolroom and started shoveling. He cleared the area and dug a hole with his spade into which he tumbled the debris.

The bell rang and he straightened. Old Mother never rang the bell for the nuns because they knew when to come for meals. That bell was for him. He laid the spade aside, carried his bucket to the well, washed his hands and walked into the house. They were waiting for him, standing in their places at the table, just as if he had never been away. He bowed his head while they prayed. When he looked up after the "Amen" they were all looking at him happily. Nobody said anything but they were glad that he was home. A man felt a thing like that. Nobody had to say anything.

There was an omelet and coarse bread, but there were vegetables, too, fresh vegetables. The farm was starting to pay off.

They resumed the English lessons after supper and Homer's ear was sharper because he had been away. They were doing better with the language but he could hear the soft echo of South Carolina coming back to him when they spoke.

Better than a phonograph accent, he thought. Used to be you could hear the turntable going around when they spoke anything in English.

He did not unveil the bathtub until after breakfast the next day. He drove the station wagon close to the house and eased the tub down from the top. He called old Mother out to see it. Sisters Gertrud and Albertine came with her. He made an awkward gesture toward the tub, not naming it. After all, these were girls who built a high fence around the privy.

"A present," he said.

He was facing Mother Maria Marthe. Her eyes squinted as though she found the sun too bright. *"Das ist gut,* Schmidt," she said, *"Das ist gut."*

She said something in German to the two nuns and went hurriedly into the house. Homer did not have to explain to her that he needed a place in which to install the tub. When she returned, she led him to a pantry off the kitchen. This was the deepest penetration that he had made into the nuns' quarters. He had not even known that the pantry existed.

"Here," she said.

It was a small room but that was her problem. He hauled the tub in and set it on its feet. He had taken some pipe as a necessary accessory to the tub and he had bought a secondhand blowtorch in the city. He cut a hole in the floor where it met the wall and angled the pipe through it, attaching it to the drain pipe of the tub and soldering it in place. He put the rubber plug in the drain and the tub was in business. He dug a trench outside the house to run the water off. They would still have to haul water because he couldn't give them a pump and a plumbing job, but this was something. He felt good about it.

He still lacked bricks, so he settled down to carpentry, making pews and kneelers like those in the church at Piedras. He lacked a lathe and he had to work with what he had, so the pews were mere benches without polish or curlicues, but he built them solidly and the day passed swiftly.

"Old Mother's got to pray me some bricks," he said softly. "If she doesn't, she's wasting my time."

He sat at the counter in Piedras while the nuns were at Mass on Sunday. He ordered his big breakfast. The sad-looking man broke eggs into the skillet and surrounded them with bacon.

"It is not reasonable that you have come back," he said.

"It makes sense to me."

"It could not. Everybody says that you are gone and this is how it had to be. They laugh at the nuns because the nuns say that you will return."

Homer's body stiffened. "I don't want to see nobody laughing at those nuns."

"This they know." The man cast a wary eye at his big customer. "Now nobody will laugh."

"No. That's right. Nobody's going to laugh."

"The padre says to them that you will return."

"How did he know?"

"That Mother Superior, she told him."

"How did she know?"

"She knew."

Homer drank his coffee, savoring the fine aroma of bacon. He had not known, himself, that he would ever come back. He had not given it a thought. How could old Mother know? He had a dark suspicion that it had something to do with her praying. She had never got it out of her head that God had given Homer Smith to her. If that was a fact, she'd be certain that he couldn't wander off. He belonged to her. That was something Homer had never liked. The idea of belonging to someone stirred a racial antagonism in him. No Negro was ever going to belong to anybody again. Not ever! He was free.

The breakfast was good and he ate it. The idea of freedom moved around in his mind while he ate, not moving in a worrisome way, merely in a curious manner. It was a strange thing, freedom. He had been free in the city. Nobody told him to do anything. He kept his own hours, ate when he wanted to eat, slept as late as he liked. Here, old Mother was always ringing bells or yelling "Schmidt" or telling him to do something. She exploded inside of herself if he didn't get up at bird-waking time. She was so certain about owning him that she never said "thank you" for anything. Not one time had she said "thank you."

"The padre, that Father Gomez, he will be very happy that you have come back to those nuns," the man behind the counter said.

"Why should he be happy?"

"He will say that it proves a religious thing."

"What religious thing?"

"Faith. It is a word for what is unreasonable. If a man believes in an unreasonable thing, that is faith. It is not reasonable that you should come back to this place and work for nothing. Nobody believed it. You have come back."

Homer ate contentedly. That was an interesting idea. He liked interesting ideas. Faith was what old Mother had. She believed that he would come back. She believed that he could build a church all by himself, maybe even without bricks. That wasn't a reasonable idea. He hadn't ever built anything all by himself. He was free, building that church, just as free as he was in the city, even more so. There wasn't anybody else to build it. He didn't need any wages. He had a full life. He had many things. He was free like the lilies of the field. It was a strange thing. As this Spanish man said, it wasn't reasonable.

"Me," the man said. "I have no faith. I do not believe in the Church. I do not go to the Mass."

Homer looked at him with interest. "I don't know what that does for you," he said. "All those other Spanish are in there sitting on those benches or doing whatever they do at Mass, not working. You're over here, working, fixing my breakfast."

"It is reasonable. You pay me. I make money."

"I never saw another customer in here during the Mass. Unless you get a hungry Baptist in your place, you don't make money."

"So, I sit here and do nothing. It is a reasonable thing. No priest tells me what to do."

The first stragglers were coming out of the church. Homer rose and paid for his breakfast. The man behind the counter baffled him in a mild way but he was not interested in him. The man could stay just as he was, where he was, being reasonable. If the man ever got faith, Sunday was going to be a hungry day in Piedras.

The nuns, as usual, were the last ones out of the church. Homer amused himself, looking big and dangerous beside the station wagon, frowning at all of these people who had laughed at his nuns, seeing them turn quickly away from him. He did not frown at Father Gomez who came out with old Mother. The priest was smiling and he extended his hand.

"It is nice to see you again," he said. "I believe that you will have a surprise or two this week, Señor Smith." He turned his head. "Don't you agree, Mother Superior?"

Mother Maria Marthe either understood, or sensed, what he was saying. She nodded and, amazingly, for the first time since Homer Smith had known her, she smiled.

"*Ja,*" she said.

The surprise was not long in developing. Early Monday morning, vehicles of various types and ages arrived at Homer's working area. Each vehicle brought adobe bricks and each driver had approximately the same speech.

"I am happy to bring these bricks for the chapel. I have had in my heart a doubt of you and I am sorry."

After his astonishment at the first two versions of the speech, Homer adjusted cheerfully to the situation. Old Padre must have preached hell to these Spanish, he thought. Wish I could have heard it.

The bricks piled up and he went to work again. The day climaxed with the beer truck and the largest donation of the day, five hundred bricks. The driver, a wide-shouldered, husky, embarrassed man made the set approach. His companion, the sad man from the café, spat at a grasshopper, missing him.

"I have come only to see this thing," he said. "I have brought no bricks."

Homer shrugged. It made no difference. This man probably did not believe in bricks. It was not reasonable that all of these bricks should be here, so they were not. The broad-shouldered man laughed. Now that he had made his speech, he was no longer embarrassed. He slapped his companion on the back and walked around the partially built chapel, shaking his head.

"You do not know well the adobe," he said.

"I'm learning."

"You should have help."

Homer resented him and he was glad to see him go. A shadow had fallen on his church which everyone else called a chapel. Now that these Spanish were bringing bricks they were going to tell him what to do and how to do it. That could not be. He had to finish it as he had begun it. It was his church. For the first time since he started work on the project, he worried. Mother Maria Marthe added to his worry. She walked around his bricks, making clucking noises like a hen that has just laid something; owning his bricks as she owned him, acting like she'd prayed them into existence.

If I hadn't come back, there wouldn't be no bricks, he thought sullenly.

Old Mother was oblivious. "Schmidt," she said. "Dese people vill help you. All iss vell."

"I don't want any help."

His mind was set on that point and when helpful neighbors came to watch and make suggestions, he was curtly hostile. They brought no brick on Tuesday or on Wednesday but men with time to spare from whatever they did normally, came in person. Some of them wanted to lay bricks and all of them were mouth experts, telling him what he should do. They were very friendly about it. When he wouldn't let them work, they sat and smoked, watching him and sometimes shaking their heads, making remarks to one another in Spanish.

They ain't commenting on how good I'm doing neither, he thought.

Thursday bothered him. He did not know whether he would still have a job with Livingston Construction Company and he was reluctant to leave his own job unguarded. There wasn't any sense in telling old

Mother to chase these Spanish because she liked the idea of having them do some of the work. She didn't understand how he felt about it. All that she cared about was getting her chapel-church built. She didn't care who built it.

Homer made two signs and placed them conspicuously on his walls. One read KEEP OFF! and the other was equally uncompromising: DON'T TOUCH ANYTHING! He drove off then to North Fork.

Orville Livingston's eyebrows moved upward and his jaw moved forward when he saw Homer Smith. "Where have you been?" he said.

"Vacation."

"Yeah? Why did you come back?"

"Had to finish my church."

"Are you going to finish it?"

"I'll finish it. Right now I'm gaining on my brick."

"Humph. Well, they ought to read you out of the Baptist Church but I'm glad you're back. I'm shorthanded."

Homer went out on a road gang and Livingston had not exaggerated his shorthandedness. The work was heavy. Thursday night Homer checked his church and no one had disturbed it. Friday night, with his two days pay, he loaded up on groceries, enjoying the adventure of pushing his cart through the supermarket again and selecting what he wanted. When he reached home and presented his sacks to old Mother, she shook her head at him.

"Nein, Schmidt," she said. "No more."

She showed him vegetables in jars which the nuns had canned for winter eating, fresh vegetables ready for the table, an entire new generation of chickens in the fowl run ready to be thinned out. He had been blind to all that. He experienced an odd twinge of disappointment.

"That's fine," he said. "That's just fine."

He had never been vitally interested in what the nuns did, or how. He knew that they worked hard and that was all that he cared to know. Now they had something to show for their work. They didn't need his groceries any more. He walked across the clearing to his church. The Spanish had been interfering in his absence. They had built a big mortar box with some of his old lumber. He sat and smoked, taking counsel with himself.

There was a way of spreading adobe on the outside of the brick and smoothing it out, a little like stone. He had studied the church in Piedras and he believed that he knew how it was done, but he had never seen anyone do it. These Spanish planned to do it for his church. That's why they built that box to do their puddling. He resented any and every hand laid on that church other than his own, but he told himself that this was a practical matter and that the Spanish knew how to do this work.

"No sense in me getting sore," he said.

Some intangible thing, some joyful spirit, had gone out of his life and he tried to call it back. He sang as he laid brick on Saturday and he was friendly to the Spanish people who came out to watch him, so friendly that he surprised them. They got in his way, trying to help him. No one attempted to mix adobe clay; everyone wanted to help lay brick.

"No!" he said. "I got my ideas. I got to do it my way."

"*Como?* There is only one way to lay the brick."

They did not understand his attitude and he had taken a positive stand at an awkward time. He had reached the point in one wall that called for the installation of a window, high up and placed, as in the church at Piedras, so that light would fall on the altar. He had the window intact in its frame, a small window that need never be opened. It was not easy to set it properly in place with the bricks holding it firm. He had measured his space carefully, but he had difficulty when he tried to set it. A short, thin man named Juan Archuleta joined him on his working platform.

"It is a matter of aggravation, this," Juan Archuleta said. "I have done it."

He broke a brick deftly, scarcely seeming to glance at it but breaking it to the exact size that he wanted. He wedged pieces into place and he spread his adobe mortar. He knew how to set a window and Homer grudgingly admitted it. The little man took no credit for what he did and made no point of it. He talked as he worked.

"I like how you sing," he said.

"A man works better singing."

"*Sí*. Singing is good. You like guitar?"

"Got one of my own."

"*Bueno*. You come to my house tonight for the dinner. Drink a little, sing a little, play the guitar."

"Sounds good."

A man couldn't stay hostile to another man who helped him work and who invited him to dinner. "I have worked much with adobe," Juan Archuleta said. "It is the stuff of this country."

He helped Homer with the twin window on the other wall and he backed him up in telling the other men that two workers on the bricks were enough. Without making a point of it, he worked over a couple of trouble spots where the wall met the chimney and enclosed the fireplace.

"You work smooth," Homer said grudgingly.

"A little work. *De nada*. You have worked much. I could not do so much. I am not a strong man."

Homer shook his head. This Juan Archuleta was easy to like; man with honey on his tongue. He met Juan's wife and his children and his neighbors. He drank white liquor that he could feel in the roots of his hair like electricity and he sang songs for his new friends. He ate food that was hotter than the liquor but strangely satisfying, and he listened to songs that he had never heard before in a language that he did not understand.

"Adios, Mariquita linda,
Yo me voy
Porque tú ya no me quieres
Como yo to quiero a ti."

He admired it. It had sadness but no misery. He could pick it up on the guitar and play along with it but he could not sing it as he sang Latin with the nuns. This language did not break down to sounds that he could carry in his head or shape with his mouth. On the faster, more cheerful music it was easier. He could make a lot of *ya-ya-ya* sounds that were almost Spanish even if they didn't mean anything.

Homer did not know when the party ended; it tapered off slowly. He rode home in Juan Archuleta's old car, singing. There was a silvery whiteness over the land, a chill in the air. He chuckled foolishly as he stood beside his station wagon watching Juan drive away. A dozen impressions of the evening whirled around in his mind but the one that rose to the surface was inconsequential.

"Those Spanish have a way with beans," he said. "Make them taste like food."

chapter six

A Livingston Construction Company truck delivered a thousand bricks on Monday morning. There was no message, no explanation offered. There did not have to be.

"Old man lost a bet with himself," Homer said. "He bet I wouldn't ever do this work. He bet I would be long gone by now."

The new bricks were far superior to any that Homer had laid; regular brickyard adobe, uniform in size and quality. It did not seem right to lay them on the upper levels with the inferior bricks below. The adobe coating, of course, would hide them but Homer considered tearing out the front of the church and using the new bricks there. He didn't mind the work but he decided against it. The people who had brought him bricks when he needed them had a right to have their bricks in the church where they were put.

He had more bricks now than he had hoped for and he decided to build his church higher. That would change the proportions but it would be more impressive. He had a driving urgency in him, a sense of time that he had not had earlier. Time had not mattered; now it did. He did not try to reason why.

The helpful Spanish brought him logs for his roof beams and they were more of a problem than ever. They were his friends and they were all over the place. Whatever they should be doing to make a living was obviously being neglected, but his blunt query—"Shouldn't you be doing something else somewhere?"—brought only shrugs and grins. They had developed a religious fervor and the finishing of the church had become important to them. They refused to accept the idea that it was his church.

"Look!" he said. "You fellows build an altar. I don't know about such things. If this chapel-church has got to have statues in it, you fix it about them. You let these bricks alone!"

They built an altar within his church while he was laying the long beams across the walls with two feet of log projecting on either side as in the Piedras church. He laid boards across the beams and, at this point, Juan Archuleta insisted upon helping him again. Together they coated the boards thickly with adobe mud. Juan helped, too, with the adobe plaster on the inside walls of the church itself.

The approach of Thursday posed a problem. If he went to work for Orville Livingston there would be no one to control the Spanish. There was no longer any purpose in his work for Livingston. The nuns didn't need groceries any more.

The man sent you all those bricks, his conscience said.

"No. He didn't. He didn't send me anything. I gave him work for wages. He sent those bricks to old Mother. Ashamed of how he said 'no' to her."

With that settled, he continued to work on the church. On Thursday afternoon, Father Gomez came out to see it. He walked all around it, making pleasant comments, then went to see Mother Maria Marthe. She came to where Homer was working after the priest left. He was whitewashing the interior and he did not want to stop.

"Schmidt," she said. "I talk to you."

"*Ja,*" he said.

It was his way of kidding her when she annoyed him. She sat on one of his pews and motioned for him to sit beside her.

"It is finish–nearly–der shapel," she said.

"Almost."

She nodded, her eyes momentarily closed. *"Ja. Gott ist gut,* Schmidt. Sunday, Father Gomez say Mass in dis shapel, der first Mass. You vill sit dere. Der front pew."

She pointed to the space before the altar where the pew had not yet been placed. She seemed very happy, very proud. She was, Homer knew, trying to do something for him, give him an honor; but his Baptist soul recoiled at the thought of sitting up front, in the first pew or any pew, at a Catholic Mass. He looked at her and he couldn't take her happiness away or do anything to hurt her.

"That will be nice," he said.

He resumed his work with even greater urgency when she left him, understanding more clearly the sense of time that drove him. He joked with the Spanish, he ate with the nuns, he continued the English lessons after supper; but only half of him did these things, the other half listened always to the ticking of an invisible clock.

On Saturday, not even the Spanish could find much to do. Homer used them in the clean-up, the removal and stacking of lumber that had been used for scaffolding, the break-up of mortar boxes, the leveling of ground. This was not very interesting so by early afternoon the Spanish had all left. Homer finished the policing himself, cleaning and leveling and removing trash.

He sat, then, smoking a cigarette and looking at his church. He had done it. Old Mother had said; "Build me a chapel-church." He had built it. He had not known how to do it, he had had no plans, adobe was a new stuff in his life–but there it was! His church stood strong with blue sky behind it, a church with angles that would be stiff and harsh in wood, soft in adobe. It had a pediment that he had made in place above the door with a crucifix at the peak. He rose and walked inside, glad to be alone.

The sunlight flowed through two windows that had come out of rowhouse bathrooms. The light took color from the diamonds in the panes and spilled that color on the whitewashed walls. The church in Piedras lacked this cathedral touch; it had only plain glass. His pews were in place and he walked down the aisle. He stood with his back to the altar and looked at the places where the five nuns would sit. His throat felt tight and he had no thoughts at all. He walked hurriedly down the aisle and out into the sunlight.

A flight of birds flew overhead. They were flying high and heading south. It was September and his spring was gone, and his summer. Another flight of birds passed over and he watched them out of sight.

Those birds got a message, he thought. A man ought to have as much sense as a bird.

The bell summoned him to supper and old Mother was feeling festive tonight. She had put a couple of her chickens in the pot and there was chicken stew. All the nuns seemed excited and happy. They had a chapel-church of their own and a priest coming to say Mass in the morning. It didn't seem like a night for English lessons. Homer brought his guitar in and played for them. He played some of the Spanish music that he remembered, not trying to sing it.

"Adios, Mariquita linda. . . ."

He played some of his own music, too, and he sang that: "Water Boy" and "Shenandoah" and "Deep River." He started playing the Latin music and Sister Albertine sang, bringing the others in. He sang Latin sounds with them and it was a happy evening, better than the night with the Spanish.

He sat for a long time beside the station wagon after the nuns had retired. He told himself that he should have said "good-by" to old Mother, but it wasn't his way to put his feelings into words. Old Mother looked into a man's heart and she had an understanding mind. When he was gone, nobody would have to tell her anything; she would just know.

He'd like to say a word to Sister Albertine, too. He'd like to tell her that he liked her singing. She wasn't so strong as the other nuns, Sister Albertine, but she did delicate things that a man liked. She was the one who drew the picture of the wooden church that he couldn't ever build. She had made pictures of him, too. Somebody sent her a package from Germany with pencils and brushes and paper and paint. He hadn't seen her paint anything but she'd made a lot of pictures of him with her pencils when he was singing or talking English at the nuns or working on the church. Better than a camera, she was. He had one of the pictures of himself that she gave him. It was signed with her name. Saying good-by to her wasn't something that he could do, either.

He looked long at his church, then he went inside. It was filled with silent shadow except where starlight filtered through his small windows. He walked down the aisle and he knew that there was something that he wanted to say to God about this church. He knelt in one of the pews and he lifted up his heart, but no words came. It wasn't something that he could talk about, not even to God.

A rabbit bounded across the clearing when he came out of the church.

It vanished and no other night creature moved or spoke. It was deep night, a late hour, and that was the best time.

The starter awakened the engine of the station wagon to noisy life and a touch of the switch sent a flow of light down the rutted road. Homer Smith drove that road to the highway and he knew that he was never coming back. A man couldn't roam forever, nor pleasure himself in strange cities indefinitely. There was a settling-down time at the end of all that. The road was lonely and he sang softly to himself as he drove.

chapter seven

The legend of Homer Smith came into being within twenty-four hours of his disappearance from the scene of his labors. Father Gomez spoke feelingly of him and a Methodist named Orville Livingston came to see the chapel that he had not believed would be built. The newspaper in North Fork ran a story with a photograph of the chapel. Because that chapel is unique in appearance and history, a reporter from the state's largest newspaper made the trip to Piedras and interviewed many people who were eager to talk of its building. Every Spanish-American in the region claimed to have known Homer Smith well, and they are a people who like tales of saints who walk the earth and of angels that take men unaware.

A man named Juan Archuleta swore that he had laid bricks beside Homer Smith and that often the bricks flew into place with no one touching them. Another man named José Gonzalez, who owned a café in Piedras, claimed that he was the intimate and the closest confidant of the chapel builder, that often a white light shown around the man and that, on one occasion, Homer Smith said to him: "God sent me to this place to build a church and to make these nuns famous. When I have done this thing you will see me no more."

Mother Maria Marthe and her nuns were reticent, reluctant to speak for publication about Homer Smith. That very reticence drew them into the legend and created curiosity. People wrote to them and sent them money, soliciting prayers. Orville Livingston, a Rotarian, was invited to speak to the Capital City Rotarians about his experience with Homer Smith and the nuns after he had spoken to his own group in North Fork. Publicity created more publicity and tourists journeyed to a section of the state which they had never seen because they were told that an unusual experience awaited them, that here was a modern shrine.

No one can explain these things. The aim of Mother Maria Marthe was publicized with the rest of the story and substantial sums of money were contributed to help her realize her aim.

Today there are several fine buildings and four new nuns under the direction of the aging Mother Superior. The buildings have electricity and modern plumbing. There are boys from broken homes, and boys who have been in difficulty with the law, studying in the classrooms, working in the fields and in the workshops. They have made their school a noted institution by their loyalty to it. The school is growing in public esteem and in facilities for service to Spanish-American young people who are easy to neglect because they are difficult to understand.

The chapel occupies the key position, with the other buildings grouped in an arc around it. It is a favorite subject of photographers and one may buy postcards of its exterior and interior in Piedras or in North Fork. Three prominent artists have painted it and one of the paintings hangs in the State Museum of Art. There is no chapel like it anywhere. It is of conventional adobe but some trick of proportion makes it memorable. There is strength in its lines and an indefinable grace. A voluble and oft-quoted sculptress has described it as "a true primitive," whatever that means. The chimney, of course, is its really distinctive feature; a brick chimney designed for a two-story house, rising above the flat-roofed adobe chapel like a steeple.

There is a fireplace halfway down the right-hand aisle of the chapel. It is a tradition with the nuns to burn logs in the fireplace on Sundays during the cold weather. The hardier tourists of the fall and winter season consider this a charming touch.

Mother Maria Marthe has grown older. Her English has improved but she still struggles with the "w" and the "th," although the struggle is scarcely apparent in the speeches that she has memorized. She is at her best when she performs her favorite task; the guiding of tourists through the buildings, climaxing always with the chapel. There is, as in the speech of several other nuns, a touch of the South in her voice, a soft slurring, an odd emphasis on certain syllables.

She directs attention first to the oil painting on the wall in the rear of the chapel. It is the painting of a powerful Negro with large features and widely spaced eyes. His head is thrown back in an attitude of exhortation, or, perhaps, of song, his lips parted to reveal two perfect rows of teeth. There is a nimbus of light around the man's head.

"This is the chapel of Saint Benedict the Moor," Mother Maria Marthe says. "That painting of the saint is the work of Sister Albertine. The model was a man named Schmidt who came to us under the direction of God. He built this chapel with his two hands under great difficulties. It is all from him."

She pauses then and her voice drops. "He was not of our faith, nor of our skin," she says, "but he was a man of greatness, of an utter devotion."

Tact **Thomas Beer**

It was widely proclaimed that Thomas Beer's interest in his own work was limited to his earliest books and that he considered the stream of short stories which he produced in the twenties and thirties no better than pot-boilers. More recently a few commentators have veered around to the belief that the stories after all had a merit which may in the end give them a life beyond that of his novels and biographies.

As an editor of *The Saturday Evening Post* (where most of the stories were published), I saw him often between the years 1920 and 1935 and on a few sad occasions later, and he always talked enthusiastically of the short story he had in work. I failed to notice in him any hint of deprecation of what he was doing. He enjoyed the affluence which the high prices we paid brought him, but in the days of the darkest depression he suggested to me that his price should be lowered. (Other writers did the same, including Booth Tarkington.)

And now about "Tact," perhaps the best of his short stories, certainly the best about Ma and Adam Egg. It is a love story, for it tells of Adam's romance with Benjamina and also of the love of food he shared with his mother. Consider this sentence: "Adam ate fourteen hot biscuits and three mounds of an ice cream that held fresh raspberries." For any reader who also truly loves food—a deathless piece of prose!

TACT

Thomas Beer

"You make me sick," said Mrs. Egg. She spoke with force. Her three daughters murmured, "Why, mamma!" A squirrel ran up an apple tree that shaded the veranda; a farm hand turned from weeding the mint bed by the garage. Mrs. Egg didn't care. Her chins shook fiercely. She ate a wafer, emptied her glass of iced tea, and spread her little hands with their buried rings on the table.

"You make me sick, girls," she said. "Dammy's been home out of the Navy precisely one year, seven weeks, an' two days, an' a month hasn't passed but what one of you've been 'phonin' me from town about what he had or ain't done unbecomin' to a boy that's engaged to Edith Sims! I don't know why you girls expect a boy that was champion heavyweight wrestler of the Atlantic Fleet an' stands six foot five inches in his shoes to get all thrilled over bein' engaged. A person that was four years in the Navy an' went clean to Japan has naturally been in love before, and–"

"Mamma!"

Mrs. Egg ate another sugar wafer and continued relentlessly "–ain't likely to get all worked up over bein' engaged to a seventeen-year-old girl who can't cook any better than a Cuban, on his own say-so." She mused: "As for his takin' Edith Sims out drivin' in overalls and a shirt, Adam John Egg is the best-lookin' person in this family and you know it. You three girls are the sent'mentalest women in the state of Ohio and I don't know how your husbands stand it. My gee! D'you expect Dammy to chase this girl around heavin' roses at her like a fool in a movie?" She panted and peered into the iced-tea pitcher, then aimed an affable bawl at the kitchen door. "Benjamina! I'd be awful obliged if you'd make up some more iced tea, please. Dammy'll be through pickin' peaches soon and he's usually thirsty about four o'clock."

The new cook came down the long veranda. The daughters stared at this red-haired girl, taller than their tall selves. Benjamina lifted the vacant pitcher and carried it silently away. Her slim height vanished into the kitchen and the oldest daughter whispered, "Mercy, mamma, she's almost as tall as Dammy!"

"She's just six feet," said Mrs. Egg with deliberate clarity meant to reach Benjamina, "but extremely graceful, I think. My gee! It's perfectly embarrassin' to ask a girl as refined as that to clear the table or dust. She went through high school in Cleveland and can read all the French in the cookbook exactly as if it made sense. It's a pleasure to have such a person in the house."

The second daughter leaned forward and said, "Mamma, that's another thing! I do think it's pretty–untactful of Dammy to take this girl's brother around in the car and introduce him to Edith Sims and her folks as if–"

"I think it was extremely sensible," Mrs. Egg puffed. "Hamish is a very int'restin' boy, and has picked up milkin' remarkably when he's only been here a week, and Dammy's taught him to sem'phore, or whatever that wiggling-your-arms thing is called. And he appreciates Dammy a lot." The plate of sugar wafers was stripped to crumbs. Mrs. Egg turned her flushed face and addressed the unseen: "Benjamina, you might bring some more cookies when the tea's ready, and some of those cup cakes you made this mornin'. Dammy ate five of them at lunch."

Benjamina answered, "Yes, Mrs. Egg" in her slow fashion.

"Mamma," said the oldest daughter, "it's all right for you to say that Dammy is absolutely perfect, but the Simses are the most refined people in town, and it does look disgraceful for Dammy not to dress up *a little* when he goes there, and he's got all those beautiful tailor-made clothes from New York."

Mrs. Egg patiently drawled, "Fern, that's an awful uninterestin' remark. Dammy looks exactly like a seal in an aquarium when he's dressed up, his things fit so smooth; but a boy that was four years in the Navy and helps milk a hundred and twenty-seven cows twice a day, besides mendin' all the machinery on the place, is *not* called upon to dress up evenings to go see a girl he's known all his life. He's twenty-two years and nine weeks old, an' capable of managin' his own concerns. –Thank you, Benjamina," she told the red-haired girl as the fresh pitcher clinked on the table and the cup cakes gleamed in yellow charm beside it. "I do hate to trouble you on such a hot day."

Benjamina smiled nicely and withdrew. Mrs. Egg ate one of the cup cakes and thought it admirable. She broke out, "My gee! There's another thing! You girls keep actin' as if Dammy wasn't as smart as should be! On the other hand, he drove up to Cleveland and looked at the list of persons willin' to work in the country and didn't waste time askin' the agency questions, but went round to Benjamina's flat and ate some choc'-

late cake. Then he loaded her and Hamish into the car and brought 'em down, all between six in the mornin' and twelve at night. I've had eight days of rest an' comfort since! My gee! Your papa's the second biggest dairyman in this state, but that don't keep me in intell'gent cooks!"

The three young matrons sighed. Mrs. Egg considered them for a moment over her glass, and sniffed, "Mercy! This has been a pleasant afternoon!"

"Mamma," said the first-born, "you can't very well deny that Dammy's awful careless for an engaged man. He ought to've got a ring for Edith Sims when he was home at Christmas and the engagement came off. And–"

Mrs. Egg lost patience. She exclaimed, "Golden Jerusalem! Dammy got engaged at Judge Randolph's party the night before he went back to Brooklyn to his ship! My gee! I never heard such idiotic nonsense. You girls act as if Edith Sims–whose ears are much too big even if she does dress her hair low–was too good for Adam Egg! She's a nice child, an' her folks are nice and all the rest of it!–Dammy," she panted as the marvel appeared, "here's the girls!"

Adam came up the veranda with a clothes basket of peaches on his right shoulder. He nodded his black head to his sisters and put the basket noiselessly down. Then he blew smoke from both nostrils of his bronze small nose and rubbed its bridge with the cigarette. He seldom spoke. Mrs. Egg filled a glass with iced tea and Adam began to absorb this pensively. His sisters cooed and his mother somewhat forgave them. They had sense enough to adore Adam, anyhow. In hours of resolute criticism Mrs. Egg sometimes admitted that Adam's nose was too short. He was otherwise beyond praise. His naked dark shoulders rippled and convulsed as he stooped to gather three cup cakes. A stained undershirt hid some of his terrific chest and his canvas trousers hung beltless on his narrow hips. Mrs. Egg secretly hoped that he would change these garments before he went to call on Edie Sims. The three cup cakes departed through his scarlet mouth into his insatiable system of muscles, and Adam lit his next cigarette. Smoke surged in a tide about his immovable big eyes. He looked at the road beyond the apple trees, then swung and made swift, enigmatic gestures with his awesome arms to young Hamish Saunders, loitering by the garage. Hamish responded with more flappings of his lesser arms and trotted down the grass. A letter carrier approached the delivery box at the gates of the monstrous farm.

"What did you sem'phore to Hamish, lamb?" Mrs. Egg asked.

Adam said "Mail" and sat down on the floor.

He fixed a black stare on the pitcher and Mrs. Egg filled his glass. Muscles rose in ovals and ropes under the hairless polish of his arm as he took the frail tumbler. His hard throat stirred and his short feet wriggled in moccasins of some soiled soft leather, indicating satisfaction. Mrs. Egg beamed. Benjamina made tea perfectly. She must tactfully tell the girl that Adam liked it. No female could hear that fact without a thrill.

"Package for you," said young Hamish, bounding up the steps. He gave Adam a stamped square box, announced "I signed for it," and retired shyly from the guests to read a post card. He was a burly lad of sixteen, in a shabby darned jersey and some outgrown breeches of Adam's. Mrs. Egg approved of him; he appreciated Adam.

The marvel tore the box to pieces with his lean fingers and got out a flat case of velvet. Two rings glittered in its satin lining. Adam contemplated the diamond of the engagement ring and the band of gold set with tiny brilliants which would forever nail Edith Sims to his perfections. His sisters squealed happily. Mrs. Egg thought how many pounds of Egg's A1 Butter were here consumed in vainglory and sighed gently. But she drawled, "My gee, Dammy! Nobody can poss'bly say you ain't got good taste in jewelry, anyhow," and shot a stare of fierce pride at her daughters. They rose. She knew that the arrival of these gauds would be known in Ilium forthwith. She said "Well, good evenin', girls," and affably accepted their kisses.

Adam paid no attention to the going of the oldest daughter's motor car; he was staring at the rings, and the blank brown of his forehead was disturbed by some superb and majestic fancy current under the dense smoothness of his jet hair. Hamish Saunders came shyly to peep at the gems and stooped his curly red head. The boy had large gray eyes, like those of his sister, and her hawk nose, which Mrs. Egg thought patrician.

"Hamish, you ain't had any tea yet, lamb. Dammy's left some. Benjamina puts in exactly sugar enough, an' I never heard of mint in iced tea before. It's awful interestin'."

Hamish soberly drank some tea and asked Adam, "Want the motor bike, Mr. Egg?"

Adam nodded. The boy went leaping down the flagged walk to the garage and busily led Adam's red motorcycle back to the veranda steps. Then he gazed with reverence at Adam's shoulders, felt his own right biceps, and sadly walked off toward the barns. The herd of the Egg Dairy Company was an agitation of twinkling horns and multicolored hides in the white-fenced yard. The ten hired men were sponging their hands at the model washstand by the colossal water tower's engine house. Mrs. Egg ate the last cup cake and looked at the town of Ilium, spread in a lizard of trees on the top of a long slope. The motor containing her female offspring was sliding into the main street. The daughters would stop at the Sims house to tell the refined Edith that her engagement ring had come.

Mrs. Egg pursed her lips courageously and said, "Dammy, you might change your duds, dear, before you take Edith her sol'taire. It's a kind of a formal occasion, sort of."

The giant pronounced lazily the one syllable "Bunk," and turned his face toward his mother. Then he said, "You've got awful pretty hands, mamma."

"Mercy, Dammy," Mrs. Egg panted, flushing. Her prodigiousness shook in the special chair of oak under the blow of this compliment. She tittered, "Well, your papa–I do hope it ain't so hot in Chicago–used to say so before I got stout."

Adam blew a snake of smoke from his left nostril and surprised her with a whole sentence. He drawled, "Was a oiler on the *Nevada* that sung a song about pale hands, pink-tipped like some kind of a flower, mamma."

"Mercy," said Mrs. Egg, "I know that song! A person sang it at the Presbyterian supper in 1910 when the oysters were bad, and some people thought it wasn't correct for a church party, bein' a pretty passionate kind of song. It was awful popular for a while after that. –Benjamina would know, her papa havin' kept a music store. I'll ask her. Help me up, lamb."

Adam arose and took his mother kindly out of her chair with one motion. Mrs. Egg passed voluminously over the sill into the kitchen and addressed her superior cook.

"There's a sent'mental kind of song that Dammy's interested in which is about some gump lovin' a woman's pale hands beside the shallow Marne or some such place."

Benjamina brushed back her blazing hair with both slender hands and looked at the rosy nails. " 'Pale Hands,' I think– No, it's the Kashmir love song. It used to be sung a great deal."

Adam said "Thanks" in the doorway.

Then he turned, jamming the jewel case into his pocket, and lounged down the steps. His shoulders gleamed like oiled wood. He picked a handful of peaches from the basket, which would have burdened two mortals, and split one in his terrible fingers. He ate a peach absently and threw the red stone at a roaming chicken, infamously busy in the nasturtiums. Mrs. Egg leaned on the side of the door. A slight nervousness made her reach for the radishes that Benjamina was cleaning. Radishes always stimulated Mrs. Egg. She ate two and hoped that Edith Sims wouldn't happen to look at Adam's back. The undershirt showed both shoulder blades and most of the sentiment "Damn Kaiser Bill" tattooed in pink across Adam. It seemed indecorous at the moment of betrothal, and Mrs. Egg winced.

Then she wondered. Adam took another peach and pressed it in a hand. Its blood welled over his shoulder and smeared the rear of the shirt brilliantly. He scrubbed it thoroughly into the back of his cropped hair and massaged his flat abdomen with a second fruit. After some study he kicked his feet out of the moccasins and doubled down in his fluid manner to rub both insteps with black grease from valves of the motorcycle. Then he signaled contentment by a prolonged pouring of smoke from his mouth, gave his mother a glance as he tucked the cast moccasins into the fork of the apple tree, and fled down the driveway with a coughing of his machine's engine, barefoot, unspeakably soiled and magnificently shimmering with peach blood.

"Oh, Lord!" said Mrs. Egg.

Benjamina looked up from the radishes and asked "What did you say?"

Mrs. Egg meditated, eating a radish. Adam had favored Benjamina with some notice in these ten days, and his approval of her cooking was manifest. He had even eaten veal goulash, a dish that he usually declined. The girl was a lady, anyhow. Mrs. Egg exploded.

"Benjamina, Dammy's up to somethin'! His sisters keep tellin' me he ain't tactful, either! My gee! He simply washed himself in peach juice and went off to give Edith Sims her engagement ring! And left his moc'sins in the apple tree where he always used to put his cigarettes when his papa didn't think he was old enough to smoke. But heaven knows, I can't see that anything ever hurt Dammy! He's always been the neatest boy that ever lived, and had all his clothes made when he was in the Navy. It's perfectly true that he ain't dressed respectable once since he got home. Mercy, the other day he went in to see Edith in a half a khaki shirt that he'd been usin' to clean the garage floor with!"

Benjamina pared a radish with a flutter of her white fingers and asked, "How long have they been engaged, Mrs. Egg?"

"He had ten days' liberty, a year ago Christmas, and was home. It perfectly upset me, because Dammy hadn't ever paid any attention to the child. They got engaged at a dance Judge Randolph gave. It was extremely sudden," Mrs. Egg pondered, "although the Simses are very refined folks and Edith's a nice girl. All this year Edie's been with her aunt in Washington, going to school.—A boy who was four years in the Navy naturally ought to know when he's in love or not. But men do fall in love in the most accidental manner, Benjamina! They don't seem to have any intentions of it. My gee! A man who takes to runnin' after a girl for her money is within my comprehensions, or because she's good-lookin'.

But what most men marry most women for is beyond me. I'm forty-six years of age," she said, "but I still get surprised at things. I think I'll lie down.–Do you man'cure your nails, or are they as pink as that all the time?"

"They're naturally pink," Benjamina said.

"They're awful pretty," Mrs. Egg yawned, pausing in her advance to the door of the living room. Then it seemed guileful to increase this praise. She added "Dammy was sayin' so," and strolled into the living room, where twenty-five photographs of Adam stood on shelves and tables.

She closed the door and stopped to eat a peppermint out of a glass urn beside the phonograph's cabinet. Excitements worked in her. She brushed a fly from the picture of Adam in wrestling tights and sank on a vast couch. The leather cushions hissed, breathing out air under her descent. She closed her eyes and brooded.–If Adam wanted to annoy Edith Sims, he had chosen a means cleverly. The girl was elaborate as to dress and rather haughty about clothes. She had praised a shirt of Judge Randolph's second son before Adam pointedly on Sunday at tea in the veranda. Perturbations and guesses clattered in Mrs. Egg's mind. Then a real clatter in the kitchen roused her.

"I milked three cows," said Hamish Saunders to his sister in a loud and complacent voice.

Benjamina said less loudly but with vigor, "Hamish, you got a post card! I saw you reading it! I told you not to write anyone where we'd gone to. Now–"

Mrs. Egg knew that the boy was wiggling. He said, "Oh, I wrote Tick Matthews. He won't tell Cousin Joe, Benjy."

"He'll tell his mother and she'll tell everyone in the building! I didn't want anyone to know where we'd gone to!"

Mrs. Egg sat up. In a little, the lad spoke with a sound of male determination. He spoke airily. His hands must be jammed into his pockets. He said, "Now, Cousin Joe ain't going to come runnin' down here after us, Benjy. You've gone off, so that ought to sort of show him you ain't going to marry him. I was asking Adam if there's any law that a person's guardian can make 'em live with him if they don't want to–"

"You told him!"

"I did not!"

The girl said, "Don't talk so loud, Hamish! Mrs. Egg's taking a nap upstairs. You told him!"

"I didn't tell him a thing! I said there was a guy I knew that had run off from his guardian and–"

Benjamina burst into queer, vexed laughter. She said, "You might as well have told him! The day he came to the flat he asked who else lived there besides us. Cousin Joe's pipes were all over the place. It–"

"Look here! There's a judge in this town, and Mrs. Egg or Adam would tell him we're not children or imbeciles or nothin'! If Cousin Joe came down here lookin' for us–" Presently he said with misery in each syllable, "Don't cry, Benjy.–But nothin'll happen.–Anyhow, you'll be twenty-one in October and the court'll give you our income, 'stead of payin' it to Cousin Joe.–Bet you a dollar it's more than he says it is!" He whistled seven notes of a bugle call and then whimpered, "Quit cryin', Benjy!"

"F-finish these radishes," Benjamina commanded; "I want to go brush my hair."

There was the light sound of her soles on the back stairs. Mrs. Egg lay down again, wishing that the urn of peppermints was within reach. In the kitchen Hamish said "Aw, hell!" and the chair by the table creaked as he slumped into it. He would pare radishes very badly, Mrs. Egg thought.

She now thought of Benjamina with admiration. Adam had seen the girl's name on a list of women willing to take service in the country, at a Cleveland agency. He had gone to interview Benjamina, Mrs. Egg gathered, because a cook on the U.S.S. *Nevada* had been named Saunders and the word looked auspicious. Accident, said Mrs. Egg to herself, was the dominant principle of life. She was much interested. Benjamina had taken proper steps to get away from an unpleasant guardian and should be shielded from any consequences. Certainly a girl who could cook to satisfy Adam wasn't to be given back to some nameless male in Cleveland, in a flat. Mrs. Egg abhorred flats. A man who would coop two children in a flat deserved no consideration. And Adam required gallons of peach butter for winter use. Mrs. Egg arose, stalked openly into the kitchen and addressed Hamish as an equal. She said, "Bub, you're an awful tactful boy, and have sense. Dammy said so himself. Honesty is my policy, an' I may as well say that I could hear all you were talkin' with Benjamina right now.–Who is this Cousin Joe you've run off from?"

Hamish cut a radish in two and wretchedly stammered, "H-he's dad's cousin. He's a louse!"

Mrs. Egg drawled, "My gee! That's a awful good description of your relation! Now, I haven't any intention to lose Benjamina when she's the best cook I ever had, an' you're not as bad at milkin' as you might be. If this person comes down here or makes any fuss I'll see to it that he don't get anywheres. So if Benjamina gets frightened you tell her that I'm goin' to look after this."

"Yes'm," said Hamish.

He looked at Mrs. Egg with an awe that was soothing. She beamed and strolled out of the kitchen. Descending the steps one by one, she came to the level walk of the dooryard and marched along it toward the barns. Mr. Egg was taking a holiday with his sister, married to a dyspeptic clergyman in Chicago, and it was her duty to aid Adam by surveying the cows. She entered the barnyard and rounded the corner of the cows' palace into a group of farm hands bent above a trotting of dice on the clay. Adam looked up from this sport and said "'Lo, mamma," cheerfully.

"My gee," Mrs. Egg faltered, regarding a pile of silver before his knees, "I never saw you win a cent at any game before, Dammy!"

The giant grinned, cast the dice, and raked three dollars toward him. His eyes were black lights. He announced, "This is my lucky day, mamma!" and all the worshipful youths chuckled as he stood away from her husband's hirelings. Then he lit a cigarette and consumed half of its length in an appalling suction. The smoke jetted from his nostrils in a flood. He patted Mrs. Egg's upper chin with a thumb and said, "She gave me the air, mamma!"

"What?"

"She told me to fly my kite! She's off me! She's goin' to marry Jim Randolph. It's all flooie.–I'd like a tub of champagne an' five fried hens for supper! Mamma," said Adam, "I ain't engaged to that girl any more!" Therewith he took all the silver from his pocket and sent it in a chiming shower up the roof of the cow barn. His teeth flashed between his parted lips and dimples invaded his brown cheeks. He swung his arms restlessly and his mother thought that he would break into a dance. Adam reflected, "It's hell what happens by accident, mamma. Was a bowl of punch in the lib'ry at that dance of Judge Randolph's Christmas time that'd knock the teeth out of a horse. Had six cups. Saw this girl's hand hangin' over the banisters when I was headin' for the front door. I kissed it. Mamma, there ain't any way of tellin' a girl in this town that you don't mean anything when you kiss her. They don't understand it."

A devastating admiration of her child made Mrs. Egg's heart cavort. His manners were sublime. He lit another cigarette and stated, "Well, that's all of that." Then, wearied with much speech, he was still.

"Mercy, Dammy! This is an awful relief! Your sisters have been holdin' forth about Edith Sims bein' much more refined than God all afternoon. I was gettin' kind of scared of her.–What's that phonograph plate, lamb?"

Adam didn't answer, but ripped the envelope from the grained disk, and Mrs. Egg saw, on the advertising, "Kashmiri Song." But her thought had sunk to a profound and cooling peace; there would be no more

Edith Sims. She drawled, "Edith's pretty awful sedate, Dammy. I don't think she'd have the sand to run off from—a person she didn't like, or make her own livin'."

The giant flung up his arms and made certain gestures. Hamish Saunders came hurtling from the house for orders. Adam said, "Go get me some clothes, kid—white. And shoes 'n' a cake of soap. Then come swimmin'. Put this plate with the rest. Hustle!" He ground his nose with a fist, staring after the boy, then said, "Nice kid, mamma."

"Mercy, yes, Dammy! Dammy, it's pretty ridiculous to have Benjamina and the boy eat in the kitchen, and it takes tact to keep a nice girl like that contented. I think they'd better take their meals with us, sweetheart."

He nodded and strode off among the regular files of apple and pear trees toward the aimless riverlet that watered the farm. Mrs. Egg felt hunger stir in her bulk. She plucked an apple leaf and chewed its fragrant pulp, marching up the walk. Benjamina was soberly chopping the chickens for dinner into convenient bits.

Mrs. Egg applauded her performance, saying, "We'd better have 'em fried, I think. Dammy prefers it. And when you've got time you might go get one of those very big green bottles of pear cider down in the cellar, honey. It's awful explosive stuff and Hamish hadn't better drink any. And lay the table for four, because it's pretty lonely for Dammy eatin' with me steadily.—Edith Sims busted their engagement this afternoon, by the way, though it isn't at all important."

"Isn't it?"

Mrs. Egg refreshed herself with a bit of cracker from the table and drawled, "Not a bit, dearie. I've never heard of anybody's heart breakin' under the age of thirty over a busted engagement. Dammy's pretty much relieved, though too polite to say so, and Edith'll marry Judge Randolph's second boy, who's a very nice kid and has curly hair, although his teeth stick out some. So it don't seem to matter except to my daughters, who'll want Dammy to go into full mourning and die of sorrow. They're tearful girls, but nice. Let me show you how Dammy likes tomatoes fried when they're done with the chicken."

"Mrs. Egg," said Benjamina, "you're—a remarkable person." The slim, pale fingers twisted themselves against her dull blue frock into the likeness of a frightened white moth. She went on, "You—you never get excited."

"My gee! I haven't any patience with excitement, Benjamina. Things either go right or they go wrong. In either case, it's no good foamin' at the mouth and tryin' to kick the roof off. I'm like Dammy. I prefer to be calm," said Mrs. Egg. "As for scatterin' rays of sunshine like a Sunday-school hymn, most people don't thank anyone to do so–nor me, when I have indigestion."

"I–I feel much calmer since I've been here," Benjamina said. "It was so hot in the flat in Cleveland, and noisy. And it's very kind of you to ask Hamish and me to eat with you and Mr. Egg."

Her hands had become steadfast. She smiled a little.

"It'll be much more sociable, honey," Mrs. Egg reflected. "Even if Dammy don't talk, he likes company, havin' been in the Navy where he had lots.–Where's the biscuit flour? There's time to make some before supper."

The kitchen dimmed and Benjamina's tall body dulled into a restful shadow. She moved without noise and her pleasant voice was low. Mrs. Egg devised biscuits in comfort and smelled Adam's cigarettes in the living room. Hamish came to stimulate the making of this meal by getting his large feet in the way, and Mrs. Egg was scolding him tranquilly when the phonograph loosed a series of lazy notes. Then it sang, fervidly, of pale hands that it had loved beside some strange name.

"It's that Kashmir business," said Mrs. Egg. "Open the door, bub, so's we can hear."

The music swelled as the door opened and a circle of smoke died in the kitchen. Mrs. Egg saw Adam as a white pillar in the gloom. The machine sobbed "Where are you now? Where are you now?" with an oily sadness.

"Real touching," Mrs. Egg mentioned.

A crashing of the orchestra intervened. Then the voice cried, "Pale hands, pink-tipped, like lotus flowers that–" The words jumbled into sounds. Mrs. Egg hungrily yawned. The tenor wailed, "I would have rather felt you on my throat, crushing out life, than waving me farewell!" and the girl stirred beside the doorway, her hands in motion. The song expired with a thin noise of violins. Adam stopped the plate. An inexplicable silence filled the house, as if this stale old melody had wakened something that listened. Then Adam lit a cigarette.

"Supper near ready, mamma?"

"Pretty near, lamb," said Mrs. Egg.

Supper was pleasant. Hamish talked buoyantly of cows. He was impressed by their stupidity and their artless qualities. Benjamina gazed at the four candles with gray eyes and smiled at nothing. Adam ate fourteen hot biscuits and three mounds of an ice cream that held fresh raspberries. He stared at the ceiling gravely, and his white shirt tightened as he breathed out the first smoke above a cup of coffee.

Then he said, "We'll go to the movies. Get your hat, Miss Saunders."

"But the dishes aren't washed!" Benjamina exclaimed.

"The kid and I'll wash 'em," Adam vouchsafed.

Mrs. Egg yawned, "Go ahead, Benjamina," and watched the girl's hands flutter as she left the green dining room.

Adam blew a ring of smoke, which drooped, dissolving about a candle. He reached across the table for the coffee pot and filled his cup, then looked at Hamish.

"What's she scared of, Kid?"

"Cousin Joe," said Hamish presently. "He's—our guardian—wants to marry her. Y'see, we have some money from dad's store. Cousin Joe's a lawyer and the bank pays him the money."

"Lived with him in Cleveland?"

Hamish groaned, "You saw where we lived! Benjy couldn't keep the place lookin' decent. He knocked his pipe out wherever he sat. But Benjy'll be twenty-one in October and the bank'll pay her the money."

"An' this Joe's a sour plum?"

"Well," said Hamish, with the manner of last justice, "he can sing pretty well."

Mrs. Egg was thinking of bed at ten o'clock when the telephone rang and the anguished voice of her oldest daughter came pouring in from Ilium: "Mamma! Dammy's got that girl in a box at the movies!"

"I'm glad," said Mrs. Egg, "that they're sitting in a box. My gee! It's hot as I ever felt it for this time of year, Fern! Benjamina's such a large person that she—"

"Oh, mamma! And it's all over town that Edith Sims is going to marry—"

"I can't pretend that I'm either surprised or sorry, Fern. As for Dammy marryin' a girl he would have had to stoop over a yard to kiss after breakfast, it never seemed a just kind of arrangement to me, although I didn't want to criticize her. The Simses are nice folks—awful refined. Mercy, but don't Dammy look well in white pants?"

"Mamma! You simply haven't any heart!"

"I'll be forty-seven in December, Fern," said Mrs. Egg. "Good night."

She drowsily ascended to her cool bedroom, where a vacuum flask of iced lemonade stood with a package of oatmeal crackers on the bedside table. In the dark she lay listening to the obliging wind that now moved in the ten acres of orchard, and sometimes she chuckled, nibbling a cracker. Finally she slept, and was wakened by Adam's voice.

"Was it a nice picture, Dammy?"

"Fair. Where's that law dictionary dad got last year, mamma?"

"It's in the pantry, under the paraffin for the preserves, sweetheart."

"Thanks," said Adam, and his feet went softly away.

Mrs. Egg resumed her slumbers composedly, and woke on the first clash of milk pails in the barnyard. Day was clear. Adam could get in the rest of the peaches and paint the garage roof without discomfort. She ate a cracker, dressing, and went down the back stairs to find Benjamina grinding coffee in a white gown that set off color in her cheeks.

"Mercy," said Mrs. Egg, "but you're up real early!"

"I don't think it can be very healthy for Mr. Egg and Hamish to wait so long for breakfast," the girl said.

"The men's cook down at the bunkhouse always has coffee for Dammy. It's a sad time that Dammy can't get himself a meal around here, honey. But it's nice to have breakfast early. I think he's hungriest in the mornin'."

"Isn't he always hungry?"

"Always," Mrs. Egg assured her, beginning to pare chilled peaches; "and he likes your oatmeal, I notice. Bein' Scotch by descent, you understand the stuff. You've been here ten days, and it's remarkable how you've learned what Dammy likes. If he was talkative it wouldn't take so much intelligence. A very good way is to watch his toes. If they move he likes what he's eatin'. My gee! It was easy to tell when he was little and went barefooted. He's too tactful to complain about anything."

"He said, driving down from Cleveland, that he hated talking much," Benjamina murmured.

Adam's black head showed above his blue milking shirt in the barnyard. Mrs. Egg watched the tall girl's gray eyes quicken as she gazed down the wet grass. Morning mist fairly smoked from the turf and the boles of apple trees were moist. Hamish was lugging pails to the dairy valiantly.

"The high school here," said Mrs. Egg, "is very good for the size of the town, and Hamish will be perfectly comfortable in winters. You mustn't be alarmed by my husband when he comes back from Chicago. It's a nervous habit he has of winkin' his left eye. It don't mean a thing. I'll try to get hold of some girl that's reasonably intell'gent to do waitin' on table and dusting, which is not good for your hands."

"It's very nice here," Benjamina said, still looking at the barnyard.

Mrs. Egg decided that she was a beautiful creature. Her color improved breath by breath, and her face had the look of a goddess on a coin. The vast woman ate a peach and inspected this virgin hopefully. Then the pale hands shot to Benjamina's throat and she whirled from the window. Hamish tumbled through the door, his shoes smeared with milk and his mouth dragged into a gash of fright.

"It's Cousin Joe! He's gettin' out of a buggy at the gate!"

"Gracious!" said Mrs. Egg.

She rose and walked into the veranda, smoothing her hair. The man limping up from the white gates was tall and his shoulders seemed broad. He leaned on a cane. He wore a hat made of rough rings of straw. Mrs. Egg greatly disliked him at once, and went down the steps slowly, sideways. Adam was lounging up from the barnyard and some farm hands followed him in a clump of tanned faces. Light made their eyes flash. The woman sighed. There might be a deal of angry talk before she got rid of the lame person in black. He advanced and she awaited him under the apple tree below the steps. When he approached she saw that his hair was dull brown and sleek as he took off his hat.

"Mrs. Egg?"

"I am," said Mrs. Egg.

The man smoothly bowed. He was less than six feet tall, but burly and not pale. His mouth smiled charmingly. He glanced at Adam, smoking on the steps, and twirled the cane in his hand. He said, "My name's Hume. I'm an attorney. I'm the guardian of Benjamina and Hamish Saunders, my cousin's children. They're here, I understand?"

"I understand," Mrs. Egg drawled, "that you ain't much of a guardian, and they're better off here."

Adam's voice came over her shoulder, "They're goin' to stay here."

Cold sweat rose in Mrs. Egg's clenched hands. She turned and saw Adam's nostrils rigid, yellow on his bronze face. She said, "Go in to breakfast, Dammy. I'm talkin' to this person."

Adam might lose his temper. He must go away. She looked at him for a moment, and the farm hands made new shadows on the turf, approaching curiously. Then Adam turned and walked into the kitchen.

"We're wasting time," the man said, always smoothly. "Benjy's my ward and she's going back to Cleveland with me."

"I don't see as that follows, precisely," Mrs. Egg panted.

"The nearest justice would."

"Then you'd better get the nearest justice to say it," said Mrs. Egg, "because Benjamina's perfectly well off here. As for sendin' her back to Cleveland for you to make love at in a flat–my gee!"

She felt herself impolitic and tactless in saying this, but rage had mounted. Her chins were shaking. The man's clothes smelled of pipe smoke. His collar wasn't clean. He was a dog. The kitchen door slammed. She dreaded that Adam might lose his temper and thrash this fellow. The man looked over her head.

"Here," said Adam, "get out of the way, mamma, please! Let's settle this! Come ahead, Benj'mina. He can't hurt you." He was leading the girl down the steps by a hand. Smoke welled from his nostrils and his eyes had partly shut. He brought the white girl to face her cousin and said, "Now! My name's Adam Egg. Benjamina's married to me. Show him your rings, kid."

The farm hands gasped and an Irish lad shooped. Adam undid his brown fingers from the pale hand. The big diamond and the circlet of little stones blazed below the rosy nails. Mrs. Egg put her palm on her mouth and a scream was a pain in her throat. She hadn't seen Adam married! He threw away the cigarette by a red motion of his tongue and drawled, "Go back in the house, kid!"

The man clamped a hand on his cane and said, "Without my permission!"

"She's twenty," Adam grunted, his shoulders tremulous under the thin blue shirt, "so what you goin' to do?"

Then nothing happened. Benjamina walked up the steps and stood with an arm about Hamish at the top. A farm hand lit a pipe. Mrs. Egg's heart beat horribly with the pain of having missed Adam's wedding. The man's face was getting green. He was odious, completely. He said, "Their property stays in my control!"

"The hell with their property!"

Nothing happened. The man stood poking his cane into the turf and turning the thick end among grass blades. Hamish came down one step. Then the man backed and whirled up his cane.

Mrs. Egg shrieked "Dammy!" and bruised her lip with her teeth.

The heavy cane seemed to balance a long while against the sun. Adam stood. The thing fell across his right shoulder and broke with a cracking sound. The blue shirt tore and Benjamina screamed. Adam's whole length shook and his lips were gray for a second. He slung out both hands and caught the fellow's throat. He said, "Now! You've 'saulted me with a dangerous weapon, see? Now, get out of here! Here's your witnesses! You hit me! All I've got to do is walk you in to a judge and you'll get a year, see? That's law! Get out of this! I could kill you," he drawled, "an' I will if you ain't out the gates in one minute!"

His shoulders heaved. The shirt split down his back. The man went spinning in a queer rotation along the grass, like some collapsing toy. Adam stood with his hands raised, watching. The figure stumbled twice. Then it lurched toward the white gates in a full run, and the farm hands yelled. Adam dropped his hands and ripped the shirt from his shoulder. A band of scarlet had risen on the bronze of his chest. He said thickly, "Damn if he ain't a husky! Hey, Hamish, get me some iodine, will you?"

Benjamina ran down the steps and dragged the rings from her fingers. She babbled, "Oh! Oh, Adam! What did you let him strike you for? I'm so sorry!" She thrust the rings into one of his palms and cried, "You shouldn't have let him hit you! He's so strong!"

"What was I goin' to say if he said to show any weddin' certificate? If he hit me it was assault, an' I could get rid of him."

Mrs. Egg wailed, "Then you ain't married, Dammy?"

"No."

Adam leaned on the apple tree and stared at Benjamina, turning the rings in his hand. After a moment the girl flushed and walked away into the orchard of rustling boughs. A morning wind made the giant's torn shirt flap. He sent his eyes to the gaping hired men and drawled "What about those cows?"

Feet thudded off on the grass. Hamish came bounding down the steps with a bottle of iodine and a handkerchief.

"My gee, Dammy," said Mrs. Egg, grasping the bottle, "if your sisters have the nerve to say you're tactless after this I'll– Sit down, lamb! Oh, Dammy, how can you think as fast as that?"

Adam lit a cigarette and blew smoke through his nostrils. His face was again blank and undisturbed. He asked, "Peaches for breakfast?"

"Anything you want, lamb! Benjamina has oatmeal ready."

He clicked the rings in his hand and his feet wriggled in the moccasins. Then he said "Mamma," strangely.

"Yes, Dammy."

"Mamma, I've put Miss Saunders in a hell of a position, sayin' we're married."

"That's so, Dammy. It'll be all over town in no time."

Adam arose from the grass and examined his mother for a whole minute. His nostrils shook somewhat. He took the engagement ring from one palm and handed it to Hamish, ordering, "Kid, you go take that to your sister and tell her it's with my compliments. I hate talkin'."

The boy's red hair went flashing under the trees. Mrs. Egg watched him halt by his sister, who was wiping her eyes beside a trunk. They conferred. Soon Hamish turned about and began to make swift signs with his arms.

Adam said, "Good enough.–I guess I'll call her Ben." He lit his next cigarette and walked up the steps.

Mrs. Egg screamed, "Dammy! Ain't you goin' to go kiss her?"

Adam's eyes opened on his mother in alarm. He said, "I'm thirsty, mamma. And I've got to get a fresh shirt. Couldn't kiss anybody in this one. It wouldn't be polite."

Then he waved his cigarette to his new love and slammed the kitchen door behind him.

The Confirmation Suit **Brendan Behan**

When Brendan Behan came from Ireland to supervise the production of his first play in this country, his work was well received, although little was known of him at the time. I did not see the play nor have I read *Borstal Boy,* his first book success. My initial acquaintance with his work came some two years ago when I picked up a large and handsomely bound volume called *Brendan Behan's Island.* It consisted of sketches of various parts of the Emerald Isle which were extremely well done. About halfway through the volume, I encountered a rather short story. It had been wedged into the book for no particular reason that I could see, because it was in no way connected with the rest of the contents. But how glad I was to make its acquaintance! Here was a story animated by the gay and sentimental spirit which I have always felt can be found in Ireland and nowhere else, a tale filled with odd quirks of story and fancy.

The regrets which all must feel as a result of his recent death will be intensified after reading this charming tale.

When Brendan Behan came from Ireland to supervise the production of his first play in this country, his work was well received, although little was known of him at the time. I did not see the play nor have I read Borstal Boy, his first book success. My initial acquaintance with his work came some two years ago when I picked up a large and handsomely bound volume called *Brendan Behan's Island*. It consisted of sketches of various parts of the Emerald Isle which were extremely well done. About halfway through the volume, I encountered a rather little story. It had been wedged into the book for no particular reason that I could see, because it was in no way connected with the rest of the sketches. But how glad I was to make its acquaintance! Here was a story animated by the gay and sentimental spirit which I have always felt can be found in Ireland and nowhere else, a tale filled with odd quirks of [illegible] and fancy.

The tragedy which all must feel as a result of his recent death will be intensified when one reads this delightful tale.

THE CONFIRMATION SUIT

Brendan Behan

For weeks it was nothing but simony and sacrilege, and the sins crying to heaven for vengeance, the big green Catechism in our hands, walking home along the North Circular Road. And after tea, at the back of the brewery wall, with a butt too, to help our wits, what is a pure spirit, and don't kill that, Billser has to get a drag out of it yet, what do I mean by apostate, and hell and heaven and despair and presumption and hope. The big fellows, who were now thirteen and the veterans of last year's Confirmation, frightened us, and said the Bishop would fire us out of the Chapel if we didn't answer his questions, and we'd be left wandering around the streets, in a new suit and top-coat with nothing to show for it, all dressed up and nowhere to go. The big people said not to mind them; they were only getting it up for us, jealous because they were over their Confirmation, and could never make it again. At school we were in a special room to ourselves, for the last few days, and went round, a special class of people. There were worrying times too, that the Bishop would light on you, and you wouldn't be able to answer his questions. Or you might hear the women complaining about the price of boys' clothes.

'Twenty-two and sixpence for tweed, I'd expect a share in the shop for that. I've a good mind to let him go in jersey and pants for that.'

'Quite right, ma'am', says one to another, backing one another up, 'I always say what matter if they are good and pure'. What had that got to do with it, if you had to go into the Chapel in a jersey and pants, and every other kid in a new suit, kid gloves and tan shoes and a scoil* cap. The Cowan brothers were terrified. They were twins, and twelve years old, and every old one in the street seemed to be wishing a jersey and pants on them, and saying their poor mother couldn't be expected to do for two in the one year, and she ought to go down to Sister Monica and tell her to put one back. If it came to that, the Cowans agreed to fight it

* School

out, at the back of the brewery wall, whoever got best, the other would be put back.

I wasn't so worried about this. My old fellow was a tradesman, and made money most of the time. Besides, my grandmother, who lived at the top of the next house, was a lady of capernosity and function. She had money and lay in bed all day, drinking porter or malt, and taking pinches of snuff, and talking to the neighbours that would call up to tell her the news of the day. She only left her bed to go down one flight of stairs and visit the lady in the back drawing room, Miss McCann.

Miss McCann worked a sewing-machine, making habits for the dead. Sometimes girls from our quarter got her to make dresses and costumes, but mostly she stuck to the habits. They were a steady line, she said, and you didn't have to be always buying patterns, for the fashions didn't change, not even from summer to winter. They were like a long brown shirt, and a hood attached, that was closed over the person's face before the coffin lid was screwn down. A sort of little banner hung out of one arm, made of the same material, and four silk rosettes in each corner, and in the middle, the letters I.H.S., which mean, Miss McCann said; 'I Have Suffered'.

My grandmother and Miss McCann liked me more than any other kid they knew. I like being liked, and could only admire their taste.

My Aunt Jack, who was my father's aunt as well as mine, sometimes came down from where she lived, up near the Basin, where the water came from before they started getting it from Wicklow. My Aunt Jack said it was much better water, at that. Miss McCann said she ought to be a good judge. For Aunt Jack was funny. She didn't drink porter or malt, or take snuff, and my father said she never thought much about men, either. She was also very strict about washing yourself very often. My grandmother took a bath every year, whether she was dirty or not, but she was in no way bigoted in the washing line in between times.

Aunt Jack made terrible raids on us now and again, to stop snuff and drink, and make my grandmother get up in the morning, and wash herself, and cook meals and take food with them. My grandmother was a gilder by trade, and served her time in one of the best shops in the city, and was getting a man's wages at sixteen. She liked stuff out of the pork butchers, and out of cans, but didn't like boiling potatoes, for she said she was no skivvy, and the chip man was better at it. When she was left alone it was a pleasure to eat with her. She always had cans of lovely things and spicy meat and brawn, and plenty of seasoning, fresh out of the German man's shop up the road. But after a visit from Aunt Jack, she would have to get up and wash for a week, and she would have to go and make stews and boil cabbage and pig's cheeks. Aunt Jack was very much up for sheep's heads too. They were so cheap and nourishing.

But my grandmother only tried it once. She had been a first-class gilder in Eustace Street, but never had anything to do with sheep's heads before. When she took it out of the pot, and laid it on the plate, she and I sat looking at it, in fear and trembling. It was bad enough going into the pot, but with the soup streaming from its eyes, and its big teeth clenched in a very bad temper, it would put the heart crossways in you. My grandmother asked me, in a whisper, if I ever thought sheep could look so vindictive, but that it was more like the head of an old man, and would I for God's sake take it up and throw it out of the window. The sheep kept glaring at us, but I came the far side of it, and rushed over to the window and threw it out in a flash. My grandmother had to drink a Baby Power whiskey, for she wasn't the better of herself.

Afterwards she kept what she called her stock-pot on the gas. A heap of bones, and as she said herself, any old muck that would come in handy, to have boiling there, night and day, on a glimmer. She and I ate happily of cooked ham and California pineapple and sock-eye salmon, and the pot of good nourishing soup was always on the gas even if Aunt Jack came down the chimney, like the Holy Souls at midnight. My grandmother said she didn't begrudge the money for the gas. Not when she remembered the looks that sheep's head was giving her. And all she had to do with the stock-pot was to throw in another sup of water, now and again, and a handful of old rubbish the pork butcher would send over, in the way of lights or bones. My Aunt Jack thought a lot about barley, too, so we had a package of that lying beside the gas, and threw a sprinkle in any time her foot was heard on the stairs. The stock-pot bubbled away on the gas for years after, and only when my grandmother was dead did someone notice it. They tasted it, and spat it out just as quick, and wondered what it was. Some said it was paste, and more that it was gold size, and there were other people and they maintained that it was glue. They all agreed on one thing, that it was dangerous tack to leave lying around, where there might be young children, and in the heel of the reel, it went out the same window as the sheep's head.

Miss McCann told my grandmother not to mind Aunt Jack but to sleep as long as she liked in the morning. They came to an arrangement that Miss McCann would cover the landing and keep an eye out. She would call Aunt Jack in for a minute, and give the signal by banging the grate, letting on to poke the fire, and have a bit of a conversation with

Aunt Jack about dresses and costumes, and hats and habits. One of these mornings, and Miss McCann delaying a fighting action, to give my grandmother time to hurl herself out of bed and into her clothes and give her face the rub of a towel, the chat between Miss McCann and Aunt Jack came to my Confirmation suit.

When I made my first Communion, my grandmother dug deep under the mattress, and myself and Aunt Jack were sent round expensive shops, and I came back with a rig that would take the sight of your eye. This time, however, Miss McCann said there wasn't much stirring in the habit line, on account of the mild winter, and she would be delighted to make the suit, if Aunt Jack would get the material. I nearly wept, for terror of what these old women would have me got up in, but I had to let on to be delighted, Miss McCann was so set on it. She asked Aunt Jack did she remember my father's Confirmation suit. He did. He said he would never forget it. They sent him out in a velvet suit, of plum colour, with a lace collar. My blood ran cold when he told me.

The stuff they got for my suit was blue serge, and that was not so bad. They got as far as the pants, and that passed off very civil. You can't do much to a boy's pants, one pair is like the next, though I had to ask them not to trouble themselves putting three little buttons on either side of the legs. The waistcoat was all right, and anyway the coat would cover it. But the coat itself, that was where Aughrim* was lost.

The lapels were little wee things, like what you'd see in pictures like *Ring* magazine of John L. Sullivan, or Gentleman Jim, and the buttons were the size of saucers, or within the bawl of an ass of it, and I nearly cried when I saw them being put on, and ran down to my mother, and begged her to get me any sort of a suit, even a jersey and pants, than have me set up before the people in this get-up. My mother said it was very kind of Aunt Jack and Miss McCann to go to all this trouble and expense, and I was very ungrateful not to appreciate it. My father said that Miss McCann was such a good tailor that people were dying to get into her creations, and her handiwork was to be found in all the best cemeteries. He laughed himself sick at this, and said if it was good enough for him to be sent down to North William Street in plum-coloured velvet and lace, I needn't be getting the needle over a couple of big buttons and little lapels. He asked me not to forget to get up early the morning of my Confirmation, and let him see me, before he went to work: a bit of a laugh started the day well. My mother told him to give over and let me alone, and said she was sure it would be a lovely suit, and that Aunt Jack would never buy poor material, but stuff that would

* A battle in 1689 where the Irish were defeated.

last forever. That nearly finished me altogether, and I ran through the hall up to the corner, fit to cry my eyes out, only I wasn't much of a hand at crying. I went more for cursing, and I cursed all belonging to me, and was hard at it on my father, and wondering why his lace collar hadn't choked him, when I remembered that it was a sin to go on like that, and I going up for Confirmation, and I had to simmer down, and live in fear of the day I'd put on that jacket.

The days passed, and I was fitted and refitted, and every old one in the house came up to look at the suit, and took a pinch of snuff, and a sup out of the jug, and wished me long life and the health to wear and tear it, and they spent that much time viewing it round, back, belly and sides, that Miss McCann hadn't time to make the overcoat, and like an answer to a prayer, I was brought down to Talbot Street, and dressed out in a dinging overcoat, belted, like a grown-up man's. And my shoes and gloves were dear and dandy, and I said to myself that there was no need to let anyone see the suit with its little lapels and big buttons. I could keep the topcoat on all day, in the chapel, and going round afterwards.

The night before Confirmation day, Miss McCann handed over the suit to my mother, and kissed me, and said not to bother thanking her. She would do more than that for me, and she and my grandmother cried and had a drink on the strength of my having grown to be a big fellow, in the space of twelve years, which they didn't seem to consider a great deal of time. My father said to my mother, and I getting bathed before the fire, that since I was born Miss McCann thought the world of me. When my mother was in hospital, she took me into her place till my mother came out, and it near broke her heart to give me back.

In the morning I got up, and Mrs. Rooney in the next room shouted in to my mother that her Liam was still stalling, and not making any move to get out of it, and she thought she was cursed; Christmas or Easter, Communion or Confirmation, it would drive a body into Riddleys, which is the mad part of Grangegorman, and she wondered she wasn't driven out of her mind, and above in the puzzle factory years ago. So she shouted again at Liam to get up, and washed and dressed. And my mother shouted at me, though I was already knotting my tie, but you might as well be out of the world, as out of fashion, and they kept it up like a pair of mad women, until at last Liam and I were ready and he came in to show my mother his clothes. She hanselled him a tanner, which he put in his pocket and Mrs. Rooney called me in to show her my clothes. I just stood at her door, and didn't open my coat, but just grabbed the sixpence out of her hand, and ran up the stairs like the hammers of hell. She shouted at me to hold on a minute, she hadn't seen my suit, but I muttered something about it not being lucky to keep a Bishop waiting, and ran on.

The Church was crowded, boys on one side and the girls on the other, and the altar ablaze with lights and flowers, and a throne for the Bishop to sit on when he wasn't confirming. There was a cheering crowd outside, drums rolled, trumpeters from Jim Larkin's band sounded the Salute. The Bishop came in and the doors were shut. In short order I joined the queue to the rails, knelt and was whispered over, and touched on the cheek. I had my overcoat on the whole time, though it was warm, and I was in a lather of sweat waiting for the hymns and the sermon.

The lights grew brighter and I got warmer, was carried out fainting. But though I didn't mind them loosening my tie, I clenched firmly my overcoat, and nobody saw the jacket with the big buttons and the little lapels. When I went home, I got into bed, and my father said I went into a sickness just as the Bishop was giving us the pledge. He said this was a master stroke, and showed real presence of mind.

Sunday after Sunday, my mother fought over the suit. She said I was a liar and a hypocrite, putting it on for a few minutes every week, and running into Miss McCann's and out again, letting her think I wore it every week-end. In a passionate temper my mother said she would show me up, and tell Miss McCann, and up like a shot with her, for my mother was always slim, and light on her feet as a feather, and in next door. When she came back she said nothing, but sat at the fire looking into it. I didn't really believe she would tell Miss McCann. And I put on the suit and thought I would go in and tell her I was wearing it this week-night, because I was going to the Queen's with my brothers. I ran next door and upstairs, and every step was more certain and easy that my mother hadn't told her. I ran, shoved in the door, saying: 'Miss Mc., Miss Mc., Rory and Sean and I are going to the Queen's. . . .' She was bent over the sewing-machine and all I could see was the top of her old grey head, and the rest of her shaking with crying, and her arms folded under her head, on a bit of habit where she had been finishing the I.H.S. I ran down the stairs and back into our place, and my mother was sitting at the fire, sad and sorry, but saying nothing.

I needn't have worried about the suit lasting forever. Miss McCann didn't. The next winter was not so mild, and she was whipped before the year was out. At her wake people said how she was in a habit of her own making, and my father said she would look queer in anything else, seeing as she supplied the dead of the whole quarter for forty years, without one complaint from a customer.

At the funeral, I left my topcoat in the carriage and got out and walked in the spills of rain after her coffin. People said I would get my end, but I went on till we reached the graveside, and I stood in my Confirmation suit drenched to the skin. I thought this was the least I could do.

[illegible]
[illegible]
[illegible]

Johnny Pye and the Fool-Killer and The Ballad of Leif the Lucky
Stephen Vincent Benét

Many stories of exceptional originality came from the pen of Stephen Vincent Benét. One of them, which he called "Johnny Pye and the Fool-Killer," is not as well known as some of the others but it seems to me certain to fill a classic page in American folklore.

Johnny was an orphan who had been left in the unkind hands of people who constantly accused him of being a hopeless fool. He used to hear steps in the stillness of night which he believed meant the approach of the Fool-Killer! His story, as it is told here, is amusing and heart-warming.

Mr. Benét's *John Brown's Body* is still vividly remembered, but how many recall that some years later he told the earliest story of American history in one hundred lines of majestic blank verse called "The Ballad of Leif the Lucky"? I have the best of reasons for remembering it because I had the honor of publishing it in the August 1937 issue of a pocket-size magazine called *American Cavalcade,* of which I was editor. I have picked it up and read it again many times through the intervening years.

I am proud to present together these two splendid samples of a great writer's work.

JOHNNY PYE AND THE FOOL-KILLER

Stephen Vincent Benét

You don't hear so much about the Fool-Killer these days, but when Johnny Pye was a boy there was a good deal of talk about him. Some said he was one kind of person, and some said another, but most people agreed that he came around fairly regular. Or, it seemed so to Johnny Pye. But then, Johnny was an adopted child, which is, maybe, why he took it so hard.

The miller and his wife had offered to raise him, after his own folks died, and that was a good deed on their part. But, as soon as he lost his baby teeth and started acting the way most boys act, they began to come down on him like thunder, which wasn't so good. They were good people, according to their lights, but their lights were terribly strict ones, and they believed that the harder you were on a youngster, the better and brighter he got. Well, that may work with some children, but it didn't with Johnny Pye.

He was sharp enough and willing enough—as sharp and willing as most boys in Martinsville. But, somehow or other, he never seemed to be able to do the right things or say the right words—at least when he was home. Treat a boy like a fool and he'll act like a fool, I say, but there's some folks need convincing. The miller and his wife thought the way to smarten Johnny was to treat him like a fool, and finally they got so he pretty much believed it himself.

And that was hard on him, for he had a boy's imagination, and maybe a little more than most. He could stand the beatings and he did. But what he couldn't stand was the way things went at the mill. I don't suppose the miller intended to do it. But, as long as Johnny Pye could remember, whenever he heard of the death of somebody he didn't like, he'd say, "Well, the Fool-Killer's come for so-and-so," and sort of smack his lips. It was, as you might say, a family joke, but the miller was a big man with a big red face, and it made a strong impression on Johnny Pye. Till, finally, he got a picture of the Fool-Killer, himself. He was a big man, too, in a checked shirt and corduroy trousers, and he went walking the ways of the world, with a hickory club that had a lump of lead in the end of it. I don't know how Johnny Pye got that picture so clear, but, to him, it was just as plain as the face of any human being in Martinsville. And, now and then, just to test it, he'd ask a grown-up person, kind of timidly, if that was the way the Fool-Killer looked. And, of course, they'd generally laugh and tell him it was. Then Johnny would wake up at night, in his room over the mill, and listen for the Fool-Killer's step on the road and wonder when he was coming. But he was brave enough not to tell anybody that.

Finally, though, things got a little more than he could bear. He'd done some boy's trick or other–let the stones grind a little fine, maybe, when the miller wanted the meal ground coarse–just carelessness, you know. But he'd gotten two whippings for it, one from the miller and one from his wife, and, at the end of it, the miller had said, "Well, Johnny Pye, the Fool-Killer ought to be along for you most any day now. For I never did see a boy that was such a fool." Johnny looked to the miller's wife to see if she believed it, too, but she just shook her head and looked serious. So he went to bed that night, but he couldn't sleep, for every time a bough rustled or the mill wheel creaked, it seemed to him it must be the Fool-Killer. And, early next morning, before anybody was up, he packed such duds as he had in a bandanna handkerchief and ran away.

He didn't really expect to get away from the Fool-Killer very long–as far as he knew, the Fool-Killer got you wherever you went. But he thought he'd give him a run for his money, at least. And when he got on the road, it was a bright spring morning, and the first peace and quiet he'd had in some time. So his spirits rose, and he chunked a stone at a bullfrog as he went along, just to show he was Johnny Pye and still doing business.

He hadn't gone more than three or four miles out of Martinsville, when he heard a buggy coming up the road behind him. He knew the Fool-Killer didn't need a buggy to catch you, so he wasn't afraid of it, but he stepped to the side of the road to let it pass. But it stopped, instead, and a black-whiskered man with a stovepipe hat looked out of it.

"Hello, bub," he said. "Is this the road for East Liberty?"

"My name's John Pye and I'm eleven years old," said Johnny, polite but firm, "and you take the next left fork for East Liberty. They say it's a pretty town–I've never been there myself." And he sighed a little, because he thought he'd like to see the world before the Fool-Killer caught up with him.

"H'm," said the man. "Stranger here, too, eh? And what brings a smart boy like you on the road so early in the morning?"

"Oh," said Johnny Pye, quite honestly, "I'm running away from the Fool-Killer. For the miller says I'm a fool and his wife says I'm a fool and almost everybody in Martinsville says I'm a fool except little Susie Marsh. And the miller says the Fool-Killer's after me—so I thought I'd run away before he came."

The black-whiskered man sat in his buggy and wheezed for a while. When he got his breath back, "Well, jump in, bub," he said. "The miller may say you're a fool, but I think you're a right smart boy to be running away from the Fool-Killer all by yourself. And I don't hold with small-town prejudices and I need a right smart boy, so I'll give you a lift on the road."

"But, will I be safe from the Fool-Killer, if I'm with you?" said Johnny. "For, otherwise, it don't signify."

"Safe?" said the black-whiskered man, and wheezed again. "Oh, you'll be safe as houses. You see, I'm a herb doctor—and some folks think, a little in the Fool-Killer's line of business, myself. And I'll teach you a trade worth two of milling. So jump in, bub."

"Sounds all right the way you say it," said Johnny, "but my name's John Pye," and he jumped into the buggy. And they went rattling along toward East Liberty with the herb doctor talking and cutting jokes till Johnny thought he'd never met a pleasanter man. About half a mile from East Liberty, the doctor stopped at a spring.

"What are we stopping here for?" said Johnny Pye.

"Wait and see," said the doctor, and gave him a wink. Then he got a haircloth trunk full of empty bottles out of the back of the buggy and made Johnny fill them with spring water and label them. Then he added a pinch of pink powder to each bottle and shook them up and corked them and stowed them away.

"What's that?" said Johnny, very interested.

"That's Old Doctor Waldo's Unparalleled Universal Remedy," said the doctor, reading from the label.

"Made from the purest snake oil and secret Indian herb, it cures rheumatism, blind staggers, headache, malaria, five kinds of fits, and spots in front of the eyes. It will also remove oil or grease stains, clean knives and silver, polish brass, and is strongly recommended as a general tonic and blood purifier. Small size, one dollar—family bottle, two dollars and a half."

"But I don't see any snake oil in it," said Johnny, puzzled, "or any secret Indian herbs."

"That's because you're not a fool," said the doctor, with another wink. "The Fool-Killer wouldn't, either. But most folks will."

And, that very same night, Johnny saw. For the doctor made his pitch in East Liberty and he did it handsome. He took a couple of flaring oil torches and stuck them on the sides of the buggy; he put on a diamond stickpin and did card tricks and told funny stories till he had the crowd goggle-eyed. As for Johnny, he let him play on the tambourine. Then he started talking about Doctor Waldo's Universal Remedy, and, with Johnny to help him, the bottles went like hot cakes. Johnny helped the doctor count the money afterward, and it was a pile.

"Well," said Johnny, "I never saw money made easier. You've got a fine trade, Doctor."

"It's cleverness does it," said the doctor, and slapped him on the back. "Now a fool's content to stay in one place and do one thing, but the Fool-Killer never caught up with a good pitchman yet."

"Well, it's certainly lucky I met up with you," said Johnny, "and, if it's cleverness does it, I'll learn the trade or bust."

So he stayed with the doctor quite a while—in fact, till he could make up the remedy and do the card tricks almost as good as the doctor. And the doctor liked Johnny, for Johnny was a biddable boy. But one night they came into a town where things didn't go as they usually did. The crowd gathered as usual, and the doctor did his tricks. But, all the time, Johnny could see a sharp-faced little fellow going through the crowd and whispering to one man and another. Till, at last, right in the middle of the doctor's spiel, the sharp-faced fellow gave a shout of "That's him all right! I'd know them whiskers anywhere!" and, with that, the crowd growled once and began to tear slats out of the nearest fence. Well, the next thing Johnny knew, he and the doctor were being ridden out of town on a rail, with the doctor's long coattails flying at every jounce.

They didn't hurt Johnny particular—him only being a boy. But they warned 'em both never to show their faces in that town again, and then they heaved the doctor into a thistle patch and went their ways.

"Owoo!" said the doctor, "ouch!" as Johnny was helping him out of the thistle patch. "Go easy with those thistles! And why didn't you give me the office, you blame little fool?"

"Office?" said Johnny. "What office?"

"When that sharp-nosed man started snooping around," said the doctor. "I thought that infernal main street looked familiar—I was through there two years ago, selling solid gold watches for a dollar apiece."

"But the works to a solid gold watch would be worth more than that," said Johnny.

"There weren't any works," said the doctor, with a groan, "but there was a nice lively beetle inside each case and it made the prettiest tick you ever heard."

"Well, that certainly was a clever idea," said Johnny. "I'd never have thought of that."

"Clever?" said the doctor. "Ouch—it was ruination! But who'd have thought the fools would bear a grudge for two years? And now we've lost the horse and buggy, too—not to speak of the bottles and the money. Well, there's lots more tricks to be played and we'll start again."

But, though he liked the doctor, Johnny began to feel dubious. For it occurred to him that, if all the doctor's cleverness got him was being ridden out of town on a rail, he couldn't be so far away from the Fool-Killer as he thought. And, sure enough, as he was going to sleep that night, he seemed to hear the Fool-Killer's footsteps coming after him—step, step, step. He pulled his jacket up over his ears, but he couldn't shut it out. So, when the doctor had got in the way of starting business over again, he and Johnny parted company. The doctor didn't bear any grudge; he shook hands with Johnny and told him to remember that cleverness was power. And Johnny went on with his running away.

He got to a town, and there was a store with a sign in the window, BOY WANTED, so he went in. There, sure enough, was the merchant, sitting at his desk, and a fine, important man he looked, in his black broadcloth suit.

Johnny tried to tell him about the Fool-Killer, but the merchant wasn't interested in that. He just looked Johnny over and saw that he looked biddable and strong for his age. "But, remember, no fooling around, boy!" said the merchant sternly, after he'd hired him.

"No fooling around?" said Johnny, with the light of hope in his eyes.

"No," said the merchant, meaningly. "We've no room for fools in this business, I can tell you! You work hard, and you'll rise. But, if you've got any foolish notions, just knock them on the head and forget them."

Well, Johnny was glad enough to promise that, and he stayed with the merchant a year and a half. He swept out the store, and he put the shutters up and took them down; he ran errands and wrapped up packages and learned to keep busy twelve hours a day. And, being a biddable boy and an honest one, he rose, just like the merchant had said. The merchant raised his wages and let him begin to wait on customers and learn accounts. And then, one night, Johnny woke up in the middle of the night. And it seemed to him he heard, far away but getting nearer, the steps of the Fool-Killer after him—tramping, tramping.

He went to the merchant next day and said, "Sir, I'm sorry to tell you this, but I'll have to be moving on."

"Well, I'm sorry to hear that, Johnny," said the merchant, "for you've been a good boy. And, if it's a question of salary—"

"It isn't that," said Johnny, "but tell me one thing, sir, if you don't mind my asking. Supposing I did stay with you—where would I end?"

The merchant smiled. "That's a hard question to answer," he said, "and I'm not much given to compliments. But I started, myself, as a boy, sweeping out the store. And you're a bright youngster with lots of go-ahead. I don't see why, if you stuck to it, you shouldn't make the same kind of success that I have."

"And what's that?" said Johnny.

The merchant began to look irritated, but he kept his smile.

"Well," he said, "I'm not a boastful man, but I'll tell you this. Ten years ago I was the richest man in town. Five years ago, I was the richest man in the county. And five years from now—well, I aim to be the richest man in the state."

His eyes kind of glittered as he said it, but Johnny was looking at his face. It was sallow-skinned and pouchy, with the jaw as hard as a rock. And it came upon Johnny that moment that, though he'd known the merchant a year and a half, he'd never really seen him enjoy himself except when he was driving a bargain.

"Sorry, sir," he said, "but, if it's like that, I'll certainly have to go. Because, you see, I'm running away from the Fool-Killer, and if I stayed here and got to be like you, he'd certainly catch up with me in no—"

"Why, you impertinent young cub!" roared the merchant, with his face gone red all of a sudden. "Get your money from the cashier!" and Johnny was on the road again before you could say "Jack Robinson." But, this time, he was used to it, and walked off whistling.

Well, after that, he hired out to quite a few different people, but I won't go into all of his adventures. He worked for an inventer for a while, and they split up because Johnny happened to ask him what would be the good of his patent, self-winding, perpetual-motion machine, once he did get it invented. And, while the inventor talked big about improving the human race and the beauties of science, it was plain he didn't know. So that night, Johnny heard the steps of the Fool-Killer, far off but coming closer, and, next morning, he went away. Then he stayed with a minister for a while, and he certainly hated to leave him, for the minister was a good man. But they got talking one evening and, as it chanced, Johnny asked him what happened to people who didn't believe in his particular religion. Well, the minister was broad-minded, but there's only one answer to that. He admitted they might be good folks–he even admitted they mightn't exactly go to hell–but he couldn't let them into heaven, no, not the best and the wisest of them, for there were the specifications laid down by creed and church, and, if you didn't fulfill them, you didn't.

So Johnny had to leave him, and, after that, he went with an old drunken fiddler for a while. He wasn't a good man, I guess, but he could play till the tears ran down your cheeks. And, when he was playing his best, it seemed to Johnny that the Fool-Killer was very far away. For, in spite of his faults and his weaknesses, while he played, there was might in the man. But he died drunk in a ditch, one night, with Johnny to hold his head, and, while he left Johnny his fiddle, it didn't do Johnny much good. For, while Johnny could play a tune, he couldn't play like the fiddler–it wasn't in his fingers.

Then it chanced that Johnny took up with a company of soldiers. He was still too young to enlist, but they made a kind of pet of him, and everything went swimmingly for a while. For the captain was the bravest man Johnny had ever seen, and he had an answer for everything, out of regulations and the Articles of War. But then they went West to fight Indians and the same old trouble cropped up again. For one night the captain said to him, "Johnny, we're going to fight the enemy tomorrow, but you'll stay in camp."

"Oh, I don't want to do that," said Johnny; "I want to be in on the fighting."

"It's an order," said the captain, grimly. Then he gave Johnny certain instructions and a letter to take to his wife.

"For the colonel's a copper-plated fool," he said, "and we're walking straight into an ambush."

"Why don't you tell him that?" said Johnny.

"I have," said the captain, "but he's the colonel."

"Colonel or no colonel," said Johnny, "if he's a fool, somebody ought to stop him."

"You can't do that, in an army," said the captain. "Orders are orders." But it turned out the captain was wrong about it, for, next day, before they could get moving, the Indians attacked and got badly licked. When it was all over, "Well, it was a good fight," said the captain, professionally. "All the same, if they'd waited and laid in ambush, they'd have had our hair. But, as it was, they didn't stand a chance."

"But why didn't they lay in ambush?" said Johnny.

"Well," said the captain, "I guess they had their orders too. And now, how would you like to be a soldier?"

"Well, it's a nice outdoors life, but I'd like to think it over," said

Johnny. For he knew the captain was brave and he knew the Indians had been brave–you couldn't find two braver sets of people. But, all the same, when he thought the whole thing over, he seemed to hear steps in the sky. So he soldiered to the end of the campaign and then he left the army, though the captain told him he was making a mistake.

By now, of course, he wasn't a boy any longer; he was getting to be a young man with a young man's thoughts and feelings. And, half the time, nowadays, he'd forget about the Fool-Killer except as a dream he'd had when he was a boy. He could even laugh at it now and then, and think what a fool he'd been to believe there was such a man.

But, all the same, the desire in him wasn't satisfied, and something kept driving him on. He'd have called it ambitiousness, now, but it came to the same thing. And with every new trade he tried, sooner or later would come the dream–the dream of the big man in the checked shirt and corduroy pants, walking the ways of the world with his hickory stick in one hand. It made him angry to have that dream, now, but it had a singular power over him. Till, finally, when he was turned twenty or so, he got scared.

"Fool-Killer or no Fool-Killer," he said to himself. "I've got to ravel this matter out. For there must be some one thing a man could tie to, and be sure he wasn't a fool. I've tried cleverness and money and half a dozen other things, and they don't seem to be the answer. So now I'll try book learning and see what comes of that."

So he read all the books he could find, and whenever he'd seem to hear the steps of the Fool-Killer coming for the authors–and that was frequent–he'd try and shut his ears. But some books said one thing was best and some another, and he couldn't rightly decide.

"Well," he said to himself, when he'd read and read till his head felt as stuffed with book learning as a sausage with meat, "it's interesting, but it isn't exactly contemporaneous. So I think I'll go down to Washington and ask the wise men there. For it must take a lot of wisdom to run a country like the United States, and if there's people who can answer my questions, it's there they ought to be found."

So he packed his bag and off to Washington he went. He was modest for a youngster, and he didn't intend to try and see the President right away. He thought probably a congressman was about his size. So he saw a congressman, and the congressman told him the thing to be was an upstanding young American and vote the Republican ticket–which which sounded all right to Johnny Pye, but not exactly what he was after.

Then he went to a senator, and the senator told him to be an upstanding young American and vote the Democratic ticket–which sounded all right, too, but not what he was after, either. And, somehow, though both men had been impressive and affable, right in the middle of their speeches he'd seemed to hear steps—you know.

But a man has to eat, whatever else he does, and Johnny found he'd better buckle down and get himself a job. It happened to be with the first congressman he struck, for that one came from Martinsville, which is why Johnny went to him in the first place. And, in a little while, he forgot his search entirely and the Fool-Killer, too, for the congressman's niece came East to visit him, and she was the Susie Marsh that Johnny had sat next in school. She'd been pretty then, but she was prettier now, and as soon as Johnny Pye saw her, his heart gave a jump and a thump.

"And don't think we don't remember you in Martinsville, Johnny Pye," she said, when her uncle had explained who his new clerk was. "Why, the whole town'll be excited when I write home. We've heard all about your killing Indians and inventing perpetual motion and traveling around the country with a famous doctor and making a fortune in dry goods and—oh, it's a wonderful story!"

"Well," said Johnny, and coughed, "some of that's just a little bit exaggerated. But it's nice of you to be interested. So they don't think I'm a fool any more, in Martinsville?"

"I never thought you were a fool," said Susie with a little smile, and Johnny felt his heart give another bump.

"And I always knew you were pretty, but never how pretty till now," said Johnny, and coughed again. "But, speaking of old times, how's the miller and his wife? For I did leave them right sudden, and while there were faults on both sides, I must have been a trial to them too."

"They've gone the way of all flesh," said Susie Marsh, "and there's a new miller now. But he isn't very well-liked, to tell the truth, and he's letting the mill run down."

"That's a pity," said Johnny, "for it was a likely mill." Then he began to ask her more questions and she began to remember things too. Well, you know how the time can go when two youngsters get talking like that.

Johnny Pye never worked so hard in his life as he did that winter. And it wasn't the Fool-Killer he thought about—it was Susie Marsh. First he thought she loved him and then he was sure she didn't, and then he was betwixt and between, and all perplexed and confused. But, finally, it turned out all right and he had her promise, and Johnny Pye knew he was the happiest man in the world. And that night, he waked up in the night and heard the Fool-Killer coming after him—step, step, step.

He didn't sleep much after that, and he came down to breakfast hollow-eyed. But his uncle-to-be didn't notice that—he was rubbing his hands and smiling.

"Put on your best necktie, Johnny!" he said, very cheerful, "for I've got an appointment with the President today, and, just to show I approve of my niece's fiancé, I'm taking you along."

"The President!" said Johnny, all dumbfounded.

"Yes," said Congressman Marsh, "you see, there's a little bill—well, we needn't go into that. But slick down your back hair, Johnny—we'll make Martinsville proud of us this day!"

Then a weight seemed to go from Johnny's shoulders and a load from his heart. He wrung Mr. Marsh's hand.

"Thank you, Uncle Eben!" he said. "I can't thank you enough." For, at last, he knew he was going to look upon a man that was bound to be safe from the Fool-Killer—and it seemed to him if he could just once do that, all his troubles and searchings would be ended.

Well, it doesn't signify which President it was—you can take it from me that he was President and a fine-looking man. He'd just been elected, too, so he was lively as a trout, and the saddle galls he'd get from Congress hadn't even begun to show. Anyhow, there he was, and Johnny feasted his eyes on him. For if there was anybody in the country the Fool-Killer couldn't bother, it must be a man like this.

The President and the congressman talked politics for a while, and then it was Johnny's turn.

"Well, young man," said the President, affably, "and what can I do for you—for you look to me like a fine, upstanding young American."

The congressman cut in quick before Johnny could open his mouth.

"Just a word of advice, Mr. President," he said. "Just a word in season. For my young friend's led an adventurous life, but now he's going to marry my niece and settle down. And what he needs most of all is a word of ripe wisdom from you."

"Well," said the President, looking at Johnny rather keenly, "if that's all he needs, a short horse is soon curried. I wish most of my callers wanted as little."

But, all the same, he drew Johnny out, as such men can, and before Johnny knew it, he was telling his life story.

"Well," said the President, at the end, "you certainly have been a rolling stone, young man. But there's nothing wrong in that. And, for one of your varied experience there's one obvious career. Politics!" he said, and slapped his fist in his hand.

"Well," said Johnny, scratching his head, "of course, since I've been in Washington, I've thought of that. But I don't know that I'm rightly fitted."

"You can write a speech," said Congressman Marsh, quite thoughtful, "for you've helped me with mine. You're a likeable fellow too. And you were born poor and worked up—and you've even got a war record—why, hell! Excuse me, Mr. President!—he's worth five hundred votes just as he stands!"

"I—I'm more than honored by you two gentlemen," said Johnny, abashed and flattered, "but supposing I did go into politics—where would I end up?"

The President looked sort of modest.

"The Presidency of the United States," said he, "is within the legitimate ambition of every American citizen. Provided he can get elected, of course."

"Oh," said Johnny, feeling dazzled, "I never thought of that. Well, that's a great thing. But it must be a great responsibility too."

"It is," said the President, looking just like his pictures on the campaign buttons.

"Why, it must be an awful responsibility!" said Johnny. "I can't hardly see how a mortal man can bear it. Tell me, Mr. President," he said, "may I ask you a question?"

"Certainly," said the President, looking prouder and more responsible and more and more like his picture on the campaign buttons every minute.

"Well," said Johnny, "it sounds like a fool question, but it's this: This is a great big country of ours, Mr. President, and it's got the most amazing lot of different people in it. How can any President satisfy all those people at one time? Can you yourself, Mr. President?"

The President looked a bit taken aback for a minute. But then he gave Johnny Pye a statesman's glance.

"With the help of God," he said, solemnly, "and in accordance with the principles of our great party, I intend . . ."

But Johnny didn't even hear the end of the sentence. For, even as the President was speaking, he heard a step outside in the corridor and he knew, somehow, it wasn't the step of a secretary or a guard. He was glad the President had said "with the help of God" for that sort of softened the step. And when the President finished, Johnny bowed.

"Thank you, Mr. President," he said; "that's what I wanted to know. And now I'll go back to Martinsville, I guess."

"Go back to Martinsville?" said the President, surprised.

"Yes, sir," said Johnny. "For I don't think I'm cut out for politics."

"And is that all you have to say to the President of the United States?" said his uncle-to-be, in a fume.

But the President had been thinking, meanwhile, and he was a bigger man than the congressman.

"Wait a minute, Congressman," he said. "This young man's honest, at least, and I like his looks. Moreover, of all the people who've come to see me in the last six months, he's the only one who hasn't wanted something—except the White House cat, and I guess she wanted something, too, because she meowed. You don't want to be President, young man—and, confidentially, I don't blame you. But how would you like to be postmaster at Martinsville?"

"Postmaster at Martinsville?" said Johnny. "But—"

"Oh, it's only a tenth-class post office," said the President, "but, for once in my life, I'll do something because I want to, and let Congress yell its head off. Come—is it yes or no?"

Johnny thought of all the places he'd been and all the trades he'd worked at. He thought, queerly enough, of the old drunk fiddler dead in the ditch, but he knew he couldn't be that. Mostly, though, he thought of Martinsville and Susie Marsh. And, though he'd just heard the Fool-Killer's step, he defied the Fool-Killer.

"Why, it's yes, of course, Mr. President," he said, "for then I can marry Susie."

"That's as good a reason as you'll find," said the President. "And now, I'll just write a note."

Well, he was as good as his word, and Johnny and his Susie were married and went back to live in Martinsville. And, as soon as Johnny learned the ways of postmastering, he found it as good a trade as most. There wasn't much mail in Martinsville, but, in between whiles, he ran the mill, and that was a good trade too. And all the time, he knew, at the back of his mind, that he hadn't quite settled accounts with the Fool-Killer. But he didn't much care about that, for he and Susie were happy. And after a while they had a child, and that was the most remarkable experience that had ever happened to any young couple, though the doctor said it was a perfectly normal baby.

One evening, when his son was about a year old, Johnny Pye took the river road, going home. It was a mite longer than the hill road, but it was the cool of the evening, and there's times when a man likes to walk by himself, fond as he may be of his wife and family.

He was thinking of the way things had turned out for him, and they seemed to him pretty astonishing and singular, as they do to most folks, when you think them over. In fact, he was thinking so hard that, before he knew it, he'd almost stumbled over an old scissors grinder who'd set up his grindstone and tools by the side of the road. The scissors grinder had his cart with him, but he'd turned the horse out to graze—

and a lank, old, white horse it was, with every rib showing. And he was very busy, putting an edge on a scythe.

"Oh, sorry," said Johnny Pye. "I didn't know anybody was camping here. But you might come around to my house tomorrow–my wife's got some knives that need sharpening."

Then he stopped, for the old man gave him a long, keen look.

"Why, it's you, Johnny Pye," said the old man. "And how do you do, Johnny Pye! You've been a long time coming–in fact, now and then, I thought I'd have to fetch you. But you're here at last."

Johnny Pye was a grown man now, but he began to tremble.

"But it isn't you!" he said, wildly. "I mean you're not him! Why, I've known how he looks all my life! He's a big man, with a checked shirt, and he carries a hickory stick with a lump of lead in one end."

"Oh, no," said the scissors grinder, quite quiet. "You may have thought of me that way, but that's not the way I am." And Johnny Pye heard the scythe go whet-whet-whet on the stone. The old man ran some water on it and looked at the edge. Then he shook his head as if the edge didn't quite satisfy him. "Well, Johnny, are you ready?" he said, after a while.

"Ready?" said Johnny, in a hoarse voice. "Of course I'm not ready."

"That's what they all say," said the old man, nodding his head, and the scythe went whet-whet on the stone.

Johnny wiped his brow and started to argue it out.

"You see, if you'd found me earlier," he said, "or later. I don't want to be unreasonable, but I've got a wife and a child."

"Most has wives and many has children," said the old man, grimly, and the scythe went whet-whet on the stone as he pushed the treadle. And a shower of sparks flew, very clear and bright, for the night had begun to fall.

"Oh, stop that damn racket and let a man think for a minute!" said Johnny, desperate. "I can't go, I tell you. I won't. It isn't time. It's–"

The old man stopped the grindstone and pointed with the scythe at Johnny Pye.

"Tell me one good reason," he said. "There's men would be missed in the world, but are you one of them? A clever man might be missed, but are you a clever man?"

"No," said Johnny, thinking of the herb doctor. "I had a chance to be clever, but I gave it up."

"One," said the old man, ticking off on his fingers. "Well, a rich man might be missed–by some. But you aren't rich, I take it."

"No," said Johnny, thinking of the merchant, "nor wanted to be."

"Two," said the old man. "Cleverness–riches–they're done. But there's still martial bravery and being a hero. There might be an argument to make, if you were one of those."

Johnny Pye shuddered a little, remembering the way that battlefield had looked, out West, when the Indians were dead and the fight over.

"No," he said, "I've fought, but I'm not a hero."

"Well, then, there's religion," said the old man, sort of patient, "and science, and–but what's the use? We know what you did with those. I might feel a trifle of compunction if I had to deal with a President of the United States. But–"

"Oh, you know well enough I ain't President," said Johnny, with a groan. "Can't you get it over with and be done?"

"You're not putting up a very good case," said the old man, shaking his head. "I'm surprised at you, Johnny. Here you spend your youth running away from being a fool. And yet, what's the first thing you do, when you're man grown? Why, you marry a girl, settle down in your home town, and start raising children when you don't know how they'll turn out. You might have known I'd catch up with you, then–you just put yourself in my way."

"Fool I may be," said Johnny Pye in his agony, "and if you take it like that, I guess we're all fools. But Susie's my wife, and my child's my child. And, as for work in the world–well, somebody has to be postmaster, or folks wouldn't get the mail."

"Would it matter much if they didn't?" said the old man, pointing his scythe.

"Well, no, I don't suppose it would, considering what's on the post cards," said Johnny Pye. "But while it's my business to sort it, I'll sort it as well as I can."

The old man whetted his scythe so hard that a long shower of sparks flew out on the grass.

"Well," he said, "I've got my job, too, and I do it likewise. But I'll tell you what I'll do. You're coming my way, no doubt of it, but, looking you over, you don't look quite ripe yet. So I'll let you off for a while. For that matter," said he, "if you'll answer one question of mine–how a man can be a human being and not be a fool–I'll let you off permanent. It'll be the first time in history," he said, "but you've got to do something on your own hook, once in a while. And now you can walk along, Johnny Pye."

With that he ground the scythe till the sparks flew out like the tail of a comet and Johnny Pye walked along. The air of the meadow had never seemed so sweet to him before.

All the same, even with his relief, he didn't quite forget, and sometimes Susie had to tell the children not to disturb father because he was thinking. But time went ahead, as it does, and pretty soon Johnny Pye found he was forty. He'd never expected to be forty, when he was young, and it kind of surprised him. But there it was, though he couldn't say he felt much different, except now and then when he stooped over. And he was a solid citizen of the town, well-liked and well-respected, with a growing family and a stake in the community, and when he thought those things over, they kind of surprised him too. But, pretty soon, it was as if things had always been that way.

It was after his eldest son had been drowned out fishing that Johnny Pye met the scissors grinder again. But this time he was bitter and distracted, and, if he could have got to the old man, he'd have done him a mortal harm. But, somehow or other, when he tried to come to grips with him, it was like reaching for air and mist. He could see the sparks fly from the ground scythe, but he couldn't even touch the wheel.

"You coward!" said Johnny Pye. "Stand up and fight like a man!" But the old man just nodded his head and the wheel kept grinding and grinding.

"Why couldn't you have taken me?" said Johnny Pye, as if those words had never been said before. "What's the sense in all this? Why can't you take me now?"

Then he tried to wrench the scythe from the old man's hands, but he couldn't touch it. And then he fell down and lay on the grass for a while.

"Time passes," said the old man, nodding his head. "Time passes."

"It will never cure the grief I have for my son," said Johnny Pye.

"It will not," said the old man, nodding his head. "But time passes. Would you leave your wife a widow and your other children fatherless for the sake of your grief?"

"No, God help me!" said Johnny Pye. "That wouldn't be right for a man."

"Then go home to your house, Johnny Pye," said the old man. And Johnny Pye went, but there were lines in his face that hadn't been there before.

And time passed, like the flow of the river, and Johnny Pye's children married and had houses and children of their own. And Susie's hair grew white, and her back grew bent, and when Johnny Pye and his children followed her to her grave, folks said she'd died in the fullness of years, but that was hard for Johnny Pye to believe. Only folks didn't talk as plain as they used to, and the sun didn't heat as much, and sometimes, before dinner, he'd go to sleep in his chair.

And once, after Susie had died, the President of those days came through Martinsville and Johnny Pye shook hands with him and there was a piece in the paper about his shaking hands with two Presidents, fifty years apart. Johnny Pye cut out the clipping and kept it in his pocketbook. He liked this President all right, but, as he told people, he wasn't a patch on the other one fifty years ago. Well, you couldn't expect it–you didn't have Presidents these days, not to call them Presidents. All the same, he took a lot of satisfaction in the clipping.

He didn't get down to the river road much any more–it wasn't too long a walk, of course, but he just didn't often feel like it. But, one day, he slipped away from the granddaughter that was taking care of him, and went. It was kind of a steep road, really–he didn't remember its being so steep.

"Well," said the scissors grinder, "and good afternoon to you, Johnny Pye."

"You'll have to talk a little louder," said Johnny Pye. "My hearing's perfect, but folks don't speak as plain as they used to. Stranger in town?"

"Oh, so that's the way it is," said the scissors grinder.

"Yes, that's the way it is," said Johnny Pye. He knew he ought to be afraid of this fellow, now he'd put on his spectacles and got a good look at him, but for the life of him, he couldn't remember why.

"I know just who you are," he said, a little fretfully. "Never forgot a face in my life, and your name's right on the tip of my tongue–"

"Oh, don't bother about names," said the scissors grinder. "We're old acquaintances. And I asked you a question, years ago–do you remember that?"

"Yes," said Johnny Pye, "I remember." Then he began to laugh–a high, old man's laugh. "And of all the fool questions I ever was asked," he said, "that certainly took the cake."

"Oh?" said the scissors grinder.

"Uh-huh," said Johnny Pye. "For you asked me how a man could be a human being and yet not be a fool. And the answer is–when he's dead and gone and buried. Any fool would know that."

"That so?" said the scissors grinder.

"Of course," said Johnny Pye. "I ought to know. I'll be ninety-two next November, and I've shook hands with two Presidents. The first President I shook–"

"I'll be interested to hear about that," said the scissors grinder, "but we've got a little business, first. For, if all human beings are fools, how does the world get ahead?"

"Oh, there's lots of other things," said Johnny Pye, kind of impatient. "There's the brave and the wise and the clever–and they're apt to roll it ahead as much as an inch. But it's all mixed in together. For, Lord, it's only some fool kind of creature that would have crawled out of the sea to dry land in the first place—or got dropped from the Garden of Eden, if you like it better that way. You can't depend on the kind of folks people think they are—you've got to go by what they do. And I wouldn't give much for a man that some folks hadn't thought was a fool, in his time."

"Well," said the scissors grinder, "you've answered my question—at least as well as you could, which is all you can expect of a man. So I'll keep my part of the bargain."

"And what was that?" said Johnny. "For, while it's all straight in my head, I don't quite recollect the details."

"Why," said the scissors grinder, rather testy, "I'm to let you go, you old fool! You'll never see me again till the Last Judgment. There'll be trouble in the office about it," said he, "but you've got to do what you like, once in a while."

"Phew!" said Johnny Pye. "That needs thinking over!" And he scratched his head.

"Why?" said the scissors grinder, a bit affronted. "It ain't often I offer a man eternal life."

"Well," said Johnny Pye, "I take it very kind, but, you see, it's this way." He thought for a moment. "No," he said, "you wouldn't understand. You can't have touched seventy yet, by your looks, and no young man would."

"Try me," said the scissors grinder.

"Well," said Johnny Pye, "it's this way," and he scratched his head again. "I'm not saying—if you'd made the offer forty years ago, or even twenty. But, well, now, let's just take one detail. Let's say 'teeth.'"

"Well, of course," said the scissors grinder, "naturally—I mean you could hardly expect me to do anything about that."

"I thought so," said Johnny Pye. "Well, you see, these are good, bought teeth, but I'm sort of tired of hearing them click. And spectacles, I suppose, the same?"

"I'm afraid so," said the scissors grinder. "I can't interfere with time, you know—that's not my department. And, frankly, you couldn't expect, at a hundred and eighty, let's say, to be quite the man you was at ninety. But still, you'd be a wonder!"

"Maybe so," said Johnny Pye, "but, you see—well, the truth is, I'm an old man now. You wouldn't think it to look at me, but it's so. And my friends—well, they're gone—and Susie and the boy—and somehow you don't get as close to the younger people, except the children. And to keep on just going and going till Judgment Day, with nobody around to talk to that had real horse sense—well, no, sir, it's a handsome offer but I just don't feel up to accepting it. It may not be patriotic of me, and I feel sorry for Martinsville. It'd do wonders for the climate and the chamber of commerce to have a leading citizen live till Judgment Day. But a man's got to do as he likes, at least once in his life." He stopped and looked at the scissors grinder. "I'll admit, I'd kind of like to beat out Ike Leavis," he said. "To hear him talk, you'd think nobody had ever pushed ninety before. But I suppose—"

"I'm afraid we can't issue a limited policy," said the scissors grinder.

"Well," said Johnny Pye, "I just thought of it. And Ike's all right." He waited a moment. "Tell me," he said, in a low voice. "Well, you know what I mean. Afterwards. I mean, if you're likely to see"—he coughed—"your friends again. I mean, if it's so—like some folks believe."

"I can't tell you that," said the scissors grinder. "I only go so far."

"Well, there's no harm in asking," said Johnny Pye, rather humbly. He peered into the darkness; a last shower of sparks flew from the scythe, then the whir of the wheel stopped.

"H'm," said Johnny Pye, testing the edge. "That's a well-ground scythe. But they used to grind 'em better in the old days." He listened and looked, for a moment, anxiously. "Oh, Lordy!" he said, "there's Helen coming to look for me. She'll take me back to the house."

"Not this time," said the scissors grinder. "Yes, there isn't bad steel in that scythe. Well, let's go, Johnny Pye."

THE BALLAD OF LEIF THE LUCKY

Stephen Vincent Benét

Leif was blown from Norway with a crew of thirty-five,
His head still buzzing with a waif word that spoke of a new land,
The yellow cub of the old sea-bear who sat in Ericstead,
Nursing his gout and his heathen gods, remembering voyages.

All Eric's sons were sailors. When the child was yet unweaned,
They bore it down in a hollow shield to wet its lips with the foam.
The boys played viking on the beach, and screamed like gulls in the cold.
The grey fog clung to the women's hair, the grey drops sprinkled the shield.

Leif was the eldest of them, a strong oar, bitted with bronze,
A longship marked for strange landfalls, a lucky skipper to serve.
He had Christ's sign on his forehead but his heart was the gannet's heart
That faces the Northwester. So he and his men set sail.

Set sail for the rocks of Greenland, but the blind storm fell on them
And for days that had no number they drove where the tempest willed,
Westward and always westward, till earth was an idle dream,
And the days of it unremembered, but the ship like a live thing still.

They had no magic shut in a box to show them North and South
Nor any course to follow, for the whole world lay behind;
There was only sea and the pole-star, and the sea was very great,
When the fog came down, they drifted, a nutshell steered by a wraith.

A nutshell lost in waste billows and blown by a warlock wind,
For these were not Christian waters, where the green berg chilled the heart,
And, down in the sea-trolls' cavern, the shapeless hosts of the deep
Sat mumbling the bones of heroes forgotten by Christ and Thor.

It was all one to Leif's shipment. If the storm came, they rode the storm.
If the warlock rose from the ocean, they would drive a spear at his side.

They slept on the bare oar-benches, when they had time to sleep,
And dreamt of grass and sweet water and roasted meat in the fire.

It is not told who sighted the first faint smudge of land,
Like an oar drifting the waters, like an elm-branch drowned in the wave,
That hail is lost in the darkness, they took no record of it.
They knew they had come a journey. That was enough for the fame.

The new land drifted toward them, they could smell the land by now.
The bearded men stared westward with blue, sea-weary eyes.
A harsh coast and a barren, with fields of ice inland.
And the stretch between sea and glacier one naked and lifeless stone.

This was the land called Helluland, the rocky-hearted waste,
Leif laughed in his throat as he looked at it. "A stone shall be thy name!"
"We have come too far to find but this, by earth and grass and bread,
Out oars, out oars, O Greenland men, and try the seas again!"

The second land they came to was a better land to find,
The white sands gleamed in the sunlight, the trees grew thick and strong,
A man might raise a hearth there and live forgotten of Time.
Leif called it Markland the Wooded and put to sea once more.

So, after two days sailing, they touched at a grassy isle
And tasted the sweet dew of the grass with lips where the salt still lay,
So they passed into shallow waters where the ship itself took ground
And did not wait for the next high tide but ran ashore with a cry.

I see them tasting that dew-sweet grass. I see them running ashore.
Through the little pools if the ebb-tide and crying out as they run.
One man took a stone and skipped it, like a child on holiday,
Another strove with his comrade like two cub-wolves in the sun.

Beyond them the virgin forest lay as it had lain from the first,
A forest of game and weather, a pure and savage domain,
No foot had ever trod it but the skin-shod foot of the wild
And the stag might die in his age there and never hear arrow fly.

The earth was a purse of bounty, the salmon leaped in the streams,
The grass withered but little for there was no frost in the year.
They built a house in the forest and lived there, caught in a dream,
For the day and the night were changed there and the sun shone winter long.

They found green vines in the forest, they found wild grapes on the vine,
They loaded the ship with timber and brought the cargo home,

But the wealth was not in the cargo, the wealth was the trodden wave
And the star tracked down past sunset till the forest rose from the sea.

They made their sagas of it when Leif was a grey old man
Fed out of a bowl by children, with hands too shaken to hold
The sword-hilt or the wine-cup or the rudder of the ship,
When Thorvald mouldered in Vineland, the arrow that slew him dust.

The voice rang from the ale-bench, the magic sang from the harp,
"Lieth a land to Westward–a star that our fathers found–
Vineland the Good they named it–it was thus that the ship set forth–
They spoke thus and they did thus–we tell the tale as it fell."

The harp uttered its music but the words were brief and plain.
The song was a skein of sea-dyed yarn that passed from hand to hand.
I make my saga of it, with short words out of the North
And dye it with earth and water and the cones of the forest-pine.

There was a land called Vineland. It was thus they came to its shore
And lived there like men enchanted for a year of Indian grace–
A phantom walks on the sea-beach, a man with a winged helm–
The ghost of a ship puts Eastward, with sun-dried grapes in its hold–

After came Thorvald and Thorfinn, and Freydis, slayer of men,
There was trading and war and murder and a white child born in the wild.
The Skraelings cast down sable-furs, in barter for scarlet cloth
And when Karsefni's bullock roared, the Skraelings ran away.

There was a fort they lived in, and clearing made with their hands,
A stream where the women washed their gear, a fire where the men told tales
And always there was the forest that listened and said no word.
The ships went back to Greenland. The wind in the forest blew.

It blew from Time, it blew upon Time, and the palisade sank down,
The grass grew over the booths of Leif and over the fire-scorched stone.
Already the crosses tottered, where Thorvald lay in his grave.
The thick grass covered them, fallen; the seasons leveled the mound.

For awhile there was still a clearing, for awhile there was trace and sign,
A scrap of red cloth, sun-faded, in a skin-clad woman's hair.
The broken blade of a war-axe, long-rusted with many rains.
Then the rune blurred out altogether. The land had mastered the rune.

The new growth covered the clearing. The wood came down to the sea.
The grape might grow for an age there and never be pressed to wine.
The gold and the iron lay hidden like spirits under the ground
And the fame slept and the evil, until Columbus came.

A Portrait Reversed **George Bradshaw**

Here is the way it starts:

"You are," Malherbes said, "like all artists, dishonourable."

"I'm afraid so."

Malherbes, who happened to be the greatest of all modernistic artists, proceeded then to explain a plan he had in his mind to his guest, who was a young American author. It was an ingenious plan but certainly not one that could be conceived with honorable intent or listened to with an agreement in which honor had a part. It is well known that in the art world buyers must beware; and this clever and, it must be acknowledged, amusing scheme was one which would make the acquisition of masterpieces a very hazardous matter, indeed.

But the story must be read to discover what this course of action was, and how it all came out.

A PORTRAIT REVERSED

George Bradshaw

If you were driving along the coast road from Cannes to Monte Carlo, say, you would find nothing much to detain you in Trou-sur-Mer. It has no casino, no great hotel, no chic beach; only two very French bars, a number of utilitarian stores and one excellent restaurant, which you would not see, as it is hidden in a cul-de-sac. But if you were interested enough to climb one of the serpentine roads which lead abruptly away from the coast you would find a number of pleasant villas, pretty squares and magnificent views.

I came to live in Trou-sur-Mer by chance and because of the view. One afternoon, lying on the sand at Juan-les-Pins, I read a book of Guy de Maupassant's, and in one of the stories he described the sun setting over Antibes from his terrace in Trou-sur-Mer: "Never," he said, "had I seen anything so astonishingly beautiful. I was haunted . . ." and so on. I made then a leisurely resolve to take a look, which I did some days later, and my eyes confirmed de Maupassant's words completely. I found that I could rent a suitable pink house with a garden; and after not too many French delays, I moved in.

The place suited me. Trou-sur-Mer was a quiet, but by no means sleepy, Riviera town. My neighbours treated me with friendly unconcern, and the tradespeople cheated me only so much as would show polite recognition that I was an American. I had a fairly set routine; I swam in the morning, had lunch, took a nap and then wrote during the late afternoon and night.

My first friend of any intimacy was the butcher, M. Biran. I stopped in occasionally to get our meat and so save my cook a trip down the hill. It appeared that some years before he had sold meat to Edith Wharton; she was a writer, she was an American. When he discovered I was not only an American but a writer, and a customer, the whole affair appeared to him as a considerable coincidence, and we had a certain amount of talk about it. Mrs Wharton, I was given to understand, however, had spent a good deal more on meat than I did.

I mention M. Biran because it was in his cool, dark shop one hot noonday that my relationship with Maurice Malherbes began.

I knew, of course, that Malherbes lived at Trou. He was as much the local monument as Picasso at Juan, or Matisse at Vence, or Maugham at Cap Ferrat. But so great was his fame that I had been too shy even to nod to him, although I saw him fairly often on the road which led past my house to his. If he was not the greatest modern painter, he was so near the top as to make differences negligible; I admired him without any possibility of criticism.

When I came into the butcher's shop this day, Malherbes was at the counter, arguing very rapidly with Biran. He was a big man, strong, as apparently all good painters must be, almost bald, with a brown beard turning white.

Biran, it was clear, was displeased and adamant. In one hand he held a bill, with the other he kept pushing a small piece of paper with a drawing upon it towards Malherbes, who kept returning it.

Finally Malherbes shrugged. Biran then ripped from its roll a very large piece of the grey-white paper which he used to wrap meat, smoothed it out on the marble counter and handed Malherbes a large black pencil. Malherbes made a few tentative circular motions in the air, and then proceeded to draw one of the most beautiful sketches of a centaur I have ever set eyes upon.

When he finished, Biran looked, nodded and then tore up the bill. Malherbes picked up a large package and left.

I said to Biran, "That is how he pays his butcher's bill, eh?"

Biran nodded. "I am by way of being something of a patron of the arts," he said, "but I am not a fool. For two months not one cent, not one drawing, and now he tries to settle for so small a picture as you saw. This is better, eh?"

"You have many of his drawings?" I said.

"Several," Biran said, and set about preparing the meat my cook had ordered.

I wanted that centaur, passionately. I have not greed for many things, but there are some pictures I cannot control myself against. "I suppose," I said, "you never consider selling any of them."

"No," said Biran.

"Ah," I said.

"Oh," he said, "occasionally, to people I know would appreciate. You understand?"

I nodded.

"That one," Biran gestured towards his treasure, "is a something you could fall in love with."

"So," I said, "sell it to me before you fall in love with it."

Biran immediately lost interest. I saw I had made a mistake. So I left, and after that, day after day, we haggled. It was my cook, of course, who finally arranged the bargain. I am afraid she did it not so much for love of me as for love of talk. The picture and the deal provided a great topic. She was very happy, and for one hundred dollars I got a picture which would have cost two thousand in any Manhattan gallery.

When Malherbes heard what had happened, he was furious. For, whatever the opinion of the local citizenry, he knew perfectly well what his pictures were worth. By way of his cook and my cook, I heard how he cursed.

But suddenly one day he appeared all smiles in my garden. Would I please, would I be so kind, but the little centaur which he had sketched for M. Biran, it had a certain–well, a certain stance–it was hard to explain these things, he said, to non-painters–which he found would be useful as a model in a picture he was now painting; in short, he wanted to incorporate the centaur into a larger work, and would I permit that he take the centaur–for a few days only, of course–to his studio so he could copy, would I be so kind?

I was immediately suspicious. If once he got my centaur away, I felt sure I would never see it again. Yet, this famous man, I could not refuse him so simple a request. So I said but of course, of course; however, would he do me one small, one infinitesimal favour?

He would.

I was, I said, such an ardent admirer of his work, that I could hardly bear the centaur out of my sight; would he, then, lend me one other picture to look at while he kept the centaur?

At this his face fell, but in a moment he narrowed his eyes and a smile appeared on his face. Yes, he would.

My fears were well-founded, for every picture I selected had some mark against it: This one was sold, those were being sent to Paris to his dealer in the morning, that one was going to the framer's, this was unfinished. He felt crestfallen, he did so want to live up to the bargain, but . . .

"Wait," he said finally. From against a wall he took a picture. "What about this?"

It was a Matisse, and one which I had heard about. Malherbes and Matisse had one day agreed to exchange pictures, and it had been their pleasure to present to each other their worst paintings. It had been a celebrated contest, but Matisse, it was agreed, had won, but only just. This was a terrible Matisse.

"No," I said, and shuddered in exaggerated disgust.

Malherbes shrugged. Obviously I was beaten.

But just by chance I turned, and through a slightly opened door I saw —well, one of the famous paintings of the twentieth century. Malherbes' Eagle with Skull—a picture I had seen in a thousand reproductions. It had been painted ten years before; it was his, I knew, and it was framed.

"I'll take that," I said.

Malherbes picked up the centaur, rolled it carefully, and threw it in my face. "Take it, take it, take it," he said. "I can draw a hundred pictures better than that. It is of no use to me. I do not need models. Get out. Take it."

Fortunately, I laughed. Fortunately, for in a moment Malherbes looked at me, and then he, too, began to laugh. He came and put his great arm on my shoulders, and we rocked together. He brought out a bottle of wine, we drank, I stayed to dinner, I looked at a hundred of his pictures he had hidden away, we talked, talked, talked; and finally, when at midnight I rolled down to my house, I had in my hand my centaur, and written on it, in a somewhat unsteady hand, was "Malherbes, *à son ami.*"

Why, in the months that followed, we became friends, I cannot tell you, but we did. He liked to talk, I liked to listen, that was part of it, but more than that we developed a genuine fondness for each other.

So much so that when in November I had to go to Paris for a couple of weeks, he decided to come too, and took me to stay at his apartment in the Rue des Grands Augustins.

I was, therefore—and it is this I have been leading up to so long—concerned from the very beginning, and intimately concerned, with the affair, the scandal, whatever you want to call it, of Malherbes' paintings —for the story broke, you remember, on the eighteenth of November.

I was directly responsible for the beginning. The second day I was in Paris, I ran into, in Morgan's bank, a fellow I had known casually for years, a very rich man who was, like M. Biran the butcher, something of a patron of the arts. He and his wife owned a lot of pictures, invested in ballet, subsidised second-rate poets, and in general did a certain amount of good. I like them well enough and they always had good food at their house. Therefore when, even after their rather too obvious surprise when I told them I was staying with Malherbes, they asked me to dinner, I accepted. As we parted, Lottie—Lottie Samuel—naturally said, "And bring the great man along, if you can."

Perhaps that "if you can" rankled, so I took Malherbes. The Samuels' apartment was one of those luxuries near the Rond Point, and we had, I must say, a dinner which even Malherbes was ecstatic about. Afterwards, rather dramatically, we were ushered along a hall to a drawing-room we had not previously seen, the door was thrown open and there, over the mantel, in the place of honour, was a really fine Malherbes. Lottie turned, after we had all exclaimed properly, to Malherbes and asked rather coyly, "Aren't you going to say anything?"

Malherbes looked blank. "What do you expect me to say?"

"Well," Lottie said, "I thought it would please you to see anything so beautiful again."

Malherbes turned away, "I assure you, madame," he said, "I have never seen that picture before in my life."

I think "commotion" is the only word to explain what occurred during the next half hour. The Samuels were appalled and, more than that, devastated. Forty thousand dollars' worth devastated. But the news, the unbelievable, electrifying news, was that this affair was no surprise to Malherbes.

"My dear people," he said, "I have known about the Malherbes forger for years. I walk along a street, and in a gallery window I will see a picture I might very well have painted–this subject, I mean–and it is signed with my name, but I have never seen it before. I have complained, certainly, but some dealers do not believe me, some do not want to. What can I do? The forger is a competent painter, he is not so good that I am ever envious of him, but he is clever. I have tried to trace him, but the pictures show up mostly from America or England. He does not paint as I do now, but in my style of fifteen or twenty years ago. I have not seen one for some time." He stopped and went over to the mantel. "Look," he said, "that picture is not more than two or three years old. You can tell by the paint. Yet I did the series like that eighteen years ago."

There was, of course, a vast amount more of conversation, but nothing more to the point. There it was. I gathered, when I shook hands in a rather strained good night with Lottie, that I had not been an entirely successful guest. Dinner had cost her forty thousand dollars, plus food.

Something I should have mentioned before is this: There was, among the dozen people at dinner that night, a foreign correspondent named Edgar Wyndam. Apparently, before he went to bed, he cabled a detailed story to his paper in New York. Within two days the repercussions began.

For, of course, the interest in the story became worldwide. The old man, like all great painters, was prolific; there were hundreds of his canvases, and now, over every one had been cast the shadow of a doubt.

Reporters from every newspaper and every wire service in Paris crowded into the apartment on Rue des Grands Augustins, for the money involved was enormous, possibly in the millions. Pictures, remember, are now, too, about the only really liquid international currency.

By the end of a week the thing happened which I suppose I should have expected: people began to bring their pictures to the apartment to have them judged. On the first day there were two, the next day five, and on the third, when Malherbes and I came home after a long lunch, there were eleven suspicious people sitting in his studio.

Of all the pictures Malherbes examined those first few days not one was a fake. But a further sensation occurred when one of the French newsmen, who had kept on with the story, asked Malherbes, "Just where can one see a forgery?"

And Malherbes replied, "In the Luxembourg. The picture called Yellow Arrangement Number Three is not mine."

The reaction to this was curious. The amount of space devoted to this piece of news—in the Paris papers, at least—was more than had been given to the original story of the forgeries. The directors of the Luxembourg Museum were by turn haughty and hurt, but there was really nothing very much they could do about it directly. Malherbes certainly ought to know his own painting. However, French officialdom is not unresourceful, and a couple of days later a newspaper piece appeared which subtly slandered the patriotism of Maurice Malherbes. The Luxembourg was a national museum, its pictures therefore national treasure; whoever plundered the national treasure was of course not a good Frenchman. Too, it implied that Malherbes was now so old and feeble that he couldn't tell his own picture if he saw it.

That, of course, excited a certain frenzy. Dozens of letters were written defending Malherbes, who was actually at the height of his power; the Luxembourg let go with another barrage, and in no time at all there had been whipped up one of those fine artistic battles royal which can occur only in Paris.

Gide and Malraux both wrote articles pointing out that Yellow Arrangement Number Three was without Malherbes' sure colour distinction; a committee of art students staged a demonstration in the Gardens; an art critic on a conservative London weekly wrote that all of Malherbes' paintings were forgeries on the fair face of culture; all of France to a man stood aghast that an Englishman should have the temerity to pronounce the word "culture." Well, well, it was lovely, and Malherbes and I, our two weeks more than over, took the Blue Train and went back to Trou-sur-Mer.

But a situation existed at home. Not an hour after we arrived Malherbes sent his cook down the hill with instructions to bring me back without fail.

"Regard," he said, when I stepped into his big white studio, and I regarded. Around the floor were strewn more than a dozen crates, and there was no doubt what they contained: pictures.

"From everywhere they come," Malherbes said. "England, America, Kansas City, Madrid, Glasgow. Look."

"What did you expect?" I said.

Malherbes began to walk up and down. "But what do I do?"

"Open them."

He made a violent gesture with his arms. "Am I a carpenter? Am I no longer a painter? Do I put away my brushes and get out a hammer?"

"You have a certain obligation," I said.

"I?"

"Naturally. You've put a sinister bar over every picture."

Malherbes considered, but he obviously wasn't impressed. Suddenly he shook a finger at me and nodded his head. "I know what I will do. I will send a telegram to everybody and say 'Don't send pictures.'"

I said, "Have you a list of everybody?"

"A list?" Malherbes said. "Where would I get a list? Ah, I see what you mean."

"Anyway," I said, "you would be unfair to yourself. Would anyone ever again believe he had a real Malherbes if you refuse? You must protect your reputation."

Malherbes nodded. "Yes, yes. But I can't have this. Look. And I have a picture I have thought of I must paint tomorrow. Well, well. We'll see."

We saw a couple of days later, when he strode into my house, his beard and cape flying, and a triumphant look in his eye. "Now it is done," he said.

"How?" I said.

"I have just been over to Nice, to the headquarters of the press wires –Reuters, Associated, and the rest of them. I have given them a message for the world."

"Did they take it?" I said.

"Of course they took it, dog."

I laughed. "It was what?"

Malherbes sat down and pushed aside all my notes I had so carefully arranged. "It came to me last night," he said, "when I could not sleep for worrying and because I had eaten too much *langouste gratinée*. Now listen."

"Yes."

"I have said, I will look at any picture—provided, of course, it is accompanied by enough money to open and shut it and pay the return freight. That is only natural, I think. Now even you will have to admit I am fair, eh?"

"But where is the catch?" I said.

"So"—Malherbes shut his eyes and waggled his head in a smile—"this is what I also said. I said I would return the real pictures, but the forgeries I would not return."

"I don't see anything so sly about that," I said.

Malherbes waved me away. "Ah. You do not know people. There I am wiser than you. In America you do not know everything. Listen, my friend. No one who owns pictures, no one, will risk losing even a false Malherbes."

"It's a fancy scheme," I said, "but if it succeeds, it's somehow basically immoral."

"Ah," Malherbes said, "but it is the world that will be immoral, not I. You wait."

Well, we did not have to wait long. The world, in a spectacular demonstration of a point, continued to send the pictures. Malherbes was, I think, taken aback. He could not quite understand what had gone wrong. His trouble was that he was a simple man—vain, I have said, yes, but he had the vanity of the creator, the man who can do, and knows it, not the vanity of the possessor, the owner. He knew his pictures were worth a great deal of money, but I think their money value was to him a thing of an instant, the instant at which his dealer took a cheque. Before that, leaning against the wall in his studio, or after, hanging on the wall in a museum, they were not money, but beauty, something to be loved. So, by that standard, even a false Malherbes could be cared for, and who would want to lose something he cared for?

But the world, from Capetown to San Francisco, took a different attitude, and the pictures continued to arrive. Finally, with a shrug, Malherbes accepted the situation, hired a framer's assistant to uncrate and crate the pictures, and himself spent, I suppose, no more than five minutes a week saying yes or no.

He said to me once, "It is not so bad, really. Most people seem to have an exaggerated idea of what it costs to undo the crates. I have managed pretty well. Besides the framer's boy, I have paid all my household bills out of what they send, and laid in a barrel of brandy besides."

"Let's hope it keeps up," I said.

"Well, I have painted a good many pictures. I was not lazy, fortunately."

I asked him another day if he had found many forgeries, but about that he was noncommittal. "Some, some," he said.

The traffic in pictures lasted about twelve or fourteen weeks, then not abruptly, but certainly, it began to fall off. By the end of March the framer's boy was let go. In April only two pictures turned up. The scandal had died down, and the collectors of the world, apparently, were satisfied.

That was the end of that.

It is not, of course, the end of my story. But I hesitate, at this point, over just how I shall go on, for one hates to admit he has been made a fool of, which I certainly was.

Well, the spring arrived, drenched in the private sunlight of the Riviera. I had worked hard all winter, and I had to use all my will power to finish, in that despoiling weather, what I was doing. Finally, almost to my satisfaction, I was done, and suddenly idle, I realized there was one thing in the world I wanted to do: go home. Within a week I was ready.

On my last night Malherbes had me to dinner. There were just the two of us, together with a selection of the finest produce of France's seas, farms and vineyards; the greatest meal, as I remember, I ever ate.

We did not have an over-amount of wine, so what happened after dinner cannot be laid to any sort of alcoholic recklessness. No, I believe Malherbes intended from the beginning to tell me what he did; in fact, I know so.

Understand the scene: We were still sitting at a big table in the studio, with wine and coffee and cheeses and fruit; we were full of inexpressibly good food, we were feeling sentimental and sad, for we did not know when we would see each other again.

Malherbes, then, suddenly laid his hands flat on the table and, looking at me steadily, said, "I can trust you."

I said, "Yes."

"You are," Malherbes said, "like all artists, dishonourable."

"I'm afraid so."

"I have known that. Come along."

Believe me, at that moment I had no idea of what was about to happen. Malherbes got up, took a key from his pocket, walked over to a door, opened it, and beckoned me to follow. The door let on to a narrow stairway, going down. At the foot of it was another door, which Malherbes also had to unlock. From there, darkness. Malherbes took my hand and led me a few steps, then, "Stand here," he said. A moment later the place was flooded with light.

We were in an underground gallery, a huge room, fifty feet long, with high ceilings and careful, brilliant illumination. It was a gallery, for on the walls were hung thirty-five or forty of the most beautiful Malherbes in the world.

When I saw, I let out my breath. "Phwew!"

Malherbes nodded. "A pleasure, eh?"

"My old friend," I said, "I have never seen so many together before in my life."

"No. No one could afford it," he laughed, "except me."

I stood silent for a moment, looking. One after another, masterpieces. Finally, "Why," I said, "are they down here, locked up? And why did you say you could trust me?"

Malherbes sucked in his cheeks. Then he said, "Because, my friend, these are the forgeries."

I said flatly, "I don't believe it."

I shall never forget the answer to that, as long as I live. Malherbes said, very quietly, "You are quite right. Let me rather say, these are the pictures I said were the forgeries."

I must have looked the way I felt, for Malherbes laughed at the face I made. "There were no forgeries," he said. "None at all. I merely wanted some of my pictures home again, and it was a way to get them."

I did not try to say anything, I simply waited for Malherbes to go on.

"I do not like to sell my pictures. They are my history and my heart, and I like to have that with me, so I can remember myself. But sometimes I have to sell, to live. The price, however, is not enough to buy what I have put in a picture; that, while I am alive, is private, and without a price. So, in a way, I rent the canvas, but I do not sell my heart."

"This is extraordinary book-keeping," I said.

Malherbes laughed. "Oh, the whole affair has been good fun, I tell you. So many times I wanted to let you in on the secret, but that would have spoiled the joke."

"But look here," I said, "it all came about by accident. That picture at the Samuels' . . ."

"Quite a good picture, and quite authentic," Malherbes said. "I was merely taking advantage of an opportunity. I had intended, when we went to Paris, to make a scene in some gallery with you. I knew you had friends who were newspapermen and you would tell them. It would have worked out the same. But when the Samuels had both a picture and a newspaperman, I seized the moment."

"I can't believe it."

"It is true. I had thought about it for some time. Then when you became so smart about that centaur—well, I decided I would play a trick on you."

"But this is international robbery," I said.

"No," Malherbes' voice was very warm and tender. "No. It is just Malherbes getting some pictures back."

"And," I said, "what about those articles by Malraux and Gide?"

"Very unfortunate for them, eh?"

"How will you explain to the Luxembourg?"

"Oh, that; it doesn't worry me. And besides, I don't intend to explain anything to the Luxembourg."

"Do you mean," I said, "that you are going to keep the pictures for good?"

Malherbes nodded. "My friend, consider," he said. "There are some things about pictures you perhaps do not know. Pictures, good pictures, have a life of their own. You lock one up in a museum, with nothing but staring, stupid faces around it, and it becomes drab. No. It needs a good room and happy people who drink a glass of wine, and quarrel maybe, and make up. It needs some feeling, then it can change and develop into a good picture. Well, now. Where are my pictures to find the right room, which means the right person? Let me explain again: A composer, to write a great concerto, must be a genius. You must be a genius to conceive a great thing, eh? But it is not necessary for the composer to perform the concerto, is it? No. That is left for the virtuoso. But–a great painter must be a great conceiver and a great executor. You never heard of a great painter who couldn't paint very well, did you? Did you?"

"No," I said.

"But here now is the point: Why are things conceived and executed? Why? I tell you: for the observer. Assuredly. And the more intelligent the observer, the more he understands the picture. Isn't that true? Now I ask you, who can best understand the conception and the execution of a Malherbes? I ask you."

"Who?" I said.

He struck his chest. "Malherbes! I can understand best. And so I can give to the pictures the best home; they will be their happiest with me. It would be unfair to them, unfair, to deny them such an opportunity."

I am afraid I laughed. "These," I said, "are all extremely poor excuses."

"I know," Malherbes said. "I have not had much time to think them up. No. I told you the truth at the beginning. I wanted these pictures home again."

I suddenly had an evil idea. "The whole thing is of course monstrous," I said. "If it ever becomes known, you will be ruined."

"Yes," Malherbes said.

Then I said, "Just how far do you think you can trust me?"

Malherbes nodded. "I have considered that already. Upstairs is a crate, wrapped up, which you are to take to America. So come now, walk with me, let us look at the pictures carefully."

Now, all these months later, here in the winter cold of New York, I read the sad and unconvincing news. Maurice Malherbes is dead of a stroke. I do not want to believe that; I hope he died of overeating.

I look at my two Malherbes and remember him. My centaur *"à son ami,"* and the other–that was already wrapped up to take to America –a magnificent oil of my garden and a corner of the house, really one of his fine ones.

I remember him, for that picture is signed in the bottom right-hand corner: "Malherbes–an obvious forgery."

The Queer Feet

G. K. Chesterton

Clubs are trumps the world over. Men are curiously gregarious and have a great desire to join clubs where women are not admitted and the members meet others of kindred interests and experiences. There are so many clubs in existence that I thought once of writing a book about them. I got far enough into the subject to count all those listed in the New York directory and to find that there were more than five hundred. This set me wondering how many there might be where an extra degree of eccentricity led them to use an unlisted telephone number. I considered also the clubs of London where there are more than in New York and where they are, I suspect, of wider variety. I concluded, wisely, that there would be altogether too much work in getting the material for such a book and abandoned the idea.

Some of the strangest clubs, of course, are those we encounter in fiction. There are, for instance, the Suicide Club (Stevenson), the Master Crooks (Oppenheim), the Renegates (Buchan), the Liars (Dunsany), the Drones (Wodehouse), the Flying Aces (Brand), and the Footmen (Dickens).

My favorite among them all is the Twelve True Fishermen, of which G. K. Chesterton tells in this splendid story, "The Queer Feet."

THE QUEER FEET

G. K. Chesterton

If you meet a member of that select club, "The Twelve True Fishermen," entering the Vernon Hotel for the annual club dinner, you will observe, as he takes off his overcoat, that his evening coat is green and not black. If (supposing that you have the star-defying audacity to address such a being) you ask him why, he will probably answer that he does it to avoid being mistaken for a waiter. You will then retire crushed. But you will leave behind you a mystery as yet unsolved and a tale worth telling.

If (to pursue the same vein of improbable conjecture) you were to meet a mild, hard-working little priest, named Father Brown, and were to ask him what he thought was the most singular luck of his life, he would probably reply that upon the whole his best stroke was at the Vernon Hotel, where he had averted a crime and, perhaps, saved a soul, merely by listening to a few footsteps in a passage. He is perhaps a little proud of this wild and wonderful guess of his, and it is possible that he might refer to it. But since it is immeasurably unlikely that you will ever rise high enough in the social world to find "The Twelve True Fishermen," or that you will ever sink low enough among slums and criminals to find Father Brown, I fear you will never hear the story at all unless you hear it from me.

The Vernon Hotel at which The Twelve True Fishermen held their annual dinners was an institution such as can only exist in an oligarchical society which has almost gone mad on good manners. It was that topsy-turvy product–an "exclusive" commercial enterprise. That is, it was a thing which paid not by attracting people, but actually by turning people away. In the heart of a plutocracy tradesmen become cunning enough to be more fastidious than their customers. They positively create difficulties so that their wealthy and weary clients may spend money and diplomacy in overcoming them. If there were a fashionable hotel in London which no man could enter who was under six foot, society would meekly make up parties of six-foot men to dine in it. If there were an expensive restaurant which by a mere caprice of its proprietor was only open on Thursday afternoon, it would be crowded on Thursday afternoon. The Vernon Hotel stood, as if by accident, in the corner of a square in Belgravia. It was a small hotel; and a very inconvenient one. But its very inconveniences were considered as walls protecting a particular class. One inconvenience, in particular, was held to be of vital importance: the fact that practically only twenty-four people could dine in the place at once. The only big dinner table was the celebrated terrace table, which stood open to the air on a sort of veranda overlooking one of the most exquisite old gardens in London. Thus it happened that even the twenty-four seats at this table could only be enjoyed in warm weather; and this making the enjoyment yet more difficult made it yet more desired. The existing owner of the hotel was a Jew named Lever; and he made nearly a million out of it, by making it difficult to get into. Of course he combined with this limitation in the scope of his enterprise the most careful polish in its performance. The wines and cooking were really as good as any in Europe, and the demeanour of the attendants exactly mirrored the fixed mood of the English upper class. The proprietor knew all his waiters like the fingers on his hand; there were only fifteen of them all told. It was much easier to become a Member of Parliament than to become a waiter in that hotel. Each waiter was trained in terrible silence and smoothness, as if he were a gentleman's servant. And, indeed, there was generally at least one waiter to every gentleman who dined.

The club of the Twelve True Fishermen would not have consented to dine anywhere but in such a place, for it insisted on a luxurious privacy; and would have been quite upset by the mere thought that any other club was even dining in the same building. On the occasion of their annual dinner the Fishermen were in the habit of exposing all their treasures, as if they were in a private house, especially the celebrated set of fish knives and forks which were, as it were, the insignia of the society, each being exquisitely wrought in silver in the form of a fish, and each loaded at the hilt with one large pearl. These were always laid out for the fish course, and the fish course was always the most magnificent in that magnificent repast. The society had a vast number of ceremonies and observances, but it had no history and no object; that was where it was so very aristocratic. You did not have to be anything in order to be one of the Twelve Fishers; unless you were already a certain sort of person, you never even heard of them. It had been in existence twelve years. Its president was Mr. Audley. Its vice-president was the Duke of Chester.

If I have in any degree conveyed the atmosphere of this appalling hotel, the reader may feel a natural wonder as to how I came to know anything about it, and may even speculate as to how so ordinary a person as my friend Father Brown came to find himself in that golden galley. As far as that is concerned, my story is simple, or even vulgar. There is in the world a very aged rioter and demagogue who breaks into the most refined retreats with the dreadful information that all men are brothers, and wherever this leveller went on his pale horse it was Father Brown's trade to follow. One of the waiters, an Italian, had been struck down with a paralytic stroke that afternoon; and his Jewish employer, marvelling mildly at such superstitions, had consented to send for the nearest Popish priest. With what the waiter confessed to Father Brown we are not concerned, for the excellent reason that that cleric kept it to himself; but apparently it involved him in writing out a note or statement for the conveying of some message or the righting of some wrong. Father Brown, therefore, with a meek impudence which he would have shown equally in Buckingham Palace, asked to be provided with a room and writing materials. Mr. Lever was torn in two. He was a kind man, and had also that bad imitation of kindness, the dislike of any difficulty or scene. At the same time the presence of one unusual stranger in his hotel that evening was like a speck of dirt on something just cleaned. There was never any borderland or anteroom in the Vernon Hotel, no people waiting in the hall, no customers coming in on chance. There were fifteen waiters. There were twelve guests. It would be as startling to find a new guest in the hotel that night as to find a new brother taking breakfast or tea in one's own family. Moreover, the priest's appearance was second-rate and his clothes muddy; a mere glimpse of him afar off might precipitate a crisis in the club. Mr. Lever at last hit on a plan to cover, since he might not obliterate, the disgrace. When you enter (as you never will) the Vernon Hotel, you pass down a short passage decorated with a few dingy but important pictures, and come to the main vestibule and lounge which opens on your right into passages leading to the public rooms, and on your left to a similar passage pointing to the kitchens and offices of the hotel. Immediately on your left hand is the corner of a glass office, which abuts upon the lounge–a house within a house, so to speak, like the old hotel bar which probably once occupied its place.

In this office sat the representative of the proprietor (nobody in this place ever appeared in person if he could help it), and just beyond the office, on the way to the servants' quarters, was the gentlemen's cloak room, the last boundary of the gentlemen's domain. But between the office and the cloak room was a small private room without other outlet, sometimes used by the proprietor for delicate and important matters, such as lending a duke a thousand pounds or declining to lend him sixpence. It is a mark of the magnificent tolerance of Mr. Lever that he permitted this holy place to be for about half an hour profaned by a mere priest, scribbling away on a piece of paper. The story which Father Brown was writing down was very likely a much better story than this one, only it will never be known. I can merely state that it was very nearly as long, and that the last two or three paragraphs of it were the least exciting and absorbing.

For it was by the time that he had reached these that the priest began a little to allow his thoughts to wander and his animal senses, which were commonly keen, to awaken. The time of darkness and dinner was drawing on; his own forgotten little room was without a light, and perhaps the gathering gloom, as occasionally happens, sharpened the sense of sound. As Father Brown wrote the last and least essential part of his document, he caught himself writing to the rhythm of a recurrent noise outside, just as one sometimes thinks to the tune of a railway train. When he became conscious of the thing he found what it was: only the ordinary patter of feet passing the door, which in an hotel was no very unlikely matter. Nevertheless, he stared at the darkened ceiling, and listened to the sound. After he had listened for a few seconds dreamily, he got to his feet and listened intently, with his head a little on one side. Then he sat down again and buried his brow in his hands, now not merely listening, but listening and thinking also.

The footsteps outside at any given moment were such as one might hear in any hotel; and yet, taken as a whole, there was something very strange about them. There were no other footsteps. It was always a very silent house, for the few familiar guests went at once to their own apartments, and the well-trained waiters were told to be almost invisible until they were wanted. One could not conceive any place where there was less reason to apprehend anything irregular. But these footsteps were so odd that one could not decide to call them regular or irregular. Father Brown followed them with his finger on the edge of the table, like a man trying to learn a tune on the piano.

First, there came a long rush of rapid little steps, such as a light man might make in winning a walking race. At a certain point they stopped and changed to a sort of slow, swinging stamp, numbering not a quarter of the steps, but occupying about the same time. The moment the last echoing stamp had died away would come again the run or ripple of light, hurrying feet, and then again the thud of the heavier walking. It was certainly the same pair of boots, partly because (as has been said) there were no other boots about, and partly because they had a small but unmistakable creak in them. Father Brown had the kind of head that cannot help asking questions; and on this apparently trivial question his head almost split. He had seen men run in order to jump. He had seen men run in order to slide. But why on earth should a man run in order to walk? Or, again, why should he walk in order to run? Yet no other description would cover the antics of this invisible pair of legs. The man was either walking very fast down one-half of the corridor in order to walk very slow down the other half; or he was walking very slow at one end to have the rapture of walking fast at the other. Neither suggestion seemed to make much sense. His brain was growing darker and darker, like his room.

Yet, as he began to think steadily, the very blackness of his cell seemed to make his thoughts more vivid; he began to see as in a kind of vision the fantastic feet capering along the corridor in unnatural or symbolic attitudes. Was it a heathen religious dance? Or some entirely new kind of scientific exercise? Father Brown began to ask himself with more exactness what the steps suggested. Taking the slow step first: it certainly was not the step of the proprietor. Men of his type walk with a rapid waddle, or they sit still. It could not be any servant or messenger waiting for directions. It did not sound like it. The poorer orders (in an oligarchy) sometimes lurch about when they are slightly drunk, but generally, and especially in such gorgeous scenes, they stand or sit in constrained attitudes. No; that heavy yet springy step, with a kind of careless emphasis, not specially noisy, yet not caring what noise it made, belonged to only one of the animals of this earth. It was a gentleman of western Europe, and probably one who had never worked for his living.

Just as he came to this solid certainty, the step changed to the quicker one, and ran past the door as feverishly as a rat. The listener remarked that though this step was much swifter it was also much more noiseless, almost as if the man were walking on tiptoe. Yet it was not associated in his mind with secrecy, but with something else–something that he could not remember. He was maddened by one of those half-memories that make a man feel half-witted. Surely he had heard that strange, swift walking somewhere. Suddenly he sprang to his feet with a new idea in his head, and walked to the door. His room had no direct outlet on the passage, but let on one side into the glass office, and on the other into the cloak room beyond. He tried the door into the office, and found it locked. Then he looked at the window, now a square pane full of purple cloud cleft by livid sunset, and for an instant he smelt evil as a dog smells rats.

The rational part of him (whether the wiser or not) regained its supremacy. He remembered that the proprietor had told him that he should lock the door, and would come later to release him. He told himself that twenty things he had not thought of might explain the eccentric sounds outside; he reminded himself that there was just enough light left to finish his own proper work. Bringing his paper to the window so as to catch the last stormy evening light, he resolutely plunged once more into the almost completed record. He had written for about twenty minutes, bending closer and closer to his paper in the lessening light; then suddenly he sat upright. He had heard the strange feet once more.

This time they had a third oddity. Previously the unknown man had walked, with levity indeed and lightning quickness, but he had walked. This time he ran. One could hear the swift, soft, bounding steps coming along the corridor, like the pads of a fleeing and leaping panther. Whoever was coming was a very strong, active man, in still yet tearing excitement. Yet, when the sound had swept up to the office like a sort of whispering whirlwind, it suddenly changed again to the old slow, swaggering stamp.

Father Brown flung down his paper, and, knowing the office door to be locked, went at once into the cloak room on the other side. The attendant of this place was temporarily absent, probably because the only guests were at dinner and his office was a sinecure. After groping through a grey forest of overcoats, he found that the dim cloak room opened on the lighted corridor in the form of a sort of counter of half-door, like most of the counters across which we have all handed umbrellas and received tickets. There was a light immediately above the semicircular arch of this opening. It threw little illumination on Father Brown himself, who seemed a mere dark outline against the dim sunset window behind him. But it threw an almost theatrical light on the man who stood outside the cloak room in the corridor.

He was an elegant man in very plain evening dress; tall, but with an air of not taking up much room; one felt that he could have slid along like a shadow where many smaller men would have been obvious and obstructive. His face, now flung back in the lamplight, was swarthy and vivacious, the face of a foreigner. His figure was good, his manners good humoured and confident; a critic could only say that his black coat was a shade below his figure and manners, and even bulged and bagged in an odd way. The moment he caught sight of Brown's black silhouette against the sunset, he tossed down a scrap of paper with a number and called out with amiable authority: "I want my hat and coat, please; I find I have to go away at once."

Father Brown took the paper without a word, and obediently went to look for the coat; it was not the first menial work he had done in his life. He brought it and laid it on the counter; meanwhile, the strange gentleman who had been feeling in his waistcoat pocket, said laughing: "I haven't got any silver; you can keep this." And he threw down half a sovereign, and caught up his coat.

Father Brown's figure remained quite dark and still; but in that instant he had lost his head. His head was always most valuable when he had lost it. In such moments he put two and two together and made four million. Often the Catholic Church (which is wedded to common sense) did not approve of it. Often he did not approve of it himself. But it was real inspiration–important at rare crises–when whosoever shall lose his head the same shall save it.

"I think, sir," he said civilly, "that you have some silver in your pocket."

The tall gentleman stared. "Hang it," he cried, "if I choose to give you gold, why should you complain?"

"Because silver is sometimes more valuable than gold," said the priest mildly; "that is, in large quantities."

The stranger looked at him curiously. Then he looked still more curiously up the passage towards the main entrance. Then he looked back at Brown again, and then he looked very carefully at the window beyond Brown's head, still coloured with the after-glow of the storm. Then he seemed to make up his mind. He put one hand on the counter, vaulted over as easily as an acrobat and towered above the priest, putting one tremendous hand upon his collar.

"Stand still," he said, in a hacking whisper. "I don't want to threaten you, but——"

"I do want to threaten you," said Father Brown, in a voice like a rolling drum, "I want to threaten you with the worm that dieth not, and the fire that is not quenched."

"You're a rum sort of cloak-room clerk," said the other.

"I am a priest, Monsieur Flambeau," said Brown, "and I am ready to hear your confession."

The other stood gasping for a few moments, and then staggered back into a chair.

The first two courses of the dinner of the Twelve True Fishermen had proceeded with placid success. I do not possess a copy of the menu; and if I did it would not convey anything to anybody. It was written in a sort of super-French employed by cooks, but quite unintelligible to Frenchmen. There was a tradition in the club that the *hors d'œuvres* should be various and manifold to the point of madness. They were taken seriously because they were avowedly useless extras, like the whole dinner and the whole club. There was also a tradition that the soup course should be light and unpretending–a sort of simple and austere vigil for the feast of fish that was to come. The talk was that strange, slight talk which governs the British Empire, which governs it in secret, and yet would scarcely enlighten an ordinary Englishman even if he could overhear it. Cabinet ministers on both sides were alluded to by their Christian names with a sort of bored benignity. The Radical Chancellor of the Exchequer, whom the whole Tory party was supposed to be cursing for his extortions, was praised for his minor poetry, or his saddle in the hunting field. The Tory leader, whom all Liberals were supposed to hate as a tyrant, was discussed and, on the whole, praised–as a Liberal. It seemed somehow that politicians were very important. And yet, anything seemed important about them except their politics. Mr. Audley, the chairman, was an amiable, elderly man who still wore Gladstone collars; he was a kind of symbol of all that phantasmal and yet fixed society. He had never done anything–not even anything wrong. He was not fast; he was not even particularly rich. He was simply in the thing; and there was an end of it. No party could ignore him, and if he had wished to be in the Cabinet he certainly would have been put there. The Duke of Chester, the vice-president, was a young and rising politician. That is to say, he was a pleasant youth, with flat, fair hair and a freckled face, with moderate intelligence and enormous estates. In public his appearances were always successful and his principle was simple enough. When he thought of a joke he made it, and was called brilliant. When he could not think of a joke he said that this was no time for trifling, and was called able. In private, in a club of his own class, he was simply quite pleasantly frank and silly, like a schoolboy. Mr. Audley, never having been in politics, treated them a little more seriously. Sometimes he even embarrassed the company by phrases suggesting that there was some difference between a Liberal and a Conservative. He himself was a Conservative, even in private life. He had a roll of grey hair over the back of his collar, like certain old-fashioned statesmen, and seen from behind he looked like the man the empire wants. Seen from the front he looked like a mild, self-indulgent bachelor, with rooms in the Albany–which he was.

As has been remarked, there were twenty-four seats at the terrace table, and only twelve members of the club. Thus they could occupy the terrace in the most luxurious style of all, being ranged along the inner side of the table, with no one opposite, commanding an uninterrupted view of the garden, the colours of which were still vivid, though evening was closing in somewhat luridly for the time of year. The chairman sat in the centre of the line, and the vice-president at the right-hand end of it. When the twelve guests first trooped into their seats it was the custom (for some unknown reason) for all the fifteen waiters to stand lining the wall like troops presenting arms to the king, while the fat proprietor stood and bowed to the club with radiant surprise, as if he had never heard of them before. But before the first chink of knife and fork this army of retainers had vanished, only the one or two required to collect and distribute the plates darting about in deathly silence. Mr. Lever, the proprietor, of course had disappeared in convulsions of courtesy long before. It would be exaggerative, indeed irreverent, to say that he ever positively appeared again. But when the important course, the fish course, was being brought on, there was–how shall I put it?–a vivid shadow, a projection of his personality, which told that he was hovering near. The sacred fish course consisted (to the eyes of the vulgar) in a sort of monstrous pudding, about the size and shape of a wedding cake, in which some considerable number of interesting fishes had finally lost the shapes which God had given to them. The Twelve True Fishermen took up their celebrated fish knives and fish forks, and approached it as gravely as if every inch of the pudding cost as much as the silver fork it was eaten with. So it did, for all I know. This course was dealt with in eager and devouring silence; and it was only when his plate was nearly empty that the young duke made the ritual remark: "They can't do this anywhere but here."

"Nowhere," said Mr. Audley, in a deep bass voice, turning to the speaker and nodding his venerable head a number of times. "Nowhere, assuredly, except here. It was represented to me that at the Café Anglais——"

Here he was interrupted and even agitated for a moment by the removal of his plate, but he recaptured the valuable thread of his thoughts. "It was represented to me that the same could be done at the Café Anglais. Nothing like it, sir," he said, shaking his head ruthlessly, like a hanging judge. "Nothing like it."

"Overrated place," said a certain Colonel Pound, speaking (by the look of him) for the first time for some months.

"Oh, I don't know," said the Duke of Chester, who was an optimist, "it's jolly good for some things. You can't beat it at——"

A waiter came swiftly along the room, and then stopped dead. His stoppage was as silent as his tread; but all those vague and kindly gentlemen were so used to the utter smoothness of the unseen machinery which surrounded and supported their lives, that a waiter doing anything unexpected was a start and a jar. They felt as you and I would feel if the inanimate world disobeyed–if a chair ran away from us.

The waiter stood staring a few seconds, while there deepened on every face at table a strange shame which is wholly the product of our time. It is the combination of modern humanitarianism with the horrible modern abyss between the souls of the rich and poor. A genuine historic aristocrat would have thrown things at the waiter, beginning with empty bottles, and very probably ending with money. A genuine democrat would have asked him, with a comrade-like clearness of speech, what the devil he was doing. But these modern plutocrats could not bear a poor man near to them, either as a slave or as a friend. That something had gone wrong with the servants was merely a dull, hot embarrassment. They did not want to be brutal, and they dreaded the need to be benevolent. They wanted the thing, whatever it was, to be over. It was over. The waiter, after standing for some seconds rigid, like a cataleptic, turned round and ran madly out of the room.

When he reappeared in the room, or rather in the doorway, it was in company with another waiter, with whom he whispered and gesticulated with southern fierceness. Then the first waiter went away, leaving the second waiter, and reappeared with a third waiter. By the time a fourth waiter had joined this hurried synod, Mr. Audley felt it necessary to break the silence in the interests of Tact. He used a very loud cough, instead of a presidential hammer, and said: "Splendid work young Moocher's doing in Burmah. Now, no other nation in the world could have——"

A fifth waiter had sped towards him like an arrow, and was whispering in his ear: "So sorry. Important! Might the proprietor speak to you?"

The chairman turned in disorder, and with a dazed stare saw Mr. Lever coming towards them with his lumbering quickness. The gait of the good proprietor was indeed his usual gait, but his face was by no means usual. Generally it was a genial copper-brown; now it was a sickly yellow.

"You will pardon me, Mr. Audley," he said, with asthmatic breathlessness. "I have great apprehensions. Your fish-plates, they are cleared away with the knife and fork on them!"

"Well, I hope so," said the chairman, with some warmth.

"You see him?" panted the excited hotel keeper; "you see the waiter who took them away? You know him?"

"Know the waiter?" answered Mr. Audley indignantly. "Certainly not!"

Mr. Lever opened his hands with a gesture of agony. "I never send him," he said. "I know not when or why he come. I send my waiter to take away the plates, and he find them already away."

Mr. Audley still looked rather too bewildered to be really the man the empire wants; none of the company could say anything except the man of wood—Colonel Pound—who seemed galvanised into an unnatural life. He rose rigidly from his chair, leaving all the rest sitting, screwed his eyeglass into his eye, and spoke in a raucous undertone as if he had half-forgotten how to speak. "Do you mean," he said, "that somebody has stolen our silver fish service?"

The proprietor repeated the open-handed gesture with even greater helplessness; and in a flash all the men at the table were on their feet.

"Are all your waiters here?" demanded the colonel, in his low, harsh accent.

"Yes; they're all here. I noticed it myself," cried the young duke, pushing his boyish face into the inmost ring. "Always count 'em as I come in; they look so queer standing up against the wall."

"But surely one cannot exactly remember," began Mr. Audley, with heavy hesitation.

"I remember exactly, I tell you," cried the duke excitedly. "There never have been more than fifteen waiters at this place, and there were no more than fifteen to-night, I'll swear; no more and no less."

The proprietor turned upon him, quaking in a kind of palsy of surprise. "You say–you say," he stammered, "that you see all my fifteen waiters?"

"As usual," assented the duke. "What is the matter with that?"

"Nothing," said Lever, with a deepening accent, "only you did not. For one of zem is dead upstairs."

There was a shocking stillness for an instant in that room. It may be (so supernatural is the word death) that each of those idle men looked for a second at his soul, and saw it as a small dried pea. One of them–the duke, I think–even said with the idiotic kindness of wealth: "Is there anything we can do?"

"He has had a priest," said the Jew, not untouched.

Then, as to the clang of doom, they awoke to their own position. For a few weird seconds they had really felt as if the fifteenth waiter might be the ghost of the dead man upstairs. They had been dumb under that oppression, for ghosts were to them an embarrassment, like beggars. But the remembrance of the silver broke the spell of the miraculous; broke it abruptly and with a brutal reaction. The colonel flung over his chair and strode to the door. "If there was a fifteenth man here, friends," he said, "that fifteenth fellow was a thief. Down at once to the front and back doors and secure everything; then we'll talk. The twenty-four pearls of the club are worth recovering."

Mr. Audley seemed at first to hesitate about whether it was gentlemanly to be in such a hurry about anything; but, seeing the duke dash down the stairs with youthful energy, he followed with a more mature motion.

At the same instant a sixth waiter ran into the room, and declared that he had found the pile of fish plates on a sideboard, with no trace of the silver.

The crowd of diners and attendants that tumbled helter-skelter down the passages divided into two groups. Most of the Fishermen followed the proprietor to the front room to demand news of any exit. Colonel Pound, with the chairman, the vice-president, and one or two others darted down the corridor leading to the servants' quarters, as the more likely line of escape. As they did so they passed the dim alcove or cavern of the cloak room, and saw a short, black-coated figure, presumably an attendant, standing a little way back in the shadow of it.

"Hallo, there!" called out the duke. "Have you seen anyone pass?"

The short figure did not answer the question directly, but merely said: "Perhaps I have got what you are looking for, gentlemen."

They paused, wavering and wondering, while he quietly went to the back of the cloak room, and came back with both hands full of shining silver, which he laid out on the counter as calmly as a salesman. It took the form of a dozen quaintly shaped forks and knives.

"You–you—" began the colonel, quite thrown off his balance at last. Then he peered into the dim little room and saw two things: first, that the short, black-clad man was dressed like a clergyman; and, second, that the window of the room behind him was burst, as if someone had passed violently through.

"Valuable things to deposit in a cloak room, aren't they?" remarked the clergyman, with cheerful composure.

"Did–did you steal those things?" stammered Mr. Audley, with staring eyes.

"If I did," said the cleric pleasantly, "at least I am bringing them back again."

"But you didn't," said Colonel Pound, still staring at the broken window.

"To make a clean breast of it, I didn't," said the other, with some humour. And he seated himself quite gravely on a stool.

"But you know who did," said the colonel.

"I don't know his real name," said the priest placidly, "but I know something of his fighting weight, and a great deal about his spiritual difficulties. I formed the physical estimate when he was trying to throttle me, and the moral estimate when he repented."

"Oh, I say–repented!" cried young Chester, with a sort of crow of laughter.

Father Brown got to his feet, putting his hands behind him. "Odd, isn't it," he said, "that a thief and a vagabond should repent, when so many who are rich and secure remain hard and frivolous, and without fruit for God or man? But there, if you will excuse me, you trespass a little upon my province. If you doubt the penitence as a practical fact, there are your knives and forks. You are the Twelve True Fishers, and there are all your silver fish. But He has made me a fisher of men."

"Did you catch this man?" asked the colonel, frowning.

Father Brown looked him full in his frowning face. "Yes," he said, "I caught him, with an unseen hook and an invisible line which is long enough to let him wander to the ends of the world, and still to bring him back with a twitch upon the thread."

There was a long silence. All the other men present drifted away to carry the recovered silver to their comrades, or to consult the proprietor about the queer condition of affairs. But the grim-faced colonel still sat sideways on the counter, swinging his long, lank legs and biting his dark moustache.

At last he said quietly to the priest: "He must have been a clever fellow, but I think I know a cleverer."

"He was a clever fellow," answered the other, "but I am not quite sure of what other you mean."

"I mean you," said the colonel, with a short laugh. "I don't want to get the fellow jailed; make yourself easy about that. But I'd give a good many silver forks to know exactly how you fell into this affair, and how you got the stuff out of him. I reckon you're the most up-to-date devil of the present company."

Father Brown seemed rather to like the saturnine candour of the soldier. "Well," he said, smiling, "I mustn't tell you anything of the man's identity, or his own story, of course; but there's no particular reason why I shouldn't tell you of the mere outside facts which I found out for myself."

He hopped over the barrier with unexpected activity, and sat beside Colonel Pound, kicking his short legs like a little boy on a gate. He began to tell the story as easily as if he were telling it to an old friend by a Christmas fire.

"You see, colonel," he said, "I was shut up in that small room there doing some writing, when I heard a pair of feet in this passage doing a dance that was as queer as the dance of death. First came quick, funny little steps, like a man walking on tiptoe for a wager; then came slow, careless, creaking steps, as of a big man walking about with a cigar. But they were both made by the same feet, I swear, and they came in rotation; first the run and then the walk, and then the run again. I wondered at first idly and then wildly why a man should act these two parts at once. One walk I knew; it was just like yours, colonel. It was the walk of a well-fed gentleman waiting for something, who strolls about rather because he is physically alert than because he is mentally impatient. I knew that I knew the other walk, too, but I could not remember what it was.

What wild creature had I met on my travels that tore along on tiptoe in that extraordinary style? Then I heard a clink of plates somewhere; and the answer stood up as plain as St. Peter's. It was the walk of a waiter—that walk with the body slanted forward, the eyes looking down, the ball of the toe spurning away the ground, the coat tails and napkin flying. Then I thought for a minute and a half more. And I believe I saw the manner of the crime, as clearly as if I were going to commit it."

Colonel Pound looked at him keenly, but the speaker's mild grey eyes were fixed upon the ceiling with almost empty wistfulness.

"A crime," he said slowly, "is like any other work of art. Don't look surprised; crimes are by no means the only works of art that come from an infernal workshop. But every work of art, divine or diabolic, has one indispensable mark—I mean, that the centre of it is simple, however much the fulfilment may be complicated. Thus, in *Hamlet,* let us say, the grotesqueness of the grave-digger, the flowers of the mad girl, the fantastic finery of Osric, the pallor of the ghost and the grin of the skull are all oddities in a sort of tangled wreath round one plain tragic figure of a man in black. Well, this also," he said, getting slowly down from his seat with a smile, "this also is the plain tragedy of a man in black. Yes," he went on, seeing the colonel look up in some wonder, "the whole of this tale turns on a black coat. In this, as in *Hamlet,* there are the rococo excrescences—yourselves, let us say. There is the dead waiter, who was there when he could not be there. There is the invisible hand that swept your table clear of silver and melted into air. But every clever crime is founded ultimately on some one quite simple fact—some fact that is not itself mysterious. The mystification comes in covering it up, in leading men's thoughts away from it. This large and subtle and (in the ordinary course) most profitable crime, was built on the plain fact that a gentleman's evening dress is the same as a waiter's. All the rest was acting, and thundering good acting, too."

"Still," said the colonel, getting up and frowning at his boots, "I am not sure that I understand."

"Colonel," said Father Brown, "I tell you that this archangel of impudence who stole your forks walked up and down this passage twenty times in the blaze of all the lamps, in the glare of all the eyes. He did not go and hide in dim corners where suspicion might have searched for him. He kept constantly on the move in the lighted corridors, and everywhere that he went he seemed to be there by right. Don't ask me what he was like; you have seen him yourself six or seven times tonight. You were waiting with all the other grand people in the reception room at the end of the passage there, with the terrace just beyond. Whenever he came among you gentlemen, he came in the lightning style of a waiter, with bent head, flapping napkin and flying feet. He shot out on to the terrace, did something to the table cloth, and shot back again towards the office and the waiters' quarters. By the time he had come under the eye of the office clerk and the waiters he had become another man in every inch of his body, in every instinctive gesture. He strolled among the servants with the absent-minded insolence which they have all seen in their patrons. It was no new thing to them that a swell from the dinner party should pace all parts of the house like an animal at the Zoo; they know that nothing marks the Smart Set more than a habit of walking where one chooses. When he was magnificently weary of walking down that particular passage he would wheel round and pace back past the office; in the shadow of the arch just beyond he was altered as by a blast of magic, and went hurrying forward again among the Twelve Fishermen, an obsequious attendant. Why should the gentlemen look at a chance waiter? Why should the waiters suspect a first-rate walking gentleman? Once or twice he played the coolest tricks. In the proprietor's private quarters he called out breezily for a syphon of soda water, saying he was thirsty. He said genially that he would carry it himself, and he did; he carried it quickly and correctly through the thick of you, a waiter with an obvious errand. Of course, it could not have been kept up long, but it only had to be kept up till the end of the fish course.

"His worst moment was when the waiters stood in a row; but even then he contrived to lean against the wall just round the corner in such a way that for that important instant the waiters thought him a gentleman, while the gentlemen thought him a waiter. The rest went like winking. If any waiter caught him away from the table, that waiter caught a lanquid aristocrat. He had only to time himself two minutes before the fish was cleared, become a swift servant, and clear it himself. He put the plates down on a sideboard, stuffed the silver in his breast pocket, giving it a bulgy look, and ran like a hare (I heard him coming) till he came to the cloak room. There he had only to be a plutocrat again—a plutocrat called away suddenly on business. He had only to give his ticket to the cloak-room attendant, and go out again elegantly as he had come in. Only—only I happened to be the cloak-room attendant."

"What did you do to him?" cried the colonel, with unusual intensity. "What did he tell you?"

"I beg your pardon," said the priest immovably, "that is where the story ends."

"And the interesting story begins," muttered Pound. "I think I understand his professional trick. But I don't seem to have got hold of yours."

"I must be going," said Father Brown.

They walked together along the passage to the entrance hall, where they saw the fresh, freckled face of the Duke of Chester, who was bounding buoyantly along towards them.

"Come along, Pound," he cried breathlessly. "I've been looking for you everywhere. The dinner's going again in spanking style, and old Audley has got to make a speech in honour of the forks being saved. We want to start some new ceremony, don't you know, to commemorate the occasion. I say, you really got the goods back, what do you suggest?"

"Why," said the colonel, eyeing him with a certain sardonic approval, "I should suggest that henceforward we wear green coats, instead of black. One never knows what mistakes may arise when one looks so like a waiter."

"Oh, hang it all!" said the young man, "a gentleman never looks like a waiter."

"Nor a waiter like a gentleman, I suppose," said Colonel Pound, with the same lowering laughter on his face. "Reverend sir, your friend must have been very smart to act the gentleman."

Father Brown buttoned up his commonplace overcoat to the neck, for the night was stormy, and took his commonplace umbrella from the stand.

"Yes," he said; "it must be very hard work to be a gentleman; but, do you know, I have sometimes thought that it may be almost as laborious to be a waiter."

And saying "Good evening," he pushed open the heavy doors of that palace of pleasures. The golden gates closed behind him, and he went at a brisk walk through the damp, dark streets in search of a penny omnibus.

Accident **Agatha Christie**

In a crowded field of eagerly inventive writers, Agatha Christie stands out, or so it seems to me, as the master of them all in the concoction of original plots and the use of unusual backgrounds. Consider these few titles: *The Murder of Roger Ackroyd, And Then There Were None, Murder in the Calais Coach, Witness for the Prosecution,* and on and on and on. Her cerebral detective, Hercule Poirot, and her intuitive little Miss Marple are pleasantly different from the tough mugs who always seem to have a highball glass in one hand and who light a fresh cigarette on every second page while they proceed with their chores of detection.

This is a short story which stands out because it tells the sequel to a murder trial and supplies a concluding situation which will bring all readers up straight in their chairs, gasping with surprise.

ACCIDENT

Agatha Christie

"And I tell you this—it's the same woman—not a doubt of it!"

Captain Haydock looked into the eager, vehement face of his friend and sighed. He wished Evans would not be so positive and so jubilant. In the course of a career spent at sea, the old sea captain had learned to leave things that did not concern him well alone. His friend Evans, late C.I.D. Inspector, had a different philosophy of life. "Acting on information received—" had been his motto in early days, and he had improved upon it to the extent of finding out his own information. Inspector Evans had been a very smart, wide-awake officer, and had justly earned the promotion which had been his. Even now, when he had retired from the force, and had settled down in the country cottage of his dreams, his professional instinct was still active.

"Don't often forget a face," he reiterated complacently. "Mrs. Anthony—yes, it's Mrs. Anthony right enough. When you said Mrs. Merrowdene—I knew her at once."

Captain Haydock stirred uneasily. The Merrowdenes were his nearest neighbours, barring Evans himself, and this identifying of Mrs. Merrowdene with a former heroine of a *cause célèbre* distressed him.

"It's a long time ago," he said rather weakly.

"Nine years," said Evans, accurate as ever. "Nine years and three months. You remember the case?"

"In a vague sort of way."

"Anthony turned out to be an arsenic eater," said Evans, "so they acquitted her."

"Well, why shouldn't they?"

"No reason in the world. Only verdict they could give on the evidence. Absolutely correct."

"Then, that's all right," said Haydock. "And I don't see what we're bothering about."

"Who's bothering?"

"I thought you were."

"Not at all."

"The thing's over and done with," summed up the Captain. "If Mrs. Merrowdene at one time of her life was unfortunate enough to be tried and acquitted of murder–"

"It's not usually considered unfortunate to be acquitted," put in Evans.

"You know what I mean," said Captain Haydock, irritably. "If the poor lady has been through that harrowing experience, it's no business of ours to rake it up, is it?"

Evans did not answer.

"Come now, Evans. The lady was innocent–you've just said so."

"I didn't say she was innocent. I said she was acquitted."

"It's the same thing."

"Not always."

Captain Haydock, who had commenced to tap his pipe out against the side of his chair, stopped, and sat up with a very alert expression:

"Hullo-ullo-ullo," he said. "The wind's in that quarter, is it? You think she wasn't innocent?"

"I wouldn't say that. I just–don't know. Anthony was in the habit of taking arsenic. His wife got it for him. One day, by mistake, he takes far too much. Was the mistake his or his wife's? Nobody could tell, and the jury very properly gave her the benefit of the doubt. That's all quite right and I'm not finding fault with it. All the same–I'd like to *know*."

Captain Haydock transferred his attention to his pipe once more.

"Well," he said comfortably. "It's none of our business."

"I'm not so sure. . . ."

"But, surely–"

"Listen to me a minute. This man, Merrowdene–in his laboratory this evening, fiddling round with tests–you remember–"

"Yes. He mentioned Marsh's test for arsenic. Said *you* would know all about it–it was in *your* line–and chuckled. He wouldn't have said that if he'd thought for one moment–"

Evans interrupted him.

"You mean he wouldn't have said that if he *knew*. They've been married how long–six years, you told me? I bet you anything he has no idea his wife is the once notorious Mrs. Anthony."

"And he will certainly not know it from me," said Captain Haydock stiffly.

Evans paid no attention, but went on.

"You interrupted me just now. After Marsh's test, Merrowdene heated a substance in a test tube, the metallic residue he dissolved in water and then precipitated it by adding silver nitrate. That was a test for chlorates. A neat, unassuming little test. But I chanced to read these words in a book that stood open on the table. *H_2SO_4 decomposes chlorates with evolution of $CL_{2}0_4$. If heated, violent explosions occur, the mixture ought therefore to be kept cool and only very small quantities used.*"

Haydock stared at his friend.

"Well, what about it?"

"Just this. In my profession we've got tests, too–tests for murder. There's adding up the facts–weighing them, dissecting the residue when you've allowed for prejudice and the general inaccuracy of witnesses. But there's another test for murder–one that is fairly accurate, but rather –dangerous! *A murderer is seldom content with one crime.* Give him time and a lack of suspicion and he'll commit another. You catch a man –has he murdered his wife or hasn't he?–perhaps the case isn't very black against him. Look into his past–if you find that he's had several wives–and that they've all died, shall we say–rather curiously?–then you *know!* I'm not speaking legally, you understand. I'm speaking of moral certainty. Once you *know,* you can go ahead looking for evidence."

"Well?"

"I'm coming to the point. That's all right if there *is* a past to look into. But suppose you catch your murderer at his or her first crime? Then that test will be one from which you get no reaction. But the prisoner acquitted–starting life under another name. Will or will not the murderer repeat the crime?"

"That's a horrible idea."

"Do you still say it's none of our business?"

"Yes, I do. You've no reason to think that Mrs. Merrowdene is anything but a perfectly innocent woman."

The ex-Inspector was silent for a moment. Then he said slowly:

"I told you that we looked into her past and found nothing. That's not quite true. There was a stepfather. As a girl of eighteen she had a fancy for some young man–and her stepfather exerted his authority to keep them apart. She and her stepfather went for a walk along a rather dangerous part of the cliff. There was an accident–the stepfather went too near the edge–it gave way and he went over and was killed."

"You don't think–"

"It was an accident. *Accident!* Anthony's overdose of arsenic was an accident. She'd never have been tried if it hadn't transpired that there was another man–he sheered off, by the way. Looked as though he weren't satisfied even if the jury were. I tell you, Haydock, where that woman is concerned I'm afraid of another–accident!"

The old Captain shrugged his shoulders.

"Well, I don't know how you're going to guard against that."

"Neither do I," said Evans ruefully.

"I should leave well enough alone," said Captain Haydock. "No good ever came of butting into other people's affairs."

But the advice was not palatable to the ex-Inspector. He was a man of patience but determination. Taking leave of his friend, he sauntered down to the village, revolving in his mind the possibilities of some kind of successful action.

Turning into the post office to buy some stamps, he ran into the object of his solicitude, George Merrowdene. The ex-chemistry professor was a small, dreamy-looking man, gentle and kindly in manner, and usually completely absent-minded. He recognized the other and greeted him amicably, stooping to recover the letters that the impact had caused him to drop on the ground. Evans stooped also and, more rapid in his movements than the other, secured them first, handing them back to their owner with an apology.

He glanced down at them in doing so, and the address on the topmost suddenly awakened all his suspicions anew. It bore the name of a well-known insurance firm.

Instantly his mind was made up. The guileless George Merrowdene hardly realized how it came about that he and the ex-Inspector were strolling down the village together, and still less could he have said how it came about that the conversation should come round to the subject of life insurance.

Evans had no difficulty in attaining his object. Merrowdene of his own accord volunteered the information that he had just insured his life for his wife's benefit, and asked Evans's opinion of the company in question.

"I made some rather unwise investments," he explained. "As a result, my income has diminished. If anything were to happen to me, my wife would be left very badly off. This insurance will put things right."

"She didn't object to the idea?" inquired Evans casually. "Some ladies do, you know. Feel it's unlucky–that sort of thing."

"Oh! Margaret is very practical," said Merrowdene, smiling. "Not at all superstitious. In fact, I believe it was her idea originally. She didn't like my being so worried."

Evans had got the information he wanted. He left the other shortly afterwards, and his lips were set in a grim line. The late Mr. Anthony had insured his life in his wife's favour a few weeks before his death.

Accustomed to rely on his instincts, he was perfectly sure in his own mind. But how to act was another matter. He wanted, not to arrest a criminal red-handed, but to prevent a crime being committed and that was a very different and a very much more difficult thing.

All day he was very thoughtful. There was a Primrose League Fête that afternoon held in the grounds of the local squire, and he went to it, indulging in the penny dip, guessing the weight of a pig, and shying at coconuts all with the same look of abstracted concentration on his face. He even indulged in half a crown's worth of Zara the Crystal Gazer, smiling a little to himself, as he did so, remembering his own activities against fortune-tellers in his official days.

He did not pay very much heed to her sing-song, droning voice till the end of a sentence held his attention.

"–and you will very shortly–very shortly indeed–be engaged on a matter of life or death–life or death to one person."

"Eh–what's that?" he asked abruptly.

"A decision–you have a decision to make. You must be very careful –very, very careful. . . . If you were to make a mistake–the smallest mistake–"

"Yes?"

The fortune-teller shivered. Inspector Evans knew it was all nonsense, but he was nevertheless impressed.

"I warn you–*you must not make a mistake*. If you do, I see the result clearly, a death. . . ."

Odd, damned odd! A death. Fancy her lighting upon that!

"If I make a mistake a death will result? Is that it?"

"Yes."

"In that case," said Evans, rising to his feet and handing over half a crown, "I mustn't make a mistake, eh?"

He spoke lightly enough, but as he went out of the tent, his jaw set determinedly. Easy to say–not so easy to be sure of doing. He mustn't make a slip. A life, a valuable human life depended on it.

And there was no one to help him. He looked across at the figure of his friend Haydock in the distance. No help there. "Leave things alone," was Haydock's motto. And that wouldn't do here.

Haydock was talking to a woman. She moved away from him and came towards Evans, and the Inspector recognized her. It was Mrs. Merrowdene. On an impulse he put himself deliberately in her path.

Mrs. Merrowdene was rather a fine-looking woman. She had a broad serene brow, very beautiful brown eyes, and a placid expression. She had the look of an Italian Madonna which she heightened by parting her hair in the middle and looping it over her ears. She had a deep, rather sleepy voice.

She smiled up at Evans; a contented, welcoming smile.

"I thought it was you, Mrs. Anthony–I mean Mrs. Merrowdene," he said glibly.

He made the slip deliberately, watching her without seeming to do so. He saw her eyes widen, heard the quick intake of her breath. But her eyes did not falter. She gazed at him steadily and proudly.

"I was looking for my husband," she said quietly. "Have you seen him anywhere about?"

"He was over in that direction when I last saw him."

They went side by side in the direction indicated, chatting quietly and pleasantly. The Inspector felt his admiration mounting. What a woman! What self-command. What wonderful poise. A remarkable woman–and a very dangerous one. He felt sure–a very dangerous one.

He still felt very uneasy, though he was satisfied with his initial step. He had let her know that he recognized her. That would put her on her guard. She would not dare attempt anything rash. There was the question of Merrowdene. If he could be warned. . . .

They found the little man absently contemplating a china doll which had fallen to his share in the penny dip. His wife suggested home and he agreed eagerly. Mrs. Merrowdene turned to the Inspector.

"Won't you come back with us and have a quiet cup of tea, Mr. Evans?"

Was there a faint note of challenge in her voice? He thought there was.

"Thank you, Mrs. Merrowdene. I should like to very much."

They walked there, talking together of pleasant ordinary things. The sun shone, a breeze blew gently, everything around them was pleasant and ordinary.

Their maid was out at the Fête, Mrs. Merrowdene explained, when they arrived at the charming old-world cottage. She went into her room to remove her hat, returning to set out the tea and boil the kettle on a little silver lamp. From a shelf near the fireplace she took three small bowls and saucers.

"We have some very special Chinese tea," she explained. "And we always drink it in the Chinese manner–out of bowls, not cups."

She broke off, peered into a cup and exchanged it for another, with an exclamation of annoyance.

"George–it's too bad of you. You've been taking these bowls again."

"I'm sorry, dear," said the Professor apologetically. "They're such a convenient size. The ones I ordered haven't come."

"One of these days you'll poison us all," said his wife with a half laugh. "Mary finds them in the laboratory and brings them back here and never troubles to wash them out unless they've something very noticeable in them. Why, you were using one of them for Potassium Cyanide the other day. Really, George, it's frightfully dangerous."

Merrowdene looked a little irritated.

"Mary's no business to remove things from the laboratory. She's not to touch anything there."

"But we often leave our teacups there after tea. How is she to know? Be reasonable, dear."

The Professor went into his laboratory, murmuring to himself, and with a smile Mrs. Merrowdene poured boiling water on the tea and blew out the flame of the little silver lamp.

Evans was puzzled. Yet a glimmering of light penetrated to him. For some reason or other, Mrs. Merrowdene was showing her hand. Was this to be the "accident"? Was she speaking of all this so as deliberately to prepare her *alibi* beforehand? So that when, one day, the "accident" happened, he would be forced to give evidence in her favour. Stupid of her, if so, because before that–

Suddenly he drew in his breath. She had poured the tea into the three bowls. One she set before him, one before herself, the other she placed on a little table by the fire near the chair her husband usually sat in, and it was as she placed this last one on the table that a little strange smile curved round her lips. It was the smile that did it.

He knew!

A remarkable woman–a dangerous woman. No waiting–no preparation. This afternoon–this very afternoon–with him here as witness. The boldness of it took his breath away.

It was clever–it was damnably clever. He would be able to prove nothing. She counted on his not suspecting–simply because it was "so soon." A woman of lightning rapidity of thought and action.

He drew a deep breath and leaned forward.

"Mrs. Merrowdene, I'm a man of queer whims. Will you be very kind and indulge me in one of them?"

She looked inquiring but unsuspicious.

He rose, took the bowl from in front of her and crossed to the little table where he substituted it for the other. This other he brought back and placed in front of her.

"I want to see you drink this."

Her eyes met his. They were steady, unfathomable. The colour slowly drained from her face.

She stretched out her hand, raised the cup. He held his breath.

Supposing all along he had made a mistake.

She raised it to her lips–at the last moment, with a shudder she leaned forward and quickly poured it into a pot containing a fern. Then she sat back and gazed at him defiantly.

He drew a long sigh of relief, and sat down again.

"Well?" she said.

Her voice had altered. It was slightly mocking–defiant.

He answered her soberly and quietly.

"You are a very clever woman, Mrs. Merrowdene. I think you understand me. There must be no–repetition. You know what I mean?"

"I know what you mean."

Her voice was even, devoid of expression. He nodded his head, satisfied. She was a clever woman, and she didn't want to be hanged.

"To your long life and to that of your husband," he said significantly and raised his tea to his lips.

Then his face changed. It contorted horribly . . . he tried to rise–to cry out. . . . His body stiffened–his face went purple. He fell back sprawling over the chair–his limbs convulsed.

Mrs. Merrowdene leaned forward, watching him. A little smile crossed her lips. She spoke to him–very softly and gently.

"You made a mistake, Mr. Evans. You thought I wanted to kill George. . . . How stupid of you–how very stupid."

She sat there a minute longer looking at the dead man, the third man who had threatened to cross her path and separate her from the man she loved. . . .

Her smile broadened. She looked more than ever like a Madonna. Then she raised her voice and called.

"George–George. . . . Oh! do come here. I'm afraid there's been the most dreadful accident. . . . Poor Mr. Evans. . . ."

The King of Paris Dies **Guy Endore**

Guy Endore has called his story of Alexandre Dumas the elder a biographical novel but he has succeeded in making it seem completely real. More than that he has found his way under the skin of this man who expressed in his own life that most vivid phase of the nineteenth century.

Even if Dumas is not read as much today as he was a half century ago, he will never be forgotten. That is more than he himself had hoped for in the days when his amazing facility was expressing itself in an almost unbelievable output of exciting and rich romance. He did not believe his books would live. But he found much compensation in the certainty that he was supplying his readers with unfailing pleasure.

His views on the subject are well worth hearing. Will Alexandre Dumas please take the stand?

THE KING OF PARIS DIES

Guy Endore

Yes, it would have been wonderful to have known this man personally. In the flesh. In his towering mass of warm flesh, never tired and never cold, six foot three in his stockinged feet. Laughing at all his enemies and his increasing host of detractors, shrugging off all their sharp darts of ridicule and saying, "What do you expect of me? I'm once and for all simply incapable of hate. Rage? Yes, I can be enraged. Because rage is brief. But hate? No, I can't hate. Hate endures."

Yes, it would have been wonderful to have known him in the flesh. Failing that, I have had the pleasure of knowing him in spirit. I have lived with this spirit of his, stayed up nights with it, taken long walks with it. Eaten with it. And gone to bed with it.

And now, when the time comes to write finis to this book, it is almost as if I were called to the funeral of a close friend.

Ah! he so loved life! He would have wanted to live and enjoy life forever. And for a time it seemed almost that he had discovered the magic of perpetual youth. It was the dying off of his friends, one by one, that shook his confidence in his own robust sturdiness. Shook it again and again until at last it was destroyed.

It was the Johannot brothers dying so young and so talented. It was Gérard de Nerval found hanging one wintry morning from a lamppost. It was his former star and mistress Marie Dorval dying in poverty and writing him a last frantic appeal from her deathbed. "Dumas, my dear Dumas, for that love that we once bore each other, please don't let me be thrown into the paupers' trench."

And he, being as usual out of funds, sold his lovely Grand Order of Nizam, the one that the Sultan of Turkey himself had hung around his neck, and bought her a plot.

And Balzac, swollen with dropsy, lying in stench and agony, while his wife entertained her lover in an adjoining room, and the doctor shaking his head and saying, "Behold the victim of fifty thousand cups of black coffee. Ten thousand nights of work, during which he kept himself awake with pot after pot of a tarlike brew."

Dumas and Victor Hugo were among the pallbearers of the body.

Oh, how many he had carried to their graves! In how many processions he had walked, and in how many black draped churches he had stood. In Notre Dame itself, steeped in black, when his good friend the son of King Louis Philippe had been thrown to his death from a horse.

How proud he had used to be, in former times, that so many people called him their friend, so that when he walked the streets or went into a café, it was everywhere: "Ah, Monsieur Dumas! Bonjour, Monsieur Dumas!" And Dumas here and Dumas there.

But in the end what did it add up to? Why, simply that the more people you knew the more funerals you eventually had to go to.

Indeed, there came a time when Paris, that city he so loved, became a nightmare to him. Romanticism had died when Baron Haussmann had ripped open the medieval city to build great modern avenues through it. And the modern people living there no longer had any respect for him. His ways were already antique. Swashbuckling. Cloak-and-dagger stuff. Trap doors. A joke!

Then a walk through Paris became a walk through a cemetery: every corner, every restaurant, almost every house, would remind him of someone who had passed on. Delphine Gay, Vigny, Murger, Musset. The number was endless.

The army of the living became ever smaller, and the army of the dead ever larger, until he felt choked. And he wanted to cry out, "Take care! We are outnumbered! *Sauve qui peut!*"

But he battled on. He devoured life. His love affairs, his cooking, became ever more extravagant, as if a champion appetite was enough to make an impregnable bastion. He wrote massively, as if he intended to use his books someday as a barricade. He threw himself into one adventure after another, as if sheer excitement would frighten away the reaper.

He traveled back and forth through France. He went to England. He went to Russia. He joined Garibaldi in the war against the Bourbons of Italy, buying a ship with his own money, stocking it with weapons of war, recruiting soldiers, hiring tailors to sew them red shirts. He even published an Italian daily newspaper. And showered Garibaldi with the advice of a man who has read deeply of the knavishness and trickery of princes and of peoples.

It is true that amidst his growing despair there still flowed the strong current of his life, like a stream of water rushing through a desert. For example, his little warship boasted a female admiral, which ordinary warships don't. And this pretty admiral gave birth to another one of

Dumas' children, Micaella, a girl, for whom Garibaldi stood godfather.

But he never stopped writing, and some authorities state that Dumas' dispatches from the Garibaldian war front entitled him to be called the world's first war correspondent. Others consider the whole business just another piece of clownishness. Larousse, the encyclopedist, had this comment to make on Dumas' dispatches: "Wasn't there once a man named Garibaldi who had something to do with this war against the Kingdom of the Two Sicilies? Or did General Dumas cashier him?"

Yes, it was all very exciting. Very alive. But no matter how fast you juggle the balls, no matter how you dazzle yourself and everyone else with the speed of your living, the days still pass by, the months pile up solid, the years move forward ponderously, and then break off suddenly like huge icebergs dropping from a polar glacier.

And yet, for Dumas, funerals were eventually to provide him with one consolation: he could be sure of seeing his son, now a dramatist more famous than his father.

The two men, tall, bareheaded, solemn-faced, stood there while the speeches droned on. Then, afterward, they embraced stiffly.

"You are well, Papa?"

"In perfect health, my boy. And you?"

"Fine, Papa."

They stood there, as if there were words that still wanted to be said. But neither spoke. A secret wedged them apart. It was as if one or the other, or both, were too embarrassed to break the silence.

Then at last, awkwardly, almost like strangers, they would shake hands and part. And Dumas, afterward, would say to a friend, "I see him only at funerals nowadays. I suppose the next time will be the occasion of my own funeral."

And yet they continued to love each other. When the *Lady of the Camellias* had been finally brought to production, Dumas had rushed from Brussels to be at the opening performance. No one had applauded so frantically as he.

What a triumph! And when the cry of "Author! Author!" had resounded through the hall, Dumas *père* had risen big and proud in his box.

"What," people had wondered, "is he going to claim that he had a hand in this too?"

"Yes," Dumas had said in a loud voice. "I demand a share of the credit. Because I am the real author–I authored the author! And who knows but that someday I shall be remembered in history only because I was the father of the playwright Alexandre Dumas."

The house had broken into wild applause, and Alexandre, who admittedly had sweated for a second or two, joined in.

And thus Dumas struggled on.

While the Cassagnacs, bribed with millions from the bloated financiers of the Empire, screamed for war against Prussia, a war that was soon to throw France to her knees, Dumas went out to the battlefield of Langensalza where the blind King of Hanover had stood with his little army against the might of Prussia and had been so brutally bowled over, and he came back to write a book, *The Prussian Terror,* warning France of her danger.

But Dumas was no longer of any consequence in France. Whether as clown or prophet, he was quite passé.

Gone were the days when customers punched each other in bookstores to reach for copies of his latest novel before it was sold out. Gone were the days when editors queued up before his study door.

Nothing was left for him but the dregs of a literary career. His books no longer sold. His plays no longer played. Out of charity a few editors still paid him small sums for bits of writing, for souvenirs, chats, squibs. And in the outlying halls he could still gather some sort of an audience for a lecture–for example, on his friend Delacroix, who had died not so long before.

As bills accumulated and money became scarce, he would not even turn down an offer to write a paragraph of publicity for a milliner.

"I'll pay you well for it," Madame Mabille assured him. "Fifty francs. But of course only when I see it in the newspapers," she added, as Dumas was already stretching out his hand for the money.

"Oh, they'll print it," he insisted. But the milliner clicked her purse shut and would not budge.

So Dumas wrote the pathetic little tale of a poor prostitute who had decided on suicide because she had no food and was even too weak to leave her tiny garret room. But before killing herself, she made one last attempt to move the heart of the kind people of Paris, writing her appeal on a bit of paper and tying it to the leg of her pet canary. Then, opening the little bird's cage, she gave it freedom.

"The poor bird," Dumas wrote, "fluttered into Madame Mabille's millinery shop. But it was too late. The young girl was already dead of starvation. The curious may still see the bird by visiting Madame Mabille's establishment, rue des Bons Enfants, and may verify the truth by the little bit of string still dangling from the bird's leg."

This little tale was picked up by all the Paris press, and hundreds of people crowded into Madame Mabille's place. After all, there's nothing moves the Parisian public to tears so much as the death of a young sinful girl.

Delighted with the results, Madame Mabille came running to Monsieur Dumas. "Here is your money," she said.

"But this is only forty-two francs," Dumas said.

"Precisely," said Madame Mabille.

"You promised me fifty," Dumas reminded her.

"Yes, but when I promised you that amount, I did not expect that I would have to run out quickly and buy a canary. That cost me eight francs."

"But you are not going to make me pay for the canary!" Dumas exclaimed.

"Isn't it because of your story that I was put to that expense?" Madame Mabille asked.

"Yes, of course," Dumas admitted.

"Then it's only right that you should pay," Madame Mabille concluded.

Since Dumas knew that no one had ever gotten the better of a Paris shopkeeper, he made no further effort to collect the eight francs.

The next morning, for the first time in nearly half a century, when he sat down to his deal table and took up his pen, he didn't write.

Day after day he sat there, pen poised, quiet. And not writing.

He sat half awake and half asleep, dozing quietly, thinking of nothing in particular.

On the great billiard table his mail accumulated, unopened and unanswered.

Before him lay his deckle-edged paper, made especially for him by a Lyons admirer who happened to be in the paper business—blue for romances, yellow for articles, green for plays, so that he would not get his manuscripts mixed up.

His eyes were as perfect as ever. His hand was just as steady.

It wasn't that he couldn't write any more. It was only that he no longer felt any urge. After fifty years the machine had suddenly stopped.

He still possessed a few of those *objets d'art* that, so he used to claim, stimulated him to creation: Moorish carvings, Bohemian glassware, Russian icons, just a fragment of the once vast booty of outlandishly shaped and garishly colored objects that he had dragged home from his endless travels, the small fragment still left over after a hundred despoiling creditors and a thousand greedy women had garnered their share.

On the wall hung the single Delacroix he still owned. And also the framed "world's largest visiting card" that Delacroix had once sketched and left at his door when he hadn't found Dumas in.

And there too hung the two letters from Abraham Lincoln. The first thanking him for $100 contributed to the Fund for the Widows of Abolitionists, but remarking that an additional $125 had been realized by selling the Dumas signature from the bottom of his letter. Lincoln's second letter thanked Dumas for the receipt of a hundred signatures which he was sure would sell quickly at a hundred dollars apiece.

But all these mementos that had usually filled him with the zest to work no longer had any effect on him.

He felt himself just another object among a lot of objects. And he remained thus–quiet, content in a strange, lethargic way.

The servants came to him for orders and for money and he simply stared at them, seeing no need to answer them. One after the other, they paid themselves off with some piece of furniture which they took out to sell and disappeared.

The days passed and Dumas dozed on. He remembered how when he had been a little child he had used to run on his tiptoes. And then finally he had come down on his heels. Yes, but only outside: inside, in his mind, in his passions, he had raced on as before. Raced on for over sixty years.

Until now. Now at last he was at rest.

The weeks passed and he did nothing. Occasionally visitors dropped in. Then Dumas would rouse himself temporarily and even get dressed and go out. And for an hour or two he would seem to be his old lively self.

But the moment he found himself alone, he relaxed. And returned to his pleasant somnolence.

One day his son made an unexpected visit.

"Bonjour, Papa," said Alexandre.

"Bonjour, *mon fils,*" said Dumas.

"How are you, Papa?"

"As you see, my boy," said Dumas. "As usual, hard at work. I have half a dozen stories and articles that I've promised to turn out." And he dipped his pen into the dry inkwell.

Alexandre saw the piles of unopened mail, the newspapers and magazines unread. With his finger he traced a track through the heavy dust that had accumulated on the mounds of blank deckle-edged paper.

"Why don't you come out and spend the summer with us at the beach?" said Alexandre. He had a little cottage at Puys, a lovely spot that George Sand had recommended.

Dumas shrugged. "Thanks. Really, I'm very comfortable here."

But he didn't resist when his son put a cape around him and led him away.

He liked to sit on the beach, in the warm sun. He heard his grandchildren screaming around him, and he smiled and dozed as if fifty years of missed sleep had now turned in their bill and were insisting on immediate payment.

Since he took no interest in the war, it was decided to say nothing to him about it. And Alexandre, seeing that the Prussian armies were headed for Paris, decided it might be safer to remain for the rest of the year at Puys.

When the cold autumn days came, Dumas began to spend less and less time up. Finally one day the maid put his clothes away. And Dumas realized that he would never wear them again.

When she emptied his pockets, she found a gold Napoleon and some change. Alexandre handed the coins to his father. Dumas laughed. "Look, my boy, that's precisely the sum with which I landed in Paris, fifty years ago. Imagine: a half century of high living and it hasn't cost me a cent. I'm still as rich as when I started out. Now let anyone accuse me of extravagance!"

The doctor came to see him, but only to confirm what was quite apparent: his body was no longer voiding its waters properly and the tissues were becoming flooded. It would be necessary, from time to time, to resort to artificial means.

Dumas understood the sentence of death and did not seem to mind.

One day his son found him in tears.

"You're in pain, Papa!" he cried out, alarmed.

Dumas shook his head.

"The children are too noisy?" Alexandre asked.

"No, son. I'm fine. But I've been thinking of the time Victor Hugo advised me not to write so fast, nor so much. 'You have money now, and reputation. Now write for the ages. Mature something that will live forever.' How I wish now that I had taken his advice to heart."

"But, Papa, you *have* written things for the ages."

"No," said Dumas. "I wanted to make myself into a legendary character. But I've failed–all around. Long ago, in my play *Antony*, I wrote: 'Oblivion is the shroud in which the dead are buried for the second time.' That line was meant for me."

Alexandre, tortured, said with simulated cheer, "But for that line alone, Papa, you should be remembered."

Dumas shook his head slowly. "No, my boy. The famous writers, the ones who really carve their names in history, they write the serious, the difficult, the incomprehensible. My works are too easy. A child can read them. And you know it's the dinner you can't digest that you remember long after you've eaten it. My stuff was always too digestible. It tasted too good. It went down too easily. Oh, I often thought of changing—but when I got to writing I could never put my mind to anything else but the problem of how to keep the reader interested, keep him excited, startled. I wanted to have him laughing or crying, amused or frightened. And never did I try to appear more intelligent than the reader. On the contrary, I strove to make the difficult as simple as possible, I wanted to share everything I knew with the reader, in the most pleasant manner possible. For this I will be forgotten."

"But, Papa, who will ever be able to forget your *Three Musketeers,* your *Monte Cristo,* your *Twenty Years After?*"

Dumas smiled incredulously. "You honestly think they are good?"

"Why, Papa, they're classics."

Dumas shook his head. "No. I don't believe it." He sighed. "I wish now that I had read them. I often promised myself that I would. But when did I have the time?"

"What?" Alexandre exclaimed, all the old ghosts rising in him again. "You never read them?"

"How could I?" Dumas asked. "I had to choose between reading and writing. I did not have time for both. So I decided to do the writing and leave the reading to the public."

"Well, you have time to read now," said Alexandre.

"But have you my books here?" Dumas asked.

"Can you imagine a French home without your books?" Alexandre said. "Without at least your *Monte Cristo* and your *Three Musketeers?* And if not, they can be purchased in every village."

He left and came back with an armload of Dumas volumes.

His father smiled sadly. "I shall scarcely have time to finish all that."

Nevertheless, he began to read. "You know, it's quite good," he said to his son once.

But in the midst of *Monte Cristo,* he became tearful. "I shall never know how it all comes out," he moaned.

Alexandre choked back his tears. "Papa," he said, "Papa . . ."

"Yes, son." The old man's eyes were closed and his voice far away.

"Forgive me, Papa. Forgive me!"

"What for, my boy?" his father asked. Those were his last words, spoken just as it seemed finally possible for father and son to have an explanation.

He had sunk into a somnolence from which he never again roused himself. Soon an attack of apoplexy in the midst of this sleep sent his daughter on the run for the priest. And while in the distance the Prussian artillery could be heard battering at Dieppe, Dumas received the last sacrament, only the fluttering of his eyelids betraying that he was aware of what was going on.

Thus he passed away. It was the fifth of December, 1870.

Magnetism **F. Scott Fitzgerald**

In the late twenties, just before the advent of the talkies changed the whole face of the motion picture world, F. Scott Fitzgerald paid his first visit to Hollywood. He found it still dominated by a group of the early great stars of the silent pictures–Mary Pickford, Greta Garbo, Douglas Fairbanks, Charlie Chaplin, Norma Talmadge, Harold Lloyd, Marguerite Clark. Their fame was world wide, their wealth was almost incalculable, and they lived in aristocratic ease on their large estates. While Fitzgerald labored to turn the formula stories which the studios owned into sprightly scenarios, he studied these secluded stars and found themes for some of his best stories.

This, I think, was the first of them–the story of a handsome young actor who was possessed of so much charm that women just naturally fell in love with him.

MAGNETISM

F. Scott Fitzgerald

The pleasant, ostentatious boulevard was lined at prosperous intervals with New England Colonial houses–without ship models in the hall. When the inhabitants moved out here the ship models had at last been given to the children. The next street was a complete exhibit of the Spanish-bungalow phase of West Coast architecture; while two streets over, the cylindrical windows and round towers of 1897–melancholy antiques which sheltered swamis, yogis, fortune tellers, dressmakers, dancing teachers, art academies and chiropractors–looked down now upon brisk buses and trolley cars. A little walk around the block could, if you were feeling old that day, be a discouraging affair.

On the green flanks of the modern boulevard children, with their knees marked by the red stains of the mercurochrome era, played with toys with a purpose–beams that taught engineering, soldiers that taught manliness, and dolls that taught motherhood. When the dolls were so banged up that they stopped looking like real babies and began to look like dolls, the children developed affection for them. Everything in the vicinity–even the March sunlight–was new, fresh, hopeful and thin, as you would expect in a city that had tripled its population in fifteen years.

Among the very few domestics in sight that morning was a handsome young maid sweeping the steps of the biggest house on the street. She was a large, simple Mexican girl with the large, simple ambitions of the time and the locality, and she was already conscious of being a luxury–she received one hundred dollars a month in return for her personal liberty. Sweeping, Dolores kept an eye on the stairs inside, for Mr. Hanaford's car was waiting and he would soon be coming down to breakfast. The problem came first this morning, however–the problem as to whether it was a duty or a favor when she helped the English nurse down the steps with the perambulator. The English nurse always said "Please," and "Thanks very much," but Dolores hated her and would have liked, without any special excitement, to beat her insensible. Like most Latins under the stimulus of American life, she had irresistible impulses toward violence.

The nurse escaped, however. Her blue cape faded haughtily into the distance just as Mr. Hannaford, who had come quietly downstairs, stepped into the space of the front door.

"Good morning." He smiled at Dolores; he was young and extraordinarily handsome. Dolores tripped on the broom and fell off the stoop. George Hannaford hurried down the steps, reached her as she was getting to her feet cursing volubly in Mexican, just touched her arm with a helpful gesture and said, "I hope you didn't hurt yourself."

"Oh, no."

"I'm afraid it was my fault; I'm afraid I startled you, coming out like that."

His voice had real regret in it; his brow was knit with solicitude.

"Are you sure you're all right?"

"Aw, sure."

"Didn't turn your ankle?"

"Aw, no."

"I'm terribly sorry about it."

"Aw, it wasn't your fault."

He was still frowning as she went inside, and Dolores, who was not hurt and thought quickly, suddenly contemplated having a love affair with him. She looked at herself several times in the pantry mirror and stood close to him as she poured his coffee, but he read the paper and she saw that that was all for the morning.

Hannaford entered his car and drove to Jules Rennard's house. Jules was a French Canadian by birth, and George Hannaford's best friend; they were fond of each other and spent much time together. Both of them were simple and dignified in their tastes and in their way of thinking, instinctively gentle, and in a world of the volatile and the bizarre found in each other a certain quiet solidity.

He found Jules at breakfast.

"I want to fish for barracuda," said George abruptly. "When will you be free? I want to take the boat and go down to Lower California."

Jules had dark circles under his eyes. Yesterday he had closed out the greatest problem of his life by settling with his ex-wife for two hundred thousand dollars. He had married too young, and the former slavey from the Quebec slums had taken to drugs upon her failure to rise with him. Yesterday, in the presence of lawyers, her final gesture had been to smash his finger with the base of a telephone. He was tired of women for a while and welcomed the suggestion of a fishing trip.

"How's the baby?" he asked.

"The baby's fine."

"And Kay?"

"Kay's not herself, but I don't pay any attention. What did you do to your hand?"

"I'll tell you another time. What's the matter with Kay, George?"

"Jealous."

"Of who?"

"Helen Avery. It's nothing. She's not herself, that's all." He got up. "I'm late," he said. "Let me know as soon as you're free. Any time after Monday will suit me."

George left and drove out an interminable boulevard which narrowed into a long, winding concrete road and rose into the hilly country behind. Somewhere in the vast emptiness a group of buildings appeared, a barn-like structure, a row of offices, a large but quick restaurant and half a dozen small bungalows. The chauffeur dropped Hannaford at the main entrance. He went in and passed through various enclosures, each marked off by swinging gates and inhabited by a stenographer.

"Is anybody with Mr. Schroeder?" he asked, in front of a door lettered with that name.

"No, Mr. Hannaford."

Simultaneously his eye fell on a young lady who was writing at a desk aside, and he lingered a moment.

"Hello, Margaret," he said. "How are you, darling?"

A delicate, pale beauty looked up, frowning a little, still abstracted in her work. It was Miss Donovan, the script girl, a friend of many years.

"Hello. Oh, George, I didn't see you come in. Mr. Douglas wants to work on the book sequence this afternoon."

"All right."

"These are the changes we decided on Thursday night." She smiled up at him and George wondered for the thousandth time why she had never gone into pictures.

"All right," he said. "Will initials do?"

"Your initials look like George Harris'."

"Very well, darling."

As he finished, Pete Schroeder opened his door and beckoned him. "George, come here!" he said with an air of excitement. "I want you to listen to some one on the phone."

Hannaford went in.

"Pick up the phone and say 'Hello,'" directed Schroeder. "Don't say who you are."

"Hello," said Hannaford obediently.

"Who is this?" asked a girl's voice.

Hannaford put his hand over the mouthpiece. "What am I supposed to do?"

Schroeder snickered and Hannaford hesitated, smiling and suspicious. "Who do you want to speak to?" he temporized into the phone.

"To George Hannaford, I want to speak to. Is this him?"

"Yes."

"Oh, George; it's me."

"Who?"

"Me–Gwen. I had an awful time finding you. They told me—"

"Gwen who?"

"Gwen–can't you hear? From San Francisco–last Thursday night."

"I'm sorry," objected George. "Must be some mistake."

"Is this George Hannaford?"

"Yes."

The voice grew slightly tart: "Well, this is Gwen Becker you spent last Thursday evening with in San Francisco. There's no use pretending you don't know who I am, because you do."

Schroeder took the apparatus from George and hung up the receiver.

"Somebody has been doubling for me up in Frisco," said Hannaford.

"So that's where you were Thursday night!"

"Those things aren't funny to me–not since that crazy Zeller girl. You can never convince them they've been sold because the man always looks something like you. What's new, Pete?"

"Let's go over to the stage and see."

Together they walked out a back entrance, along a muddy walk, and opening a little door in the big blank wall of the studio building entered into its half darkness.

Here and there figures spotted the dim twilight, figures that turned up white faces to George Hannaford, like souls in purgatory watching the passage of a half-god through. Here and there were whispers and soft voices and, apparently from afar, the gentle tremolo of a small organ. Turning the corner made by some flats, they came upon the white crackling glow of a stage with two people motionless upon it.

An actor in evening clothes, his shirt front, collar and cuffs tinted a brilliant pink, made as though to get chairs for them, but they shook their heads and stood watching. For a long while nothing happened on the stage–no one moved. A row of lights went off with a savage hiss, went on again. The plaintive tap of a hammer begged admission to nowhere in the distance; a blue face appeared among the blinding lights above and called something unintelligible into the upper blackness. Then the silence was broken by a low clear voice from the stage:

"If you want to know why I haven't got stockings on, look in my dressing room. I spoiled four pairs yesterday and two already this morning. . . . This dress weighs six pounds."

A man stepped out of the group of observers and regarded the girl's brown legs; their lack of covering was scarcely distinguishable, but, in any event, her expression implied that she would do nothing about it. The lady was annoyed, and so intense was her personality that it had taken only a fractional flexing of her eyes to indicate the fact. She was a dark, pretty girl with a figure that would be full-blown sooner than she wished. She was just eighteen.

Had this been the week before, George Hannaford's heart would have stood still. Their relationship had been in just that stage. He hadn't said a word to Helen Avery that Kay could have objected to, but something had begun between them on the second day of this picture that Kay had felt in the air. Perhaps it had begun even earlier, for he had determined, when he saw Helen Avery's first release, that she should play opposite him. Helen Avery's voice and the dropping of her eyes when she finished speaking, like a sort of exercise in control, fascinated him. He had felt that they both tolerated something, that each knew half of some secret about people and life, and that if they rushed toward each other there would be a romantic communion of almost unbelievable intensity. It was this element of promise and possibility that had haunted him for a fortnight and was now dying away.

Hannaford was thirty, and he was a moving-picture actor only through a series of accidents. After a year in a small technical college he had taken a summer job with an electric company, and his first appearance in a studio was in the rôle of repairing a bank of Klieg lights. In an emergency he played a small part and made good, but for fully a year after that he thought of it as a purely transitory episode in his life. At first much of it had offended him—the almost hysterical egotism and excitability hidden under an extremely thin veil of elaborate good-fellowship. It was only recently, with the advent of such men as Jules Rennard into pictures, that he began to see the possibilities of a decent and secure private life, much as his would have been as a successful engineer. At last his success felt solid beneath his feet.

He met Kay Tompkins at the old Griffith Studios at Mamaroneck and their marriage was a fresh, personal affair, removed from most stage marriages. Afterward they had possessed each other completely, had been pointed to: "Look, there's one couple in pictures who manage to stay together." It would have taken something out of many people's lives—people who enjoyed a vicarious security in the contemplation of their marriage—if they hadn't stayed together, and their love was fortified by a certain effort to live up to that.

He held women off by a polite simplicity that underneath was hard and watchful; when he felt a certain current being turned on he became emotionally stupid. Kay expected and took much more from men, but she, too, had a careful thermometer against her heart. Until the other night, when she reproached him for being interested in Helen Avery, there had been an absolute minimum of jealousy between them.

George Hannaford was still absorbed in the thought of Helen Avery as he left the studio and walked toward his bungalow over the way. There was in his mind, first, a horror that anyone should come between him and Kay, and second, a regret that he no longer carried that possibility in the forefront of his mind. It had given him a tremendous pleasure, like the things that had happened to him during his first big success, before he was so "made" that there was scarcely anything better ahead; it was something to take out and look at—a new and still mysterious joy. It hadn't been love, for he was critical of Helen Avery as he had never been critical of Kay. But his feeling of last week had been sharply significant and memorable, and he was restless, now that it had passed.

Working that afternoon, they were seldom together, but he was conscious of her and he knew that she was conscious of him.

She stood a long time with her back to him at one point, and when she turned at length, their eyes swept past each other's, brushing like bird wings. Simultaneously he saw they had gone far, in their way; it was well that he had drawn back. He was glad that someone came for her when the work was almost over.

Dressed, he returned to the office wing, stopping in for a moment to see Schroeder. No one answered his knock, and, turning the knob, he went in. Helen Avery was there alone.

Hannaford shut the door and they stared at each other. Her face was young, frightened. In a moment in which neither of them spoke, it was decided that they would have some of this out now. Almost thankfully he felt the warm sap of emotion flow out of his heart and course through his body.

"Helen!"

She murmured "What?" in an awed voice.

"I feel terribly about this." His voice was shaking.

Suddenly she began to cry; painful, audible sobs shook her. "Have you got a handkerchief?" she said.

He gave her a handkerchief. At that moment there were steps outside. George opened the door halfway just in time to keep Schroeder from entering on the spectacle of her tears.

"Nobody's in," he said facetiously. For a moment longer he kept his shoulder against the door. Then he let it open slowly.

Outside in his limousine, he wondered how soon Jules would be ready to go fishing.

II

From the age of twelve Kay Tompkins had worn men like rings on every finger. Her face was round, young, pretty and strong; a strength accentuated by the responsive play of brows and lashes around her clear, glossy, hazel eyes. She was the daughter of a senator from a Western state and she hunted unsuccessfully for glamour through a small Western city until she was seventeen, when she ran away from home and went on the stage. She was one of those people who are famous far beyond their actual achievement.

There was that excitement about her that seemed to reflect the excitement of the world. While she was playing small parts in Ziegfeld shows she attended proms at Yale, and during a temporary venture into pictures she met George Hannaford, already a star of the new "natural" type then just coming into vogue. In him she found what she had been seeking.

She was at present in what is known as a dangerous state. For six months she had been helpless and dependent entirely upon George, and now that her son was the property of a strict and possessive English nurse, Kay, free again, suddenly felt the need of proving herself attractive. She wanted things to be as they had been before the baby was thought of. Also she felt that lately George had taken her too much for granted; she had a strong instinct that he was interested in Helen Avery.

When George Hannaford came home that night he had minimized to himself their quarrel of the previous evening and was honestly surprised at her perfunctory greeting.

"What's the matter, Kay?" he asked after a minute. "Is this going to be another night like last night?"

"Do you know we're going out tonight?" she said, avoiding an answer.

"Where?"

"To Katherine Davis'. I didn't know whether you'd want to go——"

"I'd like to go."

"I didn't know whether you'd want to go. Arthur Busch said he'd stop for me."

They dined in silence. Without any secret thoughts to dip into like a child into a jam jar, George felt restless, and at the same time was aware that the atmosphere was full of jealousy, suspicion and anger. Until recently they had preserved between them something precious that made their house one of the pleasantest in Hollywood to enter. Now suddenly it might be any house; he felt common and he felt unstable. He had come near to making something bright and precious into something cheap and unkind. With a sudden surge of emotion, he crossed the room and was about to put his arm around her when the doorbell rang. A moment later Dolores announced Mr. Arthur Busch.

Busch was an ugly, popular little man, a continuity writer and lately a director. A few years ago they had been hero and heroine to him, and even now, when he was a person of some consequence in the picture world, he accepted with equanimity Kay's use of him for such purposes as tonight's. He had been in love with her for years, but, because his love seemed hopeless, it had never caused him much distress.

They went on to the party. It was a housewarming, with Hawaiian musicians in attendance, and the guests were largely of the old crowd. People who had been in the early Griffith pictures, even though they were scarcely thirty, were considered to be of the old crowd; they were different from those coming along now, and they were conscious of it. They had a dignity and straightforwardness about them from the fact that they had worked in pictures before pictures were bathed in a golden haze of success. They were still rather humble before their amazing triumph, and thus, unlike the new generation, who took it all for granted, they were constantly in touch with reality. Half a dozen or so of the women were especially aware of being unique. No one had come along to fill their places; here and there a pretty face had caught the public imagination for a year, but those of the old crowd were already legends, ageless and disembodied. With all this, they were still young enough to believe that they would go on forever.

George and Kay were greeted affectionately; people moved over and made place for them. The Hawaiians performed and the Duncan sisters sang at the piano. From the moment George saw who was here he guessed that Helen Avery would be here, too, and the fact annoyed him. It was not appropriate that she should be part of this gathering through which he and Kay had moved familiarly and tranquilly for years.

He saw her first when someone opened the swinging door to the kitchen, and when, a little later, she came out and their eyes met, he knew absolutely that he didn't love her. He went up to speak to her, and at her first words he saw something had happened to her, too, that had dissipated the mood of the afternoon. She had got a big part.

"And I'm in a daze!" she cried happily. "I didn't think there was a chance and I've thought of nothing else since I read the book a year ago."

"It's wonderful. I'm awfully glad."

He had the feeling, though, that he should look at her with a certain regret; one couldn't jump from such a scene as this afternoon to a plane of casual friendly interest. Suddenly she began to laugh.

"Oh, we're such actors, George—you and I."

"What do you mean?"

"You know what I mean."

"I don't."

"Oh, yes, you do. You did this afternoon. It was a pity we didn't have a camera."

Short of declaring then and there that he loved her, there was absolutely nothing more to say. He grinned acquiescently. A group formed around them and absorbed them, and George, feeling that the evening had settled something, began to think about going home. An excited and sentimental elderly lady—someone's mother—came up and began telling him how much she believed in him, and he was polite and charming to her, as only he could be, for half an hour. Then he went to Kay, who had been sitting with Arthur Busch all evening, and suggested that they go.

She looked up unwillingly. She had had several highballs and the fact was mildly apparent. She did not want to go, but she got up after a mild argument and George went upstairs for his coat. When he came down Katherine Davis told him that Kay had already gone out to the car.

The crowd had increased; to avoid a general good night he went out through the sun-parlor door to the lawn; less than twenty feet away from him he saw the figures of Kay and Arthur Busch against a bright street lamp; they were standing close together and staring into each other's eyes. He saw that they were holding hands.

After the first start of surprise George instinctively turned about, retraced his steps, hurried through the room he had just left, and came noisily out the front door. But Kay and Arthur Busch were still standing close together, and it was lingeringly and with abstracted eyes that they turned around finally and saw him. Then both of them seemed to make an effort; they drew apart as if it was a physical ordeal. George said good-by to Arthur Busch with special cordiality, and in a moment he and Kay were driving homeward through the clear California night.

He said nothing, Kay said nothing. He was incredulous. He suspected that Kay had kissed a man here and there, but he had never seen it happen or given it any thought. This was different; there had been an element of tenderness in it and there was something veiled and remote in Kay's eyes that he had never seen there before.

Without having spoken, they entered the house; Kay stopped by the library door and looked in.

"There's someone there," she said, and she added without interest: "I'm going upstairs. Good night."

As she ran up the stairs the person in the library stepped out into the hall.

"Mr. Hannaford—"

He was a pale and hard young man; his face was vaguely familiar, but George didn't remember where he had seen it before.

"Mr. Hannaford?" said the young man. "I recognize you from your pictures." He looked at George, obviously a little awed.

"What can I do for you?"

"Well, will you come in here?"

"What is it? I don't know who you are."

"My name is Donovan. I'm Margaret Donovan's brother." His face toughened a little.

"Is anything the matter?"

Donovan made a motion toward the door. "Come in here." His voice was confident now, almost threatening.

George hesitated, then he walked into the library. Donovan followed and stood across the table from him, his legs apart, his hands in his pockets.

"Hannaford," he said, in the tone of a man trying to whip himself up to anger, "Margaret wants fifty thousand dollars."

"What the devil are you talking about?" exclaimed George incredulously.

"Margaret wants fifty thousand dollars," repeated Donovan.

"You're Margaret Donovan's brother?"

"I am."

"I don't believe it." But he saw the resemblance now. "Does Margaret know you're here?"

"She sent me here. She'll hand over those two letters for fifty thousand, and no questions asked."

"What letters?" George chuckled irresistibly. "This is some joke of Schroeder's, isn't it?"

"This ain't a joke, Hannaford. I mean the letters you signed your name to this afternoon."

III

An hour later George went upstairs in a daze. The clumsiness of the affair was at once outrageous and astounding. That a friend of seven years should suddenly request his signature on papers that were not what they were purported to be made all his surroundings seem diaphanous and insecure. Even now the design engrossed him more than a defense against it, and he tried to re-create the steps by which Margaret had arrived at this act of recklessness or despair.

She had served as script girl in various studios and for various directors for ten years; earning first twenty, now a hundred dollars a week. She was lovely-looking and she was intelligent; at any moment in those years she might have asked for a screen test, but some quality of initiative or ambition had been lacking. Not a few times had her opinion made or broken incipient careers. Still she waited at directors' elbows, increasingly aware that the years were slipping away.

That she had picked George as a victim amazed him most of all. Once, during the year before his marriage, there had been a momentary warmth; he had taken her to a Mayfair ball, and he remembered that he had kissed her going home that night in the car. The flirtation trailed along hesitatingly for a week. Before it could develop into anything serious he had gone East and met Kay.

Young Donovan had shown him a carbon of the letters he had signed. They were written on the typewriter that he kept in his bungalow at the studio, and they were carefully and convincingly worded. They purported to be love letters, asserting that he was Margaret Donovan's lover, that he wanted to marry her, and that for that reason he was about to arrange a divorce. It was incredible. Someone must have seen him sign them that morning; someone must have heard her say: "Your initials are like Mr. Harris'."

George was tired. He was training for a screen football game to be played next week, with the Southern California varsity as extras, and he was used to regular hours. In the middle of a confused and despairing sequence of thought about Margaret Donovan and Kay, he suddenly yawned. Mechanically he went upstairs, undressed and got into bed.

Just before dawn Kay came to him in the garden. There was a river that flowed past it now, and boats faintly lit with green and yellow lights moved slowly, remotely by. A gentle starlight fell like rain upon the dark, sleeping face of the world, upon the black mysterious bosoms of the trees, the tranquil gleaming water and the farther shore.

The grass was damp, and Kay came to him on hurried feet; her thin slippers were drenched with dew. She stood upon his shoes, nestling close to him, and held up her face as one shows a book open at a page.

"Think how you love me," she whispered. "I don't ask you to love me always like this, but I ask you to remember."

"You'll always be like this to me."

"Oh, no; but promise me you'll remember." Her tears were falling. "I'll be different, but somewhere lost inside of me there'll always be the person I am tonight."

The scene dissolved slowly and George struggled into consciousness. He sat up in bed; it was morning. In the yard outside he heard the nurse instructing his son in the niceties of behavior for two-month-old babies. From the yard next door a small boy shouted mysteriously: "Who let that barrier through on me?"

Still in his pajamas, George went to the phone and called his lawyers. Then he rang for his man, and while he was being shaved a certain order evolved from the chaos of the night before. First, he must deal with Margaret Donovan; second, he must keep the matter from Kay, who in her present state might believe anything; and, third, he must fix things up with Kay. The last seemed the most important of all.

As he finished dressing he heard the phone ring downstairs and, with an instinct of danger, picked up the receiver.

"Hello. . . . Oh, yes." Looking up, he saw that both his doors were closed. "Good morning, Helen. . . . It's all right, Dolores. I'm taking it up here." He waited till he heard the receiver click downstairs.

"How are you this morning, Helen?"

"George, I called up about last night. I can't tell you how sorry I am."

"Sorry? Why are you sorry?"

"For treating you like that. I don't know what was in me, George. I didn't sleep all night thinking how terrible I'd been."

A new disorder established itself in George's already littered mind. "Don't be silly," he said. To his despair he heard his own voice run on: "For a minute I didn't understand, Helen. Then I thought it was better so."

"Oh, George," came her voice after a moment, very low.

Another silence. He began to put in a cuff button.

"I had to call up," she said after a moment. "I couldn't leave things like that."

The cuff button dropped to the floor; he stooped to pick it up, and then said "Helen!" urgently into the mouthpiece to cover the fact that he had momentarily been away.

"What, George?"

At this moment the hall door opened and Kay, radiating a faint distaste, came into the room. She hesitated.

"Are you busy?"

"It's all right." He stared into the mouthpiece for a moment. "Well, good-by," he muttered abruptly and hung up the receiver. He turned to Kay: "Good morning."

"I didn't mean to disturb you," she said distantly.

"You didn't disturb me." He hesitated. "That was Helen Avery."

"It doesn't concern me who it was. I came to ask you if we're going to the Coconut Grove tonight."

"Sit down, Kay?"

"I don't want to talk."

"Sit down a minute," he said impatiently. She sat down. "How long are you going to keep this up?" he demanded.

"I'm not keeping up anything. We're simply through, George, and you know it as well as I do."

"That's absurd," he said. "Why, a week ago——"

"It doesn't matter. We've been getting nearer to this for months, and now it's over."

"You mean you don't love me?" He was not particularly alarmed. They had been through scenes like this before.

"I don't know. I suppose I'll always love you in a way." Suddenly she began to sob. "Oh, it's all so sad. He's cared for me so long."

George stared at her. Face to face with what was apparently a real emotion, he had no words of any kind. She was not angry, not threatening or pretending, not thinking about him at all, but concerned entirely with her emotions toward another man.

"What is it?" he cried. "Are you trying to tell me you're in love with this man?"

"I don't know," she said helplessly.

He took a step toward her, then went to the bed and lay down on it, staring in misery at the ceiling. After a while a maid knocked to say that Mr. Busch and Mr. Castle, George's lawyer, were below. The fact carried no meaning to him. Kay went into her room and he got up and followed her.

"Let's send word we're out," he said. "We can go away somewhere and talk this over."

"I don't want to go away."

She was already away, growing more mysterious and remote with every minute. The things on her dressing table were the property of a stranger.

He began to speak in a dry, hurried voice. "If you're still thinking about Helen Avery, it's nonsense. I've never given a damn for anybody but you."

They went downstairs and into the living room. It was nearly noon—another bright emotionless California day. George saw that Arthur Busch's ugly face in the sunshine was wan and white; he took a step toward George and then stopped, as if he were waiting for something—a challenge, a reproach, a blow.

In a flash the scene that would presently take place ran itself off in George's mind. He saw himself moving through the scene, saw his part, an infinite choice of parts, but in every one of them Kay would be against him and with Arthur Busch. And suddenly he rejected them all.

"I hope you'll excuse me," he said quickly to Mr. Castle. "I called you up because a script girl named Margaret Donovan wants fifty thousand dollars for some letters she claims I wrote her. Of course the whole thing is—" He broke off. It didn't matter. "I'll come to see you tomorrow." He walked up to Kay and Arthur, so that only they could hear.

"I don't know about you two–what you want to do. But leave me out of it; you haven't any right to inflict any of it on me, for after all it's not my fault. I'm not going to be mixed up in your emotions."

He turned and went out. His car was before the door and he said "Go to Santa Monica" because it was the first name that popped into his head. The car drove off into the everlasting hazeless sunlight.

He rode for three hours, past Santa Monica and then along toward Long Beach by another road. As if it were something he saw out of the corner of his eye and with but a fragment of his attention, he imagined Kay and Arthur Busch progressing through the afternoon. Kay would cry a great deal and the situation would seem harsh and unexpected to them at first, but the tender closing of the day would draw them together. They would turn inevitably toward each other and he would slip more and more into the position of the enemy outside.

Kay had wanted him to get down in the dirt and dust of a scene and scramble for her. Not he; he hated scenes. Once he stooped to compete with Arthur Busch in pulling at Kay's heart, he would never be the same to himself. He would always be a little like Arthur Busch; they would always have that in common, like a shameful secret. There was little of the theater about George; the millions before whose eyes the moods and changes of his face had flickered during ten years had not been deceived about that. From the moment when, as a boy of twenty, his handsome eyes had gazed off into the imaginary distance of a Griffith Western, his audience had been really watching the progress of a straightforward, slow-thinking, romantic man through an accidentally glamorous life.

His fault was that he had felt safe too soon. He realized suddenly that the two Fairbankses, in sitting side by side at table, were not keeping up a pose. They were giving hostages to fate. This was perhaps the most bizarre community in the rich, wild, bored empire, and for a marriage to succeed here, you must expect nothing or you must be always together. For a moment his glance had wavered from Kay and he stumbled blindly into disaster.

As he was thinking this and wondering where he would go and what he should do, he passed an apartment house that jolted his memory. It was on the outskirts of town, a pink horror built to represent something, somewhere, so cheaply and sketchily that whatever it copied the architect must have long since forgotten. And suddenly George remembered that he had once called for Margaret Donovan here the night of a Mayfair dance.

"Stop at this apartment!" he called through the speaking tube.

He went in. The negro elevator boy stared open-mouthed at him as they rose in the cage. Margaret Donovan herself opened the door.

When she saw him she shrank away with a little cry. As he entered and closed the door she retreated before him into the front room. George followed.

It was twilight outside and the apartment was dusky and sad. The last light fell softly on the standardized furniture and the great gallery of signed photographs of moving-picture people that covered one wall. Her face was white, and as she stared at him she began nervously wringing her hands.

"What's this nonsense, Margaret?" George said, trying to keep any reproach out of his voice. "Do you need money that bad?"

She shook her head vaguely. Her eyes were still fixed on him with a sort of terror; George looked at the floor.

"I suppose this was your brother's idea. At least I can't believe you'd be so stupid." He looked up, trying to preserve the brusque masterly attitude of one talking to a naughty child, but at the sight of her face every emotion except pity left him. "I'm a little tired. Do you mind if I sit down?"

"No."

"I'm a little confused today," said George after a minute. "People seem to have it in for me today."

"Why, I thought"–her voice became ironic in midsentence–"I thought everybody loved you, George."

"They don't."

"Only me?"

"Yes," he said abstractedly.

"I wish it had been only me. But then, of course, you wouldn't have been you."

Suddenly he realized that she meant what she was saying.

"That's just nonsense."

"At least you're here," Margaret went on. "I suppose I ought to be glad of that. And I am. I most decidedly am. I've often thought of you sitting in that chair, just at this time when it was almost dark. I used to make up little one-act plays about what would happen then. Would you like to hear one of them? I'll have to begin by coming over and sitting on the floor at your feet."

Annoyed and yet spellbound, George kept trying desperately to seize upon a word or mood that would turn the subject.

"I've seen you sitting there so often that you don't look a bit more real than your ghost. Except that your hat has squashed your beautiful hair down on one side and you've got dark circles or dirt under your eyes. You look white, too, George. Probably you were on a party last night."

"I was. And I found your brother waiting for me when I got home."

"He's a good waiter, George. He's just out of San Quentin prison, where he's been waiting the last six years."

"Then it was his idea?"

"We cooked it up together. I was going to China on my share."

"Why was I the victim?"

"That seemed to make it realer. Once I thought you were going to fall in love with me five years ago."

The bravado suddenly melted out of her voice and it was still light enough to see that her mouth was quivering.

"I've loved you for years," she said–"since the first day you came West and walked into the old Realart Studio. You were so brave about people, George. Whoever it was, you walked right up to them and tore something aside as if it was in your way and began to know them. I tried to make love to you, just like the rest, but it was difficult. You drew people right up close to you and held them there, not able to move either way."

"This is all entirely imaginary," said George, frowning uncomfortably, "and I can't control——"

"No, I know. You can't control charm. It's simply got to be used. You've got to keep your hand in if you have it, and go through life attaching people to you that you don't want. I don't blame you. If you only hadn't kissed me the night of the Mayfair dance. I suppose it was the champagne."

George felt as if a band which had been playing for a long time in the distance had suddenly moved up and taken a station beneath his window. He had always been conscious that things like this were going on around him. Now that he thought of it, he had always been conscious that Margaret loved him, but the faint music of these emotions in his ear had seemed to bear no relation to actual life. They were phantoms that he had conjured up out of nothing; he had never imagined their actual incarnations. At his wish they should die inconsequently away.

"You can't imagine what it's been like," Margaret continued after a minute. "Things you've just said and forgotten, I've put myself asleep night after night remembering–trying to squeeze something more out of them. After that night you took me to the Mayfair other men didn't exist for me any more. And there were others, you know–lots of them. But I'd see you walking along somewhere about the lot, looking at the ground and smiling a little, as if something very amusing had just happened to you, the way you do. And I'd pass you and you'd look up and really smile: 'Hello, darling!' 'Hello, darling' and my heart would turn over. That would happen four times a day."

George stood up and she, too, jumped up quickly.

"Oh, I've bored you," she cried softly. "I might have known I'd bore you. You want to go home. Let's see–is there anything else? Oh, yes; you might as well have those letters."

Taking them out of a desk, she took them to a window and identified them by a rift of lamplight.

"They're really beautiful letters. They'd do you credit. I suppose it was pretty stupid, as you say, but it ought to teach you a lesson about–about signing things, or something." She tore the letters small and threw them in the wastebasket: "Now go on," she said.

"Why must I go now?"

For the third time in twenty-four hours sad and uncontrollable tears confronted him.

"Please go!" she cried angrily–"or stay if you like. I'm yours for the asking. You know it. You can have any woman you want in the world by just raising your hand. Would I amuse you?"

"Margaret——"

"Oh, go on then." She sat down and turned her face away. "After all, you'll begin to look silly in a minute. You wouldn't like that, would you? So get out."

George stood there helpless, trying to put himself in her place and say something that wouldn't be priggish, but nothing came.

He tried to force down his personal distress, his discomfort, his vague feeling of scorn, ignorant of the fact that she was watching him and understanding it all and loving the struggle in his face. Suddenly his own nerves gave way under the strain of the past twenty-four hours and he felt his eyes grow dim and his throat tighten. He shook his head helplessly. Then he turned away–still not knowing that she was watching him and loving him until she thought her heart would burst with it–and went out to the door.

IV

The car stopped before his house, dark save for small lights in the nursery and the lower hall. He heard the telephone ringing, but when he answered it, inside, there was no one on the line. For a few minutes he wandered about in the darkness, moving from chair to chair and going to the window to stare out into the opposite emptiness of the night.

It was strange to be alone, to feel alone. In his overwrought condition the fact was not unpleasant. As the trouble of last night had made Helen Avery infinitely remote, so his talk with Margaret had acted as a katharsis to his own personal misery. It would swing back upon him presently, he knew, but for a moment his mind was too tired to remember, to imagine or to care.

Half an hour passed. He saw Dolores issue from the kitchen, take the paper from the front steps and carry it back to the kitchen for a preliminary inspection. With a vague idea of packing his grip, he went upstairs. He opened the door of Kay's room and found her lying down.

For a moment he didn't speak, but moved around the bathroom between. Then he went into her room and switched on the lights.

"What's the matter?" he asked casually. "Aren't you feeling well?"

"I've been trying to get some sleep," she said. "George, do you think that girl's gone crazy?"

"What girl?"

"Margaret Donovan. I've never heard of anything so terrible in my life."

For a moment he thought that there had been some new development.

"Fifty thousand dollars!" she cried indignantly. "Why, I wouldn't give it to her even if it was true. She ought to be sent to jail."

"Oh, it's not so terrible as that," he said. "She has a brother who's a pretty bad egg and it was his idea."

"She's capable of anything," Kay said solemnly. "And you're just a fool if you don't see it. I've never liked her. She has dirty hair."

"Well, what of it?" he demanded impatiently, and added: "Where's Arthur Busch?"

"He went home right after lunch. Or rather I sent him home."

"You decided you were not in love with him?"

She looked up almost in surprise. "In love with him? Oh, you mean this morning. I was just mad at you; you ought to have known that. I was a little sorry for him last night, but I guess it was the highballs."

"Well, what did you mean when you—" He broke off. Wherever

he turned he found a muddle, and he resolutely determined not to think.

"My heavens!" exclaimed Kay. "Fifty thousand dollars!"

"Oh, drop it. She tore up the letters–she wrote them herself–and everything's all right."

"George."

"Yes."

"Of course Douglas will fire her right away."

"Of course he won't. He won't know anything about it."

"You mean to say you're not going to let her go? After this?"

He jumped up. "Do you suppose she thought that?" he cried.

"Thought what?"

"That I'd have them let her go?"

"You certainly ought to."

He looked hastily through the phone book for her name.

"Oxford—" he called.

After an unusually long time the switchboard operator answered: "Bourbon Apartments."

"Miss Margaret Donovan, please."

"Why—" The operator's voice broke off. "If you'll just wait a minute, please." He held the line; the minute passed, then another. Then the operator's voice: "I couldn't talk to you then. Miss Donovan has had an accident. She's shot herself. When you called they were taking her through the lobby to St. Catherine's Hospital."

"Is she–is it serious?" George demanded frantically.

"They thought so at first, but now they think she'll be all right. They're going to probe for the bullet."

"Thank you."

He got up and turned to Kay.

"She's tried to kill herself," he said in a strained voice. "I'll have to go around to the hospital. I was pretty clumsy this afternoon and I think I'm partly responsible for this."

"George," said Kay suddenly.

"What?"

"Don't you think it's sort of unwise to get mixed up in this? People might say—"

"I don't give a damn what they say," he answered roughly.

He went to his room and automatically began to prepare for going out. Catching sight of his face in the mirror, he closed his eyes with a sudden exclamation of distaste, and abandoned the intention of brushing his hair.

"George," Kay called from the next room, "I love you."

"I love you too."

"Jules Rennard called up. Something about barracuda fishing. Don't you think it would be fun to get up a party? Men and girls both."

"Somehow the idea doesn't appeal to me. The whole idea of barracuda fishing——"

The phone rang below and he started. Dolores was answering it.

It was a lady who had already called twice today.

"Is Mr. Hannaford in?"

"No," said Dolores promptly. She stuck out her tongue and hung up the phone just as George Hannaford came downstairs. She helped him into his coat, standing as close as she could to him, opened the door and followed a little way out on the porch.

"Meester Hannaford," she said suddenly, "that Miss Avery she call up five-six times today. I tell her you out and say nothing to missus."

"What?" He stared at her, wondering how much she knew about his affairs.

"She call up just now and I say you out."

"All right," he said absently.

"Meester Hannaford."

"Yes, Dolores."

"I deedn't hurt myself thees morning when I fell off the porch."

"That's fine. Good night, Dolores."

"Good night, Meester Hannaford."

George smiled at her, faintly, fleetingly, tearing a veil from between them, unconsciously promising her a possible admission to the thousand delights and wonders that only he knew and could command. Then he went to his waiting car and Dolores, sitting down on the stoop, rubbed her hands together in a gesture that might have expressed either ecstasy or strangulation, and watched the rising of the thin, pale California moon.

1928

The Snow Goose **Paul Gallico**

In a publisher's note with this remarkable story it was said that the type face was chosen to give a feeling of fluidity, power, and speed. The story itself has all of these and other qualities much greater–an emotional warmth and a dramatic intensity to a degree seldom encountered in fiction. Written in 1941 (one of the very few short stories to achieve a record of eight printings in its first year), it has a war setting and the author makes fine use of the historic events on the beach at Dunkirk. The story, however, is that of three main characters. Three? Decidedly, for the Lost Princess (the name the others apply to the Snow Goose) is as much a part of it as Rhayader, the lonely hermit of the lighthouse, and Frith, the tall, fair girl who lived with the fisher folk on the Great Marsh.

It is a sad tale but one which, once read, remains always in the memory.

THE SNOW GOOSE

Paul Gallico

The great marsh lies on the Essex coast between the village of Chelmbury and the ancient Saxon oyster-fishing hamlet of Wickaeldroth. It is one of the last of the wild places of England, a low, far-reaching expanse of grass and reeds and half-submerged meadowlands ending in the great saltings and mud flats and tidal pools near the restless sea.

Tidal creeks and estuaries and the crooked, meandering arms of many little rivers whose mouths lap at the edge of the ocean cut through the sodden land that seems to rise and fall and breathe with the recurrence of the daily tides. It is desolate, utterly lonely, and made lonelier by the calls and cries of the wildfowl that make their homes in the marshlands and saltings–the wildgeese and the gulls, the teal and widgeon, the redshanks and curlews that pick their way through the tidal pools. Of human habitants there are none, and none are seen, with the occasional exception of a wild-fowler or native oyster-fishermen, who still ply a trade already ancient when the Normans came to Hastings.

Grays and blues and soft greens are the colors, for when the skies are dark in the long winters, the many waters of the beaches and marshes reflect the cold and somber color. But sometimes, with sunrise and sunset, sky and land are aflame with red and golden fire.

Hard by one of the winding arms of the little River Aelder runs the embankment of an old sea wall, smooth and solid, without a break, a bulwark to the land against the encroaching sea. Deep into a salting some three miles from the English Channel it runs, and there turns north. At that corner its face is gouged, broken, and shattered. It has been breached, and at the breach the hungry sea has already entered and taken for its own the land, the wall, and all that stood there.

At low water the blackened and ruptured stones of the ruins of an abandoned lighthouse show above the surface, with here and there, like buoy markers, the top of a sagging fence-post. Once this lighthouse abutted on the sea and was a beacon on the Essex coast. Time shifted land and water, and its usefulness came to an end.

Lately it served again as a human habitation. In it there lived a lonely man. His body was warped, but his heart was filled with love for wild and hunted things. He was ugly to look upon, but he created great beauty. It is about him, and a child who came to know him and see beyond the grotesque form that housed him to what lay within, that this story is told.

It is not a story that falls easily and smoothly into sequence. It has been garnered from many sources and from many people. Some of it comes in the form of fragments from men who looked upon strange and violent scenes. For the sea has claimed its own and spreads its rippled blanket over the site, and the great white bird with the black-tipped pinions that saw it all from the beginning to the end has returned to the dark, frozen silences of the northlands whence it came.

In the late spring of 1930 Philip Rhayader came to the abandoned lighthouse at the mouth of the Aelder. He bought the light and many acres of marshland and salting surrounding it.

He lived and worked there alone the year round. He was a painter of birds and of nature, who, for reasons, had withdrawn from all human society. Some of the reasons were apparent on his fortnightly visits to the little village of Chelmbury for supplies, where the natives looked askance at his mis-shapen body and dark visage. For he was a hunchback and his left arm was crippled, thin and bent at the wrist, like the claw of a bird.

They soon became used to his queer figure, small but powerful, the massive, dark, bearded head set just slightly below the mysterious mound on his back, the glowing eyes and the clawed hand, and marked him off as "that queer painter chap that lives down to lighthouse."

Physical deformity often breeds hatred of humanity in men. Rhayader did not hate; he loved very greatly, man, the animal kingdom, and all nature. His heart was filled with pity and understanding. He had mastered his handicap, but he could not master the rebuffs he suffered, due to his appearance. The thing that drove him into seclusion was his failure to find anywhere a return of the warmth that flowed from him. He repelled women. Men would have warmed to him had they got to know him. But the mere fact that an effort was being made hurt Rhayader and drove him to avoid the person making it.

He was twenty-seven when he came to the Great Marsh. He had traveled much and fought valiantly before he made the decision to withdraw from a world in which he could not take part as other men. For all of the artist's sensitivity and woman's tenderness locked in his barrel breast, he was very much a man.

In his retreat he had his birds, his painting, and his boat. He owned a sixteen-footer, which he sailed with wonderful skill. Alone, with no eyes to watch him, he managed well with his deformed hand, and he often used his strong teeth to handle the sheets of his billowing sails in a tricky blow.

He would sail the tidal creeks and estuaries and out to sea, and would be gone for days at a time, looking for new species of birds to photograph or sketch, and he became an adept at netting them to add to his collection of tamed wildfowl in the pen near his studio that formed the nucleus of a sanctuary.

He never shot over a bird, and wild-fowlers were not welcome near his premises. He was a friend to all things wild, and the wild things repaid him with their friendship.

Tamed in his enclosures were the geese that came winging down the coast from Iceland and Spitsbergen each October, in great skeins that darkened the sky and filled the air with the rushing noise of their passage—the brown-bodied pink-feet, white-breasted barnacles with their dark necks and clowns' masks, the wild white fronts with black-barred breasts, and many species of wild ducks—widgeon, mallard, pintails, teal, and shovelers.

Some were pinioned, so that they would remain there as a sign and signal to the wild ones that came down at each winter's beginning that here were food and sanctuary.

Many hundreds came and remained with him all through the cold weather from October to the early spring, when they migrated north again to their breeding-grounds below the ice rim.

Rhayader was content in the knowledge that when storms blew, or it was bitter cold and food was scarce, or the big punt guns of the distant bag hunters roared, his birds were safe; that he had gathered to the sanctuary and security of his own arms and heart these many wild and beautiful creatures who knew and trusted him.

They would answer the call of the north in the spring, but in the fall they would come back, barking and whooping and honking in the autumn sky, to circle the landmark of the old light and drop to earth near by to be his guests again—birds that he well remembered and recognized from the previous year.

And this made Rhayader happy, because he knew that implanted somewhere in their beings was the germ knowledge of his existence and his safe haven, that this knowledge had become a part of them and, with the coming of the gray skies and the winds from the north, would send them unerringly back to him.

For the rest, his heart and soul went into the painting of the country in which he lived and its creatures. There are not many Rhayaders extant. He hoarded them jealously, piling them up in his lighthouse and the storerooms above by the hundreds. He was not satisfied with them, because as an artist he was uncompromising.

But the few that have reached the market are masterpieces, filled with the glow and colors of marsh-reflected light, the feel of flight, the push of birds breasting a morning wind bending the tall flag reeds. He painted the loneliness and the smell of the salt-laden cold, the eternity and agelessness of marshes, the wild, living creatures, dawn flights, and frightened things taking to the air, and winged shadows at night hiding from the moon.

One November afternoon, three years after Rhayader had come to the Great Marsh, a child approached the lighthouse studio by means of the sea wall. In her arms she carried a burden.

She was no more than twelve, slender, dirty, nervous and timid as a bird, but beneath the grime as eerily beautiful as a marsh faery. She was pure Saxon, large-boned, fair, with a head to which her body was yet to grow, and deep-set, violet-colored eyes.

She was desperately frightened of the ugly man she had come to see, for legend had already begun to gather about Rhayader, and the native wild-fowlers hated him for interfering with their sport.

But greater than her fear was the need of that which she bore. For locked in her child's heart was the knowledge, picked up somewhere in the swampland, that this ogre who lived in the lighthouse had magic that could heal injured things.

She had never seen Rhayader before and was close to fleeing in panic at the dark apparition that appeared at the studio door, drawn by her footsteps–the black head and beard, the sinister hump, and the crooked claw.

She stood there staring, poised like a disturbed marsh bird for instant flight.

But his voice was deep and kind when he spoke to her.

"What is it, child?"

She stood her ground, and then edged timidly forward. The thing she carried in her arms was a large white bird, and it was quite still. There were stains of blood on its whiteness and on her kirtle where she had held it to her.

The girl placed it in his arms. "I found it, sir. It's hurted. Is it still alive?"

"Yes. Yes, I think so. Come in, child, come in."

Rhayader went inside, bearing the bird, which he placed upon a table, where it moved feebly. Curiosity overcame fear. The girl followed and found herself in a room warmed by a coal fire, shining with many colored pictures that covered the walls, and full of a strange but pleasant smell.

The bird fluttered. With his good hand Rhayader spread one of its immense white pinions. The end was beautifully tipped with black.

Rhayader looked and marveled, and said: "Child, where did you find it?"

"In t' marsh, sir, where fowlers had been. What–what is it, sir?"

"It's a snow goose from Canada. But how in all heaven came it here?"

The name seemed to mean nothing to the little girl. Her deep violet eyes, shining out of the dirt on her thin face, were fixed with concern on the injured bird.

She said: "Can 'ee heal it, sir?"

"Yes, yes," said Rhayader. "We will try. Come, you shall help me."

There were scissors and bandages and splints on a shelf, and he was marvelously deft, even with the crooked claw that managed to hold things.

He said: "Ah, she has been shot, poor thing. Her leg is broken, and the wing tip, but not badly. See, we will clip her primaries, so that we can bandage it, but in the spring the feathers will grow and she will be able to fly again. We'll bandage it close to her body, so that she cannot move it until it has set, and then make a splint for the poor leg."

Her fears forgotten, the child watched, fascinated, as he worked, and all the more so because while he fixed a fine splint to the shattered leg he told her the most wonderful story.

The bird was a young one, no more than a year old. She was born in a northern land far, far across the seas, a land belonging to England. Flying to the south to escape the snow and ice and bitter cold, a great storm had seized her and whirled and buffeted her about. It was a truly terrible storm, stronger than her great wings, stronger than anything. For days and nights it held her in its grip and there was nothing she could do but fly before it. When finally it had blown itself out and her sure instincts took her south again, she was over a different land and surrounded by strange birds that she had never seen before. At last, exhausted by her ordeal, she had sunk to rest in a friendly green marsh, only to be met by the blast from the hunter's gun.

"A bitter reception for a visiting princess," concluded Rhayader. "We will call her *'La Princesse Perdue,'* the Lost Princess. And in a few days she will be feeling much better. See?" He reached into his pocket and produced a handful of grain. The snow goose opened its round yellow eyes and nibbled at it.

The child laughed with delight, and then suddenly caught her breath with alarm as the full import of where she was pressed in upon her, and without a word she turned and fled out of the door.

"Wait, wait!" cried Rhayader, and went to the entrance, where he stopped so that it framed his dark bulk. The girl was already fleeing down the sea wall, but she paused at his voice and looked back.

"What is your name, child?"

"Frith."

"Eh?" said Rhayader. "Fritha, I suppose. Where do you live?"

"Wi' t' fisherfolk at Wickaeldroth." She gave the name the old Saxon pronunciation.

"Will you come back tomorrow, or the next day, to see how the Princess is getting along?"

She paused, and again Rhayader must have thought of the wild water birds caught motionless in that split second of alarm before they took to flight.

But her thin voice came back to him: "Ay!"

And then she was gone, with her fair hair streaming out behind her.

The snow goose mended rapidly and by midwinter was already limping about the enclosure with the wild pink-footed geese with which it associated, rather than the barnacles, and had learned to come to be fed at Rhayader's call. And the child, Fritha, or Frith, was a frequent visitor. She had overcome her fear of Rhayader. Her imagination was captured by the presence of this strange white princess from a land far over the sea, a land that was all pink, as she knew from the map that Rhayader showed her, and on which they traced the stormy path of the lost bird from its home in Canada to the Great Marsh of Essex.

Then one June morning a group of late pink-feet, fat and well fed from the winter at the lighthouse, answered the stronger call of the breeding-grounds and rose lazily, climbing into the sky in ever widening circles. With them, her white body and black-tipped pinions shining in the spring sun, was the snow goose. It so happened that Frith was at the lighthouse. Her cry brought Rhayader running from the studio.

"Look! Look! The Princess! Be she going away?"

Rhayader stared into the sky at the climbing specks. "Ay," he said, unconsciously dropping into her manner of speech. "The Princess is going home. Listen! She is bidding us farewell."

Out of the clear sky came the mournful barking of the pink-feet, and above it the higher, clearer note of the snow goose. The specks drifted northward, formed into a tiny *v*, diminished, and vanished.

With the departure of the snow goose ended the visits of Frith to the lighthouse. Rhayader learned all over again the meaning of the word "loneliness." That summer, out of his memory, he painted a picture of a slender, grime-covered child, her fair hair blown by a November storm, who bore in her arms a wounded white bird.

In mid-October the miracle occurred. Rhayader was in his enclosure, feeding his birds. A gray northeast wind was blowing and the land was sighing beneath the incoming tide. Above the sea and the wind noises he heard a clear, high note. He turned his eyes upward to the evening sky in time to see first an infinite speck, then a black-and-white-pinioned dream that circled the lighthouse once, and finally a reality that dropped to earth in the pen and came waddling forward importantly to be fed, as though she had never been away. It was the snow goose. There was no mistaking her. Tears of joy came to Rhayader's eyes. Where had she been? Surely not home to Canada. No, she must have summered in Greenland or Spitsbergen with the pink-feet. She had remembered and had returned.

When next Rhayader went in to Chelmbury for supplies, he left a message with the postmistress–one that must have caused her much bewilderment. He said: "Tell Frith, who lives with the fisherfolk at Wickaeldroth, that the Lost Princess has returned."

Three days later, Frith, taller, still tousled and unkempt, came shyly to the lighthouse to visit La Princesse Perdue.

Time passed. On the Great Marsh it was marked by the height of the tides, the slow march of the seasons, the passage of the birds, and, for Rhayader, by the arrival and departure of the snow goose.

The world outside boiled and seethed and rumbled with the eruption that was soon to break forth and come close to marking its destruction. But not yet did it touch upon Rhayader, or, for that matter, Frith. They had fallen into a curious, natural rhythm, even as the child grew older. When the snow goose was at the lighthouse, then she came, too, to visit and learn many things from Rhayader. They sailed together in his speedy boat, that he handled so skillfully. They caught wildfowl for the ever increasing colony, and built new pens and enclosures for them. From him she learned the lore of every wild bird, from gull to gyrfalcon, that flew the marshes. She cooked for him sometimes, and even learned to mix his paints.

But when the snow goose returned to its summer home, it was as though some kind of bar was up between them, and she did not come to the lighthouse. One year the bird did not return, and Rhayader was heartbroken. All things seemed to have ended for him. He painted furiously through the winter and the next summer, and never once saw the child. But in the fall the familiar cry once more rang from the sky, and the huge white bird, now at its full growth, dropped from the skies as mysteriously as it had departed. Joyously, Rhayader sailed his boat into Chelmbury and left his message with the postmistress.

Curiously, it was more than a month after he had left the message before Frith reappeared at the lighthouse, and Rhayader, with a shock, realized that she was a child no longer.

After the year in which the bird had remained away, its periods of absence grew shorter and shorter. It had grown so tame that it followed Rhayader about and even came into the studio while he was working.

In the spring of 1940 the birds migrated early from the Great Marsh. The world was on fire. The whine and roar of the bombers and the thudding explosions frightened them. The first day of May, Frith and Rhayader stood shoulder to shoulder on the sea wall and watched the last of the unpinioned pink-feet and barnacle geese rise from their sanctuary; she, tall, slender, free as air, and hauntingly beautiful; he, dark, grotesque, his massive bearded head raised to the sky, his glowing dark eyes watching the geese form their flight tracery.

"Look, Philip," Frith said.

Rhayader followed her eyes. The snow goose had taken flight, her giant wings spread, but she was flying low, and once came quite close to them, so that for a moment the spreading black-tipped, white pinions seemed to caress them and they felt the rush of the bird's swift passage. Once, twice, she circled the lighthouse, then dropped to earth again in the enclosure with the pinioned geese and commenced to feed.

"She be'ent going," said Frith, with marvel in her voice. The bird in its close passage seemed to have woven a kind of magic about her. "The Princess be goin' t' stay."

"Ay," said Rhayader, and his voice was shaken too. "She'll stay. She will never go away again. The Lost Princess is lost no more. This is her home now–of her own free will."

The spell the bird had girt about her was broken, and Frith was suddenly conscious of the fact that she was frightened, and the things that frightened her were in Rhayader's eyes–the longing and the loneliness and the deep, welling, unspoken things that lay in and behind them as he turned them upon her.

His last words were repeating themselves in her head as though he had said them again: "This is her home now–of her own free will." The delicate tendrils of her instincts reached to him and carried to her the message of the things he could not speak because of what he felt himself to be, mis-shapen and grotesque. And where his voice might have soothed her, her fright grew greater at his silence and the power of the unspoken things between them. The woman in her bade her take flight from something that she was not yet capable of understanding.

Frith said: "I–I must go. Good-by. I be glad the–the Princess will stay. You'll not be so alone now."

She turned and walked swiftly away, and his sadly spoken "Good-by, Frith," was only a half-heard ghost of a sound borne to her ears above the rustling of the marsh grass. She was far away before she dared turn for a backward glance. He was still standing on the sea wall, a dark speck against the sky.

Her fear had stilled now. It had been replaced by something else, a queer sense of loss that made her stand quite still for a moment, so sharp was it. Then, more slowly, she continued on, away from the skyward-pointing finger of the lighthouse and the man beneath it.

It was a little more than three weeks before Frith returned to the lighthouse. May was at its end, and the day, too, in a long golden twilight that was giving way to the silver of the moon already hanging in the eastern sky.

She told herself, as her steps took her thither, that she must know whether the snow goose had really stayed, as Rhayader said it would. Perhaps it had flown away, after all. But her firm tread on the sea wall was full of eagerness, and sometimes unconsciously she found herself hurrying.

Frith saw the yellow light of Rhayader's lantern down by his little wharf, and she found him there. His sailboat was rocking gently on a flooding tide and he was loading supplies into her–water and food and bottles of brandy, gear and a spare sail. When he turned to the sound of her coming, she saw that he was pale, but that his dark eyes, usually so kind and placid, were glowing with excitement, and he was breathing heavily from his exertions.

Sudden alarm seized Frith. The snow goose was forgotten. "Philip! Ye be goin' away?"

Rhayader paused in his work to greet her, and there was something in his face, a glow and a look, that she had never seen there before.

"Frith! I am glad you came. Yes, I must go away. A little trip. I will come back." His usually kindly voice was hoarse with what was suppressed inside him.

Frith asked: "Where must ye go?"

Words came tumbling from Rhayader now. He must go to Dunkirk. A hundred miles across the Channel. A British army was trapped there on the sands, awaiting destruction at the hands of the advancing Germans. The port was in flames, the position hopeless. He had heard it in the village when he had gone for supplies. Men were putting out from Chelmbury in answer to the government's call, every tug and fishing boat or power launch that could propel itself was heading across the Channel to haul the men off the beaches to the transports and destroyers that could not reach the shallows, to rescue as many as possible from the Germans' fire.

Frith listened and felt her heart dying within her. He was saying that he would sail the Channel in his little boat. It could take six men at a time; in a pinch, seven. He could make many trips from the beaches to the transports.

The girl was young, primitive, inarticulate. She did not understand war, or what had happened in France, or the meaning of the trapped army, but the blood within her told her that here was danger.

"Philip! Must 'ee go? You'll not come back. Why must it be 'ee?"

The fever seemed to have gone from Rhayader's soul with the first rush of words, and he explained it to her in terms that she could understand.

He said: "Men are huddled on the beaches like hunted birds, Frith, like the wounded and hunted birds we used to find and bring to sanctuary. Over them fly the steel peregrines, hawks and gyrfalcons, and they have no shelter from these iron birds of prey. They are lost and storm-driven and harried, like the *Princesse Perdue* you found and brought to me out of the marshes many years ago, and we healed her. They need help, my dear, as our wild creatures have needed help, and that is why I must go. It is something that I can do. Yes, I can. For once–for once I can be a man and play my part."

Frith stared at Rhayader. He had changed so. For the first time she saw that he was no longer ugly or mis-shapen or grotesque, but very beautiful. Things were turmoiling in her own soul, crying to be said, and she did not know how to say them.

"I'll come with 'ee, Philip."

Rhayader shook his head. "Your place in the boat would cause a soldier to be left behind, and another and another. I must go alone."

He donned rubber coat and boots and took to his boat. He waved and called back: "Good-by! Will you look after the birds until I return, Frith?"

Frith's hand came up, but only half, to wave too. "God speed you," she said, but gave it the Saxon turn. "I will take care of t' birds. God-speed, Philip."

It was night now, bright with moon fragment and stars and northern glow. Frith stood on the sea wall and watched the sail gliding down the swollen estuary. Suddenly from the darkness behind her there came a rush of wings, and something swept past her into the air. In the night light she saw the flash of white wings, black-tipped, and the thrust-forward head of the snow goose.

It rose and cruised over the lighthouse once and then headed down the winding creek where Rhayader's sail was slanting in the gaining breeze, and flew above him in slow, wide circles.

White sail and white bird were visible for a long time.

"Watch o'er him. Watch o'er him," Fritha whispered. When they were both out of sight at last, she turned and walked slowly, with bent head, back to the empty lighthouse.

Now the story becomes fragmentary, and one of these fragments is in the words of the men on leave who told it in the public room of the Crown and Arrow, an East Chapel pub.

"A goose, a bloomin' goose, so 'elp me," said Private Potton, of His Majesty's London Rifles.

"Garn," said a bandy-legged artilleryman.

"A goose it was. Jock, 'ere, seed it same as me. It come flyin' down outa the muck an' stink an' smoke of Dunkirk that was over'ead. It was white, wiv black on its wings, an' it circles us like a bloomin' dive bomber. Jock, 'ere, 'e sez: 'We're done for. It's the hangel of death a-come for us.'

" 'Garn,' Hi sez, 'it's a ruddy goose, come over from 'ome wiv a message from Churchill, an' 'ow are we henjoying the bloomin' bathing. It's a omen, that's what it is, a bloody omen. We'll get out of this yet, me lad.'

"We was roostin' on the beach between Dunkirk an' Lapanny, like a lot o' bloomin' pigeons on Victoria Hembankment, waitin' for Jerry to pot us. 'E potted us good too. 'E was be'ind us an' flankin' us an' above us. 'E give us shrapnel and 'e give us H. E., an' 'e peppers us from the bloomin' hatmosphere with Jittersmiths.

"An' offshore is the *Kentish Maid,* a ruddy hexcursion scow wot Hi've taken many a trip on out of Margate in the summer, for two-and-six, waiting to take us off, 'arf a mile out from the bloomin' shallows.

"While we are lyin' there on the beach, done in an' cursin' becos there ain't no way to get out to the boat, a Stuka dives on 'er, an' 'is bombs drop alongside of 'er, throwin' up water like the bloomin' fountains in the palace gardens; a reg'lar display it was.

"Then a destroyer come up an' says: 'No, ye don't' to the Stuka with ack-acks and pom-poms, but another Jerry dives on the destroyer, an' 'its 'er. Coo, did she go up! She burned before she sunk, an' the smoke an' the stink come driftin' inshore, all yellow an' black, an' out of it comes this bloomin' goose, a-circlin' around us trapped on the beach.

"An' then around a bend 'e comes in a bloody little sailboat, sailing along as cool as you please, like a bloomin' toff out for a pleasure spin on a Sunday hafternoon at 'Enley."

" 'Oo comes?" inquired a civilian.

" 'Im! 'Im that saved a lot of us. 'E sailed clean through a boil of machine-gun bullets from a Jerry in a Jittersmith wot was strafin'—a Ramsgate motorboat wot 'ad tried to take us off 'ad been sunk there 'arf an hour ago—the water was all frothin' with shell splashes an' bullets, but 'e didn't give it no mind, 'e didn't. 'E didn't 'ave no petrol to burn or hexplode, an' he sailed in between the shells.

"Into the shallows 'e come out of the black smoke of the burnin' destroyer, a little dark man wiv a beard, a bloomin' claw for a 'and, an' a 'ump on 'is back.

" 'E 'ad a rope in 'is teeth that was shinin' white out of 'is black beard, 'is good 'and on the tiller an' the crooked one beckonin' to us to come. An' over'ead, around and around, flies the ruddy goose.

"Jock, 'ere, says: 'Lawk, it's all over now. It's the bloody devil come for us 'imself. Hi must 'ave been struck an' don't know it.'

" 'Garn,' I sez, 'it's more like the good Lord, 'e looks to me, than any bloomin' devil.' 'E did, too, like the pictures from the Sunday-school books, wiv 'is white face and dark eyes an' beard an' all, and 'is bloomin' boat.

" 'Hi can take seven at a time,' 'e sings out when 'e's in close.

"Our horfficer shouts: 'Good, man! . . . You seven nearest, get in.'

"We waded out to where 'e was. Hi was that weary Hi couldn't clumb over the side, but 'e takes me by the collar of me tunic an' pulls, wiv a 'In ye go, lad. Come on. Next man.'

"An' in Hi went. Coo, 'e was strong, 'e was. Then 'e sets 'is sail, part of wot looks like a bloomin' sieve from machine-gun bullets, shouts: 'Keep down in the bottom of the boat, boys, in case we meet any of yer friends,' and we're off, 'im sittin' in the stern wiv 'is rope in 'is teeth, another in 'is crooked claw, an' 'is right 'and on the tiller, a-steerin' an' sailin' through the spray of the shells thrown by a land battery somewhere back of the coast. An' the bloomin' goose is flyin' around and around, 'onking above the wind and the row Jerry was makin', like a bloomin' Morris autermobile on Winchester by-pass.

" 'Hi told you yon goose was a omen,' Hi sez to Jock. 'Look at 'im there, a bloomin' hangel of mercy.'

" 'Im at the tiller just looks up at the goose, wiv the rope in 'is teeth, an' grins at 'er like 'e knows 'er a lifetime.

" 'E brung us out to the *Kentish Maid* and turns around and goes back for another load. 'E made trips all afternoon an' all night, too, because the bloody light of Dunkirk burning was bright enough to see by. Hi don't know 'ow many trips 'e made, but 'im an' a nobby Thames Yacht Club motorboat an' a big lifeboat from Poole that come along brought off all there was of us on that particular stretch of hell, without the loss of a man.

"We sailed when the last man was off, an' there was more than seven hunder' of us haboard a boat built to take two hunder'. 'E was still there when we left, an' 'e waved us good-by and sails off toward Dunkirk, and the bird wiv 'im. Blyme, it was queer to see that ruddy big goose flyin' around 'is boat, lit up by the fires like a white hangel against the smoke.

"A Stuka 'ad another go at us, 'arfway across, but 'e'd been stayin' up late nights, an' missed. By mornin' we was safe 'ome.

"Hi never did find out what become of 'im, or 'oo 'e was—'im wiv the 'ump an' 'is little sailboat. A bloody good man 'e was, that chap."

"Coo," said the artilleryman. "A ruddy big goose. Whatcher know?"

In an officers' club on Brook Street, a retired naval officer, sixty-five years old, Commander Keith Brill-Oudener, was telling of his experiences during the evacuation of Dunkirk. Called out of bed at four o'clock in the morning, he had captained a lopsided Limehouse tug across the Channel, towing a string of Thames barges, which he brought back four times loaded with soldiers. On his last trip he came in with her funnel shot away and a hole in her side. But he got her back to Dover.

A naval-reserve officer, who had two Brixham trawlers and a Yarmouth drifter blasted out from under him in the last four days of the evacuation, said: "Did you run across that queer sort of legend about a wild goose? It was all up and down the beaches. You know how those things spring up. Some of the men I brought back were talking about it. It was supposed to have appeared at intervals the last days between Dunkirk and La Panne. If you saw it, you were eventually saved. That sort of thing."

"H'm'm'm," said Brill-Oudener, "a wild goose. I saw a tame one. Dashed strange experience. Tragic, in a way, too. And lucky for us.

Tell you about it. Third trip back. Toward six o'clock we sighted a derelict small boat. Seemed to be a chap or a body in her. And a bird perched on the rail.

"We changed our course when we got nearer, and went over for a look-see. By Gad, it was a chap. Or had been, poor fellow. Machine-gunned, you know. Badly. Face down in the water. Bird was a goose, a tame one.

"We drifted close, but when one of our chaps reached over, the bird hissed at him and struck at him with her wings. Couldn't drive it off. Suddenly young Kettering, who was with me, gave a hail and pointed to starboard. Big mine floating by. One of Jerry's beauties. If we'd kept on our course we'd have piled right into it. Ugh! Head on. We let it get a hundred yards astern of the last barge, and the men blew it up with rifle-fire.

"When we turned our attention to the derelict again, she was gone. Sunk. Concussion, you know. Chap with her. He must have been lashed to her. The bird had got up and was circling. Three times, like a plane saluting. Dashed queer feeling. Then she flew off to the west. Lucky thing for us we went over to have a look, eh? Odd that you should mention a goose."

Fritha remained alone at the little lighthouse on the Great Marsh, taking care of the pinioned birds, waiting for she knew not what. The first days she haunted the sea wall, watching; though she knew it was useless. Later she roamed through the storerooms of the lighthouse building with their stacks of canvases on which Rhayader had captured every mood and light of the desolate country and the wondrous, graceful, feathered things that inhabited it.

Among them she found the picture that Rhayader had painted of her from memory so many years ago, when she was still a child, and had stood, wind-blown and timid, at his threshold, hugging an injured bird to her.

The picture and the things she saw in it stirred her as nothing ever had before, for much of Rhayader's soul had gone into it. Strangely, it was the only time he had painted the snow goose, the lost wild creature, storm-driven from another land, that to each had brought a friend, and which, in the end, returned to her with the message that she would never see him again.

Long before the snow goose had come dropping out of a crimsoned eastern sky to circle the lighthouse in a last farewell, Fritha, from the ancient powers of the blood that was in her, knew that Rhayader would not return.

And so, when one sunset she heard the high-pitched, well-remembered note cried from the heavens, it brought no instant of false hope to her heart. This moment, it seemed, she had lived before many times.

She came running to the sea wall and turned her eyes, not toward the distant Channel whence a sail might come, but to the sky from whose flaming arches plummeted the snow goose. Then the sight, the sound, and the solitude surrounding broke the dam within her and released the surging, overwhelming truth of her love, let it well forth in tears.

Wild spirit called to wild spirit, and she seemed to be flying with the great bird, soaring with it in the evening sky, and hearkening to Rhayader's message.

Sky and earth were trembling with it and filled her beyond the bearing of it. "Frith! Fritha! Frith, my love. Good-by, my love." The white pinions, black-tipped, were beating it out upon her heart, and her heart was answering: "Philip, I love 'ee."

For a moment Frith thought the snow goose was going to land in the old enclosure, as the pinioned geese set up a welcoming gabble. But it only skimmed low, then soared up again, flew in a wide, graceful spiral once around the old light, and then began to climb.

Watching it, Frith saw no longer the snow goose but the soul of Rhayader taking farewell of her before departing forever.

She was no longer flying with it, but earthbound. She stretched her arms up into the sky and stood on tiptoes, reaching, and cried: "Godspeed! Godspeed, Philip!"

Frith's tears were stilled. She stood watching silently long after the goose had vanished. Then she went into the lighthouse and secured the picture that Rhayader had painted of her. Hugging it to her breast, she wended her way homeward along the old sea wall.

Each night, for many weeks thereafter, Frith came to the lighthouse and fed the pinioned birds. Then one early morning a German pilot on a dawn raid mistook the old abandoned light for an active military objective, dived onto it, a screaming steel hawk, and blew it and all it contained into oblivion.

That evening when Fritha came, the sea had moved in through the breached walls and covered it over. Nothing was left to break the utter desolation. No marsh fowl had dared to return. Only the frightless gulls wheeled and soared and mewed their plaint over the place where it had been.

Mooltiki **Rumer Godden**

One of the most interesting animal stories I have ever read comes from an unexpected source, a writer of delicate, lovely and perceptive prose, England's Rumer Godden. The story deals with two widely different creatures of the wild. The first is Mooltiki, an elephant described as "the camp tweeny." Tame elephants organize themselves into matriarchies, with the wisest female as the head. Mooltiki, a cranky and stupid old party, had been assigned to most of the drudgery and was not at all happy about it.

The second creature is a tiger which "seems to terrorize even the leaves into stillness" and whose entrance on the scene through the high cover of the jungle in the middle of night is told with an artistry that reduces readers to a similar degree of fear.

MOOLTIKI

Rumer Godden

Though I have spent years in India my knowledge of elephants is slight and purely domestic. I have never seen, nor do I want to see, a *keddah;* nor, as the rest of my family has often done, seen a herd wild in the jungle. I have not seen elephants dying, fighting, making love, or giving birth, all, I understand, highly mysterious processes. I know elephants only as servants.

When I was what in another country would have been the sitting-up perambulator stage I used to go for airings with my little Assamese nurse Butterfly on a big she-elephant inappropriately called Birdie. I can remember giving her a reward of some minute, picked blades of grass and leaves; it must have been like offering a human being two or three grains of salt but Birdie always took them politely.

Then there was Adela, an elephant attached to the household of a friend who was agent to one of the small states. No roads went to the palace and transport was by Adela, dignified comings and goings with suitcases. Rajah was my father's shooting elephant, and when my sisters and I grew up enough to acquire men friends, some of our courtings were done on Rajah. Just as couples go for long, aimless drives, borrowing the father's car, so we borrowed Rajah for long, leisurely rides, though the mahout was there, of course.

I remember a small elephant at the seaside in southern India. She was an elephant for hire, her chief engagements being to lend tone to marriages and feast days. She was advertised in the local paper as "docile she-elephant, used to walking in processions, ears pierced for ornaments." Then there were Secunda and Bata Scully, the two big elephants working for our friend Neil in the forestry department—and there was Mooltiki.

She does not belong in a list, for I think she was unique. My acquaintance with her was brief but I have never forgotten her. Neil, who, in a lifetime of elephants, was her owner, says he has never forgotten her either.

I met her when my sister, Nancy, her husband, Dick, and I went up to stay in the same Neil's winter camp in the Assamese jungle on the borders of Bhutan.

After a long, hot night in the train and what seemed an endless drive by lorry on the bumps and pits and ruts of a jungle road, we came out in a clearing on the river bank and saw the camp across the river. This was one of the wide rivers of the foothills, for the most part shallow with pale, pebbled shoals, then narrowing suddenly to fierce rapids. Tiger grass and forest lined both banks and, in the distance, were hills folded in a blue haze. "Bhutan," said Dick. The camp was on a sweep of land, looped by the river; we could see a tiny house on stilts that looked like matchsticks, four or five white tents, with encampments of lesser tents and a flagpole, small as a splinter. Smoke was going up from the fires and, coming to fetch us across the river, was a small grey shape. Even as it climbed out of the water and mounted the bank, declaring itself to be an elephant with a mahout on its back, it still looked small and it was grumbling to itself under its breath.

When Mooltiki had to do anything she did not like–and I have to admit that her days were filled with unpleasant tasks–she kept up this small, clearly opinionated, and private rumble. It was curious how potent it was. There was never any doubt of Mooltiki's feelings; as with other put-upon maids of all work, she would flounce and bounce, and to be flounced and bounced under when one is riding even a small elephant can be very uncomfortable indeed.

One of her tasks, as Adela's had been, was to fetch and carry baggage, stores, and passengers from the roadhead across the river. I sympathized with her; three times that morning, for our luggage and stores alone, she had to cross that river bed, braving the rapids, treading gingerly across the shoals as if the pebbles hurt her feet, and hauling herself up the banks with a creaking of the ropes that held her pad. If she paused or slowed she would get a jerk behind the ear or a jab on the head from the mahout's *ankus,* a weapon that looked like a big iron hook with a spike.

I soon saw why it was needed; straightaway, when she knelt to let us get up, I made acquaintance with one of the less endearing traits of Mooltiki. A well-schooled elephant kneels when told and allows its hind legs to be used as a mounting block to the pad which is fastened by padded ropes round its neck and stomach and by a crupper under the tail. One can hold to these, spring, kneel on the rump, and swing up. Bata Scully, Neil's big she-elephant, would even lift her master up by her trunk, raising it carefully and putting her ears forward so that he could hold to them and walk up her face; not until everyone was comfortably settled and her mahout gave the word would she rise. Not so Mooltiki; out of her small eye, which looked deep and as many-sided as a camera lens, she would watch and, I am sure, mark her victim—every time it was a woman—and when that victim, holding to the ropes, had one knee on Mooltiki's behind, the second foot just off the ground, Mooltiki would heave herself up abruptly and walk away. To fall off an uncertain elephant is dangerous; quite apart from the bump, the animal may turn round and tread on one, and many a time I have been scooped up by Bangla, the head *shikari,* just in time or have had to hang with scraped hands until the mahout's shouts and stabbings produced an effect.

That morning we were tired and shaken, but she immediately tried this on me. Then, while we were still swearing, "Abominable elephant, dangerous little brute," she did something else, a thing I have not seen another elephant do: on the long way back across the river she amused herself. She held her trunk with its nozzle just below the water and, through that small, groping spout-mouth, divided into holes and lined with pinkish skin, she blew bubbles. The pebbles in the sun were grey, almost white, but under the water they took colours, brown with a blue gleam, here and there a cabbage green one or one that was coral red; the bubbles picked up the colours of the pebbles, of the wide pale sky, and shone, iridescent. It is only people who dream and wonder who blow bubbles, children and poets—Shelley blew them; there was something of child or poet in Mooltiki. I have known her, in the forest, to pick a flower, not a branch to beat flies off or a frond to wave as most elephants do, but a flower to hold.

It was autumn and the forest was dry after the hot weather; the only flowers were the white stars of wild coffee and the red-flowering simul trees. Everywhere were great blackened patches left by the forest fires with which Neil was busy, and the smell of their smoke and charred wood was strong on the air. Soon, on these patches, sweet new grass would spring up, bringing herds of wild elephant and deer to feed.

The house on stilts was a forest lodge, used now for stores; the tents were drawn up in a semi-circle facing the river, in their centre a campfire built with logs and whole trunks of trees. The cook tent had its own fire and an oven made of clay—we once roasted a peahen whole in it—and the *shikaris,* the huntsmen, had their own camp behind, two tents just big enough for men to lie down in, a shelf woven of bamboo for holding brass platters and pots, clothes hung along a string, and a tiger's tongue stuck on a pole to dry—tiger tongues could be sold as a cure for goitre.

The elephants were farther off still, their leg chains around two trees, the ground near them littered with leaves and elephant pats.

At night the fires made the jungle seem infinitely ringed off. We would sit in wicker chairs, warmth on our feet but a gentle snow-wind, the evening wind off the hills, touching our foreheads. There was a great feeling of well-being. We were filled with whisky and dinner and listened peaceably to Bangla and the plans for tomorrow.

Bangla was a hillman, small, with tremendous hands and feet and a short supple back. His skin was a ruddy polished brown and his face was Bhutanese, flat-nosed with deep eyelids and an intelligent forehead. He often smiled at our antics, but he was said to be a bad character. "He is a bloodthirsty cut-throat," said Neil.

"If I have to have my throat cut," I said, "or to be killed, I should rather be killed by Bangla than anyone else." He was amazingly quick and deft with a knife and to see him skinning a tiger's head was a marvel. He was, even Neil admitted, a good *shikari* and, though the slightly amused smile never left him, there was not a dreadful moment, on the ladder of a *machan,* on the slippery tail of an elephant, when Bangla's brown hand did not come out to help. There were three other *shikaris* in the camp and a cook, a table-boy, a washer-up, and a camp sweeper.

Neil had to work but Dick had come to shoot, with Bangla to help him. Bangla was as courteous as he was knowledgeable. If a plan seemed to him feasible he would say, "It could be like that"; if he had to criticize, "It could not be like that," and proceed to show how it could be. Often he drew maps in the dust. The voices went on, the smell of wood ash and flowers would drift in from the night, the whisky would pass and the peace deepen, peace such as I have known only in the jungle or on the moors. It was as deep as the jungle sky where the sparks from the fire mixed with the stars; but the fire would die down. Then Neil would clap his hands, an answering rattle of chains would sound from the elephant lines, and presently a sound would approach, a reluctant, slow pad-pad of feet, a flapping of ears, and a certain unmistakable annoyed rumbling. It was Mooltiki coming to make up the fire.

It was one of her duties to build and feed it; when we were out on her and riding home she would thoughtfully pick up a young fallen tree or a big branch and carry it in, bearing it across the path when the track was wide and neatly turning it end on where it was narrow. Usually, though, she did her wood-gathering after tea and would appear from the jungle at intervals, carrying a large log in her trunk, small branches or brushwood in her mouth which made her look as if she had a moustache, and would build a pyramid, laying logs one across the other, pushing them with her foot, and leaving a pile handy for the night. She would have to come two or three times in the night to put on wood.

"Is it really necessary?" I said.

"Well, you don't want a tiger or a leopard walking through us, do you?" asked Neil.

Now, as she kicked the logs together with a careful foot, shifted their ends with her trunk, Mooltiki said clearly and unmistakably what she thought of human beings who needed fires, by elephant standards quite unnecessary. Sometimes the wood ran out and she would have to go into the dark jungle to get more. The mahout would make her put her forehead against a small tree and push; with grunts and loud sighs Mooltiki would push until the tree cracked, when she would wrench it loose with her trunk and foot. Her mahout was strict; if she threw the log down when she brought it to the fire he would make her pick it up again and put it down more gently. Then she would walk back to her bed and leaf-supper, still saying what she thought of us.

There was one pleasant thing in the day for her and that was to be bathed. Every day the mahouts took the elephants to the river. Washing an elephant is easier than washing a car or an engine, for the hose is animated, and it was a sight to see the three elephants sending fountains of water running over their backs and heads and then lying on their sides, their feet outstretched, while the mahouts scrubbed them with a besom made of jungle twigs; Mooltiki's skin gave shudders of sensuous bliss. When she was scrubbed clean, her mahout would jump clear, shout to her to get up, and once again would begin those copious pourings; but, like a naughty child, Mooltiki would never come out, and often Bata Scully, who was older and wiser and almost horribly well trained, would be called on to give her a spank. Then Mooltiki would come out at once and walk, crushed, back to camp. She had a wholesome respect for Bata Scully, but Secunda never noticed her at all.

From the beginning I was much with Mooltiki because, in a way, we were both hangers-on, which is to say, nuisances. I did not shoot, nor was I taking animal photographs, working in forestry or botany, which is why I cannot write of the camp in any expert way, while, as a jungle elephant, Mooltiki had two grave defects: she was not tall and she was not staunch. A tiger spring would have reached anyone on her back though, as I pointed out, the tiger would never have got near enough to spring because, at the first sight or smell of anything fierce, or even if a shot were fired near her, she would bolt.

Mooltiki justified her existence by working hard. She was the camp tweeny and, besides carrying all the luggage and wood, she went to the post, ten miles inland, twice a week, and every day she fetched and picked part of the food for the elephants; as each elephant ate perhaps a thousand pounds of green stuff every day, this was heavy work and we would see her toiling backwards and forwards with trailing loads of cane and leaves. Except that I liked it, I had no excuse to be in the camp —until the coming of Horatius.

A tiger had been taking cattle from one of the forest villages and the villagers came to Neil to ask if he would shoot it. Neil passed them on to Dick, who asked me if I should like to sit up with him in a *machan* built in the forest near the village.

It was surely one of the most lost villages in the world. To reach it we walked through the afternoon, on and on by the river, through grass higher than our heads, dry, dusty brown, and baking hot. At a blazed tree we struck into the jungle, walking in a nightmare forest under *sál* trees whose stems were patterned like giraffe necks; their enormous leaves in colours of beetroot and purple had fallen and rattled on the ground. In their branches were ants' nests made in shapes like great white cocoons and all round them creepers twined and hung; originally blown above the jungle, they had seeded in the tops of the trees and grew downwards in fantastic spirals and snakes.

We seemed to make a loud noise walking in the dry leaves but that was because the jungle was so quiet, quiet, dim, brooding, and, in the middle of this great tract, we came to the village, a desolate space cleared under the trees, four or five huts on stilts, a stockade and a patch of fields walled with mud. Even there the light was dim, filtered through the trees, and even the hens were quiet. In front of it was a row of white-washed stones; one side of them was Assam, the other Bhutan. The villagers, small, brown, half-naked men, had built the *machan* and under it, for bait, they had tied Horatius.

He was young, not yet bullock, but not calf, about four feet high and exceptionally solid and heavy; he was black and had a hump and two swellings of horn. The villagers had tied a bell round his neck to attract the tiger, and I tried not to look at him as I climbed past him up into the *machan*.

The rifles, a knapsack, pillows, and rugs were drawn up by rope, cut jungle was heaped round the ladder, and the *shikaris* went away, leaving us alone, and talking as they went to make the tiger, if he were near, think we had all gone. Even at half-past four in the afternoon we seemed very much alone, but the little bull was not perturbed. The sun was slanting its rays down the glade, the stems of the trees on the edge of the forest were lit, the light yellow and luminous between them, but it was growing darker in the jungle depths.

We arranged the *machan*. It was built high between three trees, a raft of cut branches tied with strips of bamboo and hidden with leaves; the smell of the dying leaves was pungent and forever afterwards that smell to me was exciting. The rugs and cushions were needed, for we might have to stay without moving till the morning. Sitting over a live kill is an art in stillness and even the sandwiches were wrapped in banana leaves that would not rustle; Dick had his and I had mine so that we should not need to speak to each other. Nothing white or conspicuous must show; the pillows had dark covers, we wore khaki and had thick coats and string gloves for, when the dew came, it would be cold. Dick fixed his torch on his rifle, I had a second rifle ready. All the time below us the bell tolled.

"It *is* cruel," I whispered. "I don't care what you say."

"Of course it's cruel, but it's one life against dozens if that tiger is left alive."

Dusk came down and there could be no more whispering. Squirrels ran down the tree and looked at us, making us start. It became dark very quickly.

A tiger usually comes early, soon after dusk, or else late, near dawn, seldom in the middle of the night. Slowly, over the forest, a listening stillness settled. The bell sounded, loudly in one moment, forlornly in another. Except for it the forest was tensely still. A leaf fell with a sound loud enough to be a tiger. Another fell after it. There was a heavy dot-dot-dot-dot, like hopping, far louder than a tiger; it was a jungle cock and his hens moving round the tree. All at once a noise came that paralysed me even though I knew what it was, a noise like a dog being torn in half, a barking deer. Again there was stillness and the bell.

Then the stillness changed. It was different. There was a root of terror in it–somewhere. The tiger was there. I could see nothing, hear nothing, though my eyes strained into the uncertain blackness; there was no sign except that the little bull was absolutely still. The expectancy went on. Something touched my cheek and I froze in horror; it was Dick's finger, pointing.

Where he pointed, with a shock of fear I saw it. If it had been lit with flares I could not have known more certainly what it was–tiger. I saw its shoulder before its head, the outline of its shoulder as it looked down the glade, a gigantic, exaggerated symmetry that reached up into the dark, that seemed to terrorize even the leaves into stillness. Then it turned its head, which brought it back into size so that it was quite near the ground, but I was even more deadly afraid of it like that.

"Why was I so afraid?" I asked Neil afterwards. "I was safe in the *machan*. Why was I afraid like that?"

"Because it was tiger," said Neil. "I am afraid every time, and how many tigers have I shot?" And he added, "A tiger carries fear. That is its power."

As its shape came forward I was still, though inwardly shaking. I lost it, saw it, lost it, then the bell was ringing so violently that there was no need for quiet.

No one would waste pity on a tiger if they had seen it kill. One trick with a victim that shows fight is to spring from behind and hamstring it, making it helpless and, without waiting to kill, begin eating. The tiger tried this with the little bull, but the bull would not be hamstrung. He fought for his life and the tiger had actually to give up this attack and go for the neck. Horatius' neck was solid, swelling muscle; he fought with all his strength and at that moment Dick shot the tiger.

In the light of the torch it lay, its head back on the grass, the white of its stomach curiously lean, one enormous paw in the air, while the sound of the shot seemed to go on and on through the jungle. The tiger did not move again, though Dick threw stones at it from the knapsack, and he let off another two shots, close together, the signal for the elephants to come.

Bata Scully came slowly and for two or three hours Horatius had to stay, tied by the dead tiger, pawing at the ground like a bull in the bull ring, blood running from his wounds. The kill is usually finished off with a shot but–"He is standing up," said Dick. "He fought for his life and he shall have it." And we named him Horatius.

He was brought into camp and tied by a rope to a tree. If anyone came near him he fought, nearly breaking his neck with the rope, but when he realized that we meant to help his wounds, he was suddenly quiet and stood still, trembling, but not moving though he snorted through his nose. It was not pleasant for any of us; he was caked with blood and dung, and when that was washed off with water and permanganate, the wounds were terrible: claw slashes down his flanks, deep teeth marks in the thigh, and deeper holes each side of the neck.

"It will go septic," Neil warned us, "and what have you to put on it? You are not to take the only iodine. What can you use?"

What? If only there had been some tar, acriflavine, anything. There was nothing but hot saline for fomentations and lanolin to block the holes and keep off the flies. It was pitifully inadequate but Nancy and I toiled, and the swelling began to go down. Horatius spent the days tied under the tree, a heap of grass beside him, and one bath towel tied round his neck to keep off the flies, another draped from his rump to his knee.

I could not leave the camp for long while he was so ill and I took to accompanying Mooltiki when she went wood-gathering or to fetch elephant food. It was always perilous to go out with her. A good elephant –Bata Scully, for instance–takes care of passengers, looking up when the mahout tells her, to see if they will escape being hit by an overhanging branch; if it seems doubtful her trunk will reach up and measure, then perhaps break off the branch. Mooltiki did not care if her whole load was swept away. Bata Scully would test a doubtful piece of ground carefully with her forefoot before putting her weight on it, while Mooltiki never looked where she was going and was quite likely to try to step into a quicksand or a bog, nor did she walk with the even pad-pad of most elephants; she had only two paces, scurry or dawdle, and if she lost her temper, which she frequently did, she was not above trying to shake us off with violent shruggings; but I could forgive her even this for the way she would fall, as I did, into a jungle dream and daze, forgetting what she had come out for, dawdling along, just looking.

There was so much to see and one never knew when one might see it: a porcupine; peacocks roosting in a low tree, their tail feathers folded and sweeping the ground; a single peacock, its crest and neck jewel green and blue; a florican; perhaps a python; monkeys. As soon as they saw us the monkeys dropped off the trees and ran. I had always thought it was the other way round, that they took to the trees and went away, swinging and leaping on the creepers. They were good-looking monkeys, deep pollen-yellow with long white tails and bluish faces, but they fled from us at sight, clutching their babies. We heard them chattering long after we had lost them in the jungle. More attractive were the cheetal, small deer with slender-boned legs and red coats spotted with white. They let us walk almost up to them on the elephant before they cantered away, hardly crackling a leaf and lifting neat little pairs of hoofs as they jumped over logs with a flick of their tails. There were hog deer, fatter, without spots, and everywhere there were butterflies: yellow ones, blue and white, dusty little black ones, and gorgeous swallowtails. All round the camp were pied kingfishers and jays, with heavenly blue in their wings and hideous quarrelsome voices.

We would wander and look, quite lost until the mahout would shout, equally startling Mooltiki and me. I would sit straighter and she would angrily begin picking up wood again.

Horatius was not improving. It was the flies; they were in a perpetual swarm around him; they would eat off the lanolin and crawl into the wounds. Now the leg, from haunch to hoof, was bloated and swollen. "I am afraid he will not do," said Neil.

Horatius was looking at us with his big, still calflike eyes, and, "Wait a little while," said Nancy. We boiled whole loaves of bread into a vast bread poultice and tied it on the wounds with dusters. Horatius appeared to like it very much.

After two days of making loaves and boiling them, the cook said he had run out of flour. No flour could be had nearer than the railhead until the lorry came at the end of the week. There was consternation until Bangla remembered that a market was held once every month in a village upstream, and that this was its day. "But that is Bhutan," said Nancy. "We haven't a permit."

Bangla smiled. "The Memsahib shall go with the cook," said Bangla, pointing at me. "They shall go for a ride. They do not want to cross the border but . . . Mooltiki is disobedient." That seemed likely enough even to satisfy Neil, and we went.

The village was on the edge of the river, twenty or thirty huts of matting and bamboo poles. A tame elephant seemed to be a curiosity and, as we came nearer, girls on their way to market threw themselves screaming off the path into the bushes, then sat up, their vegetables and chickens scattered round them, while they viewed this phenomenon of an elephant with a pad on its back, people sitting at ease–well, almost at ease–on top of it, and a little man astride the neck, driving by sticking his toes into the ears and prodding with a steel hook. Mooltiki entered the village at the head of a procession.

The market had not any stalls; it was held, simply, on the ground, and everyone left it to look at her. After she had let us get down, amid cries of admiration, she stood swaying in the middle of the only open space, where she looked almost as big as Bata Scully. It was Mooltiki's day; we were left to wander alone while she was offered sugar cane, banana leaves, and even oranges. Oranges were rare and expensive.

I walked between cloths spread with eggs, a few vegetables, bowls of roots and pulses, spice, celluloid combs and hairpins. There did not seem to be anything else except a wooden stand that displayed secondhand bottles and another with bales of cheap printed cotton and a case of gaudy beads. There were no animals, except a profusion of chickens and a small black kid curled in the dust. Every seller had the same few, cheap, common things, and in the middle a Marwari trader sat over a dirty piece of oilcloth marked with chequers and colours; when the men drifted back he gently cheated them out of most of the money they had. It was surprising what big stakes they put down, whole rupees, even five rupees.

The men were all dressed the same, in dun-white cotton breeches, black caps and waistcoats; the women nearly the same, in printed cotton skirts and bodices and coloured head-veils. The children were little replicas of their fathers and mothers, while the babies were naked. The village was the terminus of a dusty, thick-rutted road; everything was covered in dust and it all looked civilized, squalid, unappetizing. A little depressed, I went into one of the teashops; even the teashops were all the same, with a bench for customers, a platform of clay at one end topped with mats for sleeping, and a clay oven built in its side; above the oven, tea bowls were kept warm on a clay shelf.

I sat on the bench, watching the sleepy, desultory marketing going on. The cook went in search of the necessary flour and, as he was here, chickens, eggs, and some fresh vegetables as well, while Mooltiki still swayed from foot to foot, majestically eating her banana leaves. Then, from a jungle path along the road, a caravan came in and I knew there were still wild people, original, untouched by the world.

The porters were more like animals than men. They had short, brutish bodies, thick calves to their legs, faces that were flat, cheerful, and healthy-looking but quite uncomprehending. Their cheeks were red and their slit eyes were bright, reflecting everything they saw like a monkey's; they had huge fuzzes of hair gummed stiff with dirt and vermin. Their clothes, which had once been loose woollen robes, had become pelts, a veneer of the original stuff lined thick with their own grease and lice. As soon as they had put down their packs, they went straight to the bead man. It was not until they had been in the village for nearly half an hour that they saw the elephant, when they left the market in a tumult, running into the jungle and coming out on hands and knees, or hiding behind trees, clutching at each other.

With them were a chieftain and a woman. They came to the teashop; he was as fat as Henry VIII and had that king's haleness, a flat, fat, stupid, merry face, and a beautiful skin with a bloom like a fruit. He was dressed in grey, an inner and outer robe, and his hair was cut on his shoulders with a fringe under a crown of folded banana leaves.

She might have been his mother or his wife and it was obvious at once that she was a personage. She was little, merry too but with a comprehending merriness, her eyes a clear amber brown set in wrinkles. Her hair was cropped and she had small ears, flat to her head, with square silver earrings. Her mouth was small and her teeth like a child's, small and even, though she had been eating betel and they were stained poppy red. She was dressed in a blue robe with a dark red lining, blue sleeves, and the striped apron of the Bhutanese married woman.

She sat down on the bench by me. The husband stood and stared at this apparition with a white skin but she courteously did not look but made quick little remarks, probably about the market and the weather, to the teashop hostess.

Presently I said in English, "May I look at your earrings?" and touched them lightly.

The earrings would not come off, though they were shown willingly. Then I handed across my dark glasses. Through the hostess the little queen asked, "How much?" and I said with my hands, "Nothing."

The hostess wore a silver ring. I touched that and asked, "How much?"

"Eight annas," said the hostess at once.

The ring was native silver and cut with charms. When the people saw that I had bought it they crowded round the teashop offering theirs until Henry VIII got up and contemptuously drove them away. We drank tea and he called for betel leaves and, when they were brought, started to roll them.

It was then that his wife took from the pouch of her robe the small box; it was for holding the paste that flavoured the leaves, a pleasing little box made of the same native silver but finer, chased with flowers and a pattern of clouds, the lid and bottom joined by a chain. She saw my eyes on it, and when she had given Henry VIII some paste she put it into my hand.

"How much?"

For answer she took my other hand, pressed it over the box, and shook her head.

When we–the cook, his marketing, which now included a whole crate of live chickens, the mahout, Mooltiki, and I–left, the woman stood on the cliff, waving, waving. I still have the box but I never saw her again nor do I know who she was.

On the way back Mooltiki suffered from swelled head. She decided she could not bear the crate of live chickens on her back and beat at them with her trunk. The mahout screamed, we screamed, the chickens did their equivalent of screaming, but Mooltiki still slewed round. I thought she would knock us into the water but at that moment she stepped into a rapid. The water was milkily blue, running fast, and just as a child in a rage stops in mid-sob and, with tears on its cheeks, smiles, the little elephant, reduced now to her proper size, forgot the chickens and plunged her trunk into the eddies, blowing a cascade of bubbles.

As my time in the camp began to run out we were increasingly sad about Horatius. Loaf after loaf was boiled down but now the heap of grass, fresh every day, was carried away untouched and the little bull's eyes had a heavy glaze. There was even pus on his eyelids and, "I had better put a shot into him," said Neil but, "Wait," said Bangla, and I pleaded, "Wait."

On my last day but one Dick wounded a tiger that retreated into a stretch of high grass on the edge of a narrow arm of the river. An elephant was needed to get it out, but Secunda had gone with Neil on a tour of inspection, while Bata Scully had stomach trouble—an elephant with stomach trouble is an impressive sight. Mooltiki of course was ruled out for such dangerous work, yet the wounded tiger could not be left alive. Wounded, it might begin to take cattle and even men, for that is how man-eaters are made, but how was Dick to get it? He said, "I shall go to the opposite side of the river, lie up there, and wait till it comes down in the evening to drink, and shoot it across the water."

"It could be like that," said Bangla.

Dick said that the mahout must take Mooltiki round behind the stretch of grass and wait. "When I shout across, she can go in," said Dick. The mahout demurred. "She is not afraid of a dead tiger, is she?" asked Dick.

"She must not be," said Bangla, which closed the matter and, towards four o'clock, Mooltiki set out. Against my better judgment, I went with her.

"I shouldn't stay on her if I were you," said Dick. "Make her put you up a tree."

Mooltiki, with the mahout and me, walked round the back of the grass; we had only a *kukhri,* the native wide-bladed knife, between us, and it seemed to me we took a long time to find a suitable tree. "What if the tiger comes out while we are near?" I had asked Dick.

"Why should it? It won't disturb itself for an elephant."

"A tame elephant with people on its back?"

"It won't know you are on its back if you don't talk," said Dick witheringly.

The tree was bare and leafless. Mooltiki walked under the lowest branch; she had sensed that something was in the grass and it was very unwillingly that she halted to let me climb up. Standing upright on the back of a swaying elephant is difficult, particularly when one knows a wounded tiger is not far away; Mooltiki made it more difficult still. She sidled and fidgeted and, when the mahout took his attention off her for a moment to help me, she walked off. I was left hanging by my arms.

I looked down at the bald, dusty path below, singularly bald and exposed; I looked at the sinister grass. My arms felt as if they were cracking. There was no Bangla to help me this time, but terror can make one do superhuman—or subhuman—things, and I managed to wriggle myself nearer the trunk and, with my feet braced against it, in an undignified monkey fashion, climb up, though a dizzy blackness filled my eyes. After a while I felt pleased with myself. I had managed to get up and not cry out, which might have startled the tiger away.

The tree was a respectable height and overhung both grass and river. Mooltiki had disappeared and presently I saw Dick and Bangla creep into position on the opposite bank.

It was again that jungle quiet, so quiet that the river seemed to run loudly between its stones. The sun was disappearing behind the trees, there was no sunlight in the thickets of grass, only on the water where a shaft of sun lay. Then in the river three little otters began to play. They swam in quick circles after each other, only their heads, whiskers, and teeth showing above the water with long ripples to mark the steering of their tails, which they used as rudders. When they came to the shallows the whole of them showed, small and exceedingly glossy, their fur almost oily with wetness; they bounced half in, half out of the water, splashing each other as people do on the beach. All at once they reared themselves back in a row and stared, and I looked down and saw the tiger.

Distracted by the otters, I had not sensed him before. At first he was only a darkness in the grass, then slowly, very slowly, he put out a foot. I–and the otters, I thought–held our breath as he pulled himself slowly after the foot. He was long and lean, a length of stripes, his shoulders hunched and his white undercoat touching the grass. He seemed suspicious and very angry; his tail moved in jerks like that of an angry cat and he looked up and down the river. When his face turned towards me, it looked large for the rest of him, wide between the ears, almost swollen in the cheeks, touched with white. The otters slipped into the water and reared themselves up farther away to stare again while I sat so still that my bones seemed set. On the other bank a sunspot gleamed and disappeared again as the barrel of the rifle came up.

The moment settled into a long suspicious stillness. It seemed impossible that the tiger should be taken in with the quiet sky and the brooding trees, the still grass on the opposite bank, the river's cool water, and the otters, though they were harmlessly tumbling again, the water drops from their whiskers flashing in that shaft of sun. The tiger lowered his head and I heard a sound I heard from my dogs in my own house every day, the lapping of water in loud, thirsty laps.

The tiger lapped and then, with a shock, the rifle fired from the other bank. It was a long shot and it missed. He crouched, water dripping off his cheeks, snarled, and slowly retreated backwards into the grass. I heard him moving away with a slithering, rustling movement in the grass.

He was wounded and very thirsty; he did not go far and soon, surprisingly quickly, he came back to drink again, this time in a muddy inlet farther off.

There the grass stopped short of the water by several feet and I saw him clearly, crouched down in his exciting shape above the river. I had him in my field-glasses and nothing was hidden, from the pale linings of his ears to the angry tip of his tail; along his side the beautiful striped markings rippled into each other as he moved. He drank, lifted his head, and the rifle fired again.

His death was so much in the tradition of tiger deaths that I could not believe I had seen it. He gave a roar that sent echoes flying over the river to the hills, reared up like a tiger on a crest, and fell backwards; one paw beat and swooped, then he lay still.

I sat in my tree, and presently realized that I was very stiff. On the opposite bank Dick was stretching himself, and Bangla, his hands round his mouth, was hallooing to Mooltiki to come and fetch them. While the sun went down, Mooltiki waded across and came back, carrying them and grumbling and flapping her ears.

The mahout turned her to the inlet and she walked along, petulantly thumping and smacking her trunk in the grass, not looking where she was going until all at once she saw the tiger; her trunk came up and her trumpet was such an agonized squeal that Bata Scully heard and answered from the elephant lines. Mooltiki shied, but her mahout stabbed her so passionately on the forehead that at last she went in closer and Bangla was able to stand up on her pad and throw stones at the tiger; then, very cautiously and ungraciously, Mooltiki let him slide off into the grass and, covered by Dick, go to look. In a moment Bangla's thumb came up. The tiger was dead.

Bangla whistled and after a time, round the grass, came the rest of the *shikaris* and most of the camp. They roped the tiger's paws and, all together heaving, using the rope as a pulley, they hoisted the tiger onto Mooltiki's back in spite of her fuss and fury. Bangla always treated Mooltiki as if her feelings and the impressive way she showed them were childish gambols or a little woman's whims. Then Mooltiki, with the tiger riding high, came to fetch me.

I wished Bangla had come. It was nearly dark and I did not like it any more than Mooltiki. All the way home she trumpeted, rounding on herself with an angry trunk, shrugging, making the mahout cry out, a feeble little noise after hers. The tiger head lolled and bumped and blood came trickling out of its mouth while its paws went gradually stiff. The immensity of those paws was a surprise, great, sinewy lengths with pads under them like the rollers on skates, and now I saw that its coat, which had looked so velvety in the distance, was bristly and scarred and full of ticks sucking themselves fat and loathsome on blood. I wished that I and it could have gone home separately.

"You must see the skinning," said Dick, and, when I shuddered, "It isn't disgusting, it's so perfectly done." It was not even bloody. The sharp knives slipped between the skin and the tissues so that it was more like an undressing than a skinning. Tail and legs were slit down the seam–or where the seam should have been–and the paws with their claws were peeled off inside out as one would remove a glove. The mask was taken off neatly round the jaws and eyes and the tiger was left, naked and gleaming, with strappings of white and red muscles and cob-web-white tissues.

The skin was cleaned of its ticks and lice, pegged out under the shade of the hut, and rubbed with wood ash and salt; a collection of tiger chops went to the cookhouse for the servants' supper and before dawn next morning a silent procession moved through the camp, people come from the villages to get the rare and fresh meat. They carried it away on their backs or heads, or fastened a haunch to a pole between two men. Then the carcass was left to the vultures. They had appeared out of an empty sky and the trees were full of them, birds like rocs, with horrible sinister faces. In a few hours they had eaten all that was left.

Next morning when I came to dress Horatius' wounds a piece of flesh fell off into my hand and it was alive with maggots. They were in every hole and I cried out, sick and horrified. Bangla came hurrying up. "Look! Look!" I said, almost crying, but he smiled.

"Now he will get better," said Bangla, and that night when I went to see the little bull, thinking of his pain, of how he was unable to lie down and would be visited by terrors, made worse by the smell of the second tiger, Horatius was lying down and his small, humped shape looked comfortable.*

He was safe between the campfire and the *shikaris*. The fires burned high, the sparks flying up, as they always did, against the stars. The cold snow wind was blowing and, satisfied, I turned towards warmth, dinner, and whisky. Then, on the river bed, I saw a familiar small blur, Mooltiki working late. She came loaded across the river and I stayed to watch her climb wearily out of the water for the last time.

She went to the elephant lines, the tired mahout took off the load, loosened the ropes, and dropped the pad. He fastened Mooltiki's leg chains and spread an inviting meal of leaves, cane, and *dhan,* a kind of grain. Squatting beside her, he wrapped the grain in banana leaves, making envelopes which he posted in her mouth. Sometimes he spread the grain on a cloth, letting her pick it up for herself with her trunk,

* He recovered completely and went back to his village to become the leader of the herd.

which she would do to the last, last grain, but tonight she was too hungry for that; using not both hands but her trunk, she stuffed leaves in, alternately with the mahout's envelopes. She looked a happy, relaxed little elephant at last, but the life of a tweeny is hard.

The sparks in the fire had died down and Neil clapped his hands.

Miracle of the Fifteen Murderers **Ben Hecht**

What can be expected when fifteen murderers get together? A succession of killings to spread panic through the millions of a great city? A phantasmagoric series of horrors? Nothing less, surely.

Ben Hecht's characters are sometimes responsible for the deaths of people and that is all we should explain here. They had an organization of their own which they called the X Club, and they got together at intervals to discuss their experiences.

On the score of his work he once remarked: "I have seen myself like the merry and cackling fellows who once upon a time stood on the street corners of Baghdad and unfolded tales to the citizens." Unhappily, it is necessary to say now that this prolific writer, who had so steadily turned his varied talents in many directions, suffered recently a fatal heart attack. It is a sad thought that in the publishing marts and the theatrical centers of Chicago and New York and Hollywood, he will be seen no more.

MIRACLE OF THE FIFTEEN MURDERERS

Ben Hecht

There is always an aura of mystery to the conclaves of medical men. One may wonder whether the secrecy with which the fraternity surrounds its gathering is designed to keep the layman from discovering how much it knows or how much it doesn't know. Either knowledge would be unnerving to that immemorial guinea pig who submits himself to the abracadabras of chemicals, scalpels and incantations under the delusion he is being cured rather than explored.

Among the most mysterious of medical get-togethers in this generation have been those held in New York City by a group of eminent doctors calling themselves the X Club. Every three months this little band of healers have hied them to the Walton Hotel overlooking the East River and, behind locked doors and beyond the eye of even medical journalism, engaged themselves in unknown emprise lasting till dawn.

What the devil had been going on in these conclaves for twenty years no one knew, not even the ubiquitous head of the American Medical Association, nor yet any of the colleagues, wives, friends or dependents of the X Club's members. The talent for secrecy is highly developed among doctors who, even with nothing to conceal, are often as close mouthed as old-fashioned bomb throwers on their way to a rendezvous.

How then do I know the story of these long-guarded sessions? The answer is–the war. The war has put an end to them, as it has to nearly all mysteries other than its own. The world, engaged in re-examining its manners and its soul, has closed the door on minor adventure. Nine of the fifteen medical sages who comprised the X Club are in uniform and preside over combat zone hospitals. Deficiencies of age and health have kept the others at home–with increased labors.

"Considering that we have disbanded," Dr. Alex Hume said to me at dinner one evening, "and that it is unlikely we shall ever assemble again, I see no reason for preserving our secret. Yours is a childish and romantic mind, and may be revolted by the story I tell you. You will undoubtedly translate the whole thing into some sort of diabolical tale and miss the deep human and scientific import of the X Club. But I am not the one to reform the art of fiction, which must substitute sentimentality for truth and Cinderella for Galileo."

And so on. I will skip the rest of my friend's all-knowing prelude. You may have read Dr. Hume's various books, dealing with the horseplay of the subconscious. If you have, you know this bald-headed master mind well enough. If not, take my word for it he is a genius. There is nobody I know more adept at prancing around in the solar plexus swamps out of which most of the world's incompetence and confusion appear to rise. He has, too, if there is any doubt about his great talent, the sneer and chuckle which are the war whoop of the super-psychologist. His face is round and his mouth is pursed in a chronic grimace of disbelief and contradiction. You can't help such an expression once you have discovered what a scurvy and detestable morass is the soul of man. Like most subterranean workers, my friend is almost as blind as a bat behind his heavy glasses. And like many leading psychiatrists, he favors the short and balloon-like physique of Napoleon.

The last dramatic meeting of the X Club was held on a rainy March night. Despite the hostile weather, all fifteen of its members attended, for there was an added lure to this gathering. A new member was to be inducted into the society.

Dr. Hume was assigned to prepare the neophyte for his debut. And it was in the wake of the round-faced soul fixer that Dr. Samuel Warner entered the sanctum of the X Club.

Dr. Warner was unusually young for a medical genius–that is, a recognized one. And he had never received a fuller recognition of his wizardry with saw, axe and punch hole than his election as a member of the X Club. For the fourteen older men who had invited him to be one of them were leaders in their various fields. They were the medical peerage. This does not mean necessarily that any layman had ever heard of them. Eminence in the medical profession is as showy at best as a sprig of edelweiss on a mountain top. The war, which offers its magic billboards for the vanities of small souls and transmutes the hunger for publicity into sacrificial and patriotic ardors, has not yet disturbed the anonymity of the great medicos. They have moved their bushels to the front lines and are busy under them spreading their learning among the wounded.

The new member was a tense and good-looking man with the fever of hard work glowing in his steady dark eyes. His wide mouth smiled quickly and abstractedly, as is often the case with surgeons who train their reactions not to interfere with their concentration.

Having exchanged greetings with the eminent club members, who included half of his living medical heroes, Dr. Warner seated himself in a corner and quietly refused a highball, a cocktail, and a slug of brandy. His face remained tense, his athletic body straight in its chair as if it were poised for a sprint rather than a meeting.

At nine o'clock Dr. William Tick ordered an end to all the guzzling and declared the fifty-third meeting of the X Club in session. The venerable diagnostician placed himself behind a table at the end of the ornate hotel room and glared at the group ranged in front of him.

Dr. Tick had divided his seventy-five years equally between practicing the art of medicine and doing his best to stamp it out–such, at least, was the impression of the thousands of students who had been submitted to his irascible guidance. As Professor of Internal Medicine at a great Eastern medical school, Dr. Tick had favored the education-by-insult theory of pedagogy. There were eminent doctors who still winced when they recalled some of old bilious-eyed, arthritic, stooped Tick's appraisals of their budding talents, and who still shuddered at the memory of his medical philosophy.

"Medicine," Dr. Tick had confided to flock after flock of students, "is a noble dream and at the same time the most ancient expression of error and idiocy known to man. Solving the mysteries of heaven has not given birth to as many abortive findings as has the quest into the mysteries of the human body. When you think of yourselves as scientists, I want you always to remember everything you learn from me will probably be regarded tomorrow as the naïve confusions of a pack of medical aborigines. Despite all our toil and progress, the art of medicine still falls somewhere between trout casting and spook writing.

"There are two handicaps to the practice of medicine," Tick had repeated tenaciously through forty years of teaching. "The first is the eternal charlatanism of the patient who is full of fake diseases and phantom agonies. The second is the basic incompetence of the human mind, medical or otherwise, to observe without prejudice, acquire information without becoming too smug to use it intelligently, and most of all, to apply its wisdom without vanity."

From behind his table Old Tick's eyes glared at the present group of "incompetents" until a full classroom silence had arrived, and then turned to the tense, good-looking face of Dr. Warner.

"We have a new medical genius with us tonight," he began, "one I well remember in his pre-wizard days. A hyper-thyroid with kidney disfunction indicated. But not without a trace of talent. For your benefit, Sam, I will state the meaning and purpose of our organization."

"I have already done that," said Dr. Hume, "rather thoroughly."

"Dr. Hume's explanations to you," Tick continued coldly, "if they are of a kind with his printed works, have most certainly left you dazed if not dazzled."

"I understood him quite well," Warner said.

"Nonsense," Old Tick said. "You always had a soft spot for psychiatry and I always warned you against it. Psychiatry is a plot against medicine."

You may be sure that Dr. Hume smiled archly at this.

"You will allow me," Tick went on, "to clarify whatever the learned Hume has been trying to tell you."

"Well, if you want to waste time." The new member smiled nervously and mopped his neck with a handkerchief.

Dr. Frank Rosson, the portly and distinguished gynecologist, chuckled. "Tick's going good tonight," he whispered to Hume.

"Senility inflamed by sadism," said Hume.

"Dr. Warner," the pedagogue continued, "the members of the X Club have a single and interesting purpose in their meeting. They come together every three months to confess to some murder any of them may have committed since our last assembly.

"I am referring, of course, to medical murder. Although it would be a relief to hear any one of us confess to a murder performed out of passion rather than stupidity. Indeed, Dr. Warner, if you have killed a wife or polished off an uncle recently, and would care to unbosom yourself, we will listen respectfully. It is understood that nothing you say will be brought to the attention of the police or the A.M.A."

Old Tick's eyes paused to study the growing tension in the new member's face.

"I am sure you have not slain any of your relatives," he sighed, "or that you will ever do so except in the line of duty.

"The learned Hume," he went on, "has undoubtedly explained these forums to you on the psychiatric basis that confession is good for the soul. This is nonsense. We are not here to ease our souls but to improve them. Our real purpose is scientific. Since we dare not admit our mistakes to the public and since we are too great and learned to be criticized by the untutored laity and since such inhuman perfection as that to which we pretend is not good for our weak and human natures, we have formed this society. It is the only medical organization in the world where the members boast only of their mistakes.

"And now"—Tick beamed on the neophyte—"allow me to define what we consider a real, fine professional murder. It is the killing of a human being who has trustingly placed himself in a doctor's hands. Mind you, the death of a patient does not in itself spell murder. We are concerned only with those cases in which the doctor by a wrong diagnosis or by demonstrably wrong medication or operative procedure has killed off a patient who, without the aforesaid doctor's attention, would have continued to live and prosper."

"Hume explained all this to me," the new member muttered impatiently, and then raised his voice. "I appreciate that this is my first meeting and that I might learn more from my distinguished colleagues by listening than by talking. But I have something rather important to say."

"A murder?" Tick asked.

"Yes," said the new member.

The old professor nodded.

"Very good," he said. "And we shall be glad to listen to you. But we have several murderers in the docket ahead of you."

The new member was silent and remained sitting bolt-upright in his chair. It was at this point that several, including Hume, noticed there was something more than stage fright in the young surgeon's tension. The certainty filled the room that Sam Warner had come to his first meeting of the X Club with something violent and mysterious boiling in him.

Dr. Philip Kurtiff, the eminent neurologist, put his hand on Warner's arm and said quietly, "There's no reason to feel badly about anything you're going to tell us. We're all pretty good medical men and we've all done worse–whatever it is."

"If you please," Old Tick demanded, "we will have silence. This is not a sanatorium for doctors with guilt complexes. It is a clinic for error. And we will continue to conduct it in an orderly, scientific fashion. If you want to hold Sam Warner's hand, Kurtiff, that's your privilege. But do it in silence."

He beamed suddenly at the new member.

"I confess," he went on, "that I'm as curious as anybody to hear how so great a know-it-all as our young friend Dr. Warner could have killed off one of his customers. But our curiosity will have to wait. Since five of you were absent from our last gathering, I think that the confessions of Dr. James Sweeney should be repeated for your benefit."

Dr. Sweeney stood up and turned his lugubrious face and shining eyes to the five absentees.

"Well," he said in his preoccupied monotone, "I told it once, but I'll tell it again. I sent a patient to my X-ray room to have a fluoroscopy done. My assistant gave him a barium meal to drink and put him under the fluoroscope. I walked in a minute later, and when I saw the patient under the ray I observed to my assistant, Dr. Kroch, that it was amazing and that I had never seen anything like it. Kroch was too overcome to bear me out. What I saw was that the patient's entire gastro-intestinal tract from the esophagus down was apparently made out of stone. And as I studied this phenomenon, I noticed it was becoming clearer and sharper. The most disturbing factor in the situation was that we both knew there was nothing to be done. Dr. Kroch, in fact, showed definite signs of hysteria. Even while we were studying him the patient showed symptoms of death. Shortly afterward he became moribund and fell to the floor."

"Well, I'll be damned," several of the absentees cried in unison, Dr. Kurtiff adding, "What the hell was it?"

"It was simple," said Sweeney. "The bottom of the glass out of which the patient had drunk his barium meal was caked solid. We had filled him up with plaster of Paris. I fancy the pressure caused an instantaneous coronary attack."

"Good Lord!" the new member said. "How did it get into the glass?"

"Through some pharmaceutical error," said Sweeney mildly.

"What, if anything, was the matter with the patient before he adventured into your office?" Dr. Kurtiff inquired.

"The autopsy revealed chiefly a solidified gastro-intestinal tract," said Sweeney. "But I think from several indications that there may have been a little tendency to pyloric spasm which caused the belching for which he was referred to me."

"A rather literary murder," said Old Tick. "A sort of Pygmalion in reverse."

The old professor paused and fastened his red-rimmed eyes on Warner.

"By the way, before we proceed," he said, "I think it is time to tell you the full name of our club. Our full name is the X Marks the Spot Club. We prefer, of course, to use the abbreviated title as being a bit more social-sounding."

"Of course," said the new member, whose face now appeared to be getting redder.

"And now," announced Old Tick, consulting a scribbled piece of paper, "our first case on tonight's docket will be Dr. Wendell Davis."

There was silence as the elegant stomach specialist stood up. Davis was a doctor who took his manner as seriously as his medicine. Tall, solidly built, gray-haired and beautifully barbered, his face was without expression–a large, pink mask that no patient, however ill and agonized, had ever seen disturbed.

"I was called late last summer to the home of a workingman," he began. "Senator Bell had given a picnic for some of his poorer constituency. As a result of this event, the three children of a steamfitter named Horowitz were brought down with food poisoning. They had overeaten at the picnic. The Senator, as host, felt responsible, and I went to the Horowitz home at his earnest solicitation. I found two of the children very sick and vomiting considerably. They were nine and eleven. The mother gave me a list of the various foods all three of them had eaten. It was staggering. I gave them a good dose of castor oil.

"The third child, aged seven, was not as ill as the other two. He looked pale, had a slight fever, felt some nausea—but was not vomiting. It seemed obvious that he too was poisoned, but to a lesser degree. Accordingly I prescribed an equal dose of castor oil for the youngest child—just to be on the safe side.

"I was called by the father in the middle of the night. He was alarmed over the condition of the seven-year-old. He reported that the other two children were much improved. I told him not to worry, that the youngest had been a little late in developing food poisoning but would unquestionably be better in the morning, and that his cure was as certain as his sister's and brother's. When I hung up I felt quite pleased with myself for having anticipated the youngest one's condition and prescribed the castor oil prophylactically. I arrived at the Horowitz home at noon the next day and found the two older children practically recovered. The seven-year-old, however, appeared to be very sick indeed. They had been trying to reach me since breakfast. The child had 105° temperature. It was dehydrated, the eyes sunken and circled, the expression pinched, the nostrils dilated, the lips cyanotic and the skin cold and clammy."

Dr. Davis paused. Dr. Milton Morris, the renowned lung specialist, spoke.

"It died within a few hours?" he asked.

Dr. Davis nodded.

"Well," Dr. Morris said quietly, "it seems pretty obvious. The child was suffering from acute appendicitis when you first saw it. The castor oil ruptured its appendix. By the time you got around to looking at it again peritonitis had set in."

"Yes," said Dr. Davis slowly, "that's exactly what happened."

"Murder by castor oil," Old Tick cackled. "I have a memo from Dr. Kenneth Wood. Dr. Wood has the floor."

The noted Scotch surgeon, famed in his college days as an Olympic Games athlete, stood up. He was still a man of prowess, large-handed, heavy-shouldered, and with the purr of masculine strength in his soft voice.

"I don't know what kind of a murder you can call this," Dr. Wood smiled at his colleagues.

"Murder by butchery is the usual title," Tick said.

"No, I doubt that," Dr. Morris protested. "Ken's too skillful to cut off anybody's leg by mistake."

"I guess you'll have to call it just plain murder by stupidity," Dr. Wood said softly.

Old Tick cackled.

"If you'd paid a little more attention to diagnosis than to shot putting you wouldn't be killing off such hordes of patients," he said.

"This is my first report in three years," Wood answered modestly. "And I've been operating at the rate of four or five daily, including holidays."

"My dear Kenneth," Dr. Hume said, "every surgeon is entitled to one murder in three years. A phenomenal record, in fact–when you consider the temptations."

"Proceed with the crime," Tick said.

"Well"–the strong-looking surgeon turned to his hospital colleague, the new member–"you know how it is with these acute gall bladders, Sam."

Warner nodded abstractedly.

Dr. Wood went on.

"Brought in late at night. In extreme pain. I examined her. Found the pain in the right upper quadrant of the abdomen. It radiated to the back and right shoulder. Completely characteristic of gall bladder. I gave her opiates. They had no effect on her, which, as you know, backs up any gall bladder diagnosis. Opiates never touch the gall bladder."

"We know that," said the new member nervously.

"Excuse me," Dr. Wood smiled. "I want to get all the points down carefully. Well, I gave her some nitro-glycerine to lessen the pain then. Her temperature was 101. By morning the pain was so severe that it seemed certain the gall bladder had perforated. I operated. There was nothing wrong with her damn gall bladder. She died an hour later."

"What did the autopsy show?" Dr. Sweeney asked.

"Wait a minute," Wood answered. "You're supposed to figure it out, aren't you? Come on–you tell me what was the matter with her."

"Did you take her history?" Dr. Kurtiff asked after a pause.

"No," Wood answered.

"Aha!" Tick snorted. "There you have it! Blind man's buff again."

"It was an emergency." Wood looked flushed. "And it seemed an obvious case. I've had hundreds of them."

"The facts seem to be as follows," Tick spoke up. "Dr. Wood murdered a woman because he misunderstood the source of a pain. We have, then, a very simple problem. What besides the gall bladder can produce the sort of pain that eminent surgeon has described?"

"Heart," Dr. Morris answered quickly.

"You're getting warm," said Wood.

"Before operating on anyone with so acute a pain, and in the absence of any medical history," Tick went on, "I would most certainly have looked at the heart."

"Well, you'd have done right," said Wood quietly. "The autopsy showed an infraction of the descending branch of the right coronary artery."

"Murder by a sophomore," Old Tick pronounced wrathfully.

"The first and last," said Wood quietly. "There won't be any more heart-case mistakes in my hospital."

"Good, good," Old Tick said. "And now, gentlemen, the crimes reported thus far have been too infantile for discussion. We have learned nothing from them other than that science and stupidity go hand in hand, a fact already too well known to us. However, we have with us tonight a young but extremely talented wielder of the medical saws. And I can, from long acquaintance with this same gentleman, assure you that if he has done a murder it is bound to be what some of my female students would call 'a honey.' He has been sitting here for the last hour, fidgeting like a true criminal, sweating with guilt and a desire to tell all. Gentlemen, I give you our new and youngest culprit, Dr. Samuel Warner."

Dr. Warner faced his fourteen eminent colleagues with a sudden excitement in his manner. The older men regarded him quietly and with various degrees of irritation. They knew without further corroboration than his manner that this medico was full of untenable theories and half-baked medical discoveries. They had been full of such things themselves once. And they settled back to enjoy themselves. There is nothing as pleasing to a graying medicine man as the opportunity of slapping a dunce-cap on the young of science. Old Tick, surveying his colleagues, grinned. They had all acquired the look of pedagogues holding a switch behind their backs.

Dr. Warner mopped his neck with his wet handkerchief and smiled knowingly at the medical peerage. What he knew was that this same critical and suspicious attention would have been offered him were he there to recite the tale of some miraculous cure rather than a murder.

"I'll give you this case in some detail," he said, "because I think it contains as interesting a problem as you can find in practice."

Dr. Rosson, the gynecologist, grunted, but said nothing.

"The patient was a young man, or rather a boy," Warner went on eagerly. "He was seventeen, and amazingly talented. In fact, about the most remarkable young man I've ever met. He wrote poetry. That's how I happened to meet him. I read one of his poems in a magazine, and, by God, it was so impressive I wrote him a letter."

Dr. Kurtiff frowned at this unmedical behavior.

"Rhymed poetry?" Dr. Wood asked, with a wink at Old Tick.

"Yes," said Warner. "I read all his manuscripts. They were sort of revolutionary. His poetry was a cry against injustice. Every kind of injustice. Bitter and burning."

"Wait a minute," Dr. Rosson said. "The new member seems to have some misconception of our function. We are not a literary society, Warner."

"I know that," said Warner, working his jaw muscles and smiling lifelessly.

"And before you get started," Dr. Hume grinned, "no bragging. You can do your bragging at the annual surgeons' convention."

"Gentlemen," Warner said, "I have no intention of bragging. I'll stick to murder, I assure you. And as bad a one as you've ever heard."

"Good," Dr. Kurtiff said. "Go on. And take it easy and don't break down."

"I won't break down," Warner said. "Don't worry. Well, the patient was sick for two weeks before I was called."

"I thought you were his friend," Dr. Davis said.

"I was," Warner answered. "But he didn't believe in doctors."

"No faith in them, eh?" Old Tick cackled. "Brilliant boy."

"He was," said Warner eagerly. "I felt upset when I came and saw how sick he was. I had him moved to a hospital at once."

"Oh, a rich poet," Dr. Sweeney said.

"No," said Warner. "I paid his expenses. And I spent all the time I could with him. The sickness had started with a severe pain on the left side of the abdomen. He was going to call me, but the pain subsided after three days so the patient thought he was well. But it came back after two days and he began running a temperature. He developed diarrhea. There was pus and blood, but no amoeba or pathogenic bacteria when he finally sent for me. After the pathology reports I made a diagnosis of ulcerative colitis. The pain being on the left side ruled out the appendix. I put the patient on sulfaguanidin and unconcentrated liver extract and gave him a high protein diet–chiefly milk. Despite this treatment and constant observation the patient got worse. He developed generalized abdominal tenderness, both direct and rebound, and rigidity of the entire left rectus muscle. After two weeks of careful treatment the patient died."

"And the autopsy showed you'd been wrong?" Dr. Wood asked.

"I didn't make an autopsy," said Warner. "The boy's parents had perfect faith in me. As did the boy. They both believed I was doing everything possible to save his life."

"Then how do you know you were wrong in your diagnosis?" Dr. Hume asked.

"By the simple fact," said Warner irritably, "that the patient died instead of being cured. When he died I knew I had killed him by a faulty diagnosis."

"A logical conclusion," said Dr. Sweeney. "Pointless medication is no alibi."

"Well, gentlemen," Old Tick cackled from behind his table, "our talented new member has obviously polished off a great poet and close personal friend. Indictments of his diagnosis are now in order."

But no one spoke. Doctors have a sense for things unseen and complications unstated. And nearly all the fourteen looking at Warner felt there was something hidden. The surgeon's tension, his elation and its overtone of mockery, convinced them there was something untold in the story of the dead poet. They approached the problem cautiously.

"How long ago did the patient die?" Dr. Rosson asked.

"Last Wednesday," said Warner. "Why?"

"What hospital?" asked Davis.

"St. Michael's," said Warner.

"You say the parents had faith in you," said Kurtiff, "and still have. Yet you seem curiously worried about something. Has there been any inquiry by the police?"

"No," said Warner. "I committed the perfect crime. The police haven't even heard of it. And even my victim died full of gratitude." He beamed at the room. "Listen," he went on, "even you people may not be able to disprove my diagnosis."

This brash challenge irritated a number of the members.

"I don't think it will be very difficult to knock out your diagnosis," said Dr. Morris.

"There's a catch to it," said Wood slowly, his eyes boring at Warner.

"The only catch there is," said Warner quickly, "is the complexity of the case. You gentlemen evidently prefer the simpler malpractice type of crime, such as I've listened to tonight."

There was a pause, and then Dr. Davis inquired in a soothing voice,

"You described an acute onset of pain before the diarrhea, didn't you?"

"That's right," said Warner.

"Well," Davis continued coolly, "the temporary relief of symptoms and their recurrence within a few days sounds superficially like ulcers —except for one point."

"I disagree," Dr. Sweeney said softly. "Dr. Warner's diagnosis is a piece of blundering stupidity. The symptoms he has presented have nothing to do with ulcerative colitis."

Warner flushed and his jaw muscles moved angrily.

"Would you mind backing up your insults with a bit of science?" he said.

"Very easily done," Sweeney answered calmly. "The late onset of diarrhea and fever you describe rules out ulcerative colitis in ninety-nine cases out of a hundred. What do you think, Dr. Tick?"

"No ulcers," said Tick, his eyes studying Warner.

"You mentioned a general tenderness of the abdomen as one of the last symptoms," said Dr. Davis smoothly.

"That's right," said Warner.

"Well, if you have described the case accurately," Davis continued, "there is one obvious fact revealed. The general tenderness points to a peritonitis."

"How about a twisted gut?" Dr. Wood asked. "That could produce the symptoms described."

"No," said Dr. Rosson. "A vulvulus means gangrene and death in three days. Warner says he attended him for two weeks and that the patient was sick for two weeks before he was called. The length of the illness rules out intussusception, vulvulus and intestinal tumor."

"There's one other thing," Dr. Morris said. "A left-sided appendix."

"That's out, too," Dr. Wood said quickly. "The first symptom of a left-sided appendix would not be the acute pain described by Warner."

"The only thing we have determined," said Dr. Sweeney, "is a perforation other than ulcer. Why not go on with that?"

"Yes," said Dr. Morris. "Ulcerative colitis is out of the question, considering the course taken by the disease. I'm sure we're dealing with another type of perforation."

"The next question," announced Old Tick, "is, what made the perforation?"

Dr. Warner mopped his face with his wet handkerchief and said softly, "I never thought of an object perforation."

"You should have," Dr. Kurtiff smiled.

"Come, come," Old Tick interrupted. "Let's not wander. What caused the perforation?"

"He was seventeen," Kurtiff answered, "and too old to be swallowing pins."

"Unless," said Dr. Hume, "he had a taste for pins. Did the patient want to live, Warner?"

"He wanted to live," said Warner grimly, "more than anybody I ever knew."

"I think we can ignore the suicide theory," said Dr. Kurtiff. "I am certain we are dealing with a perforation of the intestines and not of the subconscious."

"Well," Dr. Wood said, "it couldn't have been a chicken bone. A chicken bone would have stuck in the esophagus and never got through to the stomach."

"There you are, Warner," Old Tick said. "We've narrowed it down. The spreading tenderness you described means a spreading infection. The course taken by the disease means a perforation other than ulcerous. And a perforation of that type means an object swallowed. We have ruled out pins and chicken bones. Which leaves us with only one other normal guess."

"A fish bone," said Dr. Sweeney.

"Exactly," said Tick.

Warner stood listening tensely to the voices affirming the diagnosis. Tick delivered the verdict.

"I think we are all agreed," he said, "that Sam Warner killed his patient by treating him for ulcerative colitis when an operation removing an abscessed fish bone would have saved his life."

Warner moved quickly across the room to the closet where he had hung his hat and coat.

"Where you going?" Dr. Wood called after him. "We've just started the meeting."

Warner was putting on his coat and grinning.

"I haven't got much time," he said, "but I want to thank all of you for your diagnoses. You were right about there being a catch to the case. The catch is that my patient is still alive. I've been treating him for ulcerative colitis for two weeks and I realized this afternoon that I had wrongly diagnosed the case–and that he would be dead in twenty-four hours unless I could find out what really was the matter with him."

Warner was in the doorway, his eyes glittering.

"Thanks again, gentlemen, for the consultation and your diagnosis," he said. "It will enable me to save my patient's life."

A half hour later the members of the X Club stood grouped in one of the operating rooms of St. Michael's Hospital. They were different-looking men than had been playing a medical Halloween in the Walton Hotel. There is a change that comes over doctors when they face disease. The oldest and the weariest of them draw vigor from a crisis. The shamble leaves them and it is the straight back of the champion that enters the operating room. Confronting the problem of life and death, the tired, red-rimmed eyes become full of greatness and even beauty.

On the operating table lay the naked body of a Negro boy. Dr. Warner in his surgical whites stood over him, waiting. The anesthetist finally nodded. The dark skin had turned ashen, and the fevered young Negro lay unconscious.

The fourteen X Club members watched Warner operate. Wood nodded approvingly at his speed. Rosson cleared his throat to say something, but the swift-moving hands of the surgeon held him silent. No one spoke. The minutes passed. The nurses quietly handed instruments to the surgeon. Blood spattered their hands.

Fourteen great medical men stared hopefully at the pinched and unconscious face of a colored boy who had swallowed a fish bone. No king or pope ever lay in travail with more medical genius holding its breath around him.

Suddenly the perspiring surgeon raised something aloft in his gloved fingers.

"Wash this off," he muttered to the nurse, "and show it to the gentlemen."

He busied himself placing drains in the abscessed cavity and then powdered some sulfanilamide into the opened abdomen to kill the infection.

Old Tick stepped forward and took the object from the nurse's hand.

"A fish bone," he said.

The X Club gathered around it as if it were a treasure indescribable.

"The removal of this small object," Tick cackled softly, "will enable the patient to continue writing poetry denouncing the greeds and horrors of our world."

That, in effect, was the story Hume told me, plus the epilogue of the Negro poet's recovery three weeks later. We had long finished dinner and it was late night when we stepped into the war-dimmed streets of New York. The headlines on the newsstands had changed in size only. They were larger in honor of the larger slaughters they heralded.

Looking at them you could see the death-strewn wastes of battles.

But another picture came to my mind—a picture that had in it the hope of a better world. It was the hospital room in which fifteen famed and learned heroes stood battling for the life of a Negro boy who had swallowed a fish bone.

In Another Country **Ernest Hemingway**

In connection with any work by Ernest Hemingway, it is never necessary to say anything about the author himself. The emphasis can safely be put on the story, in this case a heart-rending episode involving a group of wounded soldiers in the First World War. They were all being used as test cases for a new special treatment with electric machines. They were in Milan and all of them had numerous medals. One, who possessed only one medal, had been wounded within an hour of his first appearance in the trenches, his nose being blown off.

But the main character in this typically fine Hemingway story is the oldest man of the group, who had been the champion fencer of Italy and whose fine and skilled hand had been reduced to the size of a small child's. He had a young wife about whom he did not talk. In fact, he did not talk much about anything, not even when his whole world blew up about him.

[illegible] English [illegible] government [illegible] [illegible] [illegible] [illegible] [illegible] under [illegible] for a [illegible] special [illegible] with [illegible] meetings [illegible] [illegible] would [illegible] wrong [illegible] hope [illegible] the [illegible] in the [illegible] [illegible] [illegible] [illegible] Hemingway [illegible] the [illegible] the [illegible] and [illegible] [illegible] [illegible] did [illegible] [illegible]

IN ANOTHER COUNTRY

Ernest Hemingway

In the fall the war was always there, but we did not go to it any more. It was cold in the fall in Milan and the dark came very early. Then the electric lights came on, and it was pleasant along the streets looking in the windows. There was much game hanging outside the shops, and the snow powdered in the fur of the foxes and the wind blew their tails. The deer hung stiff and heavy and empty, and small birds blew in the wind and the wind turned their feathers. It was a cold fall and the wind came down from the mountains.

We were all at the hospital every afternoon, and there were different ways of walking across the town through the dusk to the hospital. Two of the ways were alongside canals, but they were long. Always, though, you crossed a bridge across a canal to enter the hospital. There was a choice of three bridges. On one of them a woman sold roasted chestnuts. It was warm, standing in front of her charcoal fire, and the chestnuts were warm afterward in your pocket. The hospital was very old and very beautiful, and you entered through a gate and walked across a courtyard and out a gate on the other side. There were usually funerals starting from the courtyard. Beyond the old hospital were the new brick pavilions, and there we met every afternoon and were all very polite and interested in what was the matter, and sat in the machines that were to make so much difference.

The doctor came up to the machine where I was sitting and said: "What did you like best to do before the war? Did you practise a sport?"

I said: "Yes, football."

"Good," he said. "You will be able to play football again better than ever."

My knee did not bend and the leg dropped straight from the knee to the ankle without a calf, and the machine was to bend the knee and make it move as in riding a tricycle. But it did not bend yet, and instead the machine lurched when it came to the bending part. The doctor said:

"That will all pass. You are a fortunate young man. You will play football again like a champion."

In the next machine was a major who had a little hand like a baby's. He winked at me when the doctor examined his hand, which was between two leather straps that bounced up and down and flapped the stiff fingers, and said: "And will I too play football, captain-doctor?" He had been a very great fencer, and before the war the greatest fencer in Italy.

The doctor went to his office in a back room and brought a photograph which showed a hand that had been withered almost as small as the major's, before it had taken a machine course, and after was a little larger. The major held the photograph with his good hand and looked at it very carefully. "A wound?" he asked.

"An industrial accident," the doctor said.

"Very interesting, very interesting," the major said, and handed it back to the doctor.

"You have confidence?"

"No," said the major.

There were three boys who came each day who were about the same age I was. They were all three from Milan, and one of them was to be a lawyer, and one was to be a painter, and one had intended to be a soldier, and after we were finished with the machines, sometimes we walked back together to the Café Cova, which was next door to the Scala. We walked the short way through the communist quarter because we were four together. The people hated us because we were officers, and from a wine-shop some one would call out, "A basso gli ufficiali!" as we passed. Another boy who walked with us sometimes and made us five wore a black silk handkerchief across his face because he had no nose then and his face was to be rebuilt. He had gone out to the front from the military academy and been wounded within an hour after he had gone into the front line for the first time. They rebuilt his face, but he came from a very old family and they could never get the nose exactly right. He went to South America and worked in a bank. But this was a long time ago, and then we did not any of us know how it was going to be afterward. We only knew then that there was always the war, but that we were not going to it any more.

We all had the same medals, except the boy with the black silk bandage across his face, and he had not been at the front long enough to get any medals. The tall boy with a very pale face who was to be a lawyer had been a lieutenant of Arditi and had three medals of the sort we each had only one of. He had lived a very long time with death and was a little detached. We were all a little detached, and there was nothing that held us together except that we met every afternoon at the hospital. Although, as we walked to the Cova through the tough part of town, walking in the dark, with light and singing coming out of the wine-shops, and sometimes having to walk into the street when the men and women would crowd together on the sidewalk so that we would have had to jostle them to get by, we felt held together by there being something that had happened that they, the people who disliked us, did not understand.

We ourselves all understood the Cova, where it was rich and warm and not too brightly lighted, and noisy and smoky at certain hours, and there were always girls at the tables and the illustrated papers on a rack on the wall. The girls at the Cova were very patriotic, and I found that the most patriotic people in Italy were the café girls—and I believe they are still patriotic.

The boys at first were very polite about my medals and asked me what I had done to get them. I showed them the papers, which were written in very beautiful language and full of *fratellanza* and *abnegazione,* but which really said, with the adjectives removed, that I had been given the medals because I was an American. After that their manner changed a little toward me, although I was their friend against outsiders. I was a friend, but I was never really one of them after they had read the citations, because it had been different with them and they had done very different things to get their medals. I had been wounded, it was true; but we all knew that being wounded, after all, was really an accident. I was never ashamed of the ribbons, though, and sometimes, after the cocktail hour, I would imagine myself having done all the things they had done to get their medals; but walking home at night through the empty streets with the cold wind and all the shops closed, trying to keep near the street lights, I knew that I would never have done such things, and I was very much afraid to die, and often lay in bed at night by myself, afraid to die and wondering how I would be when I went back to the front again.

The three with the medals were like hunting-hawks; and I was not a hawk, although I might seem a hawk to those who had never hunted; they, the three, knew better and so we drifted apart. But I stayed good friends with the boy who had been wounded his first day at the front, because he would never know now how he would have turned out; so he could never be accepted either, and I liked him because I thought perhaps he would not have turned out to be a hawk either.

The major, who had been the great fencer, did not believe in bravery, and spent much time while we sat in the machines correcting my grammar. He had complimented me on how I spoke Italian, and we talked together very easily. One day I had said that Italian seemed such an easy language to me that I could not take a great interest in it; everything was so easy to say. "Ah, yes," the major said. "Why, then, do you not take up the use of grammar?" So we took up the use of grammar, and soon Italian was such a difficult language that I was afraid to talk to him until I had the grammar straight in my mind.

The major came very regularly to the hospital. I do not think he ever missed a day, although I am sure he did not believe in the machines. There was a time when none of us believed in the machines, and one day the major said it was all nonsense. The machines were new then and it was we who were to prove them. It was an idiotic idea, he said, "a theory, like another." I had not learned my grammar, and he said I was a stupid impossible disgrace, and he was a fool to have bothered with me. He was a small man and he sat straight up in his chair with his right hand thrust into the machine and looked straight ahead at the wall while the straps thumped up and down with his fingers in them.

"What will you do when the war is over if it is over?" he asked me. "Speak grammatically!"

"I will go to the States."

"Are you married?"

"No, but I hope to be."

"The more of a fool you are," he said. He seemed very angry. "A man must not marry."

"Why, Signor Maggiore?"

"Don't call me 'Signor Maggiore.' "

"Why must not a man marry?"

"He cannot marry. He cannot marry," he said angrily. "If he is to lose everything, he should not place himself in a position to lose that. He should not place himself in a position to lose. He should find things he cannot lose."

He spoke very angrily and bitterly, and looked straight ahead while he talked.

"But why should he necessarily lose it?"

"He'll lose it," the major said. He was looking at the wall. Then he looked down at the machine and jerked his little hand out from between the straps and slapped it hard against his thigh. "He'll lose it," he almost shouted. "Don't argue with me!" Then he called to the attendant who ran the machines. "Come and turn this damned thing off."

He went back into the other room for the light treatment and the massage. Then I heard him ask the doctor if he might use his telephone and he shut the door. When he came back into the room, I was sitting in another machine. He was wearing his cape and had his cap on, and he came directly toward my machine and put his arm on my shoulder.

"I am so sorry," he said, and patted me on the shoulder with his good hand. "I would not be rude. My wife has just died. You must forgive me."

"Oh–" I said, feeling sick for him. "I am *so* sorry."

He stood there biting his lower lip. "It is very difficult," he said. "I cannot resign myself."

He looked straight past me and out through the window. Then he began to cry. "I am utterly unable to resign myself," he said and choked. And then crying, his head up looking at nothing, carrying himself straight and soldierly, with tears on both his cheeks and biting his lips, he walked past the machines and out the door.

The doctor told me that the major's wife, who was very young and whom he had not married until he was definitely invalided out of the war, had died of pneumonia. She had been sick only a few days. No one expected her to die. The major did not come to the hospital for three days. Then he came at the usual hour, wearing a black band on the sleeve of his uniform. When he came back, there were large framed photographs around the wall, of all sorts of wounds before and after they had been cured by the machines. In front of the machine the major used were three photographs of hands like his that were completely restored. I do not know where the doctor got them. I always understood we were the first to use the machines. The photographs did not make much difference to the major because he only looked out of the window.

Children's Crusade **Geoffrey Household**

An Englishman went to Palestine on a diplomatic mission and found himself a guest at dinner with two people who seemed familiar–a man holding high office in the government of the country and an intelligent and attractive woman of, clearly, equal importance. It was apparent from the start that they knew him very well and it developed finally that the three of them had shared an adventure in the earliest stage of the new country which was to become the homeland of the Jewish people.

What this adventure was must not be divulged, and so there is nothing more to be said, save this: that here is a story of great interest which is quite different from anything that Geoffrey Household has ever written before. In the telling of it, he reveals himself at the peak of his story-telling skill.

CHILDREN'S CRUSADE

Geoffrey Household

He found it hard to believe that Israel was as welcoming to every tourist. His host, Joseph Horsha, was a mere professor of history, internationally known but not so distinguished that he could lay down an invisible red carpet for any Englishman who happened to be staying in his house. Looking out over the glittering Mediterranean from the top of Carmel and green shade, Mayne's sense of well-being was near perfect, yet faintly disturbed by the suspicion that he was the subject of gossip, that everyone–Horsha, this Ben Aron woman and even the taxi driver who had brought her–knew something which he did not.

Aviva Ben Aron claimed mysteriously to have met him before, though he was quite certain she was wrong. A most exceptional woman. Calm–that had been his impression of her during lunch. Not a quality you would expect from an overworked Undersecretary of State in a new and sensitive country. It was as if she had had some experience–a superb love affair, perhaps–which gave her enough pity and self-confidence to last a lifetime.

"And all this time you have never been in Israel, when it was Palestine?" she asked.

"No. Only looked at it from afar, like Moses. I was a soldier in Egypt then. Thirty-five years ago. And, Lord, how young!"

"Gloriously young!" she answered, smiling.

"Now, just what is this attractive mystery?" he demanded. "Where did we meet?"

"I was one of the children, Mr. Mayne–one of the twenty-six."

It was like all his memories of the first war, vanished if he were alone, vivid the instant some sharer recalled them. At once he was back on the quays of Port Said, the dust blowing, the crowd of diseased and powerful Egyptian laborers laughing at a crane as it dumped on the wharf dead and dying horses from the holds of a cattle ship which had met bad weather in the Indian Ocean. The sterile, vulgarian sun pointed the details of every dried and eddying patch of filth; and meanwhile the smart Italian freighter glided to her berth with twenty-six boys and girls leaning over the rails and staring with excited eyes at the hideous Orient as if it were the gate of heaven.

He had not recognized the pattern of the future. At the end of that first and, to civilians, kindlier war there had been no need of any elaborate organization to deal with refugees and displaced persons. The Middle East had few, and those belonging to obscure and persecuted Christian sects–simple souls whose problems could be solved by the loan of a donkey to carry their baggage. As for Zionists, nobody in 1919, outside political circles, had ever heard of them. In dealing with these astonishing Jewish children, who ought to have been in school and wanted to go to Palestine, Mayne had no precedent at all to follow.

The naval authorities and the Egyptian police had passed the muddle to him, for it was obvious that the children, if allowed to land, would become the responsibility of the military government. Mayne was the Port Control Officer. What he decided would be, for the time being, accepted. He had been well aware of his exact value to his superiors: a man who knew his own mind, saved everyone trouble and was sufficiently unimportant to be sacrificed if anything went wrong.

He went up to the captain's cabin under the bridge to see what the devil this Italian thought he was about. The fellow's enthusiasm annoyed him. It appeared that the children had made an overwhelming impression upon his emotional people; but twenty-six young lunatics from unknown depths of Central Europe, with the sketchiest of papers and very little money, couldn't just be dumped on the Port Said waterfront while a rapturous captain sailed back to Italy, rubbing his hands with easy satisfaction at a good deed done.

Under the circumstances a blaze of Latin oratory was impertinent. Mayne refused to allow the children to land and posted a solid pair of sentries at the foot of the gangway.

"You had not the slightest idea of the difficulties," he said, the memory of the day and the Italian captain adding a hardness to his voice.

"It never even occurred to us that there were any," Joseph Horsha replied.

"Were you with them too, Jo? Why have you never told me?"

"Look–it was as if we had both assisted at some secret, sacred ceremony. Something to remember, not to talk of. And when we met again so many years later, I couldn't tell whether you recognized me or not. The silences of Englishmen are so effective. One has to respect them."

Mayne searched his vague memory of the children whose eyes had followed him so gaily and confidently as he went ashore to put his sentries on the gangway. There had been five girls, more stern than attractive. Perhaps that was to be expected. A girl who preferred such a mad pilgrimage to the enthralling adventure of becoming a woman was bound to lack the charm of adolescence–or rather to have ripened her character before her emotions. That would account for the gray-haired, classical grace of Aviva Ben Aron. The foundation of her was indeed a love affair–though not in the generally accepted sense.

The boys–well, of course the quest itself had singled them out. It was impossible that any boy capable of starting and finishing such an adventure should not have the face of a dreamer. They looked like young Galahads, like any sentimental Victorian engraving of ardent youth. The oddness of some of the faces–to his Gentile eye–simply didn't count. If Joseph had been one of those boys, his whole warm character was still in keeping. The blade of youth, now sharpened down to a more serviceable flexibility, was set forever into his lean, sensitive features and the eagerness of his mind.

"My name then was Joseph Wald. Horsha is the Hebrew translation."

"Wald, of course! A fiery little scamp you were!"

"Not rude, I hope?"

"None of you was ever rude. You had no need to be. You knew you were irresistible."

"That was really the impression we gave?" Aviva Ben Aron asked. "I'm glad I didn't spoil it. I was just fifteen–and an imaginative little girl."

"You weren't afraid?" Horsha asked incredulously.

"Wasn't I? To be put ashore in Port Said with no protection but you visionary male children . . ."

Perhaps those two round-faced, Midland sentries at the foot of the brow had been justified after all, Mayne thought. To the girls, at any rate, rifle and bayonet couldn't have been half so frightening as all those evil Egyptian faces. After all the years he was still offended at the Italian lack of common sense in proposing to sling overboard, like so much cargo, twenty-six starry-eyed children.

"You leave the Italians alone," Horsha told him. "Responsibility is your forte. Emotional sympathy is theirs."

"One does expect some sanity all the same."

"No! Sanity would have been out of place in dealing with us. We had made our own world, where sanity didn't exist at all."

The conspiracy, Horsha explained, had run through the high schools of Cracow like a childish epidemic. No one knew who started it; no one could tell who would resist it. Those who went down with the highest fever had been the least Jewish of Jews. That wasn't surprising. The submerged and the religious had not yet assimilated the Balfour Declaration. To them it was just another prophecy, not an immediate invitation to act.

He told of his own romantic concept as precisely as if it had been read rather than lived. His family had been cultured Poles. The medieval courts of the legends had been as familiar to him as the court of King Solomon, and morally preferable. That had been true—though perhaps in a lesser degree—for most of his companions as well.

Their Zionism was the natural flower of Christian chivalry and Jewish tradition, owing nothing at all to propaganda. A last crusade had driven the Turks from Jerusalem. A statesman of the conquerors had declared that Palestine was open to the Jews. The facts did not belong to the modern world; they were gay and stirring as the summoning song of a minstrel. What gesture could one make in answer but to put up the Star of David upon an imaginary shield, and march?

At the first secret meeting there might have been a hundred boys and girls, aged from twelve to seventeen. When the cautious had weeded themselves out, thirty were left. They came from respectable, conventional families, but the ebb and flow of war had destroyed their natural fear of movement. Soldiers in thousands tramped over Europe, seeking their legitimate or spiritual homes. Therefore children could do the same, all the way to Palestine.

They even called themselves Crusaders, without any sense of incompatibility with their Jewish traditions. Who could refuse to let them pass, provided that their voluntary dedication was plainly to be seen?

In the privacy of a ruined factory belonging to Horsha's parents they took their solemn vows—to be honorable in all their dealings, to protect the weak, to preserve chastity. That final promise, though at their age not hard to fulfill, seemed to them the most important. It was an echo not so much of saintliness as of the precepts of parents.

"It's unbelievable that we could have been so cruel to them," Aviva said.

"Birds leave the nest."

"Yes. You used that argument then. It sounded as if it meant something."

"We did warn them," Joseph protested, still with the guilty laugh of a boy.

Yes—and the parents had given parental and understanding replies. Of course the children, if they were sure, quite sure, they wanted it, could go to Palestine as soon as education was finished, as soon as the routes were open, as soon as arrangements could be made to receive them. Fathers and mothers could well afford to be sympathetic. Travel was manifestly impossible till the aftermath of war had been cleared.

But instinctively the children knew that only in a time of unrest could their crusade succeed. The world which they had imagined was close to reality. That casual, medieval society which endured for months before frontiers were formally re-established had little interest in stopping the determined traveler.

Horsha and Aviva Ben Aron, both talking at once as if they had eagerly returned to childhood, tumbled incident upon incident. The children had kept their secret profoundly well. They bought and hid packs and water bottles, and put their money, collected by small economies and the naïve, ingenious tricks of the young, into a common store. They chose for their departure the early morning of a day when there was no school, and said–for they were determined not to start with a lie–that they were off on an expedition, that they didn't know when they would be back and that they promised all to keep together. The smallest, in much need of comfort, remembered the hundreds of boys who had enlisted well under military age without telling their parents.

So fathers and mothers, patient for a whole day and three quarters of a night, discovered at last, like burghers of Hamelin, that their children had vanished and did not even guess, till a joint telegram arrived, what piper had summoned them. Meanwhile the thirty had pushed their way among peasants and demobilized soldiers from train to crowded train, and were beyond recall.

The two frontiers which they crossed were still hardly delineated, and officials easily allowed them to pass through to Vienna. They were subjects of the Austro-Hungarian Empire, and their identity cards were in order. It was nobody's business to hold them for inquiries.

But also it was nobody's business to send them back. The urgent requests of the Cracow police were presumably dropped into trays marked PENDING. Austrians who were going to remain Austrians and Austrians who were going to be Czechs had no interest in the problems of Austrians who were going to be Poles. Children bursting with health and excitement on their way to Palestine? Good luck to them! It would be time enough to bother if the Italians refused to let them pass.

At Vienna they bought several days' supply of bread and sausage, and used the last of their money to travel clear of the too curious city and its suburbs. When they got off the train they were as destitute as all the saintly beggars of history. That, indeed, was high adventure for the sake of their quest. They felt at last free. Confident and singing, they began their march over the mountain roads towards the Italian frontier two hundred miles away.

Aviva laughed like a girl at the memory.

"I've never been so sure in my life that what I was doing was right—unsurpassably right!" she said. "And ever since, when I think my conscience is happy, I have been able to test it by that day."

"We were giving joy, too," Joseph added. "I don't think any of us realized it then. We just assumed that the world was as good as the first day God made it. But to the villagers we were the return of joy and innocence after four years of war. It was enough for them to see our faces. They gave us barns and sometimes their beds to sleep in. They showered us with milk and food."

"And wine," said Aviva. "How inhuman little male saints can be!"

"No, no! You never understood. It was essential that our spirit should not be lost—that nothing should be dissipated."

"I don't know what you're talking about," Mayne reminded them.

"One of our sixteen-year-olds got drunk," Aviva explained. "The other boys court-martialed him and sent him home—or rather back to Vienna, where he fortunately had an uncle. The mayor of the village lent him money for his fare."

The mayor had done his best for the offender, too. Drunkenness wasn't such a crime, he told the children. Why, before the war the dear *Wandervögel* were often merry in the evening! Yes, he understood that they had set themselves a religious standard, but didn't the boy's shame count with them?

It did not. The young faces regarded advocate and criminal with blank severity. They knew they were right. Horsha still declared that they were right. They were following, quite blindly, a European tradition. Only that tradition, reflected in their joy and their purity of manners and living, could carry the pilgrims through to the Holy Land.

As they drew nearer to the frontier, they were told again and again that the Italians would never let them through. The Italians, said the sentimental Austrians, were not in the least like themselves. The children would meet the victors in full flush of insolence. And what of girls of fifteen and sixteen unprotected among Latins?

The whole countryside was fascinated by their march, and in committee for their welfare. It was considered that they would appear to have some official backing if they crossed the Julian Alps by rail; so friendly railway men gave them a lift in a goods train over the pass, and unloaded the twenty-nine on the frontier station.

"You must have felt pretty forlorn then," said Mayne.

No, Joseph insisted, they had not. But possibly their faces showed enough anxiety to make them appear as suppliants—enough to prevent the feeling in any sensitive official that his beloved frontier was about to be ravished against its will.

The children's unity of purpose was such that it had never occurred to them to elect or appoint a leader. But the Latin mind demanded a leader. One couldn't talk with twenty-nine children at the same time—that was reasonable, wasn't it? It was indeed, though to the children the problem was how to explain themselves at all when eight Italians were talking at once. At last there was no sound in the mountain silence but the hissing of the locomotive. The utter improbability of the situation had imposed itself.

Those kindly Italians! A sergeant of Bersaglieri laid his hand upon the shoulder of the youngest, choosing him as spokesman. He was twelve and looked, after the hardships of the journey, no more than ten. The sergeant questioned him in bad German, while the frontier officials, instantly appreciating this paternal gesture, gathered round them.

The boy spoke up boldly. Money? No, they hadn't any. Was it then so important? They had reached Italy without it, and so they could reach Palestine.

But the sea? Hadn't one to cross the sea to go to Palestine?

Yes, certainly, said the twelve-year-old spokesman, surer of his geography than the sergeant. The English who had promised them the land and who had so many ships would provide.

Italian imagination, swift to identify itself with generosity, assumed its part in promise and victory alike. Had not Italy ships? Had not Italy, too, been engaged against the Turks? And was it not a historic occasion, this arrival of pilgrim children on their frontier?

"It was you, I remember, who put that point to them, Aviva."

"Yes. I felt it so strongly that I found myself stammering it all out in spite of shyness. I was sure that we were the first of many—the first, that is, to go in a body to a Palestine that was ours again. How right children are and how absurd! A little big-eyed prophet telling the commander of an Italian frontier post that the eyes of history were on him!"

It had been enough, at any rate, for the commander to spread his wings and send a wire to Venice. Meanwhile the children, no longer laughing but still confident that these excitable strangers could not refuse them, were herded into the barracks by the friendly sergeant and given two empty rooms—a large one for the boys, a smaller for the girls.

That was their worst night. They made their first acquaintance with hungry bugs. They remembered the warnings of the Austrian peasants. Crusading gallantry rose to the occasion. Horsha and his bosom friend slept on the bare boards of the passage outside the girls' door, and awoke to find the licentious Italian soldiery tenderly tiptoeing about their military business with bare feet in order not to disturb them.

The following afternoon came a reply, permitting the Polish children who claimed to be Jews to be sent down to Venice.

"Our frontier friends couldn't have put it better," said Horsha ironically. "Polish children who claim to be Jews sounds much more sympathetic than Jewish children who claim to be Poles."

"And all that is over for us!" Aviva exclaimed. "All finished by the name Israeli!"

They caught the imagination of a people. The newspapers christened their march a new Children's Crusade. The great, grave Jewish-Italian families took them to their bosoms.

"You can't imagine how we were feted—and how it seemed somehow to spoil all the beautiful simplicity!"

Even the Church was fascinated, and held up the children as examples of the conduct to be expected of Christians as well. But Christian children, who had no comparable objective, only felt that self-discipline when presented as adventure was a fraud. What it was really worthwhile to imitate they understood. Parties, armed with axes and their fathers' carving knives, set out in stolen boats to conquer Fiume or Africa, and were brought home weeping. The Church quietly and decisively moved the pilgrims on to Rome.

At Rome it was harder still to preserve their common flame. By letters they were in touch at last with parents, and their proud sense of isolation was disturbed by remittances of money and loving reproaches. Then the Roman matrons put out as well the light of chivalry by separating girls from boys. To march singing across the foothills of the Alps had been easy. The journey through Vanity Fair was a more searching test.

The boys insisted on remaining together. Their dormitory was the vast empty salon of a palace, where the neat beds were lined against marble walls like insignificant white mice. Only their impatience saved them from being extinguished. To go on. That was all they wanted—to go on. Their hosts, though ravished by their innocent courage, found them obstinate and insensitive.

One of the girls fell in love and became engaged to be married—as young as Juliet and just as ecstatic. They thought this an indecency, plain evidence of the approaching moral rot. And then the eldest of them, a few months over seventeen, was led astray by the daughter of a Jewish family which was great but not so grave.

If he had confessed, he might have been expelled with dignity. But he boasted.

"We flung him out," said Horsha savagely, "flung him out with everything that belonged to him!"

"They had to keep their illusions," Aviva explained in half apology. "Illusion was the driving force."

"I had no idea that the girls were not in full sympathy," Joseph Horsha remarked, still with the remains of disquiet from thirty-five years before.

"We were. But it was such a relief in Rome, for a little while, not to have to play your game. Attachments had grown, you see–all very innocent and romantic."

"Not with any of us!"

She did not answer. But even if a few of the little warriors were being civilized in secret by their ladies, there was no deflecting either from their purpose. The Roman matrons found their pets untamable, and dismissed them with the magnificent gesture of a free passage to Egypt.

Presumably some diplomat, general or influential prince was ordered to approach the British authorities. He may indeed have written; but, if he did, his letter was slipped into some file reserved for the improbable and impossible. Palestine did not yet exist, only a Syria about to be divided between French and British. There was no government but the staff of Allenby's army, sorting out, with brusque military common sense, the unfamiliar complexities of Turkish administration.

At Genoa twenty-six children, overjoyed to be again together and in movement, went on board the freighter and down to a baggage room which had been roughly partitioned for the boys and girls, and furnished with camp beds. Of the original thirty, one was to be married, two had been guilty of unknightly behavior, and a fourth had died in Italy of influenza. They couldn't have said what on earth they expected to find on arrival: turbaned Turks, perhaps, or even some modern remnant of Pharaoh's linen-kilted courtiers–certainly not an impersonal military organization, with its Captain Maynes and its sentries blandly unaffected by any crusade but their own.

After the first hours of looking down from the deck upon Port Said, excitement lost its edge. Not even imagination was justified. True, there were palms and sand. But Egyptians did not ride camels; they unloaded dead horses and loaded coal. Where were the glittering caravans of the Orient, and the British cavalry which had ridden to Jerusalem? Where the curiosity or enmity that their arrival should have occasioned? The heroes of Balfour and Allenby were red-faced, red-kneed soldiers, wearing ridiculous shorts like very little boys. They entered things in notebooks and bawled at the Egyptians instead of clinking their sabers magnificently up and down the quay. This busy world had nothing in common with kindly Europe, continuous, in spite of varying scenery and manners, from Cracow to Rome.

During the morning all action was inhibited. Outside the refuge of the ship's awnings the sun smote dishearteningly upon stone and iron. The strange inhabitants of the quay continued to work. The Italian captain was fuming and unapproachable. British naval and military officers came and went, passing the eager group with noncommittal smiles.

Then the spirit of the crusade reasserted itself. There was a moment's talk, and the children picked up their packs, without any order given or any formal agreement among them, and marched together down the gangway. They ignored the casual request to hop it and the subsequent sharp command to halt. Nor was the sentry's bayonet in itself decisive.

The bayonet belonged in their world–which, after all, contained the possibility of martyrdom, though no chance of it had yet appeared. But while the boys hesitated before that unwavering point at the foot of the gangway the sentry's companion gave them a broad grin and a wink, and with a jerk of the thumb dismissed them. His confidence was unshakable as their own, and his friendly gesture intelligible; it pointed out that the bayonet was not really sharp steel but merely a wall, an unclimbable wall, around the stately park of empire. The irresistible force had met the immovable object.

"And in the end there is no way out of that," Aviva said, "but to learn to hate."

"No, you can't find parallels," Horsha went on. "There aren't any. The British, as they were in 1919–yes, and later–had the art of making the rest of the world feel ashamed of impatience. That sentry–with his tiny private share of it–was quite enough for twenty-six crusaders."

Thereafter the slow mass of bureaucracy crept over and engulfed them. Up and down that gangway, to them forbidden, passed the Egyptian police, the port authorities, the Italian consul and the agent of the line. From the conferences in the saloon the Italians emerged profane and glowering, the English unyielding and self-satisfied; and all of them combined to make the children appear in their own eyes young nuisances rather than young heroes. But never did it occur to them that they were unreasonable, or that their knightliness could be defeated. Hardest of all to bear was the young army captain, Mayne, who spoke in courtly French quite intelligible to the high school students, and merely seemed to be amused.

"You didn't mind the general," Mayne protested. "He was just as amused as I."

"We were good Polish citizens," Joseph answered. "We treated generals with respect. And he understood us. A man who isn't a boy at heart can never become a general. Half his job is to persuade men that they are really having the marvelously exciting time they dreamed of when they were twelve."

"It wasn't till much later," explained Aviva, "that we realized you had brought the general yourself."

Well, of course, he had. And it was true that he had been amused—delighted was a better word—by the glorious folly of the pilgrimage. He was surprised to find himself most reluctant to have the children's fire put out by a great wad of paper, or to return them to Italy. His sentries, as a precaution, were correct; as a solution, they were intolerable.

He persuaded the general to take the children off the ship and, pending a decision, to send them down the Suez Canal to a camp at Kantara. The old professional had been impressed by their quality—by their tremendous button-polishing capacity if they had any buttons. All the same, he insisted, some inexpensive method of returning them to Poland would have to be found. It was impossible to allow them into Palestine, utterly impossible.

"He didn't really mean us to go on, then?" Joseph asked.

"He dithered. We both did. So you were always in command of your own destiny."

It hadn't felt like it. There the children were, just as on the Italian frontier, under the benevolent control of military; but this time nobody's enthusiasm suggested that something was bound to happen. They were merely well looked after, and visited occasionally by the smiling Captain Mayne, who told them to be patient as if he had never realized that a divine impatience was their inspiring force. The only contact with the world of their imagination was that they were living in tents on the edge of the desert.

And that hard, lion-colored surface was all which separated them from Palestine? Couldn't they walk there? Hadn't all the conquerors of ancient history crossed the Sinai desert? In the gray of dawn, stealthily, an advance party set out with their water and the unexpended portion of the day's rations. Their tents were outside the military cantonments. No one saw them leave but the prowling Egyptian children—sleepers and scavengers who rose from the dust and accompanied them, mocking, capering and gesticulating obscenely. The little column marched on unconcerned, following a straight course across packed sand and gravel never disturbed by the wheel tracks of any of the armies which had cautiously hastened from Egypt into Syria. The palms of the Canal vanished over the horizon. The native children scuttled back to the safety of mud walls.

"I am always surprised that you found us," Horsha said.

"Oh, it wasn't difficult! The trouble was that I had been away. So you had two days' start, and the little wretches you left behind wouldn't say a word. But I knew exactly what you would do. Didn't I tell you that I, too, was very young then? You would march on Jerusalem by your compass."

That was their route when Mayne and his hastily borrowed cavalrymen discovered them marching east-northeast through the midday heat, stumbling, their water gone, but still in good close order. They reckoned to cover another five miles of deadly emptiness before they collapsed.

No more resistance was possible for the general. There were two good reasons for that. One was the children's determination. They could not be guarded night and day to prevent some further lunacy. The other was their chivalry. The beauty of the relationship between girls and boys was so obvious that it had never occurred to Mayne or his general that anyone could object to the proximity of their various tents. But there was no keeping out the chaplains and the welfare workers, and it was their business to protest.

The plaguing of the general increased and, like Pharaoh, he had no reasonable solution. He might have invented an excuse for putting one or two children on the new military railway to Haifa, but not twenty-six —for he was only the commander of a base. He would have had the politicians down on him, let alone Allenby's Chief of Staff.

"Did he put the blame on you?" Aviva asked.

"Only damned my eyes in a general way. There were no real reproaches. We were both emotionally affected by your spirit, you see. You had to go to Palestine. Had to go. That was why at last I gave you my promise that you should."

It had been a knightly gathering, though the banners and shields were there only in the eye of imagination. The children were drawn up in the space between the tents and took oath, eager-eyed and solemn-faced, that they would not leave the camp without permission. And in his turn Mayne gave his word of honor that he would lead them to Palestine.

"You were tremendously impressive," Horsha assured him. "You, the young Count of the Empire who had galloped up to our rescue!"

"Then it was my turn to radiate a confidence I didn't have," Mayne answered. "I remember wondering how on earth I was going to keep my word."

But the fact that he had given it was a third good reason for the general, who provided all that was in his power to provide—two lorries and rations, a week's leave for the importunate Captain Mayne and a pass which would take the whole party to Palestine so long as no one questioned it. And he wrote privately to the Chief Rabbi of Jerusalem, for he could not think of anyone else to arrange the children's reception.

"We addressed him as Your Grace," said Mayne with a chuckle. "His rank, we reckoned, must be equivalent to an archbishop. And we told the general's pet runner, who carried the letter, to be extra polite and mind his saluting."

The still Canal had just ceased to reflect the stars when the two lorries drove down it towards the desert track. The children were the first band of illegal immigrants, although, as in all their journey, they had no thought of breaking any law. Where there was none, their spirit supplied it.

Mayne, the drivers and their mates caught the infection of romance. They felt themselves explorers, and would have deliberately supplied adventure if there had not been enough in reality. The crossing of deserts by motor vehicles was then too new to be taken for granted. The lorries on their solid tires ponderously ground and bumped over irregularities of surface. Halts were frequent, and the running repairs of heavy complexity and doubtful value. The children were battered and bruised by the journey; but at night, wrapped in blankets on the sand, they abandoned themselves utterly to sleep—sleep which all their lives, said Joseph and Aviva, they remembered for its quality of peace. The next day they would have conquered.

Of this they were so sure that Mayne, against his better judgment, resumed the journey with a single lorry; the other had to be abandoned to await a tow to workshops. But even springs and axles obeyed the children. The remaining truck crept stolidly north until, instead of lonely shepherds, they saw huts with men and women sitting idle after harvest at the doors. Patches of sparse stubble began to appear among the scrub and dry thorn.

Was it at last Palestine? Well, no one could say for certain. But it was decidedly not Egypt. Two hours later the lorry limped into an Arab village and approached a group of European colonists, deep-eyed and sunburned, who waited patiently and could not yet see what precious freight was packed on blankets under the canvas hood.

Again the children asked if they had come to Palestine, and this time, though maps and politicians might be unwilling to commit themselves, history had no doubt. Mayne could not remember what he answered. He was very anxious to hand over his charge and retreat into the desert before civilians and military could overwhelm him with embarrassing questions. Nor could he trust himself to speak, for long war and sacrifice and promise, children and place and the ancient sanctities of Jew and Christian were of profound emotional power.

"You said," Aviva reminded him, "'This is Beersheba. I must leave you now.'"

Lobo **MacKinlay Kantor**

Lobo means wolf in Spanish. But the bearer of the name in this story was fifty pounds of dog, the poundage divided probably among a number of breeds. He had been a stray but with the people of El Remo he was a general favorite. He had such expensive tastes in food that sometimes his consumption of an evening included sausage, almonds, tuna fish, pickled shrimps, and candied cherries, all obtained by persistent begging from the patrons of restaurants. But Lobo had no family and no home and this made him very unhappy. Finally he succeeded in attaching himself to the author and his wife. They tried to get rid of him and failed. Then they decided to keep him and took him back to America with them.

Lobo liked America because it had such huge woods and trees and so many birds and such unfamiliar and wonderful smells. Everywhere they went, he made friends. Paws across the sea, explains the author.

Anyone who has read *The Voice of Bugle Ann* (which means nearly everyone) will know what MacKinlay Kantor can do with the story of a dog like Lobo.

[illegible]

Rowland [illegible] the [illegible]
[illegible]
[illegible]
[illegible]
[illegible]
[illegible]
[illegible]
[illegible]
[illegible]
[illegible] Then they [illegible]
[illegible]

[illegible]
[illegible]
[illegible]
[illegible]
[illegible]
[illegible]

LOBO

MacKinlay Kantor

When first we encountered him, he was disguised as a *fiesta*.

If ever I did know what particular Spanish historical occasion is celebrated on the night of February 15th, I have forgotten. It was on such a night.

The unique enterprise which Lobo had decided to grace with his presence is deemed the Montemar-El Remo complex. It is directed by the Marqués de Nájera, whose exploits on the golf courses of Andalucía vie with his hold on fame as a cavalry officer during the Rif campaigns. Angel, as he is called by intimates, is seconded in command by the lovely María Luisa Rein. From these people I learned eventually such details of Lobo's past as might have escaped the attention of ordinary biographers.

The Montemar Hotel is a sprawling white plaster building rambling along the shoulder of a hill, with the Mediterranean turning choicely blue or bitterly gray a quarter of a mile beneath. Down on those shores is the gayer portion of the concern: El Remo, a busy little restaurant by day, and by night a club where the light fantastic is tripped, and where on occasion a few of the light-minded fantastic individuals of the Gay International Set have indulged in earnest hair-pullings.

The cuisine, presided over by one Cristóbal, is above reproach if some of the guests occasionally aren't. Grouped near El Remo are cottages and a row of modern glass-fronted apartments, all a part of the same brave social scheme.

. . . A *fiesta* was in progress, and what with serpentine and confetti and noisemakers and champagne and brandy, everything was moving right well at two A.M.

By nature an abstemious man, I was not at all polluted. But my senses shivered as I watched a portion of the carnival scenery detach itself and move calmly toward us.

I murmured to my wife, "Do you see what I see?"

Irene said limply, "I guess we've had too many drinks. We ought to go home."

"Let's go–I'm with you. Serpentine doesn't just get up and walk around."

That is what the serpentine was doing. A huge parti-colored mound of the gay paper streamers progressed ominously across the dance floor.

"Serpentine's got a tail," we observed. Sure enough, the paper mountain did have a tail, a stubby sickle-shaped appendage with a white tip.

Cristóbal approached our table.

"Please, what is *that?*" We indicated the ambulatory hummock which now had turned majestically on another course.

"Ah, that. That is Lobo."

Thus began an acquaintance which ripened into friendship, which in turn ripened into obsession, which in turn ripened into madness. In the direction of Lobo (in Spanish, *wolf*) lay madness.

If you chose to introduce a Doberman, a German shepherd, and an old red-bone hound and have them somehow intermingle and beget, they might have produced something like Lobo. He had yellow eyes and droopy ears. His legs and feet were fawn-colored; and they were slim legs and tiny feet, although made of piano wire. Also tan was the mask across his face, which he wore flagrantly in a land where the wearing of masks is a felony. He had a white necktie; from this formal white decoration a pale zipper extended backward under his belly. Often I was possessed of the insane impulse to unzip that zipper but was too appalled at the notion of what I might find inside.

Lobo weighed an even fifty pounds on the dot. He could run about twice as fast as any greyhound at the Sarasota Kennel Club, at least any that I ever bet on. His teeth had been hand-forged in Seville by some master swordsmith; his tongue was a slice of palest *Serrano* ham; most of his body had been well blacked and rubbed by the best *limpiabotas* in Spain. (That is foreign talk for bootblack.)

According to Angel and María Luisa, Lobo's mother belonged to a shepherd in the hills behind the Montemar. This unhappy country matron presented the not-too-proud shepherd with a litter of puppies one cold day. The Spaniards are a philosophical race–also practical, if at times uncertain according to our standards in their moral motives. The practical and benevolent shepherd turned the puppies out to die. He said that he could feed no more dogs than the one. I suppose that most of them did die. Perhaps up there amid flint and boulders of the coastal range are lying the long-picked bones of Lobo's kin. No bones of Lobo are there.

Lobo betook himself shoreward. I can understand how his reasoning went, and so can anyone else who knew him.

"Let's see," Lobo meditated. "Shelter, of course–I don't like being rained on. . . . Food . . . yes, yes, but not ordinary food. Something exotic would be more to the point. . . . Companionship? For a certainty. And I do like a place with an open fire and red leather cushions."

So he showed up at the most expensive café on the southern coast of Spain, and moved in as manager, a grade or two above the rank held later by Cristóbal.

How long since all this had taken place?

Time means very little to the Spanish.

You would say, "How long has Lobo been here?"

"Oh, for years."

"How many years?"

"Oh, for some years, *Señor.*"

"Well, two years, three years?"

"Oh, yes."

"Four years, five years?"

The shrug. "Perhaps."

"Six years?"

"I don't know, *Señor*. He has been here for years."

Actually he had a few gray hairs when first we knew him. But a vet who looked at his teeth later said they were the teeth of a young dog. . . . *No lo sé, Señoras y Señores.*

Far from being the playboy type, he was a man of serious purpose, definitely community-minded. A native of the United States, he would have belonged–congenially, productively–to the Elks, the Masons or K of C, the Rotary Club, and probably the American Legion or the Veterans of Foreign Wars. (If a war had been going on, you wouldn't have been able to keep Lobo out of it.) A native of Spain, however, he belonged to no organization; although on good rumor he attended sessions of the Friends of New Torremolinos, the village booster organization–most especially if the meeting had a banquet attached.

He was known in every shop. All cooks and gardeners and maids knew him. The children knew him. The Civil Guards treated him with respect. "Good morning, Lobo," they would say. He would bow and continue on his course, which usually had something to eat at the end of it.

Most of the *turistas* who came to El Remo thought naturally that this beast belonged to Fermín or Antonio or Miguel or Cristóbal or Pedro or someone of the staff. At times the staff thought he belonged to the Devil. He was not in those days a cross dog. Neither was he a dirty dog, he was not a smelly dog; he did not jump up on the tables. Still the mere ubiquity of the creature was something to be contended with.

His comforts were eminently provided for at the café; the huge golden eyes did the trick. He was catholic as to his tastes. Often we saw him leisurely munching chicken bones contributed by some tot. He ate every variety of *hors d'oeuvre* in the place, although he was most partial to caviar.

His procedure consisted of approaching a table and putting his stony head on a knee or a lap. When you looked down to see what was this weight you were bearing, the weight was Lobo. You fed him, you had to, you couldn't *not* feed Lobo. That is, nineteen out of twenty people couldn't. The twentieth person (often a Swede or a German, with strict ideas as to the table deportment of dogs) would fly into a rage and flail with his napkin. Lobo sought neither to resist nor retaliate. He simply shrugged and strolled on to another table.

This is not champagne or brandy talk, Spanish or otherwise; but it does seem that I have seen him eat at least twice his weight in anchovy olives, cold sausage, almonds, tuna fish, white bread, omelette, ice cream, pickled shrimp, candied cherries, and vegetable soup in a single evening. When even his rubber belly could hold no more, he would saunter toward a cushion on the built-in bench near the fireplace. If some interloper happened to be there, he would fling himself across the interloper's feet as a hint that the spot should be vacated.

Generally he was very even as to temper—again, in those days. From time to time he traveled with a troop of native dogs ambling about the neighborhood. He was larger than most, he seemed to rule by influence rather than by brawn. I never saw him in but one fight—in those days—and then it was with a snobbish French poodle who swished into the place and apparently whispered some slighting reference to Lobo's ancestry or background.

Being seated closest to the scene of strife, and having achieved by that time a working knowledge of Lobo, I managed to save the visiting poodle from complete dismemberment. . . .

"How *dare* you!" the poodle's mistress was shrieking in five languages. "How dare you retain such a wicked beast? You should keep your dog on leash!"

"Madam," I said, "he is not my dog." Suddenly my heart was a little heavy at the thought that this was true.

If Lobo had no family of his own it was not his fault. He was willing to have a family, he courted families. Did the mighty General Carlos Martínez Amadeo Silva y Serrano appear for a quiet holiday on the seashore, complete with *la señora,* nine children, and eleven maids? Lobo moved in with them. Invariably he was welcomed as a combination court jester, tutor, night watchman, and scullion. Then, the fortnight of seaside bliss being duly expended, the Silva tribe would return to Madrid minus Lobo.

The following week one of those same cottages might be occupied by an elderly countess, with whom Lobo would promptly effect a liaison. Next month it might be an ailing English couple, or an American painter, a Swiss professor, a Copenhagen merchant, a French opera singer. Lobo must have distributed more international affections than a Hollywood playboy on his first trip to the Riviera.

Thus he developed his allergy to suitcases. Lobo dissolved at the mere sight of a suitcase being dragged from its lair. His reaction was to depart into the nearest dark closet and lie with his face turned against his tail. When the suitcase was packed and closed, and a departure grew imminent, he froze even colder–he would not lift his head. He would not come out and say Goodbye, he would not display a brave heart in the face of separation. He would simply congeal until the *camareras* shoveled him out of the way when they came to prepare the abode for new tenants.

Later, when Lobo's life was identified with my own, other people used to come proudly and declare that they too had dwelt in such intimacy. "You know, Lobo lived with *us* once. For three weeks." They seemed confident of securing prestige by the statement.

The night we returned to Spain in the early spring of 1954 for our second period of residence, we entered El Remo. Lobo greeted us with open paws. We had planned to take a house that year, probably down the coast a little farther. Angel arranged temporary quarters for us in one of the glassy apartments on the shore; without invitation, Lobo accompanied us thither when we withdrew from the table.

This apartment had been occupied until the previous week by the John Steinbecks, and I do not think that Lobo lived with them. Lobo did not like gypsies, or sadly enough, beggar children, since the latter element had been unkind to him in his infancy, and he had reason to remember cuffs, kicks, and hurtful stones. Beggar children gave him a wide berth. They would not have approached the Steinbeck establishment had Lobo been in occupancy. Mr. Steinbeck, however, is a resourceful man. He proceeded to get rid of the beggars whenever they came hissing outside the window with that supreme persistence known only to Andalucian mendicants. Mr. Steinbeck could speak no Spanish, but would erupt from his dwelling suddenly, screaming in English, "Buttered toast!" This had become a part of neighborhood tradition. It served well. Promptly the landscape would be overwhelmed with fast-fleeing brats. . . .

Lobo did exude an air of having been there before, when he trotted into the apartment. Carefully he selected the best portion of the upholstered couch, curled up, winked at us, went to sleep. He was still there in the morning, motionless, and did not even deign to stretch—until breakfast was brought and there was some reason for getting up. He took his usual continental breakfast of buttered roll and marmalade, then asked me to open the door for him. He disappeared. We did not see him again until ten o'clock at night, when the very earliest-dining Spaniards begin to gather. Then he consumed dinner along with us, and moved in again for the night.

On the third day we were invited to a party. It was to be a large assemblage, and common sense and a certain degree of sophistication suggested that we should decline. The hostess was a member of the Gay International Set—by no means one of the hair-pullers—but still there were bound to be the usual Hollywood types, Left Bank types, Monaco types, Costa Brava types, with a good prospect of several people plunging fully clad into the swimming pool before the night was over.

Few diners were present when we walked into El Remo about ten or a little later, and certainly there was no Lobo in sight.

"Where is Lobo?" I asked.

"*Don* MacKinlay, he has gone to the party. Were you not invited to the party? Everyone has gone to the party."

We chattered out something about still being weary from our trip.

"Oh, yes," said Cristóbal. "I know that Lobo is there, because he saw them fetching in the food very early, and preparing tables in the Contessa's patio. He went up there immediately."

This night Lobo had decided to cast discretion to the winds, to become in name and deed one of the G.I.S. It was four o'clock A.M., and we were sound asleep, when the most horrible caterwauling burst forth outside our door, punctuated by a scratching assault on the panel. I arose and opened the door. Lobo staggered in. He had had too much to drink as well as too much to eat. He barely made it to the couch, and didn't get up until noon.

We started explaining suitcases to him a couple of days later.

"You see, Lobo, we have taken a house about five *kilómetros* down the beach, and of course that is too far from El Remo for your comfort. So—"

But we were talking to thin air, because he had gone into the closet. There was just that shiny black rear with its four-leaf-clover design of tan at a strategic place; that was all we could see.

He didn't move, not even after we crowded our bags into the car.

Irene bent over him tenderly. "Lobo, aren't you even going to say goodbye?"

He did follow us into the yard, but after one look at the loaded car he lay down and turned his face away.

"I almost hate to leave him," Irene mourned as we drove off.

"Why, heavens. He wouldn't be happy anywhere else. El Remo is his *home,* the only place he knows," and I had almost convinced myself of this by the time we reached our new quarters on the precipice at La Verdad.

Following a few meals cooked over charcoal, we felt that since we were the proud possessors of a regular kitchen and a regular stove, we would try a little roasting or baking. Most Spanish stoves might be good for fogging up an Air Force Base to conceal it from visual attack by the enemy; ours was no exception. A storm of smoke drove us out. We left the windows open and fled to El Remo.

Promptly a solid head was dumped on each of our four knees in turn, and Lobo expressed his pleasure by gobbling most of our dinners. Then he disappeared; we presumed that he had gone among other tables to beg for further sustenance–as if he needed it!–and after a postprandial visit to the bar, we went out to our car. The windows had been left open; this was still the off season, with very few cars parked beside the café, and no such fripperies as parking-lot attendants and the like.

Lobo was seated in the car. He had no license, but he was in the driver's seat.

I shoved him over between us. "Let's take him home for a visit. Might be fun."

"Now, don't you start that," said Irene.

"Oh, what's the harm? He can visit us for a couple of days, and then we'll bring him back and dump him down here the next time we come. He'd much rather be *here* than *there.* Anyone knows that."

Anyone didn't know that. We dumped him in due course a few nights later. I was rather sick of having him under foot all the time, and I was busy working on *Andersonville,* and I didn't see how Lobo could help me very much. Accordingly we came back for a Sunday evening snack; once we had seen him retreat toward the patio to join dancers and diners there, we tiptoed quietly to the car and drove away.

All he did was to go up to the big coastal highway, the main artery which bisects the hillside area between El Remo and the Montemar Hotel. He lay beside the road for two days and two nights. The *Guardia Civil* told me so later, for they saw him and wondered about it.

We started to drive in to Málaga. Our car stood out more or less in that land of few automobiles, most of them of darker hue. We were driving a sedan with a cream-colored body and rust-colored top; it could be spotted far away.

As we whirred past the intersection I saw a shape beside the road.

"Is that Lobo back there?"

Irene turned for a look through the rear window. "It is indeed Lobo back there. He is coming at exactly ninety miles per hour."

There were some trucks around, there was a flock of sheep to be circled. I didn't want to see Lobo mashed before our very eyes, so hastily I pulled over to the side of the road and slowed down. He overtook the car like Mr. John Landy passing somebody in a wheel chair. He took off in a running dive when he was about fifteen feet away. Fortunately the window by the driver's seat was open, because that was his target.

When a fifty-pound plummet of solid dog lands smack on your stomach and chest, you know that you have been hit.

He said to us, "I couldn't imagine where you'd gone! You weren't down at El Remo; but I decided that you'd be driving along the highway one of these times, so I just waited there. Thanks a lot for stopping."

We went groaning to Málaga, where I left Lobo incarcerated in the car under the watchful eyes of the little crippled public-parking-attendant, and found a store where I could buy a collar and a leash. I bought Lobo a fine red collar. He had never worn a collar; I thought the red would be gay. No, he had never worn a collar in his life, nor had he been on leash either, as far as we knew; but delicately he trod the crowded sidewalks, overseeing our shopping, as if he had a half-dozen diplomas from obedience schools. There was nothing to do now but to take him back to La Verdad, where he'd remain in residence until our departure.

During an interlude he visited the local veterinarian in Torremolinos, whose quarters and talents were more suited to the drenching of oxen than the conducting of a boarding kennel. We had promised to move over to Mallorca for some sixteen days, homework and all, and we just couldn't see lugging Lobo to Madrid and thence by air to the Balearic Islands.

"He'll be perfectly all right up there at that so-called vet's," I assured Irene and my conscience. "Anyway, I know he needs to be wormed, and he ought to have a rabies shot, and he should have a good scrubbing, because probably he's never had a good scrubbing. I know that he plunges into the sea now and then; but that's not like soap and elbow grease."

I left Lobo in the car outside the vet's, while I went in to explain. . . .

A poor dog, I said. . . . A beggar dog who has adopted us temporarily. . . . I would like to leave him for a while, until our return. He needs to be wormed, bathed, etc. . . .

El veterinario listened sympathetically and suggested that I bring the dog inside. We appeared, at opposite ends of the leash. The vet's eyes widened with delight.

"Why, mercy sakes," he said, or the Andalucian equivalent thereof. "I thought you said this was a *poor* dog–an unknown! Why, this is *El Lobo!*"

. . . Our friend brooded a good deal while we were gone, according to later report. The vet said that he was *muy desconsolado*. Lobo awarded us a flattering reception on our return.

. . . We found that he was given to mysterious illnesses. He had a couple of them that summer–times when he would lie in a chair or on the floor and not move of his own volition for several days; and he would not eat a bite, and would drink nothing. Once I took him up to the vet's for examination; after his temperature was taken and found to be normal, the vet only shook his head and gave Lobo a *laxante*. The animal perked out of it in a couple of days, and went bounding about the cliffs again.

During this season Lobo began to realize that he was become a man of substance. His disposition underwent a slight if corrosive change. For the first time he growled at the Civil Guard.

In Spain, quite sensibly, many of the guards dwell in family barracks, complete with wives and children. One of these establishments was on a hilltop directly across the road from our place at La Verdad. Hence it was customary for the guards, who at a later hour would have to report for duty at the central office in Torremolinos, to take up stations outside our gateway, and there await the American who might drive toward the village on morning errands. Sometimes there was one man, sometimes two or three, all very handsome in neat green uniforms, with Tommy guns slung amiably over their shoulders and black hats shining. It was Standing Operating Procedure for them to wait there, and Standing Operating Procedure for me to stop, ask if they should like a lift, and fling open the door. The first time I did this, Lobo nearly flung himself out of it. He had decided that the car was his, and he saw no reason why the *policía* should take over. I counseled him severely and he remained quiet, but with ears up. A rumbling growl moved in the caverns of his body as the trim military figures climbed into the rear seat.

"Why, here is *El Lobo,*" they said. "Lobo, how are you today?"

Grrrrr.

They forgave him the slight without resentment; probably they thought it was quite natural. One guard said, "Lobo is now very rich."

I told him firmly, "Lobo is not rich. He is the same dog he always was."

"Ah, yes. But, *Señor,* he is rich by comparison. You see, Lobo had nothing before; now he has a beautiful home, and of course a handsome large American car. Yes," he said contentedly, "Lobo is rich. *Es verdad.*"

Grrrrr, said Lobo.

Also in this same month romance lifted her pretty head. Romance appeared for shy and tentative calls, which increased to daily frequency as the summer season–and the lady's own season–advanced. We didn't know her name, we called her Perrita; she belonged to some one of the guards across the way. She was yaller-dog as to color, and owned somewhat the proportions of a mule deer, and stood nearly as tall as one. The net result of this disparity in stature was complete frustration on the part of Lobo, no matter how willing he was to achieve wedded bliss. Finally Perrita gave up in disgust and married a taller dog down the road. . . . Sometimes I've seen the same thing happen in the human species: generally speaking, it seems unwise for shorter men to fall in love with much taller women.

We began to hear rumors. "Is it true? Are you taking Lobo back to the United States when you return?"

"Nothing could be further from the truth."

"You should take him. He loves to be with you."

We felt that it would take more than a merely expressed preference on Lobo's part to compel us to submit to such an ordeal. An ordeal also would it be for him. We planned not to proceed directly to the United States, but to drive to Madrid, thence through the Pyrenees into France, all the way up through France; and we would leave the car at a seaport while we went–by boat, air, and train–to look after some business in England, Denmark, Germany.

"You think that would be a kindness to the dog?" I demanded witheringly of these self-appointed advisors. "Why, the poor thing would have to be shut up in a kennel, week after week."

. . . I had made a few tentative queries, and had even secretly consulted a book of rules and regulations at the consulate in Málaga. . . . Not much trick about getting him into the United States, in case we really wanted to do so. All he had to have was a rabies certificate, and a deposition of good health, signed by a doctor shortly before embarkation. Then, if he stood up under scrutiny of the Public Health Officer in New York (and didn't take a piece out of him) he could be admitted at once. It was entirely discretionary with the officer.

But in the meantime–

France he could get into: no trouble about that. In England, dogs must be quarantined for six months. No exceptions; not if you are Prince Philip himself.

"Just think of Lobo, accustomed to all this freedom, bounding about the stone staircases and cliffs, scampering along the shore, jumping like an ibex from rock to rock. Think of his languishing in a French kennel! It's too hideous to contemplate. We certainly shall *not* take Lobo. He is very happy at El Remo; he has his friends; he has plenty to eat." Etc., etc.

Men and women propose, Lobos dispose.

Community opinion seemed to be about equally divided. Some people asserted staunchly that we were right–imprisonment would be a cruelty of the worst kind. Others said, wasn't it terrible for those Kantors to go away and abandon their dog?

Our dog, indeed. I scowled at Lobo and felt almost that he needed to be abandoned. "Far as that is concerned," I said with sternness one late summer's evening, "shouldn't tonight be the night?" We had just returned from a dinner party, and Irene was yawning.

I said, "I thought I'd go by El Remo, have a drink or two, and say goodbye to the staff. We've got dates every night until we leave, so we shan't be going back there for dinner. This is as good a night as any other to leave Lobo. Pack your bags, Lobo." Which feat Lobo performed by bounding into the car again and sitting up expectantly.

Irene reached in, put her arms around him, hugged and petted him, and then went quickly down the steps toward our house, going rapidly because she wanted neither Lobo nor me to see her cry.

During the few minutes it took us to drive along the highway I expatiated on the comforts and glories of that café which was in fact Lobo's hostelry. . . . The season was in full swing, the parking lot was filled with little cars, attendants darted here and there with flashlights. There was a uniformed boy outside the door, another cheerful greeter inside. The joint was certainly jumping.

Lobo made his usual recognition grunts. These were a series of piglike sounds which he had originated. They meant, "Oh yes, we're back *here*. I know this place. Yes, yes. Well, well." I used to ask him whether he thought he was dog or pig; but he would only give a lopsided glance and keep on grunting.

Lobo set a course for the patio where people were still dining, and I found the Marqués de Nájera at the bar. I told him of my plan. On this very night I would abandon Lobo; or, not liking the word *abandon* under the circumstances, I should say that I would *return* Lobo to his own domicile.

"Yes, yes, I quite agree with you," said the host. "A very good idea. He might cry around for a day or two after you depart, but he will be much happier here than in a kennel."

Angel is not a drinking man, but I believe he recognized desperation in my attitude. We lingered for a time at the bar. The marques's pink face shone even pinker under his neatly clipped gray locks, he stabbed the air with his finger for emphasis. I tried to convince the marques, the marques tried to convince me, I tried to convince myself, that this thing was right. Best make a clean break. Deeds, not words, were needed to affirm and underline the process of getting rid of Lobo.

Cristóbal came by. His unoccupied moments are few, but I managed to grab him during one of them. I took him aside and folded into his palm–not exactly a king's ransom in *pesetas,* but at least a duke's.

"Lobo must lack for nothing this winter."

"Don MacKinlay," said Cristóbal, "Lobo has never lacked for anything."

"Nevertheless, he might get sick and need to go to the doctor. He might– Oh well, you will take good care of him, won't you?"

"We do not take care of Lobo," said Cristóbal with dignity. "Lobo takes care of us."

I peered out on the pretty little lawn below the orchestra's platform. All the regular Saturday night celebrants were gathered, and as usual there were newcomers and transients. I saw familiar faces, familiar bald heads or patent leather ones. I saw María Luisa, her dark eyes flashing as she danced; I saw the lawyer from Málaga, the motion-picture director from Barcelona.

Also I saw a black tail with a white tip, a tail shaped like a sickle, moving casually among farther tables. I turned away.

The marques had to join people at dinner. We shook hands, embraced, parted. Cristóbal and I shook hands, embraced, parted. Antonio the musician took a break and came to the bar. We shook hands, embraced, parted.

Well, I thought, you won't get anywhere this way. Come on, get moving. . . .

Quietly I went toward the outer door which opened upon a graveled driveway in the opposite direction from the patio. The inner doorman sprang forward. There was a frown between his brows.

"Señor, where is Lobo?"

"Lobo," I said, "is among the tables in the patio, and there he will remain. Shhhh."

Shhhh, repeated the inner doorman.

I descended the steps. The outer doorman, or doorboy (*Botones,* we call him there, since he wears many buttons on his uniform) came up, also frowning.

"But, *Señor,* have you not forgotten *El Lobo?*"

"I have not forgotten *El Lobo,*" I said. "I can never forget him. Shhhh."

Shhhh, said *Botones.*

I went around through the dark driveway, past innumerable little cars. The parking-lot attendant came up through the gloom, his light flashed.

"Ah, *Señor!* But where is the dog?"

"Shhhh," I said. "The dog is among the dancers and tables of food on the patio. Shhhh."

Shhhh, said the parking-lot attendant.

We moved upon my car through darkness. Now, with so many strangers about, so many transients at this height of season, it behooved anyone to keep his car locked.

The attendant flashed his light . . . *and who should be waiting there?* A beautiful line from Alfred Noyes. I remember that Noyes said it was Bess, the landlord's daughter, plaiting a dark red love-knot into her long black hair. . . . Who should be waiting there, indeed?

He had black hair but he was plaiting no love-knot into it. He stood, red collar ashine, amber eyes gleaming, tail swaying with assurance.

I unlocked the door and he swarmed into the interior. *"Hombre,"* I said huskily, "let's go to America."

We were overly optimistic in assuming that because Lobo had been informed verbally of his projected adventure, he would shrug off promptly all allergy to suitcases, traveling bags, and the like. In fact he never did lose the allergy. Any object which looked as if it might contain clothing or possessions packed for a journey meant just one thing to Lobo: it meant that people were going to go away and leave him. The fear was too deeply rooted, it had flourished too long, it could not be changed. Sometimes I even caught him regarding my briefcase with gravest suspicion.

. . . Felipe carried the last of our bags up the forty-nine steps to where I was struggling to force all our European-Continental possessions into and upon the top of one sedan. It was more or less like the clowns in Ringlings' circus—those several dozen figures who rushed cheering out of one small coupe after it was driven into the ring; except in this case I was trying to get clowns into the car, not take them out.

. . . Irene peered into the depths of the closet where Lobo had been monkishly entombed for the past forty-eight hours.

"Come along, Lobo."

Naturally we always addressed him in Spanish.

"You will accompany us in the car."

The creature bounced into a sitting position and regarded her, eyes rolling, jaws agape. She started to repeat the reassurance, when he gave a dive past her, nearly upsetting her; he plunged through the patio and soared up the several flights of stairs. He emerged from the pink-geranium-smothered hill (again a circus comparison: he reminded me of that character who used to be shot out of a cannon). In mid-trajectory, however, he halted, then flopped to the ground. He had seen all those suitcases. This must mean the end after all. It was not until Irene herself had labored up the steps, opened the car door, and pointed, that he really knew. Jet-propelled by the inexhaustible fuel of his desire, he annihilated gravity and space, and lay gasping atop the highest piled wardrobe container in the rear seat. There was just room for him between the roof and the layers of baggage.

Felipe and Anita came to say their *adiós* but Lobo heeded not. As we drove through the gate and down the highway, I could see him in the mirror. His was also a rear vision, his face turned toward the back window, his ears sagging, as in coma he regarded the Andalucian home existence which he was leaving. He did not even growl at the *Guardia Civil* when they gave us a rifle salute in farewell.

Like all sisters of her sex, Irene had been tempted into a wonderful bargain which in this case consisted of a pair of green shoes, burnished with nailheads, which a local cobbler was going to fashion for her at a price so ridiculously small that she would have insulted her femininity had she not yielded to the temptation. (The fact that she was never able to wear the shoes after she got them is beside the point.) Delivery had been promised for lo these many weeks. She reminded the cobbler forcefully that we were to depart on this day, and that the shoes must be ready: she herself would stop to pick them up.

Thus we drove into Torremolinos for a repeat farewell, since already we had done our duty by grocer, butcher, druggist, and the rest. We parked in a narrow street which, though crowded and dirty, is dignified by the name of Generalissimo Franco, when someone spied Lobo.

"You are about to depart," we were told shrilly. "But look–do you not see? Lobo is in the car."

"Yes, we know."

"But–Lobo?" The voices rose higher. "Do you mean to say–? Is it true? *Madre de Dios!* Is Lobo to accompany you?"

"It is true."

Yells arose on every side. People began to flock from the stores. "María! Pepe! Antonio! Matilde! Observe! Lobo! In the car! Lobo is to travel in the *coche!* Lobo is going to other nations! . . . Is it true, *Señor?* Is Lobo to go to North America?"

"It is true."

Children pressed in the first rank, adults squeezed behind them, mules came to observe. Not a one of them drew as much as the courtesy of a direct glance from Lobo, who lay collapsed, brassy eyes brooding.

"Enrique! Pablo! Bepa! Lobo–in the car! He goes to many countries! He goes to *los Estados Unidos!*"

. . . We were halfway to Jaén before Lobo emerged from his state of shock sufficiently to threaten two herdsmen who shambled past in the dusk when we were having Sevenses.

Now ensued an interesting series of events both for ourselves, for the black-and-tan beast who ordered our lives, and for sundry hotelkeepers, bartenders, waiters, chambermaids. By custom or legality there was nothing wrong in Lobo's sharing our intimacy. Of course everyone knows that Spain is a backward nation. To my notion the nation is nothing like so backward as those States of our Country which prohibit the appearance of dogs in public restaurants. I should much prefer to enjoy my meal with certain dogs under table than with certain people sitting across from me. But little matter now. . . . No eyebrows were raised at Lobo in any café or hostelry throughout Spain or France. (Not until we reached Le Havre, where it seems they are somewhat satiated with American tourists who purchase cute poodle puppies in Paris, transport them to Le Havre to await the sailing of their vessels, and in the past have attempted with futility to housebreak their newly acquired pets upon the best carpeting. I think the refusal of the Le Havre hotel authorities to admit Lobo was rather solidly founded.)

The leash had become an essential in Lobo's traveling equipment, since to his mind all tables were meant to be begged at, and all kitchens to be explored. He accepted his restraint philosophically; and since we were more or less fed up with Spanish cookery (and longed for nothing so much as homemade Spanish rice according to an Iowa recipe, and not at all like the Spanish rice of Spain), Lobo was deeded larger portions of our own fare than had previously come his way.

I shall never forget the fabulous evening in Roquefort, where we deviated from main routes and traveled on back roads, drawn by the mysterious scent of cheese caverns. A certain restaurant there is heavily starred in the guide books. In this place we sat down for the evening meal. Baked Roquefort cheese in light piecrust–I forgot what they call it–was out of this world; and so the steak would have been, the first decent-looking steak I'd seen in many a month. In Andalucía steaks are carved from the very bravest of bulls by means of electric saws and diamond drills.

However, I have neglected to state that I am just as allergic to grilled garlic as was Lobo to steamer trunks. It was my own fault I had not told the waiter. I should have known that they would saturate my sirloin with minute insertions of garlic, drench it with a marinade of garlic, serve it in a garlic sauce. Muttering curses at my own stupidity, I set to work to carve the steak for you-guess-whom.

He was under the table, and put his head up between my knees with the scarf of cloth concealing his eyes and draping his brown mask like a nun's cowl. Promptly at intervals a pink cavern opened, a chunk of beef was dropped in; then, at the stated interval, the pink cavern reopened. It was one of the most interesting disappearing acts I ever saw. That steak was at least three inches thick, and proportionately wide. . . . Lobo seemed fretful when we took him for his evening walk. I think he thought he had had his *canapé* but when did the dinner begin?

His compulsion in the direction of food was something like that endured by Mr. Burl Ives. Mr. Ives spent a lean infancy and childhood amid fellow sharecroppers in southern Illinois, where the butter was spread very thinly–when indeed there was any butter to spread–and where sometimes even the bread was cut much too thinly. In his modern existence as an internationally admired minstrel and actor, Mr. Ives tries vigorously to compensate for the fact that forty years ago there were not enough beans in the pot, and sometimes no bacon at all.

When you are dwelling with Burl, often you are awakened in the middle of the night by a slow thunderous tread in the hall, a squeak and opening and closing of the front door, which is repeated in reverse process some time later. Then comes the rustle of innumerable midnight delicatessen paper bags in the kitchen. In the morning when you go out you find empty cartons with the marks of potato salad and pickled herring still apparent–sausage rinds, seeds, peelings, empty cream containers, soggy receptacles in which various pasties and Boston cream pies have previously been housed. It looks rather as if Henry the Eighth has been entertaining the Yeomen of the Guard in one small kitchen. A few walls away, some three hundred and thirty-three pounds of Ives lie in deep and contented repose.

Lobo also may have had nagging recollection of the sharp-ribbed puppy which was himself, trailing down harsh hillsides above the Mediterranean, and sniffing drearily into ditches which bore not a single morsel of garbage . . . all before his guardian angels conducted him to El Remo.

Carennac is a picturesque village on the Dordogne River in France.

There we were ensconced for some time in an ancient abbey turned into hotel, where I worked on my novel even harder than ever, where Irene painted, and Lobo lay on our two old B-10 jackets with a wary eye turned toward the antique Gothic doorway–just in case one of the tourists who sometimes visited the flagged courtyard might intrude.

It was at this place that I requested of Lobo a written report for the Society for Psychical Research.

In sunset afterglow, weary from toil, the three of us would prowl among shrubbery and walls behind the old chapel. On the first occasion my eye was caught by a coal-black aperture–some sort of tunnel extending down into a dank and mossy area beneath the structure. I was unaccompanied this first time; I went to the car, got a flashlight, and proceeded to examine the chamber. There was nothing in there except a few garden tools, but somehow a storied sepulchral quality was present.

Later that same evening, chaperoned by my two domestic pets, I essayed further investigation. Irene went in boldly enough; Lobo balked at the entrance. He could not be budged. He spread his muscular legs, his deer's feet might have been set in concrete. No matter how I pulled or tugged or persuaded, he was rigid. The hair was up on his back, his ears were raised, and all he said was, "If you want to get me into that place, you'll have to kill me first." Twice at later date I attempted to meet this challenge, and was vanquished. It was not merely darkness that he feared–he had pranced gaily into far blacker holes than this. He had been with me in caves and cellars of various kinds, but into this particular spot he would not venture.

It piqued my curiosity. I sought out the proprietor and asked him the original nature of that room.

"Well," he said. "It was a– The whole place is quite old, you know."

"But what was that subterranean room you now use to put the garden tools in?"

"Oh, it's very difficult to say, *Monsieur*. You see, during the centuries that have elapsed, the room has undoubtedly been used for various purposes." He wriggled uncomfortably.

"O.K.," I said. "Was it the crypt?"

He ducked his head, nodded, fled away. I did not attempt to escort Lobo into any more crypts.

We worked our way up through central and western France toward the inevitable, if temporary, parting in Le Havre. There, in the hotel originally befouled by poodles, our companion was relegated to a dungeon in the basement for one sorry night. Recognizing belatedly that the air was damp and that the place was too uncomfortable for even a toughened veteran like Lobo, I had a bright idea, and bedded him down in the car itself, parked in front of the hotel.

This to Lobo was the height of luxury and satisfaction. That car represented assurance to him; it represented us, it represented his new life. I saw that in the future it would be unnecessary to remove visible bags against the incursion of car thieves. In wildest flight of fancy I could not envision the bold prowler who might attempt to force one of those doors, when inside there existed an arsenal of gleaming teeth and a snarl which would have frightened *El Cid* himself.

Lobo was so entranced with his new lodgings that he refused to budge each morning, and had to be hauled out bodily. The old jackets were fleecy, security was here, he doted on security. He knew always that we would come to the car again. He had a pan of water on the floor in the front seat; seldom did it seem to be touched. All night long he dreamed his dreams and, I firmly believe, wrote his poems and offered his quiet invocation to the Goddess of Security.

The eve of our sailing for England was arrived, and we felt that we were leaving our friend in good hands. There was a genial veterinarian who, on viewing Lobo, asserted that he was far too fine an animal to languish in one of the small pens adjacent to the doctor's city office. He explained that in cases like this he always took the dogs to his mother's place in the country. With light hearts we accepted this plan. Lobo wagged and danced, not knowing that we would soon disappear.

Our actual leave-taking occurred abruptly and without planning on my part, since the veterinarian-kennel-keeper had told me that he must have Lobo's rabies-shot certificate. I fetched it over to him, with Lobo along, of course; then we were stricken simultaneously with the same idea. It was only a few hours until I should have to bring him anyway—why not leave him now? Accordingly he cavorted off with the kennel-keeper, confident that *entremeses* were about to be served in the rear.

I returned to the hotel and found Irene come back from shopping. She was grieved. "I didn't get to say goodbye to Lobo."

"Oh, Lobo's fine. The last I saw him the doctor had him on a leash—"

Irene considered for a time. "Just give him a couple of days," she said. "Lobo will have the doctor on a leash."

In fact we did not believe that we were leaving him marooned on a linguistic desert island. He had shown a remarkable aptitude for languages. I don't know what all he spoke before we came along. . . . Andaluz was his native tongue. I am sure that he spoke considerable Castilian and perhaps Catalonian, gained from other contacts on the beach. He could not have dwelt long in the polyglot Montemar-El Remo surroundings without at least a smattering of German, Dutch, and French, with a few Scandinavian words thrown in. I think also that he knew some Arabic; he looked as if he did.

Already he had given us a striking demonstration of his ability to absorb English. The month before, in Pau, we endured a rainy afternoon during which all Irene wanted to do was put a new canvas on a stretcher-frame, and all Lobo wanted to do was sleep. We were domiciled in a remodeled chateau on the edge of town, and garages were not far off.

"I think," I called across the living room and into the bedroom where Irene sat on the floor with a mouth full of tacks, "I think that this is a good afternoon for me to take the car down to the garage and have that little matter fixed"—whatever it was—"so I think I'll go now."

I addressed my wife in Midwestern United States, which is our mutual native tongue. Now, mind you, Lobo was sound asleep on the bed; furthermore, neither of us could recall ever having addressed him before in any language except Spanish. In a split second a black-and-tan projectile was fired off the bed and exploded into the target area beside the front door. He stood quivering, bright-eyed, ears up, tail aloft. He said, "Actually I had been intending to sleep the rest of the afternoon, but of course if you're going to the garage—"

We looked at each other helplessly.

"You'd better take him," said Irene. "Perhaps he can help you, when you have trouble with the garage people with your French."

We had not expected to find any other than that which we found on our return after three or four weeks in London, Copenhagen, and West Germany: Lobo was speaking French fluently. We had sent him two or three postcards along the way, and obviously he forgave us for our desertion. ("Why should they send postcards to Lobo?" cried veterinarian and staff. "He cannot read!")

But he could speak French. When the girl assistant brought him out to me at a special rendezvous arranged by telegram from Paris, and which reunion took place within half an hour after our arrival in Le Havre, Lobo was busy in conversation with her. She was talking of the country house, of *Grand'mère,* of the other dogs; and Lobo was joining in, obviously understanding every word she uttered.

We came together. I was assaulted with tongue and claws. I paid my bill and stumbled out. "Let's go right over to the garage," I said, hailing a taxi. "So we can get the car out, and you can have a decent place to sleep tonight."

Like the greater part of Le Havre, the garage area has been rebuilt from scratch since World War II, and this particular garage is a handsome edifice with ramps leading from floor to floor, and room for scores of automobiles on every story.

An old man took us up in an elevator, and we got off at floor Number Five. I unsnapped the leash from Lobo's collar. He raced up and down the aisles of silent parked vehicles.

He found the car quicker than I could have found it–far quicker, I know, than could the old attendant, for he was one of those people who go by card and number. He was still squinting at the ticket and trying to decide in which row the car might be, when Lobo notified us that the car *had* been found, with grunts amplified out of all natural proportion by the peculiar acoustics of the place. I unlocked the door, Lobo flew into the rear seat. The attendant regarded him with something akin to fear, all the way down, as we poked around the short hairpin curves.

Two days later British soil, in the shape of the S.S. *Mauretania,* was treated to its most singular Spanish invasion since the unsuccessful attempt in 1588. . . . Out at sea, I had a little difficulty with the good-looking young assistant-ship's-butcher who was detailed to the care and feeding of canine passengers. I remonstrated about the vast masses of food which were pushed into Lobo's cell.

"But he wants it, sir! He keeps asking for more, he does. I don't know what he does with it all, to be sure. He seems quite hungry. I *did* cut down his rations–"

Even then, there was a certain complication because of Lobo's very strictly conceived toilet habits. The only place allotted to the exercise of dogs was the aft end of the tourist deck; there Lobo and I repaired six or eight times a day. Definitely there was a rule against keeping dogs in one's stateroom–not on the French Line, but on this one. I saw an elderly woman sneaking a suspicious-looking bundle back and forth–something wrapped up in an old raincoat–but even then I didn't protest. A real live Lobo, domiciled in our cabin until we reached New York, would have been just too much.

. . . Trouble was, he had the idea that the deck was a room. It was a room that was not a room. We would go all the way aft, and Lobo would brace himself and stare down at the wake and give grunts as if he recognized the wake of some small vessel in which, many incarnations agone, he had moved through the war-tossed Mediterranean. For several days he simply would not Do Anything. One did not Do Things in rooms, and certainly the deck was a room, because it had a floor. It was a great relief to me when outraged Nature finally threw up her hands, and the deck needed special treatment. Undoubtedly it was a great relief to Lobo as well.

The chief difficulty which I encountered on the voyage was clerical.

Not long before we reached New York, I received a message from the old baggagemaster, who insisted that I must come to see him about my dog. Baggagemasters take care of the business of booking dogs aboard steamships. Mr. MacWilliams was a Scotsman with well-established ideas of protocol when it comes to filling out papers.

"I am sorry, sir," he said. "Your papers on your dog are no complete."

"But what's wrong?" We spread the papers out. "Look here, you've got everything: you've got my home address, date of shipment, certificate of good health signed by the French veterinarian within ten days of embarkation. You've got the rabies certificate, you've got–"

His finger indicated one blank square. "You have no put down the *breed* of the dog. Now, will you please to give me the *breed* of the dog?"

I said, "That would be very interesting."

He regarded me disapprovingly through his spectacles. "I can no put *that* down on the paper."

I took a deep breath. Irene and I had discussed Lobo's possible lineage; we knew that he came from the Montemar region, and also that he was prone to worry. "Very well," I said. "If the truth must be known, he is a Montemar Worrier."

The baggagemaster gripped his pencil. "How do you spell it?" Letter by letter, I spelled it out. There is no doubt that Lobo was the first Montemar Worrier–and probably the last–ever to be admitted to the United States.

I was apprehensive about New York. What would happen? Would officials come aboard, would they attempt to take specimens of Lobo's blood? I shuddered to think of what might occur if this came about. Would they pull his eyelids apart? Would they stick things down his throat, and up–elsewhere? I wished that I had some compendium of law through which I might search to gain an idea of exactly what penalty befell the avowed owner of a dog who undertook to carry out a one-dog *pogrom* among Public Health officials.

"But what do I do?" I asked, on that last morning. "Do I wait in the lounge for the officials? Does Lobo ride off on a pile of freight, or does he walk off with me, or what?"

"Just take him along with you," said Mr. MacWilliams. "If yon official wants to see you, he'll find you with no trouble on the quay." Thus Lobo marched on clicking toenails down the gangplank and became an immigrant.

As for the Public Health officials, we saw not hide nor hair of them. The customs officer studied the item on our declaration: *One Lobo. Acquired through self-adoption in Spain. Weight: fifty pounds. Color:*

black-tan-and-white. Intrinsic value: uncertain, and then tried to strike up a conversation with Lobo in Gaelic. . . . I still have the papers. Maybe he was never officially admitted after all.

It wasn't until I walked Lobo through the streets of New York that I began to realize how like a carefully bred dog he did look. He was all of a pattern, he didn't look like a mongrel. His doe-colored stockings were all of the same size, his tan mask well-balanced; there was the set and feeling of a breed about him. No mere ascribing of possible parentage through the process of free love among German shepherds, Dobermans, and hounds seemed to suffice. It wasn't until quite a time afterward, when—Lobo-less—Irene and I ventured on back roads of the Basque country, that we came to know what he was in fact, although it had been suggested a time or two.

He was a Basque shepherd. If we saw one we saw forty Lobos in the Basque country. We saw two or three that could have been his littermates; but I fear that I shall never own another Basque shepherd. . . .

How Lobo's father ever found his way down the long rugged Iberian Peninsula to Mediterranean shores, I leave to be decided by the canine archaeologists, ethnologists, genealogists, and historians who should deal with this fascinating subject in the future. As it was, in New York people kept coming up to me on the street and wanting to know what kind of dog that was. I always said that he was a Montemar Worrier, which satisfied in every case. One old lady informed me that indeed that's what he was—a Montemar Worrier—she remembered now; her sister used to have one of those.

Lobo and I left Irene surrounded by doting grandchildren in Westchester, and sought Florida quickly. Again we had the ton of baggage to be transported; but this time Lobo could share the front seat with me; although now, on alien shores, he had a propensity for putting his head in my lap. This I regarded as a safety hazard. We had a few words and cuffs on the subject; after that he behaved properly—thrusting his head out of the right window, and observing critically the Howard Johnson edifices along the Jersey Turnpike.

In Maryland an interesting experience befell when—perforce, of necessity, as is the habit of motorists—I decided suddenly to stop by the wayside and take a stroll into a thicketed area. Lobo tumbled out along with me, and went around through the woodland like a runaway jeep, except that he made more noise about it. I discovered that his grunts were not all recognition grunts (or maybe they were: this reincarnation idea, you see, although he had never heard of Bridey Murphy). They were also inquisitive grunts.

"Goodness sake, what is this—what are all these trees? What are all these bushes? What are all these smells? Ah-ha, above all, the smells! Well, what is this, anyway?"

The idea struck me full force. It is a strange experience to proceed into the mild forests of Maryland, with a dog of obvious maturity, and realize that the dog has never been in *woods* before.

There are no woods in the locality from which Lobo sprang. There are a few trees bordering gardens, a very few bordering the roads; there are olive groves, and some tiny groves of poplars grown as a crop. Nothing more. The rest is rocks, wasteland, low tough herbage. No thickets, no bushes, no wild brakes.

There was something touching about all this . . . I wondered how he would go plunging through the bit of Florida jungle which has not been Yankeeized, and which we own. (He went plunging, all right. He came home twice without his collar.)

Few bridegrooms ever lugged their brides across fabled thresholds with more excitement than that with which I escorted Lobo to our beach, once we were safe on Siesta Key. His hard racing feet tore the white packed sand. . . . Birds, birds! He was after them full pelt. Of course I knew that he could never catch one; but he did not know that, and never learned the fact. Water would smash as he struck it, the birds would go squawking. . . .

Coconuts were more vulnerable to his attack. A green coconut, shell and all, washed up on the beach, is a heavisome thing, God wot. To me they weighed just as much as so many atomic bombs, but to Lobo they were peanuts. How he got his jaws around them I'll never know, but he did. Not only did he get his jaws around them, but he would bear them off at full gallop. I have seen him do this with coconuts which weighed roughly a quarter of Lobo's own weight. If you are a man of ordinary size, try clamping a forty-pound burden in your jaws, and dashing off with it.

Lobo had several private coconut hoards: one under pines on the beach, a couple among palms out in the yard. These treasured toys were doled out to him in frolicksome moments. But unfortunately coconuts were not the only objects against which he now directed his threat.

The old parable of rags to riches had come true again. In Spain a penniless beggar, Lobo was tolerant as to disposition. He drew no property lines around El Remo or the Montemar. Let who would come and go, was his philosophy.

Not so after he had acquired a seaside home in Florida, with a couple of cars thrown in. He was more avaricious than Hetty Green, more savage than Simon Girty, less charitable than Ebenezer Scrooge.

"Good grief!" he would roar at the top of his lungs, dashing through the gallery and across the living room and out to the porch, slashing the rugs as he came. "Look out there on the beach! There's an old man walking on *my beach*. I can't *stand* this. He needs to be torn limb from limb! Please open the door and let me out! I want to go down there and *assassinate* him–"

I thought of the smug but discerning Civil Guard, far back in the Province of Málaga, who observed, "Lobo is very rich now." In vain did I explain, cajole, and set examples of hospitality and benevolence. He was far gone into a most predatory sort of snobbery. If people didn't belong on his property, they didn't belong on it. That went for practically all humans.

As for dogs, he would pay ardent court to those females who were in a courting mood; would calmly ignore other females or the especial type of spinsters with which the canine world is so frequently blessed. But–a *male* dog–I was kept busy snatching at Lobo's collar, and explaining to the world that he was not truly vicious–he was just savage, and had an exaggerated sense of property rights and controls.

Our two small grandsons came with their parents to spend the Christmas holidays, and we watched Lobo narrowly. I heard him growl just once. He had an ear infection and Mike, the elder, pulled his sore ear. I explained to Mike, and he did not do this again. On the other hand, I came in one day to find the smaller boy in his play pen with Lobo lying just outside the wooden bars. Tommy had fastened his grubby mitts on Lobo's muzzle, and was kneading flesh and nostrils energetically. Lobo was not uttering a sound, nor was he trying to move away; he was just taking it from the baby. We breathed more easily after that.

As if to compensate for whatever inconvenience his highhanded defense of the home caused us, Lobo now offered assistance of an acceptable kind. Heart and soul he became dedicated to helping me in my work.

In Spain he had paid but little heed: I went out each day in the car with my portable typewriter installed on a folding chair which served as table. I took a basket of lunch, bottle of wine, my briefcase and whatever reference books had been selected for the day's activity. That was all right with Lobo; most of the time he was content to remain at home, lying on cool tiles, leisurely inspecting Irene's painting as it progressed.

But *Andersonville* had grown from an originally promised one-hundred-and-fifty-thousand-word novel into a novel of a projected three-hundred-and-fifty-thousand words. . . . There are such things as deadlines in the publishing business; mechanical details of manufacturing have to be set up in advance; thus they were starting to put the book into type long before I had finished it. Uneasy lies the head of an author under such circumstances. . . .

I dared not let a day pass without a substantial amount accomplished, and sometimes I was very near the breaking point. Friends and relatives urged me to slow down, take a trip, go away somewhere—but I knew I'd be working every day I was gone, so what could be gained in going?

I began to find Lobo in the car each morning when I went to the garage. He sensed that I needed help and was willing to offer such as he could give. The house was unendurable as a workplace most of the time, even with the telephones shut off, because of people who came to the door, and my vulnerability to such interruptions. I had to drive afield, usually into the Myakka wilderness east of Sarasota, or to a lonely spot down the Tamiami Trail where I could not be reached or interfered with.

I took to fetching along Lobo's lunch as well as my own. He never interfered with my typing; I left the rear door open when parked in the shade, and Lobo could hop in and out as the spirit moved him. There was only one difficulty: forever he was coming back hobbling from the effects of sandspurs. I would have to extract myself from behind the typewriter and succor the needy—always rewarded by a slobbery tongue well applied.

He did feel that we should sleep together when we took our naps. It was disconcerting to be aroused from stupor by the crushing blow of his compact body as he flung himself over the seat on top of me.

There came a day when I thought I could work no more. My head ached, my eyes hurt, my finger tips were filmy. I had been at it daily, without exception, for over fifteen months. *You can't finish,* evil voices were crying. *You can't. You can't. Don't try. It's too much. It's too big. It's too long. It's too tiring. You can't do it. You're no stronger than anyone else. Flesh and brain can endure only so much. Emotions break, and discipline vanishes, and you're tired, tired, tired.*

I managed to back the car out of the garage, but couldn't turn it away toward the driveway from the live-oak shade. Lobo was in the rear seat. Over on the right-hand side of the front seat, the typewriter waited on its stand—grimly, implacably, presenting that threatening countenance which typewriters have forever turned toward exhausted writers. I put my head back on the seat and was close to tears.

Then there came a heavy breathing in my ear. A nose was thrust close.

"Lobo, what shall I do?" My own voice sounded far away and flogged. "I can't go on. What shall I do—quit? Quit for a while, try later, put the book off? What shall I do?"

With a single bound he was over the ridge. He was in the front seat, sitting bolt upright behind the typewriter, staring ahead. Then he swung his head to the left, grinned, rolled his eyes.

"You mean," I faltered, "that I've got to go to work anyway? That I've got to go out in the car and at least try to do *something?*"

He bent down, put his head on the seat, pushed with his hind legs, stood on his head, and smashed over across my lap.

"O.K.," I groaned. Away we drove. I wrote twenty-seven hundred words in the next two hours or so. They were pretty good words—or so at least some of the critics thought who quoted them later.

. . . The Pulitzer Prize seemed a long way off in those days; so did the films, so did the critical response, so did the fortune which would be earned for booksellers, publishers, the Federal Government, the book clubs, editors, agents, and even myself. But Lobo knew. Assuredly he knew.

It was pretty tough on Irene, managing him when I was away. I had to go back to the Andersonville region several times; there was a research trip to Mississippi, and so on. During each of these periods Lobo appointed himself High Sheriff of Siesta Key, and lay most of the time either at Irene's feet or upon her bed. The mildest step of dry cleaner, spring-water man, or mere casual caller was sufficient to bring him into a defensive attitude similar to that of the Iberian women who tore out their hair to braid it for bowstrings. Not the most thorny commando in the world could have entered the house without first riddling Lobo with his burp gun.

Once Irene had flu while I was gone, and our friend and family doctor, Tom Garrett, came to attend her. Tom went out of that bedroom faster than he came in. This was not even reasonable, because Lobo knew Tom, and tolerated him socially. But I was gone, and he was *pro tem* guardian of bed, board, and belfry.

There was nothing sensible in his attitude, and I am not apologizing for him. In short, he was a damn nuisance about this sort of thing. No dog should behave in such wise. But I had come to the terrifying opinion that Lobo was not actually a dog.

I asked him about it one day, when we were coming home from work.

"Is it true," I inquired in my most carefully constructed Spanish, which I fear isn't very carefully constructed, but was always understandable to Lobo, "is it true that you are not in fact a dog, but are actually a king of the Moors?"

He had the answer to that one too. He stood on his head, to show me that he was a veritable emperor of the Moors.

He had spent all his years, uncertain though they were as to number, in trying to find a home of his own and people of his own. He had found them, and now nothing in the world must interfere with his possession of them.

. . . Did he ever dream of the whitewashed farmhouses, the noisy village street, the mules, the creaking carts, the green-uniformed constabulary he had left thousands of miles behind? An echo was there one night for him to hear; he heard it and responded.

We were sitting in the living room with friends, and Lobo was flat on his back, sound asleep on our bed at the other end of the house, all four paws dangling in the air. I knew this because I had seen him so a few minutes before. . . . People were asking about the Holy Week processions current throughout Spain, and we were trying to give a description —trying to make them see the images with their jewels, the flare of ten thousand candles, the robed figures walking, the drums and bugles and weird Moorish pipes coming on ahead.

"Why," I said, "I have an album, a recording made over there. The Girl With the Combs—a fat gypsy woman who is one of the finest *saeta* singers in Spain. It sounds like the real stuff. Let me play it for you—"

I put on the record. First there came the throb and shuffle of feet. You could imagine the heavy *paso* being lifted onto thirty or forty shoulders, the striving bodies, the ragged cord-soled sandals scraping uneven pavement stones. You could hear bugles beginning to talk, the pound of drums as slatternly fifteen-year-old musicians in their baggy khaki uniforms rolled and marched. *La niña* started in with her chant. Her voice swept on high, the traditional arrow of song above the sound of marchers, the military hullabaloo, the religious illusion.

Then another sound intermingled with this, and it did not come from the Hi-Fi. It was a series of grunts, approaching steadily up the long hall which led from our bedrooms. *Unh, unh, unh, unh, unh?* Here he came, recognition sounds floating ahead.

Unh, unh, unh, unh?

He was in the middle of the living room, ears lifted, body tensed, face turned toward the corner where the instrument lived. The gypsy's voice soared on; she wailed about the agony of Our Dear Lord; bugles blatted, drums throbbed.

Unh, unh, unh, unh? He was gone into the corner to stand close to the amplifier, and he was still sniffing, but his nose told him nothing, *nada*.

He was not home, he was not back in Spain. Oh, yes, this was home, but . . . there was a memory, he had heard sounds . . . where did they come from? Because there was no actuality here. No smell. Only the sounds which he had learned in puppyhood. . . . Finally he collapsed, flopped on the floor, went to sleep, paid no more heed.

Once I knew and loved a man who was a notorious tightwad. He was often inconsiderate of others—he was not even very good in his profession, nor very dependable, although he managed to make quite a lot of money. He did not ever do little thoughtful things for other people, he seldom repaid favors to friends, he did not always sacrifice himself too sublimely on community projects. Yet when he died the whole town wept. Everybody adored him, no one knew quite why. Everyone missed him; they miss him still.

Thus it was with Lobo. He was a gourmand; he set a high record for selfishness; he was far too savage for comfort; he was always wanting to go in and out of doors just because he wanted to go in and out of doors. He was a thief: he stole a roast in New York, a steak in Sarasota, two pounds of ground beef at La Verdad. He lay on beds, he begged at table, he left a cloud of shed hairs wherever he moved—cars and furniture were coated with them. (Months after he left us, I was still picking black white-tipped hairs off the ceiling of one automobile—and how they ever got there is more than I know. I suppose it was when he stood on his head and waved his tail in the air.)

Lobo gave no alarms of fire. So far as I know he never saved a child from drowning, or a traveler from freezing to death in the snow. He bit inoffensive Other Dogs. He lay right in the middle of all the main avenues, and you were forever falling over him.

By ordinary standards of polite conduct, Lobo was a mess. Yet the majesty and mystery which he exuded reached far. People were mad for him, even the ones he growled at.

Friends would call up with informal invitations to dinner, and were always careful to state that Lobo was especially included. Once established in the kitchen—say, at Ed Beattie's—he got in the maid's way every minute, and Mardelle loved it.

. . . He went along with me to Newtown areas where most of the Sarasota servants live, to help take the laundry to Hattie May. Immediately soft dusky voices would speak lovingly from neighboring porches. "Why, there's Lobo. Hello, Lobo. Don't you remember me, Lobo?" His ears would sprout, nostrils sniff in awareness, his saffron eyes would be polished and sharp.

He knew far too much for his own good and for my own. He knew on that last morning, the eighth of August, when I left him at the vet's in Scarsdale, New York. We were up there temporarily; we had to be in order to attend to the preliminaries of publishing *Andersonville*.

This was just a routine thing: he seemed to need worming attention again, I would leave him to be wormed. But the vet heard a suspicious cough, and asked a few questions, and said he should like to make some tests. The next day we heard the verdict: heartworms–the parasites which dwell in subtropical regions, but now I hear are making their wicked way North.

"It won't be much," the doctor said. "I'll start his series of shots . . . he'll have to be here all of this week, and next week you can bring him in every other day."

. . . He didn't want to be left there. Lobo said, "Please do not leave me. There is something I fear," and he twisted in circles at the end of his leash, and kept thrusting his head between my legs, and quivering. It hurts like to hell to remember that now. . . . They gave him the first shot that evening, and it killed him *pronto.*

Nobody could understand. The doctor got another doctor out of bed in the dead of night. They worked hard, they called the laboratory from which the serum had come. Nothing was wrong with it. They got chemists out of bed and talked to them. But nothing could be done, although they tried to do everything.

The next day there was an autopsy, and we thought of the weird illnesses which had seemed to possess Lobo at La Verdad. Still that wasn't all the answer, and we have never found some of the answer yet.

Other veterinary physicians must have cried in the past; but it so happens that that was the first time I ever saw one do so.

We took Lobo up to the Hartsdale Canine Cemetery and put him into the hillside. There he lies, the eight-thousand-eight-hundred-and-ninety-first pet to sleep there. He has his stone–in Spanish, of course. It says: *Adiós, Amigo.*

The people at the place have been catering to bereaved humans for a long time, and so they know just what to do. They put flowers on his grave in summer and evergreens in winter. There he rests in the clutch of his adopted land–adopted through choice, no one can gainsay that.

So we left him on that tenth of August, and I took Irene home. Then I did what a good many other men would have done: I headed for the nearest bar.

It happened to be Buddy Kennedy's bar on Central Avenue. When Buddy saw my face he knew there was very bad news. Lobo used to go in there with me, and everyone knew him. Buddy is sentimental, like most ex-vaudevillians; we had our tears together.

An amiable Irishwoman was sipping a beer down the bar. She said, "You know, I'd like to tell you something. I dearly loved a mutt one time; he came to my door in the snow, half-starved, and I took him in, and he brought the sunshine into my life. When he died I couldn't take it. Our priest was an old family friend, and I said to the priest, 'But why did my Paddy have to be run over? I loved him so–I wanted him with me always.' And the priest said, 'Daughter, you never really *had* your Paddy dog. You never *owned* him. He was loaned to you by God, as are all good people and beasts. And God needed him somewhere else, perhaps, to help some other people as he helped you. So he took him back.'"

I could barely thank the woman, but the comfort of her little story stayed with me. That is the way I began to think of Lobo then; that is the way I think of him now, and always shall. A strange and endearing form of Spanish Lend-Lease. . . . Paws across the sea, and all that sort of thing.

The Man Who Was **Rudyard Kipling**

In 1890 a remarkable young man of twenty-five named Rudyard Kipling wrote a story which he called "The Man Who Was." There was no special antagonism toward Russia at the time (the Crimean War had been fought more than thirty years before), nor was anyone seriously concerned with the possibility of an eventual conflict between east and west. Both of these future developments were, however, clearly indicated in the story, which was written in the high traditional style that he began to display in the important work still ahead of him–*The Jungle Books, Kim,* and the best of his *Barrack-Room Ballads*.

Somerset Maugham, who does not stir himself easily to praise, says this of Kipling: "He is our greatest story teller. I don't believe he will ever be equalled. I am sure he can never be excelled."

Whenever I have an urge to dip into Kipling, which is often, I am very likely to begin first with "The Man Who Was."

The Man Who Was — Rudyard Kipling

In 1890 a remarkable young man of twenty-five named Rudyard Kipling wrote a story which he called "The Man Who Was." There was no special antagonism toward Russia at the time (the Crimean War had been fought more than thirty years before), nor was anyone seriously concerned with the possibility of an eventual conflict between East and West. Both of these future developments were, however, clearly indicated in the story, which was written in the high traditional style that he began to develop in the important work still ahead of him—*The Jungle Books*, *Kim*, and the best of his *Barrack-Room Ballads*.

Somerset Maugham, who does not give himself easily to praise, says this of Kipling: "He is our greatest story teller. I don't believe he will ever be equalled. I am sure he can never be excelled."

Whenever I have an urge to dip into Kipling, which is often, I am very likely to begin first with "The Man Who Was."

THE MAN WHO WAS

Rudyard Kipling

The Earth gave up her dead that tide,
Into our camp he came,
And said his say, and went his way,
And left our hearts aflame.

Keep tally—on the gun-butt score
The vengeance we must take,
When God shall bring full reckoning,
For our dead comrade's sake.

Ballad.

Let it be clearly understood that the Russian is a delightful person till he tucks in his shirt. As an Oriental he is charming. It is only when he insists upon being treated as the most easterly of western peoples instead of the most westerly of easterns that he becomes a racial anomaly extremely difficult to handle. The host never knows which side of his nature is going to turn up next.

Dirkovitch was a Russian—a Russian of the Russians—who appeared to get his bread by serving the Czar as an officer in a Cossack regiment, and corresponding for a Russian newspaper with a name that was never twice alike. He was a handsome young Oriental, fond of wandering through unexplored portions of the earth, and he arrived in India from nowhere in particular. At least no living man could ascertain whether it was by way of Balkh, Badakshan, Chitral, Baluchistan, or Nepal, or anywhere else. The Indian Government, being in an unusually affable mood, gave orders that he was to be civilly treated and shown everything that was to be seen. So he drifted, talking bad English and worse French, from one city to another, till he forgathered with Her Majesty's White Hussars in the city of Peshawur, which stands at the mouth of that narrow swordcut in the hills that men call the Khyber Pass. He was undoubtedly an officer, and he was decorated after the manner of the Russians with little enamelled crosses, and he could talk, and (though this has nothing to do with his merits) he had been given up as a hopeless task, or cask, by the Black Tyrone, who individually and collectively, with hot whisky and honey, mulled brandy, and mixed spirits of every kind, had striven in all hospitality to make him drunk. And when the Black Tyrone, who are exclusively Irish, fail to disturb the peace of head of a foreigner—that foreigner is certain to be a superior man.

The White Hussars were as conscientious in choosing their wine as in charging the enemy. All that they possessed, including some wondrous brandy, was placed at the absolute disposition of Dirkovitch, and he enjoyed himself hugely–even more than among the Black Tyrone.

But he remained distressingly European through it all. The White Hussars were 'My dear true friends,' 'Fellow-soldiers glorious,' and 'Brothers inseparable.' He would unburden himself by the hour on the glorious future that awaited the combined arms of England and Russia when their hearts and their territories should run side by side, and the great mission of civilising Asia should begin. That was unsatisfactory, because Asia is not going to be civilised after the methods of the West. There is too much Asia and she is too old. You cannot reform a lady of many lovers, and Asia has been insatiable in her flirtations aforetime. She will never attend Sunday school or learn to vote save with swords for tickets.

Dirkovitch knew this as well as any one else, but it suited him to talk special-correspondently and to make himself as genial as he could. Now and then he volunteered a little, a very little information about his own sotnia of Cossacks, left apparently to look after themselves somewhere at the back of beyond. He had done rough work in Central Asia, and had seen rather more help-yourself fighting than most men of his years. But he was careful never to betray his superiority, and more than careful to praise on all occasions the appearance, drill, uniform, and organisation of Her Majesty's White Hussars. And indeed they were a regiment to be admired. When Lady Durgan, widow of the late Sir John Durgan, arrived in their station, and after a short time had been proposed to by every single man at mess, she put the public sentiment very neatly when she explained that they were all so nice that unless she could marry them all, including the Colonel and some Majors already married, she was not going to content herself with one hussar. Wherefore she wedded a little man in a rifle regiment, being by nature contradictious; and the White Hussars were going to wear crape on their arms, but compromised by attending the wedding in full force, and lining the aisle with unutterable reproach. She had jilted them all–from Basset-Holmer the senior Captain to little Mildred the junior subaltern, who could have given her four thousand a year and a title.

The only persons who did not share the general regard for the White Hussars were a few thousand gentlemen of Jewish extraction who lived across the border, and answered to the name of Pathan. They had once met the regiment officially and for something less than twenty minutes, but the interview, which was complicated with many casualties, had filled them with prejudice. They even called the White Hussars children of the devil and sons of persons whom it would be perfectly impossible to meet in decent society. Yet they were not above making their aversion fill their money-belts. The regiment possessed carbines—beautiful Martini-Henry carbines that would lob a bullet into an enemy's camp at one thousand yards, and were even handier than the long rifle. Therefore they were coveted all along the border, and since demand inevitably breeds supply, they were supplied at the risk of life and limb for exactly their weight in coined silver—seven and one half pounds weight of rupees, or sixteen pounds sterling reckoning the rupee at par. They were stolen at night by snaky-haired thieves who crawled on their stomachs under the nose of the sentries; they disappeared mysteriously from locked arm-racks, and in the hot weather, when all the barrack doors and windows were open, they vanished like puffs of their own smoke. The border people desired them for family vendettas and contingencies. But in the long cold nights of the northern Indian winter they were stolen most extensively. The traffic of murder was liveliest among the hills at that season and prices ruled high. The regimental guards were first doubled and then trebled. A trooper does not much care if he loses a weapon—Government must make it good—but he deeply resents the loss of his sleep. The regiment grew very angry, and one rifle-thief bears the visible marks of their anger upon him to this hour. That incident stopped the burglaries for a time and the guards were reduced accordingly, and the regiment devoted itself to polo with unexpected results; for it beat by two goals to one that very terrible polo corps the Lushkar Light Horse, though the latter had four ponies apiece for a short hour's fight, as well as a native officer who played like a lambent flame across the ground.

They gave a dinner to celebrate the event. The Lushkar team came, and Dirkovitch came, in the fullest full uniform of a Cossack officer, which is as full as a dressing-gown, and was introduced to the Lushkars, and opened his eyes as he regarded. They were lighter men than the Hussars, and they carried themselves with the swing that is the peculiar right of the Punjab Frontier Force and all Irregular Horse. Like everything else in the Service it has to be learnt, but, unlike many things, it is never forgotten, and remains on the body till death.

The great beam-roofed mess-room of the White Hussars was a sight to be remembered. All the mess plate was out on the long table—the same table that had served up the bodies of five officers after a forgotten fight long and long ago—the dingy, battered standards faced the door of entrance, clumps of winter-roses lay between the silver candlesticks, and the portraits of eminent officers deceased looked down on their successors from between the heads of sambhur, nilghai, markhor, and, pride of all the mess, two grinning snow-leopards that had cost Basset-Holmer four months' leave that he might have spent in England, instead of on the road to Thibet and the daily risk of his life by ledge, snow-slide, and grassy slope.

The servants in spotless white muslin with the crest of their regiments on the brow of their turbans waited behind their masters, who were clad in the scarlet and gold of the White Hussars, and the cream and silver of the Lushkar Light Horse. Dirkovitch's dull green uniform was the only dark spot at the board, but his big onyx eyes made up for it. He was fraternising effusively with the captain of the Lushkar team, who was wondering how many of Dirkovitch's Cossacks his own dark wiry down-countrymen could account for in a fair charge. But one does not speak of these things openly.

The talk rose higher and higher, and the regimental band played between the courses, as is the immemorial custom, till all tongues ceased for a moment with the removal of the dinner-slips and the first toast of obligation when an officer rising said, 'Mr. Vice, the Queen,' and little Mildred from the bottom of the table answered, 'The Queen, God bless her,' and the big spurs clanked as the big men heaved themselves up and drank the Queen upon whose pay they were falsely supposed to settle their mess-bills. That Sacrament of the Mess never grows old, and never ceases to bring a lump into the throat of the listener wherever he be by sea or by land. Dirkovitch rose with his 'brothers glorious,' but he could not understand. No one but an officer can tell what the toast means; and the bulk have more sentiment than comprehension. Immediately after the little silence that follows on the ceremony there entered the native officer who had played for the Lushkar team. He could not, of course, eat with the mess, but he came in at dessert, all six feet of him, with the blue and silver turban atop, and the big black boots below. The mess rose joyously as he thrust forward the hilt of his sabre in token of fealty for the Colonel of the White Hussars to touch, and dropped into a vacant chair amid shouts of: '*Rung ho,* Hira Singh!' (which being translated means 'Go in and win'). 'Did I whack you over the knee, old man?' 'Rissaldar Sahib, what the devil made you play that kicking pig of a pony in the last ten minutes?' '*Shabash,* Rissaldar Sahib!' Then the voice of the Colonel, 'The health of Rissaldar Hira Singh!'

After the shouting had died away Hira Singh rose to reply, for he was the cadet of a royal house, the son of a king's son, and knew what was due on these occasions. Thus he spoke in the vernacular:—'Colonel Sahib and officers of this regiment. Much honour have you done me. This will I remember. We came down from afar to play you. But we were beaten' ('No fault of yours, Rissaldar Sahib. Played on our own ground y' know. Your ponies were cramped from the railway. Don't apologise!') 'Therefore perhaps we will come again if it be so ordained.' ('Hear! Hear! Hear, indeed! Bravo! Hsh!') 'Then we will play you afresh' ('Happy to meet you') 'till there are left no feet upon our ponies. Thus far for sport.' He dropped one hand on his sword-hilt and his eye wandered to Dirkovitch lolling back in his chair. 'But if by the will of God there arises any other game which is not the polo game, then be assured, Colonel Sahib and officers, that we will play it out side by side, though *they,*' again his eye sought Dirkovitch, 'though *they,* I say, have fifty ponies to our one horse.' And with a deep-mouthed *Rung ho!* that sounded like a musket-butt on flagstones, he sat down amid leaping glasses.

Dirkovitch, who had devoted himself steadily to the brandy–the terrible brandy aforementioned–did not understand, nor did the expurgated translations offered to him at all convey the point. Decidedly Hira Singh's was the speech of the evening, and the clamour might have continued to the dawn had it not been broken by the noise of a shot without that sent every man feeling at his defenceless left side. Then there was a scuffle and a yell of pain.

'Carbine-stealing again!' said the Adjutant, calmly sinking back in his chair. 'This comes of reducing the guards. I hope the sentries have killed him.'

The feet of armed men pounded on the verandah flags, and it was as though something was being dragged.

'Why don't they put him in the cells till the morning?' said the Colonel testily. 'See if they've damaged him, sergeant.'

The mess sergeant fled out into the darkness and returned with two troopers and a corporal, all very much perplexed.

'Caught a man stealin' carbines, sir,' said the corporal. 'Leastways 'e was crawlin' towards the barricks, sir, past the main road sentries, an' the sentry 'e sez, sir——'

The limp heap of rags upheld by the three men groaned. Never was seen so destitute and demoralised an Afghan. He was turbanless, shoeless, caked with dirt, and all but dead with rough handling. Hira Singh started slightly at the sound of the man's pain. Dirkovitch took another glass of brandy.

'*What* does the sentry say?' said the Colonel.

'Sez 'e speaks English, sir,' said the corporal.

'So you brought him into mess instead of handing him over to the sergeant! If he spoke all the Tongues of the Pentecost you've no business——'

Again the bundle groaned and muttered. Little Mildred had risen from his place to inspect. He jumped back as though he had been shot.

'Perhaps it would be better, sir, to send the men away,' said he to the Colonel, for he was a much privileged subaltern. He put his arms round the rag-bound horror as he spoke, and dropped him into a chair. It may not have been explained that the littleness of Mildred lay in his being six feet four and big in proportion. The corporal seeing that an officer was disposed to look after the capture, and that the Colonel's eye was beginning to blaze, promptly removed himself and his men. The mess was left alone with the carbine-thief, who laid his head on the table and wept bitterly, hopelessly, and inconsolably, as little children wept.

Hira Singh leapt to his feet. 'Colonel Sahib,' said he, 'that man is no Afghan, for they weep *Ai! Ai!* Nor is he of Hindustan, for they weep *Oh! Ho!* He weeps after the fashion of the white men, who say *Ow! Ow!*'

'Now where the dickens did you get that knowledge, Hira Singh?' said the captain of the Lushkar team.

'Hear him!' said Hira Singh simply, pointing at the crumpled figure that wept as though it would never cease.

'He said, "My God!"' said little Mildred. 'I heard him say it.'

The Colonel and the mess-room looked at the man in silence. It is a horrible thing to hear a man cry. A woman can sob from the top of her palate, or her lips, or anywhere else, but a man must cry from his diaphragm, and it rends him to pieces.

'Poor devil!' said the Colonel, coughing tremendously. 'We ought to send him to hospital. He's been man-handled.'

Now the Adjutant loved his carbines. They were to him as his grandchildren, the men standing in the first place. He grunted rebelliously: 'I can understand an Afghan stealing, because he's built that way. But I can't understand his crying. That makes it worse.'

The brandy must have affected Dirkovitch, for he lay back in his chair and stared at the ceiling. There was nothing special in the ceiling beyond a shadow as of a huge black coffin. Owing to some peculiarity in the construction of the mess-room this shadow was always thrown when the candles were lighted. It never disturbed the digestion of the White Hussars. They were in fact rather proud of it.

'Is he going to cry all night?' said the Colonel, 'or are we supposed to sit up with little Mildred's guest until he feels better?'

The man in the chair threw up his head and stared at the mess. 'Oh, my God!' he said, and every soul in the mess rose to his feet. Then the Lushkar captain did a deed for which he ought to have been given the Victoria Cross–distinguished gallantry in a fight against overwhelming curiosity. He picked up his team with his eyes as the hostess picks up the ladies at the opportune moment, and pausing only by the Colonel's chair to say, 'This isn't *our* affair, you know, sir,' led them into the verandah and the gardens. Hira Singh was the last to go and he looked at Dirkovitch. But Dirkovitch had departed into a brandy-paradise of his own. His lips moved without sound, and he was studying the coffin on the ceiling.

'White–white all over,' said Basset-Holmer, the Adjutant. 'What a pernicious renegade he must be! I wonder where he came from?'

The Colonel shook the man gently by the arm, and 'Who are you?' said he.

There was no answer. The man stared round the mess-room and smiled in the Colonel's face. Little Mildred, who was always more of a woman than a man till 'Boot and saddle' was sounded, repeated the question in a voice that would have drawn confidences from a geyser. The man only smiled. Dirkovitch at the far end of the table slid gently from his chair to the floor. No son of Adam in this present imperfect world can mix the Hussars' champagne with the Hussars' brandy by five and eight glasses of each without remembering the pit whence he was digged and descending thither. The band began to play the tune with which the White Hussars from the date of their formation have concluded all their functions. They would sooner be disbanded than abandon that tune; it is a part of their system. The man straightened himself in his chair and drummed on the table with his fingers.

'I don't see why we should entertain lunatics,' said the Colonel. 'Call a guard and send him off to the cells. We'll look into the business in the morning. Give him a glass of wine first though.'

Little Mildred filled a sherry-glass with the brandy and thrust it over to the man. He drank, and the tune rose louder, and he straightened himself yet more. Then he put out his long-taloned hands to a piece of plate opposite and fingered it lovingly. There was a mystery connected with that piece of plate, in the shape of a spring which converted what was a seven-branched candlestick, three springs on each side and one in the middle, into a sort of wheel-spoke candelabrum. He found the spring, pressed it, and laughed weakly. He rose from his chair and inspected a picture on the wall, then moved on to another picture, the mess watching him without a word. When he came to the mantelpiece he shook his head and seemed distressed. A piece of plate representing a mounted hussar in full uniform caught his eye. He pointed to it, and then to the mantelpiece with inquiry in his eyes.

'What is it–oh, what is it?' said little Mildred. Then as a mother might speak to a child, 'That is a horse. Yes, a horse.'

Very slowly came the answer in a thick, passionless guttural–'Yes, I –have seen. But–where is *the* horse?'

You could have heard the hearts of the mess beating as the men drew back to give the stranger full room in his wanderings. There was no question of calling the guard.

Again he spoke–very slowly, 'Where is *our* horse?'

There is but one horse in the White Hussars, and his portrait hangs outside the door of the mess-room. He is the piebald drum-horse, the king of the regimental band, that served the regiment for seven-and-thirty years, and in the end was shot for old age. Half the mess tore the thing down from its place and thrust it into the man's hands. He placed it above the mantelpiece, it clattered on the ledge as his poor hands dropped it, and he staggered towards the bottom of the table, falling into Mildred's chair. Then all the men spoke to one another something after this fashion, 'The drum-horse hasn't hung over the mantelpiece since '67.' 'How does he know?' 'Mildred, go and speak to him again.' 'Colonel, what are you going to do?' 'Oh, dry up, and give the poor devil a chance to pull himself together.' 'It isn't possible anyhow. The man's a lunatic.'

Little Mildred stood at the Colonel's side talking in his ear. 'Will you be good enough to take your seats, please, gentlemen!' he said, and the mess dropped into the chairs. Only Dirkovitch's seat, next to little Mildred's, was blank, and little Mildred himself had found Hira Singh's place. The wide-eyed mess-sergeant filled the glasses in dead silence. Once more the Colonel rose, but his hand shook, and the port spilled on the table as he looked straight at the man in little Mildred's chair and said hoarsely, 'Mr. Vice, the Queen.' There was a little pause, but the man sprang to his feet and answered without hesitation, 'The Queen, God bless her!' and as he emptied the thin glass he snapped the shank between his fingers.

Long and long ago, when the Empress of India was a young woman and there were no unclean ideals in the land, it was the custom of a few messes to drink the Queen's toast in broken glass, to the vast delight of the mess-contractors. The custom is now dead, because there is nothing to break anything for, except now and again the word of a Government, and that has been broken already.

'That settles it,' said the Colonel, with a gasp. 'He's not a sergeant. What in the world is he?'

The entire mess echoed the word, and the volley of questions would have scared any man. It was no wonder that the ragged, filthy invader could only smile and shake his head.

From under the table, calm and smiling, rose Dirkovitch, who had been roused from healthful slumber by feet upon his body. By the side of the man he rose, and the man shrieked and grovelled. It was a horrible sight coming so swiftly upon the pride and glory of the toast that had brought the strayed wits together.

Dirkovitch made no offer to raise him, but little Mildred heaved him up in an instant. It is not good that a gentleman who can answer to the Queen's toast should lie at the feet of a subaltern of Cossacks.

The hasty action tore the wretch's upper clothing nearly to the waist, and his body was seamed with dry black scars. There is only one weapon in the world that cuts in parallel lines, and it is neither the cane nor the cat. Dirkovitch saw the marks, and the pupils of his eyes dilated. Also his face changed. He said something that sounded like *Shto ve takete,* and the man fawning answered, *Chetyre.*

'What's that?' said everybody together.

'His number. That is number four, you know.' Dirkovitch spoke very thickly.

'What has a Queen's officer to do with a qualified number?' said the Colonel, and an unpleasant growl ran round the table.

'How can I tell?' said the affable Oriental with a sweet smile. 'He is a –how you have it?–escape–run-a-way, from over there.' He nodded towards the darkness of the night.

'Speak to him if he'll answer you, and speak to him gently,' said little Mildred, settling the man in a chair. It seemed most improper to all present that Dirkovitch should sip brandy as he talked in purring, spitting Russian to the creature who answered so feebly and with such evident dread. But since Dirkovitch appeared to understand no one said a word. All breathed heavily, leaning forward, in the long gaps of the conversation. The next time that they have no engagements on hand the White Hussars intend to go to St. Petersburg in a body to learn Russian.

'He does not know how many years ago,' said Dirkovitch facing the mess, 'but he says it was very long ago in a war. I think that there was an accident. He says he was of this glorious and distinguished regiment in the war.'

'The rolls! The rolls! Holmer, get the rolls!' said little Mildred, and the Adjutant dashed off bare-headed to the orderly-room, where the muster-rolls of the regiment were kept. He returned just in time to hear Dirkovitch conclude, 'Therefore, my dear friends, I am most sorry to say there was an accident which would have been reparable if he had apologised to that our Colonel, which he had insulted.'

Then followed another growl which the Colonel tried to beat down. The mess was in no mood just then to weigh insults to Russian Colonels.

'He does not remember, but I think that there was an accident, and so he was not exchanged among the prisoners, but he was sent to another place–how do you say?–the country. *So,* he says, he came here. He does not know how he came. Eh? He was at Chepany'–the man caught the word, nodded, and shivered–'at Zhigansk and Irkutsk. I cannot understand how he escaped. He says, too, that he was in the forests for many years, but how many years he has forgotten–that with many things. It was an accident; done because he did not apologise to that our Colonel. Ah!'

Instead of echoing Dirkovitch's sigh of regret, it is sad to record that the White Hussars livelily exhibited un-Christian delight and other emotions, hardly restrained by their sense of hospitality. Holmer flung the frayed and yellow regimental rolls on the table, and the men flung themselves at these.

'Steady! Fifty-six–fifty-five–fifty-four,' said Holmer. 'Here we are. "Lieutenant Austin Limmason. *Missing.*" That was before Sebastopol. What an infernal shame! Insulted one of their Colonels, and was quietly shipped off. Thirty years of his life wiped out.'

'But he never apologised. Said he'd see him damned first,' chorused the mess.

'Poor chap! I suppose he never had the chance afterwards. How did he come here?' said the Colonel.

The dingy heap in the chair could give no answer.

'Do you know who you are?'

It laughed weakly.

'Do you know that you are Limmason–Lieutenant Limmason of the White Hussars?'

Swiftly as a shot came the answer, in a slightly surprised tone, 'Yes, I'm Limmason, of course.' The light died out in his eyes, and the man collapsed, watching every motion of Dirkovitch with terror. A flight from Siberia may fix a few elementary facts in the mind, but it does not seem to lead to continuity of thought. The man could not explain how, like a homing pigeon, he had found his way to his own old mess again. Of what he had suffered or seen he knew nothing. He cringed before Dirkovitch as instinctively as he had pressed the spring of the candlestick, sought the picture of the drum-horse, and answered to the toast of the Queen. The rest was a blank that the dreaded Russian tongue could only in part remove. His head bowed on his breast, and he giggled and cowered alternately.

The devil that lived in the brandy prompted Dirkovitch at this extremely inopportune moment to make a speech. He rose, swaying slightly, gripped the table-edge, while his eyes glowed like opals, and began:

'Fellow-soldiers glorious–true friends and hospitables. It was an accident, and deplorable–most deplorable.' Here he smiled sweetly all round the mess. 'But you will think of this little, little thing. So little, is it not? The Czar! Posh! I slap my fingers–I snap my fingers at him. Do I believe in him? No! But in us Slav who has done nothing, *him* I believe. Seventy–how much–millions peoples that have done nothing–not one thing. Posh! Napoleon was an episode.' He banged a hand on the table. 'Hear you, old peoples, we have done nothing in the world–out here. All our work is to do; and it shall be done, old peoples. Get a-way!' He waved his hand imperiously, and pointed to the man. 'You see him. He is not good to see. He was just one little–oh, so little–accident, that no one remembered. Now he is *That!* So will you be, brother soldiers so brave–so will you be. But you will never come back. You will all go where he is gone, or'–he pointed to the great coffin-shadow on the ceiling, and muttering, 'Seventy millions–get a-way, you old peoples,' fell asleep.

'Sweet, and to the point,' said little Mildred. 'What's the use of getting wroth? Let's make this poor devil comfortable.'

But that was a matter suddenly and swiftly taken from the loving hands of the White Hussars. The Lieutenant had returned only to go away again three days later, when the wail of the Dead March, and the tramp of the squadrons, told the wondering Station, who saw no gap in the mess-table, that an officer of the regiment had resigned his new-found commission.

And Dirkovitch, bland, supple, and always genial, went away too by a night train. Little Mildred and another man saw him off, for he was the guest of the mess, and even had he smitten the Colonel with the open hand, the law of that mess allowed no relaxation of hospitality.

'Good-bye, Dirkovitch, and a pleasant journey,' said little Mildred.

'*Au revoir,*' said the Russian.

'Indeed! But we thought you were going home?'

'Yes, but I will come again. My dear friends, is that road shut?' He pointed to where the North Star burned over the Khyber Pass.

'By Jove! I forgot. Of course. Happy to meet you, old man, any time you like. Got everything you want? Cheroots, ice, bedding? That's all right. Well, *au revoir,* Dirkovitch.'

'Um,' said the other man, as the tail-lights of the train grew small. 'Of –all–the–unmitigated–—!'

Little Mildred answered nothing, but watched the North Star and hummed a selection from a recent Simla burlesque that had much delighted the White Hussars. It ran–

I'm sorry for Mister Bluebeard,
I'm sorry to cause him pain;
But a terrible spree there's sure to be
When he comes back again.

My Revelations as a Spy **Stephen Leacock**

One of the first things I did when I became editor of *Maclean's Magazine* was to write to Canada's great humorist, Stephen Leacock, at McGill University, suggesting that he send me some articles. I did not receive a reply. But one day, returning from lunch, I was told by the receptionist that a man had been in to see me and had left a manuscript. There was a note with it in obscure handwriting which I finally deciphered as "Hope you like this." The signature was harder to make out than the curious symbols that the experts encountered when they were working on the Rosetta Stone. But on the manuscript it appeared in fine, plain, exciting typescript, Stephen Leacock.

He did an article for me each month for nearly ten years and contributed more than any other writer to our circulation climb. The articles I liked best were his comic excursions into international complications. Of these the best was "My Revelations as a Spy."

MY REVELATIONS AS A SPY

Stephen Leacock

In many people the very name "Spy" excites a shudder of apprehension; we Spies, in fact, get quite used to being shuddered at. None of us Spies mind it at all. Whenever I enter a hotel and register myself as a Spy I am quite accustomed to see a thrill of fear run round the clerks, or clerk, behind the desk.

Us Spies or We Spies–for we call ourselves both–are thus a race apart. None know us. All fear us. Where do we live? Nowhere. Where are we? Everywhere. Frequently we don't know ourselves where we are. The secret orders that we receive come from so high up that it is often forbidden to us even to ask where we are. A friend of mine, or at least a Fellow Spy–us Spies have no friends–one of the most brilliant men in the Hungarian Secret Service, once spent a month in New York under the impression that he was in Winnipeg. If this happened to the most brilliant, think of the others.

All, I say, fear us. Because they know and have reason to know our power. Hence, in spite of the prejudice against us, we are able to move everywhere, to lodge in the best hotels, and enter any society that we wish to penetrate.

Let me relate an incident to illustrate this: a month ago I entered one of the largest of the New York hotels which I will merely call the B. hotel without naming it: to do so might blast it. We Spies, in fact, never *name* a hotel. At the most we indicate it by a number known only to ourselves, such as 1, 2, or 3.

On my presenting myself at the desk the clerk informed me that he had no room vacant. I knew this of course to be a mere subterfuge; whether or not he suspected that I was a Spy I cannot say. I was muffled up, to avoid recognition, in a long overcoat with the collar turned up and reaching well above my ears, while the black beard and the moustache, that I had slipped on in entering the hotel, concealed my face. "Let me speak a moment to the manager," I said. When he came I beckoned him aside and taking his ear in my hand I breathed two words into it. "Good heavens!" he gasped, while his face turned as pale as ashes. "Is it enough?" I asked. "Can I have a room, or must I breathe again?" "No, no," said the manager, still trembling. Then, turning to the clerk: "Give this gentleman a room," he said, "and give him a bath."

What these two words are that will get a room in New York at once I must not divulge. Even now, when the veil of secrecy is being lifted, the international interests involved are too complicated to permit it. Suffice it to say that if these two had failed I know a couple of others still better.

I narrate this incident, otherwise trivial, as indicating the astounding ramifications and the ubiquity of the international spy system. A similar illustration occurs to me as I write. I was walking the other day with another man, on upper B. way between the T. Building and the W. Garden.

"Do you see that man over there?" I said, pointing from the side of the street on which we were walking on the sidewalk to the other side opposite to the side that we were on.

"The man with the straw hat?" he asked. "Yes, what of him?"

"Oh, nothing," I answered, "except that he's a Spy!"

"Great heavens!" exclaimed my acquaintance, leaning up against a lamp-post for support. "A Spy! How do you know that? What does it mean?"

I gave a quiet laugh—we Spies learn to laugh very quietly.

"Ha!" I said, "that is *my* secret, my friend. *Verbum sapientius! Che sarà sarà! Yodel doodle doo!*"

My acquaintance fell in a dead faint upon the street. I watched them take him away in an ambulance. Will the reader be surprised to learn that among the white-coated attendants who removed him I recognized no less a person than the famous Russian Spy, Poulispantzoff. What he was doing there I could not tell. No doubt his orders came from so high up that he himself did not know. I had seen him only twice before—once when we were both disguised as Zulus at Buluwayo, and once in the interior of China, at the time when Poulispantzoff made his secret entry into Thibet concealed in a tea-case. He was inside the tea-case when I saw him; so at least I was informed by the coolies who carried it. Yet I recognized him instantly. Neither he nor I, however, gave any sign of recognition other than an imperceptible movement of the outer eyelid. (We Spies learn to move the outer lid of the eye so imperceptibly that it cannot be seen.) Yet after meeting Poulispantzoff in this way I was not surprised to read in the evening papers a few hours afterward that the uncle of the young King of Siam had been assassinated. The connection between these two events I am unfortunately not at liberty to explain; the consequences to the Vatican would be too serious. I doubt if it could remain top-side up.

These, however, are but passing incidents in a life filled with danger and excitement. They would have remained unrecorded and unrevealed, like the rest of my revelations, were it not that certain recent events have to some extent removed the seal of secrecy from my lips. The death of a certain royal sovereign makes it possible for me to divulge things hitherto undivulgeable. Even now I can only tell a part, a small part, of the terrific things that I know. When more sovereigns die I can divulge more. I hope to keep on divulging at intervals for years. But I am compelled to be cautious. My relations with the Wilhelmstrasse, with Downing Street and the Quai d'Orsay, are so intimate, and my footing with the Yildiz Kiosk and the Waldorf-Astoria and Childs' Restaurants are so delicate, that a single *faux pas* might prove to be a false step.

It is now seventeen years since I entered the Secret Service of the G. empire. During this time my activities have taken me into every quarter of the globe, at times even into every eighth or sixteenth of it.

It was I who first brought back word to the Imperial Chancellor of the existence of an Entente between England and France. "Is there an Entente?" he asked me, trembling with excitement, on my arrival at the Wilhelmstrasse. "Your Excellency," I said, "there is." He groaned. "Can you stop it?" he asked. "Don't ask me," I said sadly. "Where must we strike?" demanded the Chancellor. "Fetch me a map," I said. They did so. I placed my finger on the map. "Quick, quick," said the Chancellor, "look where his finger is." They lifted it up. "Morocco!" they cried. I had meant it for Abyssinia but it was too late to change. That night the warship *Panther* sailed under sealed orders. The rest is history, or at least history and geography.

In the same way it was I who brought word to the Wilhelmstrasse of the *rapprochement* between England and Russia in Persia. "What did you find?" asked the Chancellor as I laid aside the Russian disguise in which I had travelled. "A *Rapprochement!*" I said. He groaned. "They seem to get all the best words," he said.

I shall always feel, to my regret, that I am personally responsible for the outbreak of the present war. It may have had ulterior causes. But there is no doubt that it was precipitated by the fact that, for the first time in seventeen years, I took a six weeks' vacation in June and July of 1914. The consequences of this careless step I ought to have foreseen. Yet I took such precautions as I could. "Do you think," I asked, "that you can preserve the *status quo* for six weeks, merely six weeks, if I stop spying and take a rest?" "We'll try," they answered. "Remember," I said, as I packed my things, "keep the Dardanelles closed; have the Sandjak of Novi Bazaar properly patrolled, and let the Dobrudja remain under a *modus vivendi* till I come back."

Two months later, while sitting sipping my coffee at a Kurhof in the Schwarzwald, I read in the newspapers that a German army had invaded France and was fighting the French, and that the English expeditionary force had crossed the Channel. "This," I said to myself, "means war." As usual, I was right.

It is needless for me to recount here the life of busy activity that falls to a Spy in wartime. It was necessary for me to be here, there and everywhere, visiting all the best hotels, watering-places, summer resorts, theatres, and places of amusement. It was necessary, moreover, to act with the utmost caution and to assume an air of careless indolence in order to lull suspicion asleep. With this end in view I made a practice of never rising till ten in the morning. I breakfasted with great leisure, and contented myself with passing the morning in a quiet stroll, taking care, however, to keep my ears open. After lunch I generally feigned a light sleep, keeping my ears shut. A table d'hôte dinner, followed by a visit to the theatre, brought the strenuous day to a close. Few Spies, I venture to say, worked harder than I did.

It was during the third year of the war that I received a peremptory summons from the head of the Imperial Secret Service at Berlin, Baron Fisch von Gestern. "I want to see you," it read. Nothing more. In the life of a Spy one learns to think quickly, and to think is to act. I gathered as soon as I received the despatch that for some reason or other Fisch von Gestern was anxious to see me, having, as I instantly inferred, something to say to me. This conjecture proved correct.

The Baron rose at my entrance with military correctness and shook hands.

"Are you willing," he inquired, "to undertake a mission to America?"

"I am," I answered.

"Very good. How soon can you start?"

"As soon as I have paid the few bills that I owe in Berlin," I replied.

"We can hardly wait for that," said my chief, "and in case it might excite comment. You must start to-night!"

"Very good," I said.

"Such," said the Baron, "are the Kaiser's orders. "Here is an American passport and a photograph that will answer the purpose. The likeness is not great, but it is sufficient."

"But," I objected, abashed for a moment, "this photograph is of a man with whiskers and I am, unfortunately, clean-shaven."

"The orders are imperative," said Gestern, with official hauteur. "You must start to-night. You can grow whiskers this afternoon."

"Very good," I replied.

"And now to the business of your mission," continued the Baron. "The United States, as you have perhaps heard, is making war against Germany."

"I have heard so," I replied.

"Yes," continued Gestern. "The fact has leaked out–how, we do not know–and is being widely reported. His Imperial Majesty has decided to stop the war with the United States."

I bowed.

"He intends to send over a secret treaty of the same nature as the one recently made with his recent Highness the recent Czar of Russia. Under this treaty Germany proposes to give to the United States the whole of equatorial Africa and in return the United States is to give to Germany the whole of China. There are other provisions, but I need not trouble you with them. Your mission relates, not to the actual treaty, but to the preparation of the ground."

I bowed again.

"You are aware, I presume," continued the Baron, "that in all high international dealings, at least in Europe, the ground has to be prepared. A hundred threads must be unravelled. This the Imperial Government itself cannot stoop to do. The work must be done by agents like yourself. You understand all this already, no doubt?"

I indicated my assent.

"These, then, are your instructions," said the Baron, speaking slowly and distinctly, as if to impress his words upon my memory. "On your arrival in the United States you will follow the accredited methods that are known to be used by all the best Spies of the highest diplomacy. You have no doubt read some of the books, almost manuals of instruction, that they have written?"

"I have read many of them," I said.

"Very well. You will enter, that is to say, enter and move everywhere in the best society. Mark specially, please, that you must not only *enter* it but you must *move*. You must, if I may put it so, get a move on."

I bowed.

"You must mix freely with the members of the Cabinet. You must dine with them. This is a most necessary matter and one to be kept well in mind. Dine with them often in such a way as to make yourself familiar to them. Will you do this?"

"I will," I said.

"Very good. Remember also that in order to mask your purpose you must constantly be seen with the most fashionable and most beautiful women of the American capital. Can you do this?"

"Can I?" I said.

"You must if need be"—and the Baron gave a most significant look which was not lost upon me—"carry on an intrigue with one or, better, with several of them. Are you ready for it?"

"More than ready," I said.

"Very good. But this is only a part. You are expected also to familiarize yourself with the leaders of the great financial interests. You are to put yourself on such a footing with them as to borrow large sums of money from them. Do you object to this?"

"No," I said frankly, "I do not."

"Good! You will also mingle freely in Ambassadorial and foreign circles. It would be well for you to dine, at least once a week, with the British Ambassador. And now one final word"—here Gestern spoke with singular impressiveness—"as to the President of the United States."

"Yes," I said.

"You must mix with him on a footing of the most open-handed friendliness. Be at the White House continually. Make yourself in the fullest sense of the words the friend and adviser of the President. All this I think is clear. In fact, it is only what is done, as you know, by all the masters of international diplomacy."

"Precisely," I said.

"Very good. And then," continued the Baron, "as soon as you find yourself sufficiently *en rapport* with everybody, or I should say," he added in correction, for the Baron shares fully in the present German horror of imported French words, "when you find yourself sufficiently in enggeknüpfterverwandtschaft with everybody, you may then proceed to advance your peace terms. And now, my dear fellow," said the Baron, with a touch of genuine cordiality, "one word more. Are you in need of money?"

"Yes," I said.

"I thought so. But you will find that you need it less and less as you go on. Meantime, good-bye, and best wishes for your mission."

Such was, such is, in fact, the mission with which I am accredited. I regard it as by far the most important mission with which I have been accredited by the Wilhelmstrasse. Yet I am compelled to admit that up to the present it has proved unsuccessful. My attempts to carry it out have been baffled. There is something perhaps in the atmosphere of this republic which obstructs the working of high diplomacy. For over five months now I have been waiting and willing to dine with the American Cabinet. They have not invited me. For four weeks I sat each night waiting in the J. hotel in Washington with my suit on ready to be asked. They did not come near me.

Nor have I yet received an invitation from the British Embassy inviting me to an informal lunch or to midnight supper with the Ambassador. Everybody who knows anything of the inside working of the international spy system will realize that without these invitations one can do nothing. Nor has the President of the United States given any sign. I have sent word to him, in cipher, that I am ready to dine with him on any day that may be convenient to both of us. He has made no move in the matter.

Under these circumstances an intrigue with any of the leaders of fashionable society has proved impossible. My attempts to approach them have been misunderstood—in fact, have led to my being invited to leave the J. hotel. The fact that I was compelled to leave it, owing to reasons that I cannot reveal, without paying my account, has occasioned unnecessary and dangerous comment. I connect it, in fact, with the singular attitude adopted by the B. hotel on my arrival in New York, to which I have already referred.

I have therefore been compelled to fall back on revelations and disclosures. Here again I find the American atmosphere singularly uncongenial. I have offered to reveal to the Secretary of State the entire family history of Ferdinand of Bulgaria for fifty dollars. He says it is not worth it. I have offered to the British Embassy the inside story of the Abdication of Constantine for five dollars. They say they know it, and knew it before it happened. I have offered, for little more than a nominal sum, to blacken the character of every reigning family in Germany. I am told that it is not necessary.

Meantime, as it is impossible to return to Central Europe, I expect to open either a fruit store or a peanut stand very shortly in this great metropolis. I imagine that many of my former colleagues will soon be doing the same!

Ask Me No Questions **Mary McCarthy**

This long story accomplishes three objectives. First, it is a portrait of an elderly lady of many unusual traits, who had been a great beauty and has still retained much of her distinction of looks. Second, it paints a picture of life in Seattle, from the end of the last century through the first decades of the present. This is the Seattle of wealth, of large and somewhat old-fashioned homes, of an easy life with a beguiling background. Finally, it offers some light, in skillfully indirect ways, on the relationships between the gentile and Jewish sections in Seattle society. It is, in fact, a tabloid novel, but all the better for avoiding the pitfall of building up minor characters and charting the course of their lives and romances.

It is quite different from *The Group* but it holds attention with a sureness seldom encountered in stories of this length.

Ask Me No Questions Mary McCarthy

This long story accomplishes three objectives. First, it is a portrait of an elderly lady of many unusual traits, who has been a great beauty and has still retained much of her distinction of looks. Second, it paints a picture of life in Seattle from the end of the last century through the first decades of the present. This is the Seattle of wealth, of large and somewhat old fashioned houses, of unhurried life with a family background. Finally, it offers some light, in slightly different ways, on the relationships between the gentile and Jewish sections of Seattle society. It is, in fact, a tabloid novel, but all the better for avoiding the pitfall of building up minor characters and charting the course of their lives and romances.

It is quite different from *The Cicerone* but it holds attention with a sureness seldom encountered in stories of this length.

ASK ME NO QUESTIONS

Mary McCarthy

There was something strange, abnormal, about my bringing-up; only now that my grandmother is dead am I prepared to face this fact. When she died, she had not divulged her age; none of her children knew it, and whatever birth date they found in her papers has remained a secret to me. She was well over eighty, certainly, and senile when she finally "passed away," three years ago, in her tall Seattle house—under her gold taffeta puff, doubtless, with her rings on her fingers and her blue-figured diamond wristwatch on her puckered wrist. Probably she herself no longer knew how old she was; she was confused the last time I saw her, six years ago, when I flew West to be with her after she had broken her hip. Going over family photographs, which we spread out on her bed, she nodded and smiled eagerly, sitting up among her pillows like a macaw on its perch, in her plumage of black hair and rouge and eyebrow pencil and mascara. She recognized the faces—her husband, Grandpa Preston, with a mustache, her husband clean-shaven, her son in a World War I uniform, her nephews, her younger son in a sailor suit, my mother dressed as a Spanish dancer, my mother in a ball gown—but she was vague about the names. "My father," she decided after studying an obituary photograph of Grandpa, clipped out of a newspaper. "Son," "husband," and "father" were all one to her. She knew who I was, right enough, and did not mix me up with my dead mother, but this was not very flattering, since it was usually the people she had loved that she could not keep apart, melting them into a single category—father-son-husband—like the Mystery of the Trinity. One relation whom she had quarrelled with she picked out instantly, while I was still fumbling for the name. "That's Gertrude!" she proclaimed victoriously. Then she made a face—the same face she made when the cook brought her something she did not like on her tray. I reminded her that she had made up with Gertrude years ago, but she shook her head. "Bad," she said childishly. "Gertrude said bad things about me."

"You," she said one day, suddenly pointing. "You wrote bad things about me. Bad." It was not true; I had never written about her at all. But when I told her so, she would not listen, nor would she say where she had derived her notion. This was exactly like her; she collected stray grudges like bits of colored ribbon and would never tell where they came from. Nobody had ever known, for instance, the exact cause of her falling-out with Gertrude. That day, sitting by her bed, I tried to coax her into a better frame of mind. She turned her head away on the pillow and shut her eyes; long, sharp lines ran down, like rivulets of discontent, from her nose to the corners of her mouth. A hopeless silence followed. It troubled me to see her like this; those deep, bitter lines were new to me, yet it must have taken years to indent them. I did not know whether to leave or stay, and I wished the nurse would come in. "You wrote about my husband," she abruptly charged, opening her eyes and frowning over her high-bridged nose. This was a sign that she was far away; in her clear moments she spoke of him to me as "Grandpa." "Yes," I agreed. "I wrote about Grandpa."

It transpired that this had made her very angry, though she had never alluded to it in any of her letters. But why, precisely, she was angry, I could not find out from her. Certainly I had not said anything that she could call "bad" about Grandpa. It occurred to me that she was jealous because she had not been included in these writings; moreover, my grandfather had been shown with other women—a Mother Superior, a fictional aunt, myself. When she accused me of putting her in, did she really mean that she felt left out? She was capable of such a contradiction even before her mind had clouded. Or did she suppose that *she* was the aunt—a disagreeable personage? Hopeless, hopeless, I repeated to myself. It had always been like this. You could never explain anything to her or make her see you loved her. She rebuffed explanations, as she rebuffed shows of affection; they intruded on her privacy, that closely guarded preserve—as sacrosanct as her bureau drawers or the safe with a combination lock in her closet—in which she clung to her own opinion. "Look, Grandma," I began, but then I gave it up.

I was going to say that (a) I had not written about her in any shape or disguise, and (b) if I had not, it was not because I considered her unimportant but because I knew she would hate to have her likeness taken. For nearly forty years, she had refused to be photographed. The last picture made of her, a tinted photograph, stood on her chiffonier; it showed an imperious, handsome matron in a low-cut beaded evening dress and a gauzy scarf, with her hair in a pompadour and her young son at her knee. This remained her official image, and nothing would persuade her to let it be superseded. In the four-generations pictures made when my brothers and I were children—my great-grandfather, my grandfather, my mother, and the babies—my grandmother is absent. The last time I had come to visit her, with my own baby, in 1939, just before the war, I had begged her to let us take pictures of this new family group. But she would not allow it. In the snapshots I have of that summer, my grandmother again is absent; a shadow on the lawn, near the playpen, in one of them may indicate where she was standing. Yet I dared not draw these facts to her attention, for there was a story behind them, the story of her life—a story that was kept, like her age, a secret from those closest to her, though we all guessed at it and knew it in a general way, just as we all knew, in a general way, calculating from our own ages and from the laws of Nature, that she had to be over eighty when she died.

Starting to tell that story now—to publish it, so to speak, abroad—I feel a distinct uneasiness, as though her shade were interposing to forbid me. If I believed in the afterlife, I would hold my peace. I should not like to account to her in whatever place we might meet; Limbo is where I can best imagine her, waiting for me at some Victorian stairhead, with folded arms, and cold cream on her face, as she used to wait in her pink quilted Japanese bathrobe or the green one with the dragons when I turned my key softly in the front door at two or three in the morning, with a lie, which I hoped not to need, trembling on my lips. She would never forgive me for what I am about to do, and if there is an afterlife, it is God who will have to listen to my explanations.

My first recollection of her is in her gray electric, her smartly gloved hands on the steering bar, or tiller. How old I was, I am not sure, but it was long before my family left Seattle when I was six. The gray box would glide up to the curb in front of our brick house on Twenty-fourth Avenue, and we would see her step out, wearing a dressy suit, braided or spangled, and a hat with a dotted veil that was pulled tight over her high-bridged nose, so that the black furry dots against her skin looked like beauty patches. On her feet, over her shoes, were curious cloth covers fastened with pearl buttons; my father said that they were called "spats," and that some men wore them, too. She had come to see my mother, and smelled of perfume. The electric would be parked for a long time outside our house; one day my brothers and I climbed in and got it started rolling. My mother spanked us with her tortoise-shell comb, but my father boasted of the exploit. "How did the little tykes do it?" he would say, laughing; we must all have been well under six.

Next, I think I see her in our bathroom, telling my mother that we must each have our own towel with our name above it, so that we would not keep catching colds from each other. When she left that afternoon, there was a brand-new towel for each of us hanging folded on the towel rack, with our name written out on a little label pasted on the wall behind each towel: "Roy" and "Tess" for our parents, and "Mary," "Kevin," and "James Preston" for us children; my littlest brother, Sheridan, was too young to have one. I was impressed by this arrangement, which seemed to me very stylish. But the very next day my father spoiled it by using one of our towels, and soon they were all scrambled up again and the labels fell off. This was the first (and, I think, the only) time I felt critical of my debonair Irish father, for I knew that the strange lady would be cross with him if she could see our bathroom now.

On Sundays, sometimes, we were taken to lunch at her house, out by Lake Washington. Two things we loved to do there. One was to crawl under the table while the grownups were still eating and find the bulge or little mound in the carpet where there was a bell she stepped on when she wanted the maid to come in. The bulge in the carpet was rather hard to locate, with all the feet and the women's skirts in the way, but eventually we found it and made the bell ring. It was nice under there, with the white tablecloth hanging down all around us like a tent. The carpet was thick and soft and furry, and if we peered out, we could see exotic birds on the wallpaper. I don't remember anyone's telling us not to get under the table, but one Sunday, perhaps the last time we went there, we could not find the bulge at all, and I remember the strange, scary feeling this gave me, as though I had been dreaming or making up a story and there had never been any bulge or bell in the first place. It did not occur to us that the bell must have been removed to keep us from annoying the maid, and the mystery of its disappearance used to plague me, long after we had left Seattle, like some maddening puzzle. I would lie awake in my new bed, thinking about the bell and wishing I could be given another chance to look for it. Five years later, when I was brought back to that house to live, a girl of eleven (and it remained my official home until I was twenty-one), I had the great joy, the vindication, of finding the bell just where I thought it should be, between her feet and mine.

The other thing we liked to do was, after lunch, to roll down her terraces, which dropped in grassy tiers from her tall house all the way, I remembered, to Lake Washington. We rolled and rolled, almost into the water, it seemed, and nobody stopped us until it was time to go home, our white Sunday clothes smeared with green stains. The grass was like velvet, and there were flower beds all around, and a smell of roses; a sprinkler was going somewhere, and there were raspberries that we ate off bushes. Alas, when I came back, I found I had been dreaming. The grounds did not go down to the lake but only to the next block, below, and there was only one grass terrace; the second one was wild, covered with blackberry prickers, and it had always been so, they said. I rolled a few times down the bank, but it was not the same; only five or six turns and I had reached the bottom; I could not recapture the delicious dizzy sensation I remembered so well. And the raspberries, which I had been looking forward to eating, did not belong to us but to the people next door.

The strange lady was supposed to be my grandmother, but I did not think of her that way when I was little. She did not have white hair, for one thing, like my other grandmother–the real one, as I considered her. Nor did she do embroidery or tapestry work, or stare at us over her glasses. She did not have glasses–only a peculiar ornament on a chain that she put up to her eyes when she wanted to look at something. With her queer electrical car that ran soundlessly and was upholstered inside in the softest gray, like a jewel case, her dotted veil, her gloves, which had bumps in them (made by her rings, I discovered later), her bell, and her descending terraces, she was a fairy-tale person who lived in an enchanted house, which was full of bulges, too–two overhanging balconies, on the lake side, and four bays and a little tower. (She had a fairy-tale sister, different from herself–tall, with white hair piled on top of her head in a long, conical shape, a towering mountain peak or a vanilla ice-cream cone. We were taken to see her one day, and her house was magic also. She had a whole polar bear for a rug, and her floor shone like glass and made you slip when you walked on it; her house was like a winter palace or like the North Pole, where Santa Claus came from.) I did not love the strange lady in the electric, but I loved the things she had.

The last time I saw her, in this pristine, fairy-tale period, was in the Hotel Washington, where we were staying because our house had been sold and we were moving away from Seattle. She was riding in the elevator, wearing a funny white mask, like the one the doctor had worn when they took my tonsils out; I heard the word "epidemic," and I think she told my mother that we should have masks, too, when we rode up and down in the elevator–a thing we were fond of doing. But I did not like the masks.

We were very sick on the train and they took us off with stretchers and wheelchairs. I was still sick when I saw her again, in a place where she did not belong–a place called Minneapolis, where my other grandmother lived. Lying in an iron bed in my other grandmother's sewing room, I watched the door open, and the strange lady came in, with a different kind of veil on–a black one, which hung all the way down over her face. She flung it back, and her face looked dreadful, as if she had been crying. Then she sat down on my bed, and her husband, Grandpa Preston, sat on a straight chair beside it. She sobbed, and her husband patted her, saying something like "Come now, Gussie," which appeared to be her name. She wiped her tears with a handkerchief; they went away on tiptoe, telling me to be a good girl. I did not understand any of this; my reason was offended by her turning up here in Minneapolis when I knew she lived in Seattle. No one enlightened me; I heard the word "flu," but it was months before it dawned on me that the occasion had been my parents' funeral. Yet when I surmised, finally, that Mama and Daddy were not coming back, I felt a certain measure of relief. One mystery, at least, was cleared up; the strange lady had come and cried on my bed because her daughter was dead. I did not see her again till five years later, when she was standing in the depot in Seattle, in a hat with a black dotted veil pulled tight across her face, which was heavily rouged and powdered. By this time, I knew that she was my grandmother, that she was Jewish, and dyed her hair.

The last of these items was a canard. Her hair was naturally black, black as a raven's wing and with a fine silky gloss, like loose skeins of embroidery thread. When she was over eighty and bedridden, the first sprinkling of white hairs began to appear in her thick, shining permanent. Brushing it, the nurses used to marvel ("Wonderful, isn't it? You'd swear, at first, it was dye"), but this triumph over her calumniators came too late. The nurses could testify, my uncles and their wives could testify, I could testify, but whom were we to tell? Within the immediate family, we had always given her the benefit of the doubt, though I recall my grandfather's uneasy face when she went to have her first permanent, for in those days dyed hair did not take well to the process and was reputed to turn green or orange. It was the outsiders—the distant in-laws, the ladies who bowed to my grandmother in the shops and then turned aside to whisper something—whom I should have liked to make eat their words now, and in particular my other grandmother, with her reiterated, crushing question "Who ever saw natural hair *that* color?" But she was in her mausoleum, unavailable for comment, and the others were gone, too. My grandmother had outlived them all—an unfortunate state of affairs. Moreover, she herself was no longer in a condition to appreciate or even understand her victory; on her energetic days she would ask me to fetch her hand mirror from her bureau, and, frowning into it, would set herself to plucking out those stray white hairs, not realizing that they were the proof she had long been needing to show that her hair was truly black.

She had been a beautiful woman—"the most beautiful woman in

Seattle," my friends' mothers used to tell me, adding that my mother, in her day, had been the most beautiful woman in Seattle, too. I can see it in the case of my mother, but my grandmother does not appear beautiful to me in the few photographs that exist of her as a young woman. Handsome, I would say, with a long, narrow, high-nosed, dark-eyed, proud, delicate face, the pure forehead topped by severe, somewhat boyish curls, such as the Romantic poets used to cultivate. A Biblical Jewish face that might have belonged to the young Rachel when Jacob first saw her. Her ears were pierced, and in one photograph she is wearing a pair of round, button-style earrings that lend her, somehow, a Russian appearance; in another, where she is posed with my mother as a little girl, her hair is caught in a big dark hair ribbon that gives her the air of a student. She has a gentle, open, serious mien—qualities I would never associate with the sharp, jaunty woman I knew or with the woman of the mature photograph on her chiffonier. Perhaps fashions in photography are responsible for the difference or perhaps her character changed radically during the early years of her marriage. The long, dreamy countenance became short, broad, and genial; the wide eyes narrowed and drew closer together. The change is so profound as to evoke the question "What happened?" The young woman in the photographs looks as though she could be easily hurt.

She came to Seattle from San Francisco, where her father had been what she called a "broker." Whether or not she meant a pawnbroker, I never could discover. He was a Forty-niner, having gone out to California in the gold rush, after a year in Pennsylvania. He had left Europe during the troubles of '48, and I like to think he was a political émigré, but I do not know. I do not know, though I once asked her, what part of Europe he came from. Poland, I suspect; her name, however, was German: Morganstern. Her first name was Augusta. These few sketchy facts were all she seemed to know of her early life and family history, and it puzzled her that anyone should want to find out more. "All those old things, Mary," she would say to me half grumpily. "Why do you keep asking me all those old things?" Like many great beauties, she had little curiosity; for nearly ten years she did not know the name of the family who had moved into the house next door to us.

Her parents had died when she was quite young—in her teens—and she and her younger sister, my Aunt Rosie, came to live in Seattle with an older sister, Eva, who had married a fur importer named Aronson; this was the lady with the polar-bear rug. The girls had had some private education; my grandmother, at one time, used to play the piano—rather prettily, I imagine. She had a pleasing speaking voice and a surprising knowledge of classical music. "Were you rich or poor?" I asked her once, trying to learn the source of these accomplishments. "My father had a nice business," she replied. She had read the Russian novelists; when I sought to introduce her to Tolstoy and Dostoevski, she gave her dry laugh and said they had been the popular writers of her youth. All her life, she retained a taste for long novels that went on from generation to generation, on the model of "War and Peace." She hated short stories, because, she said, just as you got to know the characters, the story ended; it was not worth the trouble. Her sister Rose was fourteen when the two arrived in Seattle; Aunt Rosie went out and inspected the University of Washington, which had just been started, and decided she knew more than the professors did—a fact she faced up to ruefully, since she had been yearning for a higher education.

Aunt Rosie was a very different person from my grandmother, yet they talked together on the phone for nearly an hour every day and often went "downtown" together in the afternoon, my grandmother stopping by at her house to pick her up in the electric, later in the Chrysler or the La Salle. Aunt Rosie was a short, bright, very talkative, opinionated woman, something of a civic activist and something of a bohemian. She had married an easygoing New York Jew, Uncle Mose Gottstein, a juicy, cigar-smoking man who ran a furniture store, subscribed to the New York *Times,* and liked to chat about current events, his cigar tilted at a reflective angle, upward, in his cherry-red mouth. He and Aunt Rosie often sat up all night in their first-floor bedroom, with its big walnut double bed, Uncle Mose in his nightgown reading the newspapers, and Aunt Rosie playing a solitaire, which she would not leave till it came out. Uncle Mose had fond recollections of Lüchow's (Jimmy Durante, he said, used to be a singing waiter there), and their big bedroom, strewn with newsprint and playing cards and smelling of cigar smoke, was like a club or a café. Aunt Rosie and her husband and their two sons always sat there, even in the daytime, instead of in the living room or the little parlor, which was lined with signed photographs of opera stars and violinists and pianists. Aunt Rosie had "known them all;" in her youth, she had been a vocal soloist, much in demand for weddings and special services in Seattle's Protestant churches. Later, she had managed the musical events at Seattle's Metropolitan Theatre; the high point of her life had been a trip she took to Vancouver with Chaliapin, about whom Uncle Mose liked to twit her, his small, moist eyes (he later developed cataracts) beaming behind his glasses, his apple cheeks flushed. Aunt Rosie had met other artists besides Chaliapin and the various divas, including Mary Garden and Galli-Curci, who had inscribed their photographs to her; thanks to her theatre connection, she had known Houdini and The

Great Alexander and could explain the magicians' acts by the fact that there was a trapdoor on the Metropolitan Theatre's stage. When I knew her, she was running the Ladies' Musical Club.

Aunt Rosie was poor–compared to her sisters. Her husband was the kind of man who is chronically unsuccessful in business–the genial uncle nearly every Jewish family possesses who has to be helped out by the others. Aunt Rosie had a plain "girl" to give her a hand with the housework; she dressed very unmodishly and lived in a somewhat rundown section, in a smallish frame house that needed painting. She was active in the temple as well as in the musical world. The cookbook of the Ladies' Auxiliary of the Temple de Hirsch, a volume got up for charity and much used in our family–I still own a copy–has many recipes contributed by Mrs. M. A. Gottstein. Her chicken stewed with noodles, hamburger in tomatoes, and rhubarb pie are quite unlike the recipes contributed by Mrs. S. A. Aronson, my other great-aunt, which begin with directions like this: "Take a nice pair of sweetbreads, add a cup of butter, a glass of good cream, sherry, and some foie gras." Or her recipe for baked oysters: "Pour over each caviar and cream, and dot with bits of butter. Serve hot."

Aunt Rosie, with her energy, her good heart and rattling, independent tongue, was a popular woman in Seattle, among all classes and kinds. Society ladies fond of music gushed over "the wonderful Mrs. Gottstein;" poor Jewish ladies in the temple praised her; Protestant clergymen respected her (they used to try to convert her when she was younger, she told me, because she sang their anthems with such feeling); judges, politicians, butchers, poor tailors, clerks in bookstores all knew Aunt Rosie. She had not let the Protestant ministers tempt her away from her religion, but she was a truly open person, able to cross barriers naturally because she did not notice they were there. Most of the Jews in Seattle lived a life apart, concerned with *bar mitzvahs* and weddings, and family and business affairs; a few, with German-sounding names, managed to cross into the Gentile world and get their sons pledged to regular fraternities at the University, leaving temple and observances behind them. Aunt Rosie was a unique case. Her Jewishness–that is, her bounce and volubility–was a positive asset to her in her dealings with the Gentile ascendancy. If my grandmother's marriage (to a Gentile) had made it a little easier for Aunt Rosie to get around, Aunt Rosie, I think, never suspected it; she had a lively self-conceit and no social envy or ambition. To her good-humored mind, being Jewish was simply a matter of religion.

Each of the three sisters had a different attitude toward her Jewish heritage, perhaps in each case conditioned by the man she had married.

Aunt Eva–Mrs. Aronson, whose husband, Uncle Sig, had long since passed on–was a typical wealthy widow of Jewish high society. She travelled a good deal, with a rather hard, smart set who had connections in Portland, San Francisco, and New York, and even in Paris; she gambled, and went to resorts and fashionable hotels in season; when she was in Seattle, she was a habitué of the Jewish country club, where they golfed in the daytime and played bridge for very high stakes at night. The scale of living of these people–widows and widowers, bachelors and divorcees, for the most part–was far beyond anything conceived of by the local Christian *haute bourgeoisie,* which was unaware of their existence. This unawareness was mutual, at least in the case of Aunt Eva, who, gyrating with perfect aplomb on her roulette wheel of hotels, yachts, race tracks, and spas, her white hairdress always in order, seemed ignorant of the fact that there was a non-Jewish society right under her nose, whose doings were recorded in the newspapers, daily and Sunday, whose members were "seen lunching" at the Olympic Hotel on Mondays, or golfing at the Seattle Golf Club, near The Highlands, or sunning at the tennis club on the lake.

Aunt Eva, I think, hardly realized that the world contained persons who were not Jewish. She, too, never knew envy; her nature was serene and imperturbable. My grandmother's mixed marriage never seemed to give Aunt Eva a qualm; her tall unawareness was sublime, a queenly attribute. If my grandfather was not "of the tribe," as my Irish relations used to call it suggestively, she did not give any sign of perceiving it. The "unpleasant" was barred by Aunt Eva, who seldom read anything and talked in magnificent generalities. She was fond of the theatre, and when she was not travelling, she used to go every week to see the Henry Duffy stock company in Seattle. My grandmother, Aunt Rosie, and I had strong opinions about these players ("He's a perfect stick," my grandmother almost invariably complained of the leading man), but to Aunt Eva there were no distinctions. Every play she saw she pronounced "very enjoyable." And the actors "took their parts well." We used to laugh at her and try to get her to acknowledge that the play was better some weeks than others. But Aunt Eva would not cross that Rubicon; she smelled a rat. To her, all the plays and players were equal, and equally, blandly good.

Toward the end of her life, she suffered cruelly from indigestion (the foie gras and the cup of butter, doubtless), and it was an awful thing to watch her, after a Sunday luncheon at our house, majestic and erect, walk about our back living room, her lips bubbling a little and her face pale-vanilla-colored and contorting slightly from spasms of pain. "Gas," she would say, with dignity. It tortured me to see this highly aristocratic lady reduced by her stomach to what I felt must be a horrible embarrassment for her, but her unawareness seemed to extend to the "unpleasant" aspect of her sufferings; she entertained them, as it were, graciously, like a hostess. My grandfather showed her great sympathy during these ordeals of hers; she was his favorite, I think, among my grandmother's relations. Having helped her with her business affairs, he must have come to realize that Aunt Eva, unlike her sisters, was extremely stupid. Perhaps this regal stupidity, like that of a stately white ox, elicited his chivalry, for he was a gallant man, or perhaps the slow, measured pace of her wits allowed him to forget that she was one of the Chosen (another classic epithet dear to my Irish relations).

How did my grandfather feel about the Jews? Again, I do not know; this was one of the many mysteries that surrounded our family life. He almost never attended church, except to be a pallbearer at a funeral, but he was by birth a Presbyterian Yankee, the son of a West Point man who was head of a military college in Norwich, Vermont, commanded a Negro regiment during the Civil War, and was retired as a brigadier general. Simon Manly Preston was my great-grandfather's name (wife: Martha Sargent, born in New Hampshire), and he lived to be ninety-nine; his last years were passed in Seattle, where he was one of the local curiosities. All his progeny, including Uncle Ed, another West Point man, who died in his fifties, were eventually drawn to Seattle: my grandfather, Harold; my Great-Uncle Clarence; and my Great-Aunt Alice, who married a law partner of my grandfather's, Eugene H. Carr, and lived for a time in Alaska. My grandfather first came West working as a geodetic surveyor during his college vacation (he started at Cornell and finished at what is now Grinnell College, in Iowa), and when he had his A.B. degree, he decided to read law in Seattle. It was then that he must have first met my grandmother, aged circa seventeen, who was living in the house of the fur importer, Sigismund Aronson. Did this name ring strangely in my grandfather's Yankee ears? Possibly not. Seattle was a frontier town, where you could expect to meet all kinds—French and Dutch and Germans, aristocrats and plebeians. Many of our first families had aristocratic pedigrees (the de Turennes, the von Phuls), yet it used to be said of every first family that the great-grandfather "came here with his pack on his back." My grandmother was courted by a number of suitors, including one, George Preston, who had the same last name as my grandfather. She had Jewish beaux also, I discovered, and, as far as I could make out, she did not distinguish between the two kinds. They were assorted young men who took her driving; that was all.

"As far as I could make out"—this matter was impossible to probe with my grandmother. I don't think I ever used the word "Jewish" in any connection when talking with her. I sensed she would not like it. I used to think about the word a lot myself, when I first came back to Seattle and was sent as a five-day boarder to a Sacred Heart Convent. I thought about it partly because of the ugly innuendoes dropped by my father's people, but chiefly because I was in love with my cousin, Aunt Rosie's tall, ravishing son Burton, who was twenty-one, ten years older than I, and I worried, being a Catholic, about the impediments to our marriage: the fact that he was my first cousin once removed, and the difference in religion—would he have to be baptized? This passion of mine was secret (or at least I hope it was), but even if it had not been, I could not have discussed the problem with my grandmother because of that unmentionable word.

I myself had a curious attitude, I now realize, in which the crudest anti-Semitism ("Ikey-Mose-Abie," I used to chant, under my breath, to myself in the convent) mingled with infatuation and with genuine tolerance and detachment. I *liked* Uncle Mose and Aunt Rosie far better than any other older people I knew, and "Ikey-Mose-Abie" represented what I supposed others would think of them. It was a sort of defiance. If I identified a little bit of myself with those others, my dead mother had gone much further; one day I found a letter she had written to my Grandmother McCarthy in which she spoke of an evening "with the Hebrews." Finding this letter was one of the great shocks of my adolescence. It destroyed my haloed image of my mother, and the thought that her mother must have read it, too (for there it was, in my desk, put away for me with other family keepsakes), nearly made me ill.

Perhaps I was too sensitive on my grandmother's behalf. No secret was ever made of the family connection with Aunt Rosie and Aunt Eva, and whenever my grandmother gave a tea, it always appeared in the paper that Mrs. M. A. Gottstein and Mrs. S. A. Aronson poured. I used to hear about some distant cousin's having a *bar mitzvah,* and once I was taken to a Jewish wedding, which fascinated me because it was held at night in a hotel ballroom. Nevertheless, there was *something,* a shying away from the subject, an aversion to naming it in words—so persistent that I was startled, one morning, when I was about sixteen, to hear my grandmother allude to "my faith." I had been talking to her about my disbelief in God, and to my surprise she grew quite agitated. She no longer practiced her faith, she declared, but she was certain that there was a kind God who understood and who watched over everything. She spoke with great feeling and emphasis—a rare thing in our relationship.

It was characteristic of her queer, oblique nature that I should have chanced to find out that she had had Jewish suitors by idly asking her the names of the young men she had driven out with. She gave them with perfect readiness, but without any indication that such a name as Schwabacher or Rosenblatt would tell a story to me. If it had been a major step to marry outside her own people, she did not seem to recall this any more, and, of course, I could not ask her.

Yet in other respects she was remarkably frank. "How did you come to marry Grandpa?" I asked her one night, when I was home on a visit after I myself had married. "Rosie and I didn't get along with Uncle Sig," she answered matter-of-factly.

So that was all; I could hardly believe my ears, and wondered whether she realized the enormity of what she was saying. "But why did you pick Grandpa instead of one of the others?" I pressed her, determined, for Grandpa's sake, that she should answer that it had been because of his eyes or his mustache or his intellect. She appeared to search her memory, in vain. "Oh, I don't know, Mary," she said, yawning. "You *must* know," I retorted. She thought he would be good to her, she finally conceded.

This archaic view of the function of a husband astonished me. But for her, as I soon learned, it was the prime, the only, consideration. "Is he good to you?" she asked me, another night, on that same visit, speaking of my new husband. I had to stop and think, because marriage had never presented itself to me in this light. "Why, yes, I suppose so," I said slowly. "Yes, of course he is." My grandmother nodded and reopened her evening newspaper. "That's all right, then." The subject of my new husband was closed. "Grandpa was always good to me," she resumed tranquilly, turning to the racing column and beginning to mark her selections for the next day's pari-mutuel.

What did these words mean? Kindness, patience, forbearance—or fur coats and jewelry? Or was it all the same thing? Love, evidently, was as foreign a concept to her as this "goodness" was to me. She did not want to hear about love; it irritated her. The words "I love him" were meaningless sounds to her ears; if I uttered them in her hearing, which at length I had the sense not to do, I might as well have been talking Chinese. She did not care for love stories, which she pronounced trash, and she used to make fun of the movie actors who were my heroes as a young girl. "He has such thick lips," she used to say of Ronald Colman, mimicking his expression by thrusting out her own lower lip. "And that mustache! Think of kissing that bristly mustache!" Ricardo Cortez, she said, mimicking his expression, "looked as if he had a stomach ache." Yet her own favorite was Adolphe Menjou. My grandfather liked Lewis Stone.

She was not so much cynical as prosaic. She made fun of the young men who used to come to take me out when I was home from college on vacations by seizing on some small detail of their appearance and relentlessly exaggerating it: curly hair, rosy cheeks, full lips, large ears. This was not done maliciously but in high-humored jest, as though *she* were the young girl mocking her suitors behind their backs to her audience of sisters. I never minded it (though I had minded about Ronald Colman), but it struck me as unfair in the abstract; the part was always greater to her than the whole, and some of the things she noticed would have escaped the attention of anyone but a phrenologist.

Her marriage had been successful, and she attributed this to a single simple recipe, like one of the Household Hints in the back of the Temple de Hirsch cookbook, on how to clean ermine (rub with corn meal) or how to extract grease from papered walls (flannel and spirits of wine). She had never let a quarrel continue overnight. No matter how mad she was at Grandpa, she told me, she always kissed him good night. And, a corollary, no matter how mad she was in the morning, she always kissed him goodbye before he went to the office. She passed this recipe on to me gravely after I had been divorced; if I would just follow it, I would never have any more trouble, she was certain. This advice made me smile; it was so remote in its application to my case. But she shook her head reprovingly as she stood in front of her mirror, undoing her pearls for the night. "Remember, Mary," she enjoined. "All right," I said lightly. "I'll remember. 'Always kiss him good night.' " She had felt the moment as a solemn one, like the time she had spoken of "my faith," yet in an instant she, too, was smiling broadly. An anecdote had occurred to her, and she began to tell me, acting out both parts, of a morning when Grandpa had left for his office without the usual morning salute. . . . From one point of view, her entire married life was a succession of comic anecdotes, of which she was both butt and heroine.

These anecdotes began before her marriage, with the time the horse ran away with her and George Preston in the buggy, and Grandpa was terribly jealous. Then there was her honeymoon: how he had taken her back to Iowa to visit his family, who had settled there after the Civil War. It was winter, and before they left, my grandfather kept asking her whether she had enough clothes. She answered yes each time, but the question puzzled and offended her, for she took it as a criticism of her wardrobe. "I had very nice clothes," she explained. What he meant, it turned out, was long underwear, but he was too delicate to name it, so she went ignorantly on to Newton, Iowa, in her fine batiste-and-lace underclothing; she could never tolerate anything else next to her skin—

silk was too coarse. In the barbarous Midwestern climate, she nearly froze to death, she declared, and she came out in chilblains all over. She nearly died of boredom also.

The provinciality of her in-laws horrified her. She had never met people like this, whose idea of a social evening was to stand around the stove, clad in long underwear and heavy dark clothing, the men cracking one joke after another. She could see that her in-laws, with the exception of Great-Grandpa Preston, did not like her. "They thought I was fast and stuck-up." She could not eat their food or put on the union suit they offered her. They were displeased by her elegant clothes and by her smiles and laughter. They only laughed, shortly, at the humorless jokes they told. Alone in her bedroom with her husband, she cried and cried, and finally she made him have a telegram sent to himself calling him back to Seattle. After the telegram came, her father-in-law, the General, took them to Chicago, which was supposed to be a treat. But they put up at an awful boarding house, where she could not eat the food, either. The two men stayed out all day, looking at sights like the stockyards, and the other boarders scared her, they were so rough and crude in their manners. That was the end of her honeymoon, and on the train going back she made my grandfather promise that he would never take her to Newton again.

Later, they went to Chicago for the World's Fair with my Aunt Eva, and this was the subject of another anecdote. She and Aunt Eva were left at a stop in Montana, when the train drew out unexpectedly while they were buying postcards in the station. Another passenger, a man, seeing their predicament, jumped out of the train and said to my grandmother, "Can I be of assistance to you, Madam?" Somehow (I forget the details), he managed to get the train to come back for them or to wait at the next station for them to arrive by carriage. But my grandfather was terribly jealous; as soon as he saw them again, he accused my grandmother of having got off the train to be with the strange man. And she never could convince him differently all the rest of her life.

There was the time the house caught on fire while my grandmother was downtown shopping. When she boarded the Cherry Street trolley to go home (her house was way out, almost in the country, then), the conductor said to her, "Mrs. Preston, your house is on fire," and she arrived on the scene to find the fire engine there and their one-eyed maid, Tilda (yes, so my grandmother swore), carrying the piano out of the house balanced on one hand, like a tray; all the little boys in the neighborhood were sitting on the lawn reading her love letters from my grandfather, which they had found in a bureau drawer. There was the time her riding horse ran away with her, down in Gearhart, Oregon, and there was an incident, I think, with a rowboat. There was the time she came to our house, when my mother had been taken to the hospital to have our little brother, and found the three of us sitting on the floor of the living room making a bonfire of my father's lawbooks and pointing his loaded revolver at each other.

My grandmother was a gifted *raconteuse* when she could be induced to tell one of her stories. She acted out all the parts zestfully, particularly her own, and short trills of unwilling laughter proceeded from her as she spoke; when she had finished, she would have to wipe her eyes with a handkerchief. This power of being amused at herself, this perpetual dismay, made one see her in these disconcerting situations, which had a classic plot–the plot of a nightmare, really.

Someone, usually a man, laconically breaks her an untoward piece of news, or fails to break it successfully, as in the case of the long underwear. Or it is a runaway horse, a runaway train, a runaway buggy, a rocking boat, a loaded revolver; my grandmother is always helpless while some uncontrollable event unfolds before her eyes. (There was the story of the crazy piano tuner who without a by-your-leave walked into her parlor and took the piano apart as my grandmother watched, unable to stop him, bewitched by his flow of talk: "A beautiful instrument, Madam. . . . So you have neglected your lovely musical gift [an imitation of him shaking his head]. Believe me, Madam, you owe it to the world and to your husband and family to take up the instrument again. . . ." At the end of the story, naturally, the dismembered piano was lying on the floor; he had forgotten how to put it together again.) She is always the loser in these anecdotes; she never gets the better of the situation with a biting retort, as she often did in real life. But because she is the heroine, she is usually rescued, in the nick of time.

In my grandmother's narratives, it is the other person who is self-possessed, full of an almost supernatural assurance–the stranger alighting from the moving train in a single airy bound, like an acrobat sliding down a rope to bow at her feet. She is forever disconcerted, put out of countenance, dumb-struck. In reality, *she* was the disconcerting one, short of speech when she was not telling a story (and to get her to tell a story usually took a lot of coaxing), impassive, forbidding. Most people, including all my friends, were afraid of her.

The first thing that would have struck an outsider about her in her later years–that is, when she was in her sixties and seventies–was the oddity of her appearance. If you saw her downtown, shopping in Frederick's or Magnin's–and she never did anything but shop any afternoon of her life, excluding Sundays, matinée days, and the days of the race meetings—you would probably ask the salesgirl who she was: a woman of medium height, a little plump but not fat, wearing a small, high-crowned hat topped with ribbons or feathers, pumps with Cuban heels, fabric gloves, an onyx-and-diamond *lorgnon,* a smart dress in black or navy, printed or solid-color, with a fur piece over it—silver fox or baum marten. This would be in summer. In the fall, she might be wearing a dark-green wool ensemble, or a black one trimmed with monkey, or a beige one trimmed with beige broadtail or caracul. In the winter, she would have on her mink or her Persian or her squirrel or her broadtail. She would be proceeding at a stately walk through the store, stopping to finger something at a counter, smiling at the salespeople, nodding. Her clothes in themselves should not have attracted attention. She disliked bright colors and never wore anything but black, navy, dark green, beige, or wine. Nor were the styles youthful or extreme. She was careful about her skirt lengths; her dresses were lavish in tucks and shirring, but the cut was simple and discreet. She wore small pearl earrings and a short string of pearls; her rings were concealed by her gloves. Underneath the gloves, her nails were natural-color, polished with a buffer. Nor did her toilet table contain a lipstick. Yet the whole effect she made was of an indescribable daring.

It was partly the black hair, so improbably black and glossy. It was partly the mascara and the eyeshadow surrounding her narrow black watchful eyes, though these aids to beauty were not applied carelessly but with an infinite discretion. It was the rouge, perhaps, most of all, the rouge and the powder and the vanishing cream underneath. When she perspired, on a warm day, the little beads of sweat on her eagle nose under her nose veil and on her long upper lip would produce a caked look that seemed sad, as though her skin were crying. Yet not even her cosmetics and the world of consummate artifice they suggested could account for the peculiarly florid impression she made as she moved across the store, peering through her *lorgnon* at the novelties and notions, and vanished into the elevator, up to the lending library or the custom-made or the hat department—her favorite purlieus—where elderly salespeople, *her* salespeople, would hurry up to greet her, throwing their arms around her, just as though they had not seen her the day before.

"Have you got anything for me?" my grandmother would demand of Mrs. Slaughter, the red-haired hat lady at Frederick's, surveying the premises with a kind of jesting coquetry, a hand on her hip. This was the same tone she took with the clerks in the circulating library or with the butcher on the telephone—a tone of challenging banter, as though she defied these people, her suitors, to please her.

On a good day, Mrs. Slaughter would bring out two or three hats she had "put away" for my grandmother in a special cupboard. "They just came in," she would whisper. "I've been saving them for you." My grandmother would try them on before the mirror, tilting her head sidewise and back in an odd way she had, at once vain and highly self-critical. If she liked one of them well enough, she would walk to the full-length mirror and assay herself, thrusting one small foot forward and balancing back and forth, seeming to weigh herself and the hat in the scales of judgment. To my disappointment, watching her, she never bought on the spot. She would set the hat or hats down on the table, as if she were through with them, and Mrs. Slaughter, who seemed to be a mind reader, would whisk them back into the special cupboard, where they would wait, out of sight of other customers, for several days or even a week, while my grandmother arrived at a decision. She was the same with her shoes and dresses; she would even coquette with a piece of meat. It was as though she would not give these things the satisfaction of letting them see that she liked them. To her, every piece of merchandise, suing for her favor, appeared to enter the masculine gender and to be subject, therefore, to rebuff. Yet the salespeople were all eager to oblige her, for she was a good customer and, more than that, underneath her badinage, always good-humored.

It pleased her to pretend to be cross with them; indeed, in all her dealings she had an air of just consenting to be mollified. Her veteran salespeople would flatter her ("You're looking younger every day, Mrs. Preston. Nobody would believe this young lady was your granddaughter. Make her pass for your daughter"), and my grandmother would hide her gratification in a short, tart, scathing laugh. Actually, they were proud of her, for she did look remarkably young, despite her blazonry of makeup; she *could* have passed for my mother. They were genuinely fond of her. "Take care of yourself," they would call after her, and some of them used to kiss her. My grandmother pretended to be suspicious of these manifestations; a muscle moved, like a protest, in her cheek while the kiss was being planted.

She was lonely. That was the thing that made her seem so garish and caused people to turn their heads when she went by. Loneliness is a garish quality, and my grandmother's wardrobe and elaborate toilette appeared flamboyant because they emphasized her isolation. An old woman trying to look young is a common enough sight, but my grandmother was something stranger and sadder—a hermit all dressed up for a gala, a recluse on stubborn parade. Tagging along, I was half conscious, even as a little girl, of the bizarre figure my grandmother cut, and if I had not known her, my imagination might have woven some story around her for a school composition—the holocaust, at the very least, of all her nearest and dearest, her husband gone to prison, her children branded as traitors. . . .

But in fact, during the years I knew her best—the years after I had left the convent and was in boarding school in Tacoma—she had a husband; two sons, whom she saw every day (one of them lived at home and went to the University, and the other lived across the street with an exemplary wife); two sisters, whom she saw nearly every day; a sister-in-law, Aunt Alice Carr, who lived downtown in the Sorrento Hotel; a granddaughter (myself) who came home from school for vacations; a cook; and an old gardener who had been with her twenty-five years—the original family coachman. All these people were devoted to her. She was independent; she had her own investments and drove her own car. Every winter, my grandfather took her to California, where they ate at the best restaurants and lived at the best hotels and went to the races at Tijuana, over the border. He was a distinguished citizen, with a prosperous law practice, a reputation for immense integrity, and countless friends and cronies. During my sophomore year in boarding school, he took her to New York, where they saw nearly every play on the boards and she had an outfit made by a smart new designer in a new color called "kasha," an exact copy of an outfit worn by Katharine Cornell in "The Green Hat," and he took her to Washington, where they had an interview with Calvin Coolidge.

She had nothing to complain of in life. There was nothing wrong with her health, except for a mild diabetic condition, which the best local specialist was controlling, and a high blood pressure that was not dangerous but that gave her headaches in the afternoons. Nor did she complain; she was a little fretful sometimes when she was having her headaches, but she possessed an equable temper—the result, no doubt, of self-discipline. She and I used to quarrel, and she had much to find fault with in my conduct. She worried a good deal about her younger son's late hours. But she was never cross or nagging. It was only much later, when she grew senile, that she became difficult to deal with, capricious and fault-finding, sending the cook downtown to return a mascara applier that dissatisfied her, pushing her food away, soughing and making faces.

But until she reached her second childhood she seemed, on the surface, a contented woman, well situated in life, self-contained, unemotional. The only blights she had suffered, so far as I knew, were the unseasonable death of my mother and a mastoid operation that had left her with some scars just under her ears, in her neck and lower cheeks. If she was cold to me for a few days, or stopped speaking, abruptly, to Gertrude, or feuded with my grandfather's brother, Uncle Clarence, these were mere quirks—the privileges of beauty—that did nobody any harm. She was not a demonstrative person, but neither were her sons or her husband or her daughter-in-law; they all seemed to have been cut from the same bolt of cloth. I was the only member of the family—not counting Aunt Rosie—who was excitable.

When I was brought back from Minneapolis to live with my grandparents, I was impressed by our house and its appurtenances, much as I had been as a young child—the bay-window seat in the parlor, the cabinet with opaline Tiffany glass and little demitasse cups, all different, the grass wallpaper, the pongee-silk curtains, the sleeping porches upstairs, the hawthorn tree in front of the house, the old carriage block with the name "PRESTON" carved on it, the date "1893" over the front door, the Kelvinator in the kitchen, the bell system, the generator in the garage that charged the electric, the silver samovar, the Rhine-wine glasses (never used), with green bowls and crystal stems. To me, the house was like a big toy, full of possibilities for experiment and discovery; I was constantly changing my sleeping quarters—out to the sleeping porch behind my bathroom, upstairs to the little room under the eaves on the cook's floor, back again to my green-and-violet bedroom. Once I even got permission to sleep outdoors, in the moonlight, on the back lawn, overlooking the lake.

The room I was given had been redone for me; I had lots of pretty new clothes, made by my grandmother's own dressmaker; the gardener drove me about in the electric and let me practice steering; I did not have to wear glasses any more, as I had had to in Minneapolis, and I could read anything I wanted to in my grandfather's library: Dickens and Frank Stockton and Bulwer-Lytton and Sienkiewicz, and the Elsie Dinsmore books, which had belonged to my mother. I could look through the stereoscope, or play an old record of "Casey at the Bat" on the new Victrola. Everything we had seemed superior to anything anyone else had—the flowers in our garden, the vegetables on the table, which we grew ourselves in the lower garden instead of getting them from the store, as other people did. We had strawberry beds, too, and rows of currant bushes, a crab-apple tree and two kinds of cherry trees, black and Royal Ann, and—something very special for Seattle—my grandmother's favorite, an apricot tree. At Christmas, we had our own holly, cut from a tree in the front yard; the idea that this was better than other holly persisted in my grandmother's mind to the very end, for every year until she died, a box would arrive for me, just before Christmas, in New England, from Seattle, packed full of holly from the Preston tree. My grandmother's gardening was a distinguished, personal thing; she never joined a garden club or pored over seed catalogues, or exchanged slips or compared notes with other gardeners. Every morning after breakfast, she gave directions to the old gardener, descending from the back porch in a farmer's straw hat and a smock, with a basket over her arm, to pick flowers for the day's bouquets and supervise the new asparagus bed he was laying out or the planting of the new variety of sweet corn they were trying.

She was greedy, in a delicate way, picking daintily at her food, yet finishing off a whole bowl of fresh apricots or a dozen small buttered ears of the tenderest white corn. She had a cormorant's rapacity for the first fruits of the season: the tiniest peas, the youngest corn, baby beets cooked with their greens. This emphasis of hers on the youth of the garden's produce made her fastidious appetite seem a little indecent—cannibalistic, as though she belonged to a species that devoured its own young. "Take a spring chicken," many of her recipes began, and the phrase often salted her conversation. "She's no spring chicken," she would say of another woman. Baby beets, new potatoes, young asparagus, embryonic string beans, tiny Olympia oysters, tiny curling shrimps, lactary ears of corn—like my grandmother's clothes, our food was almost too choice, unseemly for daily use. The specialties of our table were like those of a very good hotel or club: Olympia-oyster cocktail and devilled Dungeness crabs; a salad, served as a first course, that started with a thick slice of tomato, on which was balanced an artichoke heart containing crabmeat, which in turn was covered with Thousand Island dressing and sprinkled with riced egg yolk; a young salmon served in a sherry sauce with oysters and little shrimps; eggs stuffed with chicken livers. We ate this company food every day; every meal was a surprise, aimed at pleasing some member of the family, as though we were all invalids who had to be "tempted." On Sundays, the ice cream, turned by the gardener in the freezer on the back porch, was chosen to suit me; we had strawberry (our own strawberries), peach, peppermint (made from crushed candy canes), and the one I was always begging for—bisque. Our icebox always contained a bowl of freshly made mayonnaise and a bowl of Thousand Island dressing, and usually a chicken or a turkey and a mold or *bombe* with maraschino cherries, whipped cream, and macaroons or ladyfingers in it. My grandmother's own palate was blander than the rest of the family's. I associate her with sweetbreads, with patty shells, and with a poulette sauce.

Or, if I shut my eyes, I can see her at the head of the table, on a summer morning, wearing her horn-rimmed reading glasses, the newspaper before her on a silver rack; there is a dish of fresh apricots in the middle of the table, and as she reads, her bare, plump white arm, as if absently, stretches out toward this dish; her slender, tapering fingers pinch the fruit, and she selects the choicest, ripest one. The process is repeated until the dish is empty, and she does not look up from her paper. I had a tremendous appetite myself ("If she assimilated all she ate, she'd be a mountain," my older uncle's wife used to comment after a Sunday-night supper), but my grandmother's voracity, so finical, so selective, chilled me with its mature sensuality, which was just the opposite of hunger. I conceived an aversion to apricots—a tasteless fruit anyway, I considered—from watching her with them, just as though I had witnessed what Freud calls the primal scene. Now I, too, am fond of them, and whenever I choose one from a plate, I think of my grandmother's body, full-fleshed, bland, smooth, and plump, cushioning in itself, close held—a secret, like the flat brown seed of the apricot.

This body of hers was the cult object around which our household revolved. As a young girl, I knew her shoe size and her hat size and her glove size, her height and weight, the things she ate and didn't eat, her preferences in underwear and nightgowns and stockings, the contents of her dressing table in the bathroom, down to the pumice stone that she used for removing an occasional hair from under her arms; one of her beauty attributes was that her white, shapely arms and legs were almost totally hairless, so that she never had to depend on a depilatory or a razor. No other woman has ever been known to me in such a wealth of fleshly, material detail; everything she touched became imbued for me with her presence, as though it were a relic. I still see her clothes, plumped to her shape, hanging on their velvet-covered hangers in her closet, which was permeated with the faint scents of powder and perfume, and the salty smell of her perspiration; she comes back to me in dress shields, in darned service-sheer stockings (for morning), in fagoting and hemstitching, in voile and batiste, in bouclé and monkey fur, in lace dyed écru with tea.

I never saw her undressed. Once, when she was in her seventies, I did catch a disturbing glimpse of her thighs, which were dazzling, not only in their whiteness and firmness but in the fineness of the skin's texture—closer to a delicate chiffon than to silk or satin. Disturbing because I knew she would not want to be looked at, even in admiration. She shared with my grandfather the mysteries of the big bathroom, but until she became bedridden, no one else, I think, ever saw her in less than her corset, camisole, and petticoat.

The big bathroom, which had a sofa covered with worn Oriental carpeting and an old-fashioned deep tub with claw feet, was the temple of her beauty, and I never went into it, even as a grown woman, without feeling as if I were trespassing. For me, as a young girl, it had all the attractions of the forbidden, and as soon as my grandmother left the house in the afternoon, I would fly in to examine her salves and ointments, buffers and pencils and swabs, brushes and tweezers, her jars and bottles from Elizabeth Arden, Dorothy Gray, Marie Earle, Helena Rubinstein, and Harriet Hubbard Ayer, her skin food, neck lotion, special astringent, and anti-wrinkle emollient, Hinds Honey and Almond, cucumber lotion, Murine, special eye lotion, Velva Cream, mascara, eyeshadow, dry rouge, paste rouge, vanishing cream, powders, chin strap, facial mask. One day, I found a box of something called Turkish Delight, which I took, from its name, to be a beauty preparation used in harems.

The room had a queer, potpourri smell; my grandmother seldom threw anything away, and some of her cosmetics were so old they had gone rancid. Another odor, medicinal, sometimes hung about the room in the morning; I smelled it on the days when I was allowed to have my hair washed in the basin there, by my grandmother's "woman." Actually, as I learned many years later, what I smelled was bourbon whiskey; my grandfather, though a temperate man, was accustomed to have two shots of bourbon before breakfast. The only other signs of his presence were a bottle of Eau Lilas Végétal—a purple cologne—on my grandmother's dressing table and some corn plasters in one of its drawers. He kept his shaving things, as I recall, in a small dressing room that opened off the big bathroom. You could find almost anything there: medicine, bath salts, an unopened bottle of Virginia Dare, family photographs, fishing tackle, Christmas presents that were being hidden, newspaper clippings that dated back to the time when my grandfather had been running for United States Senator. (He was defeated by Levi Ankeny, of Walla Walla.)

The temptation to try out some of my grandmother's beauty aids got the better of me when I was twelve. Unfortunately (like her Household Hint for a successful marriage), most of them had no bearing on my particular problems. "Not for the Youthful Skin," cautioned one astringent, and there was nothing in her crowded drawers for freckles. I did not need eyebrow pencil; my eyebrows were too thick already, and I had recently performed the experiment of shaving half of them off in the convent, while my grandparents were in California. My nose was my chief worry; it was too snub, and I had been sleeping with a clothespin on it to give it a more aristocratic shape. Also, I was bowlegged, and I was wondering about having an operation I had heard about that involved having your legs broken and reset. The dressing table offered no help on these scores, and, failing to find a lipstick and being timorous of the curling iron, I had to be satisfied with smearing a little paste rouge on my lips and putting dry rouge on my cheekbones (to draw attention away from the nose) and pink powder all over my face. I myself could see little change, but my grandmother could, and as soon as she came home that afternoon, a terrible scene took place, for I felt so guilty at what I had done that I would not admit I had been "into" her dressing table, even when confronted with the proof in the disarrayed drawers and the rouge that came off on the handkerchief she applied firmly to my cheek.

She did not actually, as I learned later, think that what I had done was so bad; it was the lying that offended her. But I was convinced that I had committed a real crime, so terrible that I might be sent away from home. The idea that I was not to touch my grandmother's things had impressed itself on my excitable mind like a Mosaic commandment. I had left the well-codified Catholic world in which my young childhood had been spent, and in this new world I could no longer tell what was a mortal and what a venial sin. The bathroom figured to me as the center of everything in the Preston family life from which I was excluded. I had begun to wonder about this family life a little; it was not as much fun as I had thought at first. In spite of the glamour that lay on it like a spell, I was not having as good a time, nearly, as my schoolmates had. Yet when I tried to determine what was different, the only thing I could put my finger on then was that, unlike other people, we did not have a regular lunch at home, and that at the time most people were lunching my grandmother was in the bathroom with the door shut.

This seems a small complaint, but the clue to everything was there. When I think of our house now, the strongest memory that comes back to me is of shut doors and silence. My young uncle, five years older than I was, had his own apartments, reached by a dark set of stairs that branched off the main staircase at the landing; my grandmother and grandfather had their separate chain of rooms, connected by a series of inner doors; the cook had her own, on the third floor, though she had to tiptoe down to share my bathroom; the gardener lived over the garage in rooms I never saw. There was no guest room.

During the greater part of the day, the upstairs hall was in gloom, because every door opening off it, except mine, was shut. The common rooms downstairs—the library, parlor, and living room—were seldom used in the daytime by anyone but me. The rest of the family kept to their own quarters; you would have thought the house was empty when everyone was home. I remember those summer mornings during school vacations. The mornings of the long years of my teens were so alike that they might have been one morning. The silence was profound. Every member of the family, except me, was taciturn—the cook and the gardener, too. After a wordless breakfast (my grandfather had already gone to the office), I was left to my own devices while my grandmother went out to the garden, picked flowers, then arranged them in the pantry; every vase in the house was renewed daily, but I was not allowed to help with the bouquets. Then she climbed the stairs to her bedroom; the door was shut and stayed shut for an hour or more while she talked on the telephone to her sisters and the butcher. During this period, the stillness was broken only by the hum of the vacuum cleaner and the sound of the mail dropping through the slot in the front door.

There was never any interesting mail, just the *National Geographic, Vogue,* and the *American Boy* (which my grandfather, for some reason, had subscribed to for me), some ads and charitable appeals addressed to "The Honorable Harold Preston," and perhaps a letter from Aunt Eva or Aunt Alice Carr. After a time that seemed interminable, while I lay on the sofa reading and waiting for something to happen, the door to the old nursery upstairs, where my grandfather slept and my grandmother did her sewing, would open—a signal to me that I could come up if I wanted. Then, for another hour, we would sit opposite each other in the bay window, my grandmother mending, or looking through the latest copy of *Vogue,* I staring out the window and trying to start a conversation.

"What did Aunt Rosie have to say?" I would begin. "Oh, nothing," she would answer. "Just talk. You know Rosie." Or "Uncle Mose isn't feeling so well." Or "She had a letter from Mortie in New York." Silence. When she was finished with the magazine, she would pass it on to me, and I would study the society notices of weddings and engagements, but there was never anything from Seattle. New York, Chicago, Boston, San Francisco—that was all. You would think, to read *Vogue,* that nothing ever happened in Seattle, a supposition that, from where *I* sat, was true. Yet I never lost hope; I think I somehow expected to find my own name in those columns, just as I somehow expected that, down below, a roadster would turn the corner with a boy in it who had discovered that I existed. My interest in boys was one of the many subjects I could not discuss with my grandmother; I was not supposed to be aware of them until I was in college. Indeed, the only topics we had in common were clothes and movie actors and actresses. She disliked the kind of books I read and would have disliked the girls I saw if she had had any inkling of what they were like. She would never give her opinion of any member of the family, including those she was "mad" at. For all my fishing, I could never find out even a simple thing, such as what she thought of me.

The liveliest time we had, in all the mornings we sat opposite each other in the nursery, was when I wrote in for a Vogue pattern to make a tennis dress. If I could have learned to sew, or she had had the patience to teach me, we might have found a medium in which we could communicate. The tennis dress, thanks to her help, did not come out too badly, and, encouraged, I wrote for another pattern–a model far too old for me, in tiers of crêpe de Chine that were supposed to shade from a pale yellow, through apricot, to flame. This dress was never finished; I found the blushing remains of it in a hall cupboard on my last visit home.

The dressmaking phase, of which my grandfather entertained great hopes, was a failure. We could never be "like mother and daughter" to each other, in spite of what people said. She could not bear to watch me sewing without a thimble and with a long thread that had a slightly dirty knot on the end of it. If I started on a piece of mending, my ineptitude always drove her to finish it.

Much of my adolescent boredom and discontent sprang from the fact that I had absolutely nothing to do but read and play the Victrola. I was not allowed in the kitchen, except to fix a sandwich for my lunch, because of a historic mess I had made with a batch of marshmallows; as with the dawn-colored dress, I had been too ambitious for a beginner. All I know today of sewing I learned in boarding school and, earlier, from the nuns in the convent, and the only person who was willing to show me anything about cooking was the old gardener-chauffeur, who used to come in and make German-fried potatoes for his lunch. On the cook's day out, he would let me watch him and then try it myself. In our family now, we have a dish called, in his memory, chauffeur-fried potatoes; they are very good.

My grandmother herself did not eat lunch as a regular thing, and at twelve o'clock, or sometimes earlier, my audience was over. She would get up from her chair and retire to the bathroom, shutting the door into the hall behind her. In a minute, her bedroom door closed, the nursery door closed. From then on till a time that varied between two and three o'clock, she was invisible; no one was allowed to disturb her. She was getting ready to go downtown. This sortie was the climax of her day. Her bedroom door would open, revealing her in festive array; every outfit she wore, like every meal, was a surprise. The car would be waiting in front of the old carriage block, and we would set off, sometimes stopping for Aunt Rosie. The next two or three hours would be spent in the stores, trying on, ransacking counters. My grandmother was not much interested in bargains, though we never missed a sale at Helen Igoe's or Magnin's; what she cared about was the "latest wrinkle" in dresses or furs or notions–news from the fashion front. During these hours, she reached her highest point of laconic animation and sparkle; she shopped like an epigrammatist in top form, and the extravagance of her purchases matched her brilliant hair and bobbing feathers and turkey walk and pursy pink cheeks.

But at a quarter of five, wherever we were, my grandmother would look at her watch. It was time to pick up Grandpa in front of his club, where he always played a rubber of bridge after leaving the office. At five o'clock, punctually, he would be on the sidewalk, anxiously surveying the traffic for us. The car would draw up; he would climb in and kiss my grandmother's cheek. "Have a good day?" he would ask. "All right," she would reply, sighing a little. We would get home at five-thirty; dinner was at six, punctually. During the meal, my young uncle would be queried as to how he had passed his day, and he would answer with a few monosyllables. My grandmother would mention the names of any persons she had seen on her shopping tour. My grandfather might praise the food. "Allee samee Victor Hugo," he would say, referring to a restaurant in Los Angeles. After dinner, my married uncle would drop in with his wife, perhaps on their way out to a party. My other uncle, yawning, would retire to his quarters. The doorbell might ring. I would run to answer it, and two or three of his friends would tramp past me upstairs to his rooms. The door on the landing would shut. In a little while, he would lope down the stairs to say that he was going out. He would kiss his mother and father, and my grandfather would say to him, "Home by eleven, son." My grandfather and grandmother, having finished the evening papers, would start playing double Canfield, at which my grandmother nearly always won. "I'll have to hitch up my trousers with a safety pin," my grandfather would say to me, jesting, as he paid over her winnings; this expression signified to him the depths of poverty.

Then he might go downtown to his club for a game of poker, or he might stay in his deep chair, smoking a cigar and reading a book that always seemed to be the same book: "The Life and Letters of Walter Hines Page." My grandmother would take up her circulating-library book, I would take up mine, and silence would resume its sway over the household. The only sound would be the turning of a page or the click of the door on the kitchen landing as the cook went upstairs to bed. Rarely, the telephone would ring, and I would rush to get it, but it was never anything interesting—someone for my uncle, or a girl for me, asking what I was doing. Or my grandmother would glance over at me as I lay stretched out on the sofa with my copy (disappointing) of "Mademoiselle de Maupin": "Mary, pull your dress down." At ten o'clock, she would close her book, sighing, and start out to the front hall, on her way to bed. "Going up, Mama?" my grandfather would say if he was at home, raising his gray eyes with an invariable air of surprise. "I think so, Harry," she would reply, sighing again, from the stairs. The stairs creaked; her door closed; the bathroom door closed. Soon my grandfather would put down his book and his paper knife, offer his cheek to me for a kiss, and follow her up the stairs. The nursery door would shut.

Occasionally, we would all go to the movies, or to the theatre if a New York company was in town; my grandfather did not care for stock. We saw "The Student Prince" and "No! No! Nanette!" I remember, and "Strange Interlude," which my grandmother pronounced "talky." On Thursday nights, we might go out to dinner at my grandfather's club. On Sundays, the cook left a supper prepared for us; my married uncle and his wife always came to this meal, no matter how many invitations they had to turn down, and sometimes Aunt Eva or Aunt Alice. These suppers usually ended with our going to the movies afterward; we were always home by eleven.

About once a year, or possibly every two years, my grandmother gave a tea and we had the caterer in. That was the only entertaining we did. Except for Aunt Alice and Aunt Eva (both widows), we never gave anyone dinner outside the immediate family. We never had Uncle Mose and Aunt Rosie, or Uncle Clarence and his wife, Aunt Abbie (a vegetarian pair), or any of my cousins and their wives, or my grandfather's partners and theirs. My grandmother's brother Elkan, whom she saw rarely but was not on bad terms with, was never, to my knowledge, in our house, nor were his wife or his numerous progeny. This leads me to wonder whether it was not the Jewish connection that had put the bar on entertaining. "If we have one in the house, we'll have them all," my grandfather may have said. But we did have Aunt Eva, frequently, and once, a great exception, her daughter from Portland, to Sunday lunch. The only other exception that comes back to me was a dinner we gave for old Judge Gilman, of the Great Northern, and his wife; I remember this because the men were served whiskey before dinner, the only time this ever happened in our house. But why we had Judge and Mrs. Gilman I do not know; I think it puzzled me at the time by introducing into my head the question of why we did not have other people, since on this occasion a good time was had by all.

Up to then, it had never occurred to me that my family was remarkably inhospitable. I did not realize how strange it was that no social life was ever planned for me or my young uncle, that no young people were invited for us and no attempt made to secure invitations on our behalf. Indeed, I did not fully realize it until I was over thirty and long a mother myself. If I did not have an ordinary social set but only stray, odd friends, I blamed this on myself, thinking there was something wrong with me, like a petticoat showing, that other people could see and I couldn't. The notion that a family had responsibility for launching the younger members was more unknown to me than the theorem of Pythagoras, and if anybody had told me of it, I think I would have shut my ears, for I loved my family and did not wish to believe them remiss in any of their obligations. The fact that they would not let me go out with boys was an entirely different case. I saw their side of it, even though I disagreed violently; they were doing it for my own good, as they conceived it.

And yet I knew there was something odd about my grandmother's attitude toward outsiders. She would never go up to Lake Crescent, in the Olympic Mountains, with my grandfather and my young uncle and me in the summertime, where, amid my grandfather's circle of friends and their descendants, we had the only regular social life I ever experienced in the West. Life in the mountain hotel was very gay, even for the old people—Judge and Mrs. Battle, Colonel Blethen, Mr. Edgar Battle, Mr. Claude Ramsay, Mr. and Mrs. Boole—in my grandfather's set. They had card games on the big veranda and forest walks up to the Marymere waterfall; they went on motorboat expeditions and automobile expeditions; they watched the young people dance in the evening and sent big tips to the chef in the kitchen. I could not understand why my grandmother preferred to stay in Seattle, pursuing her inflexible routine.

She was funny that way—that was the only explanation—just as she was funny about not letting my young uncle or me ever have a friend stay to dinner. In all the years I lived with my grandmother, as a child and as a woman, I can only recall two occasions when this rule was broken. The second one was when she was bedridden and too feeble, morally, to override my determination to ask a poet who was teaching at the University to stay and have supper with me. I felt a little compunction, though the nurse and the cook assured me that it would be all right—she would forget about it the next minute. But her pretty voice, querulous, was heard from upstairs at about eight-thirty in the evening: "Mary, has that man gone home yet?" And all through the rest of my visit she kept reverting crossly to the subject of "that man" who had stayed to supper; it was no good explaining to her that he had no means of getting home, that he lived in rooms way out at the University and took his meals in diners and tearooms, that he was an old friend to whom some hospitality was due in my native city. Nor could I laugh her out of it. "Why didn't he go home for his dinner?" she reiterated, and those dark, suspicious words were very nearly the last I heard from her.

This ungraciousness of my grandmother's was a deeply confirmed trait. It was not only that she resisted offering meals to anyone outside the immediate family; she took exception to a mere caller. There was a silver tray for calling cards on the hall table, but most of the cards in it were yellow with age; my grandmother was always downtown shopping at the hour when calls were normally paid. If I had a girl in for the evening, we could not really talk until my grandmother had gone to bed, and often she would outstay the guest, sitting in a corner with her book and glancing at us from time to time as we sat on the sofa endeavoring to improvise a dialogue. We could tell she was listening, but she did not talk herself. Suddenly, looking up, she would make the gesture to me that meant "Pull your skirt down."

My uncle's situation was the same, but he had the advantage of having his own sitting room, where his friends could congregate. For the most part, my grandmother ignored their presence; she would nod to them curtly if she chanced to meet them in the hall. The girls he knew were never asked to the house; he could never give a party.

Yet she was not an unkindly woman. She was good to her servants and their families, and on some occasions, if she was persuaded to unbend and tell an anecdote, she could be positively cordial. Her house, with its big rooms and wide porches, had been built, it would seem, with a hospitable *intention*. And in my mother's day, so I was told, things had been very different; the house had been full of young people. The silver and crystal and cut glass had not always been put away in the cupboard; there had been music and dancing, and my mother's school and college friends had spent night after night on the sleeping porches without even the necessity of a permission.

My mother had been my grandmother's darling. The fact that we did not entertain, I was given to understand, was related to my mother's death. My grandmother had resented her marriage to my father; according to my Irish relations, she would not have a priest in the house, and so the ceremony had been performed on the lawn. I do not believe this story, which is contradicted by other accounts, but it is true that my grandmother resented the Catholic Church, to which my mother was eventually converted. Dr. Sharples, the family physician, had told my father, it seems, that my mother's health would not stand her repeated pregnancies, but my father went right ahead anyway, refusing to practice birth control. Actually, my mother's death had nothing to do with childbearing; she died of the flu, like so many young women, during the great epidemic. But this would not have deterred a woman like my grandmother from holding my father and the Church responsible. That was perhaps the reason she took no interest in my three brothers, who were still living with my father's people in Minneapolis; she sent them checks and gifts at birthdays and Christmas, and remembered them later in her will, but during the years I lived with her, the three little boys who had been born against her judgment were very remote from her thoughts. Possibly I was enough of a handful for a woman of her age; nevertheless, it seems odd, unfeeling, that dry lack of concern, when she well knew that their lot was not happy. But happiness, like love, was a concept she had no real patience with.

As for the impassibility or aloofness she showed sometimes toward me, this may have been due to an absence of temperamental sympathy (could she have thought I had my father's traits?), or it may have been because I reminded her painfully of my mother (I was always conscious of a resemblance that did not go far enough; everyone was always telling me how "good" my mother had been).

For three years after my mother's death, one of her friends told me, my grandmother did not go out socially. Five years, said another. And this prolonged mourning was always offered as the official explanation of any oddities in our household. My grandmother, people said, lowering their voices, had never recovered from the shock of my mother's death. As a child, I could not quite believe this; it was impossible for me to imagine this contained, self-centered woman overcome by a passion of grief. Without being a psychologist, I felt somehow that her obdurate mourning was willful and selfish.

Children generally feel this about any adult emotion that is beyond their ken, but in my grandmother's case I think I was on the track of something real. Her grief had taken a form peculiar to herself, stamped, as it were, with her monogram—the severe "AMP," in scroll lettering, that figured on her silver, her brushes and combs, her automobile. Her grief had the character of an inveterate hostility. One of my mother's friends recently wrote me a letter describing how my grandmother had hurt her feelings by refusing to speak to her for a year after my mother's death whenever they met in the stores. "Your grandmother could not stand the sight of me," she sadly decided.

And that is how I see my grandmother, bearing her loss like an affront, stubborn and angry, refusing to speak not only to individual persons but to life itself, which had wounded her by taking her daughter away. Her grief was a kind of pique, one of those nurtured *grievances* in which she specialized and which were deeply related to her coquetry. If I had only her photographs to go on, I might doubt the legend of her beauty; what confirms it for me is her manner of grieving, her mistrust of words, her refusal to listen to explanations from life or any other guilty suitor. Life itself was obliged to court her—in vain, as it appeared, for she had been mortally offended, once, twice, three times.

What the first offense was, I do not know, but I presume it had something to do with her Jewish pride and sensitiveness; some injury was dealt her early in her marriage, and it may have been a very small thing —a chance word, even—that caused her to draw back into an august silence on this topic, a silence that lasted until her death. The second one I know about. This was the tragic face-lifting that took place—in 1916 or 1917, I imagine—when she was in her forties and my mother was still living. Perhaps she really did have a mastoid operation at some later period (I rather think she must have), but the disfiguring pouchy scars I have spoken of that started on her cheeks and went down into her neck were the work of a face-lifter, who, as I understand the story, had pumped her face full of hot wax.

Such accidents were common in the early days of face-lifting, and the scars, by the time she was sixty, were not especially noticeable. It was only that her cheeks had a puffy, swollen appearance, which her makeup did not conceal—in fact, if anything, enhanced, for though she did not know it, she always looked better in the morning, before she put on the rouge and powder that made her skin's surface conspicuous. But when the scars were new, they must have been rather horrifying, and that was surely the reason for the dotted veils she wore, pulled tight across her face. The photographs break off at the time of the operation. That was when she stopped speaking to the camera, and, according to one informant, my grandmother left Seattle for a year after the tragedy.

"According to one informant"—the story of the face-lifting was well known in Seattle, and yet in the family no mention was ever made of it, at least in my hearing, and I learned of it from outsiders, my father's people, friends of my mother's, who naturally were unable to supply all the details. I was grown up when I learned it, and yet that same unnatural tact that kept me from ever using the word "Jewish" to my grandmother kept me from prying into the matter with the family. "Your grandmother's tragedy"—so I first heard the face-lifting alluded to, if I remember rightly, by one of my friends, who had heard of it from her mother. And I will not query the appropriateness of the word in terms of the Aristotelian canon; in this case, common usage seems right. It was a tragedy—for her and for her husband and family, who, deprived of her beauty through an act of folly, came to live in silence, like a house accursed.

My grandmother's withdrawal from society must have dated, really, from this period, and not from the time of my mother's death, which came as the crowning blow. That was why we were so peculiar, so unsocial, so, I would add, slightly inhuman; we were all devoting ourselves, literally, to the cult of a relic, which was my grandmother's body, laved and freshened every day in the big bathroom, and then paraded before the public in the downtown stores.

I was living in New York when my grandfather died, of a stroke, one morning, when he was seventy-nine, in the big bathroom. My grandmother's ritual did not change. She still dressed and went downtown at the same hours, returning at the time when she would have picked him up at his club. She was cheerful when I saw her, a year or so after this. She went to the races and had a new interest, night baseball; we went to the ballpark together. Once in a great while, she would lunch and play bridge with a group of women friends, with whom she had resumed connections after twenty years. But she did not, to my knowledge, ever have them to her house; they met at the Seattle Golf Club usually, the best (non-Jewish) country club.

Like many widows, she appeared to have taken a new lease on life; I had never seen her so chatty, and she was looking very handsome. I remember an afternoon at the races, to which she drove Aunt Rosie and me in her car, at a speed of seventy miles an hour; she herself was well over seventy. The two sisters, one a lively robin and the other a brilliant toucan, chaffed and bantered with the sporting set in the clubhouse. Conscious of their powers and their desirability, they were plainly holding court. Aunt Rosie did not bet but advised us; my grandmother, as usual, won, and I think I won, too. That night, or in the small hours of the morning, Aunt Rosie died.

It was something that she had eaten at the races, Dr. Sharples thought; an attack of indigestion caused a heart block. He believed at first that he could save her, and I had persuaded my grandmother to go to bed, confident that Aunt Rosie would be almost herself the next day. But in the middle of the night the phone rang. I ran to get it. It was Uncle Mose: "Rosie just went." My grandmother understood before I could tell her, before I had set down the telephone. A terrible scream—an unearthly scream—came from behind the closed door of her bedroom; I have never heard such a sound, neither animal nor human, and it did not stop. It went on and on, like a fire siren on the moon. In a minute, the whole household was roused; everybody came running. I got there first. Flinging open her bedroom door (even then with a sense of trepidation, of being an unwarranted intruder), I saw her, on her bed, the covers pushed back; her legs were sprawled out, and her yellow batiste nightgown, trimmed with white lace, was pulled up, revealing her thighs. She was writhing on the bed; the cook and I could hardly get hold of her. My uncle appeared in the doorway, and my first thought (and I think the cook's also) was to get that nightgown down. The spectacle was indecent, and yet of a strange boudoir beauty that contrasted in an eerie way with the awful noise she was making, more like a howl than a scream, and bearing no resemblance to sorrow. She was trying, we saw, to pull herself to her feet, to go somewhere or other, and the cook helped her up. But then, all at once, she became heavy, like a sack full of stones. The screaming stopped, and there was dead silence.

Eventually, I forget how, but thanks chiefly to the cook, we got her calmed down to the point where she was crying normally. Perhaps the doctor came and administered a sedative. I sat up with her, embracing her and trying to console her, and there was something sweet about this process, for it was the first time we had ever been close to each other. But suddenly she would remember Rosie and shriek out her name; no one could take Rosie's place, and we both knew it. Then I felt like an utter outsider. It seemed clear to me that night, as I sat stroking her hair, that she had never really cared for anyone but her sister; that was her secret. The intellectual part of my mind was aware that some sort of revelation had been made to me—of the nature of Jewish family feeling, possibly. And I wondered whether that fearful, insensate noise had been classic Jewish mourning, going back to the waters of Babylon. Of one thing I was certain: my grandmother was more different from the rest of us than I could ever have conceived.

Uncle Mose was taking it well, I learned the next morning. It was only my grandmother, so unemotional normally, who had given way to this extravagant grief, and the family, I gathered, were slightly embarrassed by her conduct, as though they, too, felt that she had revealed something—something that, as far as they were concerned, would have been better left in the dark. But what *had* she revealed, as they saw it? Her essential Jewishness? I could never find out, for I had to take the train East that very day, with my baby, and when I came back, several years later, no one seemed to remember anything unusual about the occasion of Aunt Rosie's death.

"That's my sister!" my grandmother would exclaim, eagerly pointing, when we came to a photograph of Aunt Rosie. "My sister," she would say of Aunt Eva, in a somewhat grander tone. She always brightened when one of her sisters turned up in the photograph collection, like a child when it is shown its favorite stuffed animal. I think she was a little more excited at the sight of Aunt Rosie. By that time, I imagine, she had forgotten that her sisters were dead—or, rather, the concept death no longer had any meaning for her. They had "gone away," she probably believed, just as children believe that this is what happens to their dead relations. I used to stand ready to prompt her with the names, but she did not seem to need or want this; her sisters' relationship to her was what mattered, and she always got that straight. "Aunt Rosie," I would observe, showing her a picture of a small, smiling, dark woman in a big marabou hat. "My sister," her voice would override me proudly, as if she were emending my statement.

The clothes in the old photographs amused her. She had not lost her interest in dress, and was very critical of my appearance, urging me, with impatient gestures, to pull my hair forward on my cheeks, and surveying me with pride when I had done so; it gave a "softer" look. If I did not get it right, she would pull her own black waves forward, to show me what she meant. Though she could no longer go downtown, she still kept to the same schedule. Every day at twelve o'clock, the nurse would close my grandmother's door and the doors to the nursery and the bathroom, reopening them between two and three, when the beauty preparations had been completed. "You can come in now. Your grandmother is all prettied up." One afternoon, responding to the summons, I found my grandmother frowning and preoccupied. There was something the matter, and I could not make out what it was. She wanted me to get her something, the "whatchamacallit" from her bureau. I tried nearly everything–brush, comb, handkerchief, perfume, pincushion, pocketbook, photograph of my mother. All of them were wrong, and she grew more and more impatient, as if I were behaving like an imbecile. "Not the *comb*–the whatchamacallit!" Finally, for she was getting quite wrought up, I rang for the nurse. "She wants something," I said. "But I can't make out what it is." The nurse glanced at the bureau top and then went swiftly over to the chiffonier; she picked up the hand mirror that was lying there and passed it silently to my grandmother, who at once began to beam and nod. "She's forgotten the word for mirror," the nurse said, winking at me. At that moment, the fact that my grandmother was senile became real to me.

Exactly Eight Thousand Dollars Exactly and The Sun-Dodgers

John O'Hara

In addition to a now imposing list of novels, John O'Hara has written a great many short stories. They cover all activities of the American scene and have won him deserved acclaim. Critics have fallen into the habit of calling him the American de Maupassant. Some of them have qualified this by awarding him a niche a little below that occupied by the French writer. I am not sure I agree with this downgrading. At any rate, I find that I read the O'Hara stories with more enjoyment than I do those of de Maupassant.

I am not offering the two stories which follow, "Exactly Eight Thousand Dollars Exactly" and "The Sun-Dodgers," as being, in my opinion, his best.

I selected them because I happen to like both of them very much.

EXACTLY EIGHT THOUSAND DOLLARS EXACTLY

John O'Hara

What had once been a pleasant country club, its members consisting largely of young couples on the way up, was now an "industrial park"; and on the old site of the tennis courts was a long, low, windowless building, a laboratory for research in synthetics. The clubhouse was still recognizable beneath the renovations that had converted it into executive offices, but the first and eighteenth fairways were leveled off and covered with blacktop, a parking area for the plant employees. At approximately the location of the second tee there was a roped-off space, with a sign that warned against getting too close to the helicopter which transported plant officials to the municipal airport. One reminder of the former character of the place remained: a golf cart carried officials from the helicopters to the executive offices. A ten-foot-high fence surrounded the entire property and above the fence was strung barbed wire. The fence proper was painted white, but there is no way to make barbed wire look like anything but barbed wire.

The man in the small Renault stopped his car at the gate, and a man in uniform, with a badge that said "Security Officer" and a revolver holster, bent over to speak to the driver of the car. "Good afternoon, sir. May I help you?" The *may* sounded false and sissy, as though it seemed false and sissy to the officer himself.

"Yes, thanks. I'm here to see Mr. D'Avlon."

"Yes sir. Name please?"

"Mr. Charles D'Avlon," said the driver of the car.

"Oh, right. You're expected, Mr. D'Avlon." The guard could not refrain from a surprised look at the small car. "Will you just pin this badge on your lapel and return it to the officer on duty on your way out?" Charles D'Avlon accepted a plastic square which had a safety pin attached to the reverse side; on the obverse side was printed "VISITOR–D'Avlon Industries–355–This badge must be worn at all times while visitor is on Company property. Please return to Security Officer, Main Gate, on completion of visit."

"Where do I park?"

"A space reserved for you, Number 355, executive parking. That'll be that third row. One, two, three. Please leave your key in the car."

"Oh? Why?"

"That's regulations, sir. All cars."

"My brother's, too?"

"Yes sir. Mr. Henry D'Avlon leaves his key in the car just the same as I do."

"A somewhat different car from mine, though, I imagine."

"Well, you see that black and gray Rolls? That's your brother's. But the key's in it just the same. That's in case we have to move the cars in a hurry."

"In an emergency?"

"Correct."

"Such as an explosion?"

"Any emergency that comes up," said the guard. He did not like the word explosion or the slightly frivolous tone of D'Avlon's remark. "By the time you got your car parked the escort will be there to escort you to Executives' Reception." The guard went back into his glass sentry box and picked up a telephone. D'Avlon drove to the parking space.

The escort was a younger man in a uniform similar to the guard's but without the revolver. "Your first visit, I understand," said the escort.

"My first visit to the plant. I've been here before, but when it was a golf club."

"Oh, yes. That was quite some time ago."

"I would think before you were born."

"I guess *so,*" said the young man.

"Are we waiting for someone else?"

"Just waiting for you to pin your badge on."

"Even if I'm with you?"

"Everybody has to wear his badge. You wouldn't get ten feet without it."

"What would happen to me?"

"Be detained. If you didn't have a satisfactory explanation you'd be arrested for trespassing. You saw all those signs on the fence. This is a pretty efficient operation."

"Is that since the explosion?"

"We've always taken security precautions here," said the young man, evasively.

"Why don't *you* carry a gun?"

"What makes you think I don't?" The young man reached in his pocket and brought out a .25 automatic. "It's no .38, but a lot of women have got rid of a lot of husbands with one of these. They aren't bulky, slip into your pants pocket, and some visitors don't feel right walking with a man with a holster. But if you hit a man in the throat with one of these slugs, he wouldn't be much use."

"Can you hit a man in the throat?"

"In the eye, with a little time and the right distance. Some cops call it a jealousy gun. And we practice firing it. The women don't even practice, and look what they do with it. It's a mean little fellow. This way, sir."

The handsome young woman in Executives' Reception bowed and smiled at Charles D'Avlon and apparently pushed a button that released the lock on the door into a corridor. At any rate she did not speak to D'Avlon or to the young security officer. "This way, sir," said the young man. They rode one flight up in an automatic elevator, then proceeded to the end of the second-story corridor, to a door marked President. The young man held that door open for Charles D'Avlon, and a man rose to greet the stranger.

"Okay, Mr. Lester?" said the security officer.

"Okay, Van," said the man addressed. He was about forty-five, wore half-shell glasses and a blue four-in-hand that was embroidered with what appeared to be a long exclamation point. His dark blue suit had narrow lapels and his pocket handkerchief, neatly folded, showed enough to reveal, in the very center, the initials D.W.L. "Have a seat, Mr. D'Avlon. Your brother will be right with you. You have a nice trip out?"

"Out from town, or out from Connecticut?"

"Well–from Connecticut."

"Oh, it was all right. Gave me a chance to see a lot of the country."

"Didn't you use to live here?"

"Oh, sure. We were born here, but it's all changed. I used to play golf here when I was a young man. Do you know where you're sitting?"

"How do you mean?"

"You're sitting in the ladies' can. That's what this was. The ladies' locker-room."

"I wasn't with the company then."

"There wasn't any company then."

"No, I guess not," said Mr. Lester. He sat with his hands folded on his desk.

"Go ahead with your work, if you want to. Don't let me hold you up," said Charles D'Avlon.

"I'm waiting for–there he is," said Mr. Lester. He rose as the door at his right was opened.

"Hello, Chiz," said the man in the doorway. "Come on in."

"Hello, Henry," said Charles D'Avlon. The brothers shook hands and Charles entered the president's office.

It was a corner room with a magnificent view of the rolling countryside and a distant mountain. "I was just telling your man Lester, his office is in the ladies' can."

"Well, that proves one thing," said Henry. "You haven't changed much. You always liked to throw people a little off balance."

"Don't be disagreeable, Henry. It's tough enough to be here under the circumstances. Don't make it tougher."

"Chiz, you're the one that always makes things tougher for yourself."

"I didn't say you made things tougher. I just said they were tough enough. I swore I'd never ask you for a nickel, but here I am."

"Yes," said Henry. "Well, we got right to the point. How much do you want?"

"A lot."

"Oh, I guessed that. If it was a little you wouldn't feel you had to make such a long trip. How much, Chiz?"

"Eight thousand dollars."

"All right. But why eight? Why not five, or why not ten? I'm curious to know how you arrived at the figure eight thousand."

"I thought it would sound businesslike."

"As though you'd figured it out very carefully. Okay, it does," said Henry. He spoke into the inter-com on his desk. "Dale, will you make out a cheque, my personal account, eight thousand dollars, payable to Charles W. D'Avlon, and bring it in for my signature as soon as it's made out? Thank you."

"Aren't you interested in what I want it for?" said Charles.

"Not very much. You have some story, and it comes to eight thousand dollars. You probably need five, but you thought you might as well get three extra."

"That's right," said Charles. "But I hate to waste the story. I had a good one."

"Write it and sell it to a magazine."

"I can't write. If I could write I'd have plenty of material, but first you said you were interested in why I said eight thousand, and in the next breath you don't want to hear my story."

"I wanted to see if you'd admit it was a story. If you hadn't admitted it I'd have had the cheque made out for four thousand. But you were frank, and that's as close as you ever come to being honest. So you get your eight thousand."

"If I'd known it was going to be this easy–"

"No. You might have got ten, but no more."

"Then give me ten."

"Not a chance," said Henry. There were two light taps on the door, Lester came in and laid the cheque on Henry's desk and departed. Henry signed and pushed the cheque toward his brother.

"Cheque protector and everything. Exactly eight thousand exactly," said Charles. "Now I'm interested to know why you gave me any money at all. You didn't have to. Does it give you a sense of power? Does it go with that Rolls-Royce you have down there, and all this high-powered security stuff?"

"To a certain extent I guess it does. But there's more to it than that, Chiz."

"Of course."

"You see, I've always wondered when you'd finally put the touch on me. Not that I lay awake nights, but I knew you would some day. And now you have, for eight thousand dollars. I'm getting off light. Because you must know damn well that this is all you'll ever get from me."

"That occurred to me."

"When we were boys and you used to knock me around I used to feel sort of sorry for you. You'd beat the hell out of me and walk away with something of mine. A fielder's glove, or a necktie. But what you didn't know was that I was dying to *give* you the God damn glove or tie. Anything you asked for of mine, you could have had. But you preferred violence and theft, and naturally I could take only so much and then I began to hate you."

"And still do."

"Does that surprise you? Yes. Because as you grew older that was the way you were with everybody, all through your life. If you look out that window you'll see a research laboratory where the tennis courts used to be. One night after a dance I was getting in that little Oakland I had, that Grandmother gave me for my twenty-first birthday. You ought to remember it, you smashed it up, you son of a bitch. Anyway, I didn't have a date and I was by myself and I heard a girl crying. It was Mary Radley, sitting on the bench between the first and second courts. She was ashamed to go back to the clubhouse with her dress all torn. You. You didn't have to be brutal with Mary Radley. Nobody did, but especially you. But that was your way, and that was when I first realized that it wasn't just a question of being a bully to your kid brother. You were a bully, net."

"Okay," said Charles. "Well, it's your turn to be the bully. Thanks for the money."

"Wait a minute. I haven't finished. I want you to hear a few things, and you'll damn well listen or I'll stop payment on that cheque."

"Captive audience. All right," said Charles.

"You've never changed. Both your wives took all they could stand, your children don't want to be anywhere near you. Have you ever wondered why?"

"Not very much. The children were brought up by their mothers, and their mothers saw to it that I didn't get any of the best of it. I wrote them off very early."

"Not your daughter. You showed up at her graduation and made her leave her mother and stepfather to go on some excursion with you. Whimsical cruelty, that was. Because you then sent her back to her mother and never did any more about her. Not a thing, financially or otherwise."

"Her mother has plenty of glue. One thing I did for my children was make sure they had rich mothers."

"Yes. Who also could afford *you* before there were any children, and after."

"The fact of the matter is that both my wives proposed to me, Henry."

"I have no doubt of it. You were very skillful. I understand your first wife forced you to accept a wedding present of two hundred thousand dollars."

"Two-fifty. A quarter of a million. All long since gone, I regret to say."

"But your second wife—"

"An iron-bound trust. I couldn't get my hooks on any of that. Where did you find out so much about my affairs?"

"When I was around trying to raise the money to get this business started, I encountered a certain amount of resistance because of the name. Even when they found out I wasn't you, people were still very dubious, especially New York and Philadelphia people. Don't ever go back to Philadelphia, Chiz. They really don't like you there."

"I'm desolated."

"You're not, but you ought to be."

"I really am. There are a couple of rich widows in Philadelphia that could make me entirely independent of people like you. But the Girard Trust Company and that other one, they probably take a dim view of me. It's too bad, too, because both of these women, or I should say either one of them could make me comfortable in my old age. I'm crowding sixty, you know."

"Oh, I know."

"The next fifteen years, I don't look forward to them the way things are at present. You may have to take me on as a night watchman."

"Fat chance. And that brings me to another point I was going to make. Or my earlier point about your being a bully. Do you realize that before you came in this room I already knew that you'd been shooting off your mouth about the explosion we had here three years ago? Our Security people couldn't believe their ears. The first man you talked to lost a brother in that explosion. The second man, the young fellow, was very badly burned and had to have skin-grafting operations that took over a year. But your feeble jokes, aside from any question of taste, were your way of bullying people, the way you used to be to caddies and waiters when this was the club. Five men were killed in that explosion, and it's no joke around here. It's no joke anywhere. For your information, both Security officers were convinced that you were an impostor, that you weren't my brother at all. For your additional information, Chiz, I wish they'd been right."

Charles D'Avlon rose. "Well, that sounds pretty final," he said. He went over to the window and looked out at the laboratory. "Mary Radley," he said. "She was certainly a little tramp."

[illegible]

[illegible] addition, since I was going through the [illegible] any ordinary [illegible] [illegible] [illegible]

[illegible] "What was [illegible] pulled out all the stops [illegible] [illegible] got you in a little trouble."

THE SUN-DODGERS

John O'Hara

Back in the long nighttime of the Twenties and Thirties, when so many of the people I knew had jobs that made them sun-dodgers, Jack Pyne was known derisively as a mystery man. He was even called *the* mystery man, but it was not said in a way that would make you want to meet him or to inquire into the reason for calling him that. We all have our secrets, and Jack Pyne undoubtedly had his, but when he was referred to as a mystery man it was a term of contempt. In our set it was universally known that Jack Pyne made his living by peddling gossip to the Broadway columnists. They paid him no money, but Jack Pyne always had some chorus girls or bit players who paid him twenty-five dollars a week to get their names in the papers. The chatter writers would mention his clients in return for his acting as a spy or a messenger boy or procurer. You would be surprised to learn the names of some of the girls who once were clients of Jack Pyne. You might even be shocked and incredulous.

When business was good Jack Pyne sometimes had three or four clients, some of them paying him more than twenty-five dollars a week, and when business was exceptionally good Jack Pyne might have four individual clients, a second-rate night club, and a Broadway show. The night club seldom paid him any cash, but he was on the cuff there for meals and, within reason, free drinks for newspaper men. There were occasional periods when Jack Pyne probably had an income of close to two hundred dollars a week from the chorus girls and a hundred and fifty dollars a week as press agent for a musical comedy, in addition to the food and liquor he got free from the night clubs. It was in that way that he got the nickname of mystery man. "Who's Jack Pyne hustling for a buck now? The mystery man," someone once said. "Jack Pyne, the man of mystery."

We had favorite joints and favorite tables in the joints, and in the course of a single night, any night, we would move from a favorite table in one joint to a favorite table in one or two other joints, more or less according to a schedule. Jack Pyne always knew where we could be found at any hour between eleven P.M. and six o'clock in the morning. In our group there were, among the regulars, four or five newspaper men, a Broadway doctor, a Broadway attorney, one or two lyric-writers, a playwright, two or three press agents, a bookmaker, a detective from the Broadway Squad, sometimes a Catholic priest, a vaudeville actor turned sketch writer, a salesman for a meat packer, a minor poet, a real estate speculator, a radio announcer. At no time were all these men together at the same table, but they were the regulars of our group. There were other groups: the mobster group, the song-writing and music-publishing group, the gamblers, the minor hoods, and in the course of a night we might be visited briefly by members of the other groups, with the exception of the minor hoods. They kept to themselves because they did not want to go anywhere near a newspaper man; they did not want to be seen talking to a newspaper man. As a group, a class, they were the cruelest, stupidest, most evil men I have ever known, and I was afraid of them. I was not afraid of the big shots; they, with their new importance and power, generally behaved themselves in public, but the smallies, as we called the minor hoods, were unpredictable, reckless, and we knew the stories about them and their savagery. They were not all young men; some of them were in their forties and fifties, and I had a theory that the reason the older ones survived was that they had been out of circulation, in prison, and thus invulnerable to the high mortality rate among smallies. It was not only a theory I had; some of them had been in prison before Prohibition went into effect and came out to find that highjacking and gang warfare paid better than armed robbery and felonious assault, and not only paid better but were safer in that prosecution had become more difficult and the mobs retained cleverer attorneys. A man who had gone to prison for homicide in 1916 and was released in ten years would discover that in his absence an almost ideal situation had been created. If he could make a connection with an established mob he might easily make a living on a standby basis, with nothing to do but remain on call until the mob had some punishment to dole out. And if the punishment involved murdering a member of an opposition mob, the legal authorities often could not or would not make an arrest. The smallies were killing each other off in private mob warfare, and if you noticed that one of the familiar faces was missing from the smallies' table, you could usually guess why. But you had to guess, most of the time. I didn't know many of them by name, although I knew them by sight, and even when their bodies were found in Bushwick or in Dutchess County, the newspaper photographs did not identify them for me. One man with half his face shot away and curled up in the back of a sedan looks much the same as another man who died in the same circumstances. A man who had been soaked with gasoline as well as stabbed or shot might be the missing face from the smallies' table, but I could only guess.

When the tabloids came out with stories and pictures of a mobster's murder the regulars at our table postponed discussion of it, but we could not help looking at the smallies' table to see how they were taking it. Sometimes their table would be vacant, which usually meant that one or more of the smallies had been picked up by the police and the others were in hiding. The big shots were always at their own table, gabbing away as though nothing had happened, and probably from their point of view nothing had; the murder we were reading about had been ordered weeks before, and the actual killing was old hat to the big shots. This was New York, not Chicago, and it has never ceased to amaze me how few of the real big shots got killed. But of course there is the old saying that generals die in bed, too.

If we often stole glances at the smallies' table, they in turn spent a lot of time staring at us. Plainly they resented us and our presence; obviously they thought we did not belong in the same joints that they frequented—and in a way they were right, but we were sun-dodgers and had no place else to go. If they had had their way they could easily have got rid of us, and without working us over. I know I would not have gone to a joint after being warned off by a couple of those hoods. They had a neat trick of pushing a man to the sidewalk, laying his leg across the curbstone, and jumping on it. No guns, no knives, no acid. They had a hundred other tricks, too, to maim or cripple people, of either sex, who got in their way. But the big shots' visits to our table gave us a sort of *laissez-passer,* which, though it increased the smallies' resentment of our presence, protected us from abuse. I must qualify that statement a little bit: they would not have abused the detective from the Broadway Squad. *He* abused *them,* sometimes beat them up just to keep in practice. But he was a special case, a terrifying man with fist and boot, and not really one of our group. Two things were always, always said of Tommy Callaghan: he was a law unto himself, and he led a charmed life. He has been written about in articles and in fiction, and I think there was even a movie that was more or less based on his career. His attitude and policy were expressed very simply. "I hate hoods," he would say, and he made no distinction between the big shots and the smallies. One of the biggest of the big shots always had to tip his hat to Tommy Callaghan, no matter where they ran into each other; at the fights in the Garden, at the race track, or in a hotel lobby. But this is not a repetition of the legend of

Tommy Callaghan. In this chronicle he plays a minor part, and having introduced him I will go on until I need him later in the story.

However, since I have been rambling along with digressions where I felt like making them, I want to put in a warning to those readers who may still retain an impression of those days and those people that may be charming, but has nothing to do with the truth. Broadway really was not populated by benevolent bookmakers who gave all their money to the Salvation Army, and bootleggers who were always looking around for a paraplegic newsboy who needed surgery, and crapshooters who used their tees and miss-outs–crooked dice–in order to finance a chapel. There is something about the words rogue and rascal that brings a smile to the eyes of people who never spent any time with rogues and rascals. And I have never been able to accept the paradox of the prostitute who was faithful to one man. The big shots and the smallies that I saw–and I saw dozens of them–were unprincipled, sadistic, murderous bullies; often sexually perverted, diseased, sometimes drug addicts, and stingy. The women were just as bad, except when they were worse. The picture of a band of jolly Robin Hoods on Times Square is all wrong and not very romantic to those who knew that perhaps the most spectacular gambler of them all was nothing but a shylock–a usurer–and a fixer. And now back to Jack Pyne.

The joint that usually was our last stop before going home was a place called The Leisure Club, Fiftieth Street near Eighth Avenue, on the second story. It had several things to recommend it: it stayed open until nine o'clock in the morning; it was considered neutral territory by the important mob leaders; the booze was basically good liquor that had been cut only once; and it was not expensive. The Leisure offered no entertainment more elaborate than a colored piano player who also sang dirty songs. His name was Teeth, the only thing he would answer to. He played quite good piano, in spite of not having eighty-eight notes to work with. It was a studio piano, and he had to be inventive to do right by Youmans and Gershwin and Kern on an abbreviated keyboard. The dirty songs were the work of anonymous composers, and they were the same dirty songs that could be heard in little joints all over town, or parodies of songs by Cole Porter and Noel Coward. It was rather high-class stuff for a joint like The Leisure, most of it too subtle for the big shots and the smallies, but their girl friends liked it.

The Leisure had not caught on with the Park Avenue-Junior League-Squadron A crowd, probably because they would be flocking to Harlem at just about the same hour that The Leisure was showing signs of action. In any event, The Leisure was strictly a Broadway joint, not for post-debutantes or squash players. It was for show people, newspaper men, various kinds of hustlers, and mobsters, in addition to the regulars whom I have already mentioned. Since for most of the customers it was the last place before going home, it was usually well filled, with no new male faces from night to night. There were, of course, new girls from the musical comedies and other night clubs, and women who had come in from out of town; but some of these girls and women soon became steady customers too.

At The Leisure our group gathered at a booth in the middle of a row of booths. When we were more than nine in number the waiters would put a table against the booth table as an extension, but that seldom was necessary. We hardly ever numbered fewer than five or more than nine, and eight was the most comfortable; four on each side of the table and two at the open end. I describe the seating arrangements because I never saw anyone make room for Jack Pyne. If he joined our table, he had to sit at the open end. And I never heard anyone actually ask him to sit down.

He would come in, say a few words to the hatcheck girl, and head for our table. "Hello, there, you muggs," he would say.

Somebody would say, "Jack," and the others would nod–or not nod. There was one fellow, a newspaper reporter, who would be a bit more loquacious. "Why, hello there, Jack. We were just talking about you."

"Oh, yeah? What'd you say?"

"Just saying what a great fellow you were. We just got finished taking a vote."

"Come off it."

"On the level. We're raising a little purse to send you on a trip. Where would you rather go, Jack? Devil's Island? You speak French, don't you, Jack?"

"Lay off, lay off, you muggs."

There was no insult he would not take, whether it concerned his honesty, his morals, his manhood, his appearance, or his methods of earning a living. The newspaper reporter who suggested Devil's Island (and who had first called him a mystery man) would mention an extraordinary sexual perversion and suddenly say, "What's it like, Jack? I hear that's what you go for." Always, when they were making a fool of him, he would pretend to think they were kidding him, as though they would only kid a man they were fond of. But it was all insulting, often straight-factual, and finally not very funny. We all had a crack at insulting Jack Pyne, but he was so totally lacking in self-respect and so completely unable or unwilling to make any kind of retort that we finally did lay off, and he became a bore. I think we began to hate him then. He was a bore, and a terribly cheap individual, and because we had given up the mean sport of insulting him, he convinced himself that he was one of the boys.

We all read the same newspapers and heard the same gossip, and that went for Jack Pyne. He had the same information we had out of the newspapers, but now he had opinions as well. He was one of the boys, and he would hold forth on politics and sports and other topics of the day, and I've never known anyone who could be so consistently wrong about everything. We would sit in glassy-eyed silence while he told us what he thought was going to happen at City Hall or the Polo Grounds or the Garden. And why. If there were only four or five of us at the table we would fiddle with matchbooks, make rings on the table with our highball glasses, and neither look at Jack nor say a word to him. Then when he had said his say we would resume talking, but not about the topic Jack had just discussed. We would not agree with him, we would not contradict him; we would simply ignore all he had said. Almost literally we were giving him the freeze. When our group was larger, when there were so many of us that the waiter added the extra table, Jack Pyne was no problem. The larger group always meant that one of the Broadway columnists was present, and Jack Pyne knew better than to interrupt their monologs. The Broadway columnists were his gods, his heroes—and his bread and butter.

You may wonder why we put up with Jack Pyne. The answer is easy: in the beginning he had been a pathetic clown, and later there was no way to get rid of him. And I guess we were not very selective on the late shift. The meat salesman was no Wilson Mizner, the radio announcer no Oliver Herford, the Broadway doctor no James Abbott MacNeill Whistler. We did not pretend to be the Algonquin Round Table, and there was no test of wit that a man had to pass to be welcome in our group. We were brought together by the circumstances of our jobs and their unconventional hours, and the attraction of convivial drinking. The married men among us never brought their wives, and the rest of us rarely brought a girl. Our conversation would have bored women, and women would have inhibited our conversation. From this distance I could not repeat one of our conversations, not so much because the talk was rough—although it was that—as because it was so immediately topical. It was lively, but evanescent, and the interruptions by Jack Pyne only gave us a chance to get our breath.

Then one night—say around four o'clock in the morning—the character of our meetings began to change. It was not something we noticed at the time, but I know now that the change began when one of the smallies came to our table and said to Jack Pyne, "Hey, Pincus, I want to talk to you." Jack got up and followed the gangster to an empty table. They talked for five minutes or so, and Jack came back to our table and the gangster returned to his group.

"Who's your friend, Jack?" said the newspaper reporter. "I don't remember seeing him before. Don't want to see him again, either."

"I went to school with him. We grew up together," said Jack Pyne.

"He didn't look as if he went to school very long."

"No. I knew him in sixth grade. Seventh grade. Around then," said Jack Pyne.

"He's been away?"

"I'll say he has. He was doing five to ten up the river. He only got out about a month ago."

"What was the rap, Jack?"

"Why, I guess it was felonious assault. I didn't ask him, but I remember hearing about it. I think he was up twice. I don't know. I don't know for sure."

"He knew you. He made you the minute you came in tonight."

"Yeah. Yeah, I guess he did. I guess he was kind of expecting me."

"What has he, got some little broad he wants you to get her picture in the paper?"

"I didn't say that, did I?" said Jack Pyne.

"You didn't say anything, but that's a pretty good guess, isn't it? Your fame has spread far and wide, Jack. You're getting somewhere. Who's the broad? We'll find out, so don't be coy."

"Ella Haggerty. She's in the Carroll show."

"Mixed up with a hood like that? She does better than that, Jack."

"Not now she doesn't, and she better not. He's stuck on her."

"She doesn't need you to get her picture in the paper. I know Ella. You guys know Ella Haggerty."

Some of us did, and some of us didn't.

"I know her myself," said Jack Pyne. "She recommended me. She told Ernie to hire me, and Ernie said he went to school with me."

"Small world. What's Ernie's last name?"

"Black, he goes by. Ernie Black. It used to be Schwartz."

"Well, what the hell? Mine used to be Vanderbilt, but Buckley's easier to remember. I'll tell you something, Jack. Your friend Ernie, whether it's Black or Schwartz, he's got himself a very expensive lady friend."

"I know that."

"You know whose girl she was for a couple of years."

"I know."

"And where he had her living and all that? Those fur coats and diamonds."

"I been to her apartment. I know all that," said Jack Pyne.

"You know all that. Then what's she doing with some smallie like this Ernie Black? You don't go from J. Richard Hammersmith to some cheap hood just out of stir."

"She did."

"She did, but you better find out why, and you better get your money in advance. The way I see it, Jack, you've got nothing but trouble ahead of you. This coffee-and-cakes mobster, he hasn't got enough dough to keep her in bath salts. So he's going to have to get big all of a sudden, and how do you get big in his racket? You know as well as I do. From where he is, you start by killing somebody. That's the only way to make a fast big score. Homicide."

"I know, I know," said Jack Pyne.

"And even then you don't get rich, unless you happen to kill somebody very big. And if you kill somebody very big, you end up very dead. Jack, you ought to get out of this contract as quickly and as gracefully as you can."

"I can't," said Pyne. "I made a contract."

"Then leave town."

"Sure. Where would I go? My show closed Saturday and I got expenses."

"Well, if you don't want to take my advice, that's up to you," said Buckley.

"Who's the banker tonight?" said Jack Pyne.

"I am," I said.

Jack tossed me a five-dollar bill. "I had two drinks. Give me three bucks change."

I did so, and he left.

"You know," said Buckley. "I wouldn't be surprised if I accomplished something tonight. I think we finally got rid of the mystery man."

"Is that what you were doing?" I said.

"Sure. Everything I said was true, but Pyne hadn't looked at it that way. It just needed me to point out certain disadvantages."

Buckley was entirely correct. Days, then weeks, then years passed, and no more was seen of Jack Pyne. It was as though the sewer had swallowed him up. Our group, I have said, changed in character, and I may be putting too much emphasis on the effect Jack Pyne's disappearance produced. But there is no use denying the coincidence that the only time we were visited by one of the smallies, one of our number disappeared. We didn't talk about the coincidence, but one of the smallies had invaded our territory despite the implied protection we enjoyed from the big shots.

Several months after Jack Pyne vanished a body was fished out of the

East River. It was identified as Ernie Black, *né* Schwartz, and the mutilations indicated to police that Black had been tortured in gangster fashion. I advanced the theory that we might soon be welcoming Jack Pyne back to the fold, but I was wrong. Wherever he had gone, he liked it better than The Leisure, and not long after that The Leisure itself was raided and permanently closed. We had to find a new late spot, and in so doing we lost some of our group and recruited some newcomers. Then I changed jobs and got married and moved to Great Neck, and began leading a very different life from the one I had known.

That was more than thirty years ago. We have grandchildren now, and my wife and I last year bought a little house near Phoenix, Arizona. I have my retirement pay, a few securities, and an unsteady income from my writing. I occasionally sell a piece to a magazine and I have written two books, one of which did well as a paperback. Our two daughters are married and living in the East, and until about a month ago it looked as though we had it made. We liked Arizona; the climate suited us, we made new friends, we had no money worries, the future looked good. So did the past. Our new friends seemed to be entertained by my reminiscences of the old days, and now and then I could convert my reminiscences into an honest buck. For instance, I wrote a story about Ella Haggerty that I sold as fiction but was almost straight fact. Ella married a clarinet player in 1930 or '31 and shortly after that dropped out of sight. The piano player from The Leisure, the man known as Teeth, went to Paris, France, during the depression and became a great hit. He was married briefly to an English lady of title, and after World War II he was awarded the Medal of Resistance, which must have amused him as much as it did me. I had a letter from him in 1939. He was thinking of writing his memoirs even then, and he particularly called my attention to his new name–Les Dents. "It sounds like 'let's dance' if you pronounce it English style but I talk mostly French these days," he wrote. Only one of the former big shots is still alive. He is living, I believe, in Hot Springs, Arkansas. My friend Buckley, the newspaper reporter, was killed in the War. He and another correspondent, riding in a jeep in Italy, hit a land mine. His old paper established the Buckley Scholarship at a school of journalism, a memorial he would object to as he hated the very word journalism. My friends of the old days who have survived are in the minority, and Madge and I have our aches and pains as well as the obituary pages to remind us of the passage of time, but things were going all right until last month, when one afternoon Madge came to my workroom and said a man wanted to see me. "Who is he?" I said.

"I didn't ask him his name, but he wanted to make sure you had worked on the old New York *World*."

"Probably a touch," I said.

I went out to our tiny patio, and a man got up to greet me. He was wearing a white sombrero, the kind that costs about seventy-five dollars, and a gabardine coat and trousers that in the West they call a stockman's suit. "You don't remember me?"

"I'm afraid I don't," I said.

"Well, I shouldn't have expected you to. It's a long, long time," he said. Then, suddenly, he said: "Jack Pyne."

"Jack Pyne," I repeated. *"Jack Pyne?"*

"You think I was dead?"

"As a matter of fact I did," I said.

"Now you recognize me?"

"Yes, of course," I said. "Sit down. What can I get you to drink?"

"Not a thing," he said. "I just happened to hear in a roundabout way that you were living out here, so I took it in my head to look you up. I bought your book. You must be coining money. I see it every place I go. Airports. Drug stores. You coulda cut me in." He smiled to show he was joking. "I reccanized Ella Haggerty, and I said to my wife, I said I introduced him to her."

"But you didn't," I said.

"I know I didn't, but it impressed the hell out of my missus. Like we took a trip over to Europe a couple of years ago, and did you ever hear of the famous entertainer, Les Dents? You know who that is?"

"Yes. Teeth, from the old Leisure Club."

"Oh, you knew that. Well, he remembered me right off. I was twenty pounds lighter then. Good old Teeth. He sat and talked with the wife and I for a couple hours, and all those French people and the international set, they couldn't figure out who we were."

"What are you doing now, Jack?"

"Well, I got a couple of things going for me. Different things. I got my money all invested in various enterprises. I only live about ten miles from here. You ought to come and take a look at my place. You have a car, don't you? Or I could send one for you."

"We have a car," I said. "But, Jack, what ever happened to you? You just disappeared into thin air."

"You mean way back? Oh, I just took it into my head one night, what was I wasting my time sitting around those night spots. So I sold my business–"

"What business?"

He shook his head somewhat pityingly. "Jack Pyne. I had one of the first if not *the* first really successful public relations concerns. You know, your memory ain't as good as it ought to be. I noticed a couple things in your book. Sure it was fiction, but you sure did take a lot of liberties. I mean, didn't you know Ella was my girl? I kept that dame for three years. She cost me a fortune. Maybe you were afraid I'd sue you for libel, but that's not the way I operate. I told my wife, I said this book was about an old girl friend of mine. That was before I read the book, and then she asked me which one was me and I said I guess you were afraid I'd sue you for libel. I wouldn't take an old friend into court. You ought to know me better than that."

"Well, I'll put you in my next book."

"No, don't do that. You don't have to make amends. But you and your wife come out and have dinner at my house and I'd like to straighten you out on those days. You remember Pete Buckley?"

"Sure."

"Always pestering me to meet Ella, but I said to him one night, I was glad to help him out any time he needed a send-in with one of those underworld characters. I knew them all. But it was one thing to tell my mob friends a guy was all right, and a very different story to introduce a thirty-five-dollar-a-week police reporter to my girl. I sent them a cheque when they had that memorial for Pete. Very sarcastic when he made his load, but a great newspaper man when he was sober. Great. No doubt about it." He stood up. "Old pal, I gotta see a couple executives downtown, but you and I are going to have a lot of fun together, cutting up the old touches. Right?"

We have not gone to his house, although we have heard it is one of the showplaces. But we see him a great deal. A great deal. He has found out where we are and he knows when we'll be home. It is a sad thing after so many years to have a house you love seem to turn into a night club table. Suddenly I miss Pete Buckley, too.

Clothe the Naked

Dorothy Parker

The unexpected plot twist at the finish of a story was not invented by O. Henry but he used it with greater frequency and more skill perhaps than anyone else. His purpose, of course, was to leave his readers with the impact of that turn of events which came in the last few sentences.

Dorothy Parker ends her unusual story of Big Lannie, the hard-working colored servant, and her blind grandson, with a development which contains the element of surprise. But it is much more than a trick ending; it is an emotional climax which readers could not have foreseen but which is both logical and conclusive. It lifts the story to a high emotional level.

"Clothe the Naked" is beautifully conceived and told.

CLOTHE THE NAKED

Dorothy Parker

Big Lannie went out by the day to the houses of secure and leisured ladies, to wash their silks and their linens. She did her work perfectly; some of the ladies even told her so. She was a great, slow mass of a woman, colored a sound brown-black save for her palms and the flat of her fingers that were like gutta-percha from steam and hot suds. She was slow because of her size, and because the big veins in her legs hurt her, and her back ached much of the time. She neither cursed her ills nor sought remedies for them. They had happened to her; there they were.

Many things had happened to her. She had had children, and the children had died. So had her husband, who was a kind man, cheerful with the little luck he found. None of their children had died at birth. They had lived to be four or seven or ten, so that they had had their ways and their traits and their means of causing love; and Big Lannie's heart was always wide for love. One child had been killed in a street accident and two others had died of illnesses that might have been no more than tedious, had there been fresh food and clear spaces and clean air behind them. Only Arlene, the youngest, lived to grow up.

Arlene was a tall girl, not so dark as her mother but with the same firm flatness of color. She was so thin that her bones seemed to march in advance of her body. Her little pipes of legs and her broad feet with jutting heels were like things a child draws with crayons. She carried her head low, her shoulders scooped around her chest, and her stomach slanted forward. From the time that she was tiny, there were men after her.

Arlene was a bad girl always; that was one of the things that had happened to Big Lannie. There it was, and Big Lannie could only keep bringing her presents, surprises, so that the girl would love her mother and would want to stay at home. She brought little bottles of sharp perfume, and pale stockings of tinny silk, and rings set with bits of green and red glass; she tried to choose what Arlene would like. But each time

Arlene came home she had bigger rings and softer stockings and stronger perfume than her mother could buy for her. Sometimes she would stay with her mother over a night, and sometimes more than a week; and then Big Lannie would come back from work one evening, and the girl would be gone, and no word of her. Big Lannie would go on bringing surprises, and setting them out along Arlene's bed to wait a return.

Big Lannie did not know it, when Arlene was going to have a baby. Arlene had not been home in nearly half a year; Big Lannie told the time in days. There was no news at all of the girl until the people at the hospital sent for Big Lannie to come to her daughter and grandson. She was there to hear Arlene say the baby must be named Raymond, and to see the girl die. For whom Raymond was called, or if for anyone, Big Lannie never knew.

He was a long, light-colored baby, with big, milky eyes that looked right back at his grandmother. It was several days before the people at the hospital told her he was blind.

Big Lannie went to each of the ladies who employed her and explained that she could not work for some while; she must take care of her grandson. The ladies were sharply discommoded, after her steady years, but they dressed their outrage in shrugs and cool tones. Each arrived, separately, at the conclusion that she had been too good to Big Lannie, and had been imposed upon, therefore. "Honestly, those niggers!" each said to her friends. "They're all alike."

Big Lannie sold most of the things she lived with, and took one room with a stove in it. There, as soon as the people at the hospital would let her, she brought Raymond and tended him. He was all her children to her.

She had always been a saving woman, with few needs and no cravings, and she had been long alone. Even after Arlene's burial, there was enough left for Raymond and Big Lannie to go on for a time. Big Lannie was slow to be afraid of what must come; fear did not visit her at all, at first, and then it slid in only when she waked, when the night hung motionless before another day.

Raymond was a good baby, a quiet, patient baby, lying in his wooden box and stretching out his delicate hands to the sounds that were light and color to him. It seemed but a little while, so short to Big Lannie, before he was walking about the room, his hands held out, his feet quick and sure. Those of Big Lannie's friends who saw him for the first time had to be told that he could not see.

Then, and it seemed again such a little while, he could dress himself, and open the door for his granny, and unlace the shoes from her tired feet, and talk to her in his soft voice. She had occasional employment—

now and then a neighbor would hear of a day's scrubbing she could do, or sometimes she might work in the stead of a friend who was sick—infrequent, and not to be planned on. She went to the ladies for whom she had worked, to ask if they might not want her back again; but there was little hope in her, after she had visited the first one. Well, now, really, said the ladies; well, really, now.

The neighbors across the hall watched over Raymond while Big Lannie looked for work. He was no trouble to them, nor to himself. He sat and crooned at his chosen task. He had been given a wooden spool around the top of which were driven little brads, and over these with a straightened hairpin he looped bright worsted, working faster than sight until a long tube of woven wool fell through the hole in the spool. The neighbors threaded big, blunt needles for him, and he coiled the woolen tubes and sewed them into mats. Big Lannie called them beautiful, and it made Raymond proud to have her tell him how readily she sold them. It was hard for her, when he was asleep at night, to unravel the mats and wash the worsted and stretch it so straight that even Raymond's shrewd fingers could not tell, when he worked with it next day, that it was not new.

Fear stormed in Big Lannie and took her days and nights. She might not go to any organization dispensing relief, for dread that Raymond would be taken from her and put in—she would not say the word to herself, and she and her neighbors lowered their voices when they said it to one another—an institution. The neighbors wove lingering tales of what happened inside certain neat, square buildings on the cindery skirts of the town, and, if they must go near them, hurried as if passing graveyards, and came home heroes. When they got you in one of those places, whispered the neighbors, they laid your spine open with whips, and then when you dropped, they kicked your head in. Had anyone come into Big Lannie's room to take Raymond away to an asylum for the blind, the neighbors would have fought for him with stones and rails and boiling water.

Raymond did not know about anything but good. When he grew big enough to go alone down the stairs and into the street, he was certain of delight each day. He held his head high, as he came out into the little yard in front of the flimsy wooden house, and slowly turned his face from side to side, as if the air were soft liquid in which he bathed it. Trucks and wagons did not visit the street, which ended in a dump for rusted bedsprings and broken boilers and staved-in kettles; children played over its cobbles, and men and women sat talking in open windows and called across to one another in gay, rich voices. There was always laughter for Raymond to hear, and he would laugh back, and hold out his hands to it.

At first, the children stopped their play when he came out, and gathered quietly about him, and watched him, fascinated. They had been told of his affliction, and they had a sort of sickened pity for him. Some of them spoke to him, in soft, careful tones. Raymond would laugh with pleasure, and stretch his hands, the curious smooth, flat hands of the blind, to their voices. They would draw sharply back, afraid that his strange hands might touch them. Then, somehow ashamed because they had shrunk from him and he could not see that they had done so, they said gentle good-bys to him, and backed away into the street again, watching him steadily.

When they were gone, Raymond would start on his walk to the end of the street. He guided himself by lightly touching the broken fences along the dirt sidewalk, and as he walked he crooned little songs with no words to them. Some of the men and women at the windows would call hello to him, and he would call back and wave and smile. When the children, forgetting him laughed again at their games, he stopped and turned to the sound as if it were the sun.

In the evening, he would tell Big Lannie about his walk, slapping his knee and chuckling at the memory of the laughter he had heard. When the weather was too hard for him to go out in the street, he would sit at his worsted work, and talk all day of going out the next day.

The neighbors did what they could for Raymond and Big Lannie. They gave Raymond clothes their own children had not yet worn out, and they brought food, when they had enough to spare and other times. Big Lannie would get through a week, and would pray to get through the next one; and so the months went. Then the days on which she could find work fell farther and farther apart, and she could not pray about the time to come because she did not dare to think of it.

It was Mrs. Ewing who saved Raymond's and Big Lannie's lives, and let them continue together. Big Lannie said that then and ever after; daily she blessed Mrs. Ewing, and nightly she would have prayed for her, had she not known, in some dimmed way, that any intercession for Mrs. Delabarre Ewing must be impudence.

Mrs. Ewing was a personage in the town. When she went to Richmond for a visit, or when she returned from viewing the azalea gardens in Charleston, the newspaper always printed the fact. She was a woman rigorously conscious of her noble obligation; she was prominent on the Community Chest committee, and it was she who planned and engineered the annual Bridge Drive to raise funds for planting salvia around the cannon in front of the D.A.R. headquarters. These and many others were her public activities, and she was no less exacting of herself in her private life. She kept a model, though childless, house for her husband and herself, relegating the supervision of details to no domestic lieutenant, no matter how seemingly trustworthy.

Back before Raymond was born, Big Lannie had worked as laundress for Mrs. Ewing. Since those days, the Ewing wash tubs had witnessed many changes, none for the better. Mrs. Ewing took Big Lannie back into her employment. She apologized for this step to her friends by the always winning method of self-deprecation. She knew she was a fool, she said, after all that time, and after the way that Big Lannie had treated her. But still, she said—and she laughed a little at her own ways—anyone she felt kind of sorry for could always get round her, she said. She knew it was awful foolish, but that, she said, was the way she was. Mr. Ewing, she said behind her husband's hearing, always called her just a regular little old easy mark.

Big Lannie had no words in which to thank Mrs. Ewing, nor to tell her what two days' assured employment every week could mean. At least, it was fairly assured. Big Lannie, as Mrs. Ewing pointed out to her, had got no younger, and she had always been slow. Mrs. Ewing kept her in a state of stimulating insecurity by referring, with perfect truth, to the numbers of stronger, quicker women who were also in need of work.

Two days' work in the week meant money for rent and stovewood and almost enough food for Raymond and Big Lannie. She must depend, for anything further, on whatever odd jobs she could find, and she must not stop seeking them. Pressed on by fear and gratitude, she worked so well for Mrs. Ewing that there was sometimes expressed satisfaction at the condition of the lady's household linen and her own and her husband's clothing. Big Lannie had a glimpse of Mr. Ewing occasionally, leaving the house as she came, or entering it as she was leaving. He was a bit of a man, not much bigger than Raymond.

Raymond grew so fast that he seemed to be taller each morning. Every day he had his walk in the street to look forward to and experience, and tell Big Lannie about at night. He had ceased to be a sight of the street; the children were so used to him that they did not even look at him, and the men and women at the windows no longer noticed him enough to hail him. He did not know. He would wave to any gay cry he heard, and go on his way, singing his little songs and turning toward the sound of laughter.

Then his lovely list of days ended as sharply as if ripped from some bright calendar. A winter came, so sudden and savage as to find no comparison in the town's memories, and Raymond had no clothes to wear out in the street. Big Lannie mended his outgrown garments as long as she could, but the stuff had so rotted with wear that it split in new places when she tried to sew together the ragged edges of rents.

The neighbors could give no longer; all they had they must keep for their own. A demented colored man in a near-by town had killed the woman who employed him, and terror had spread like brush fire. There was a sort of panic of reprisal; colored employees were dismissed from their positions, and there was no new work for them. But Mrs. Ewing, admittedly soft-hearted certainly to a fault and possibly to a peril, kept her black laundress on. More than ever Big Lannie had reason to call her blessed.

All winter, Raymond stayed indoors. He sat at his spool and worsted, with Big Lannie's old sweater about his shoulders and, when his tattered knickerbockers would no longer hold together, a calico skirt of hers lapped around his waist. He lived, at his age, in the past; in the days when he had walked, proud and glad, in the street, with laughter in his ears. Always, when he talked of it, he must laugh back at that laughter.

Since he could remember, he had not been allowed to go out when Big Lannie thought the weather unfit. This he had accepted without question, and so he accepted his incarceration through the mean weeks of the winter. But then one day it was spring, so surely that he could tell it even in the smoky, stinking rooms of the house, and he cried out with joy because now he might walk in the street again. Big Lannie had to explain to him that his rags were too thin to shield him, and that there were no odd jobs for her, and so no clothes and shoes for him.

Raymond did not talk about the street any more, and his fingers were slow at his spool.

Big Lannie did something she had never done before; she begged of her employer. She asked Mrs. Ewing to give her some of Mr. Ewing's old clothes for Raymond. She looked at the floor and mumbled so that Mrs. Ewing requested her to talk *up*. When Mrs. Ewing understood, she was, she said, surprised. She had, she said, a great, great many demands on her charity, and she would have supposed that Big Lannie, of all people, might have known that she did everything she could, and, in fact, a good deal more. She spoke of inches and ells. She said that if she found she could spare anything, Big Lannie was kindly to remember it was to be just for this once.

When Big Lannie was leaving at the end of her day's work, Mrs. Ewing brought her a package with her own hands. There, she said, was a suit and a pair of shoes; beautiful, grand things that people would think she was just a crazy to go giving away like that. She simply didn't know, she said, what Mr. Ewing would say to her for being such a crazy. She explained that that was the way she was when anyone got around her, all the while Big Lannie was trying to thank her.

Big Lannie had never before seen Raymond behave as he did when she brought him home the package. He jumped and danced and clapped his hands, he tried to speak and squealed instead, he tore off the paper himself, and ran his fingers over the close-woven cloth and held it to his face and kissed it. He put on the shoes and clattered about in them, digging with his toes and heels to keep them on; he made Big Lannie pin the trousers around his waist and roll them up over his shins. He babbled of the morrow when he would walk in the street, and could not say his words for laughing.

Big Lannie must work for Mrs. Ewing the next day, and she had thought to bid Raymond wait until she could stay at home and dress him herself in his new garments. But she heard him laugh again; she could not tell him he must wait. He might go out at noon next day, she said, when the sun was so warm that he would not take cold at his first outing; one of the neighbors across the hall would help him with the clothes. Raymond chuckled and sang his little songs until he went to sleep.

After Big Lannie left in the morning, the neighbor came in to Raymond, bringing a pan of cold pork and corn bread for his lunch. She had a call for a half-day's work, and she could not stay to see him start out for his walk. She helped him put on the trousers and pinned and rolled them for him, and she laced the shoes as snug as they would go on his feet. Then she told him not to go out till the noon whistles blew, and kissed him, and left.

Raymond was too happy to be impatient. He sat and thought of the street and smiled and sang. Not until he heard the whistles did he go to the drawer where Big Lannie had laid the coat, and take it out and put it on. He felt it soft on his bare back, he twisted his shoulders to let it fall warm and loose from them. As he folded the sleeves back over his thin arms, his heart beat so that the cloth above it fluttered.

The stairs were difficult for him to manage, in the big shoes, but the very slowness of the descent was delicious to him. His anticipation was like honey in his mouth.

Then he came out into the yard, and turned his face in the gentle air. It was all good again; it was all given back again. As quickly as he could, he gained the walk and set forth, guiding himself by the fence. He could not wait; he called out, so that he would hear gay calls in return, he laughed so that laughter would answer him.

He heard it. He was so glad that he took his hand from the fence and turned and stretched out his arms and held up his smiling face to welcome it. He stood there, and his smile died on his face, and his welcoming arms stiffened and shook.

It was not the laughter he had known; it was not the laughter he had lived on. It was like great flails beating him flat, great prongs tearing his flesh from his bones. It was coming at him, to kill him. It drew slyly back, and then it smashed against him. It swirled around and over him, and he could not breathe. He screamed and tried to run out through it, and fell, and it licked over him, howling higher. His clothes unrolled, and his shoes flapped on his feet. Each time he could rise, he fell again. It was as if the street were perpendicular before him, and the laughter leaping at his back. He could not find the fence, he did not know which way he was turned. He lay screaming, in blood and dust and darkness.

When Big Lannie came home, she found him on the floor in a corner of the room, moaning and whimpering. He still wore his new clothes, cut and torn and dusty, and there was dried blood on his mouth and his palms. Her heart had leapt in alarm when he had not opened the door at her footstep, and she cried out so frantically to ask what had happened that she frightened him into wild weeping. She could not understand what he said; it was something about the street, and laughing at him, and make them go away, and don't let him go in the street no more, never in the street no more. She did not try to make him explain. She took him in her arms and rocked him, and told him, over and over, never mind, don't care, everything's all right. Neither he nor she believed her words.

But her voice was soft and her arms warm. Raymond's sobs softened, and trembled away. She held him, rocking silently and rhythmically, a long time. Then gently she set him on his feet, and took from his shoulders Mr. Ewing's old full-dress coat.

The Worker in Sandalwood **Marjorie Pickthall**

There is always a demand for Christmas stories and every year publishers put them out hopefully. But when it comes down to popular favor, we always go back to one that was published in 1843. It was then that Charles Dickens delighted a circle of friends by reading to them the manuscript of *A Christmas Carol.* It is still read to a circle of millions every Christmas over the air and the book continues to sell in the thousands. This, despite the quite worthy successors which continue to appear.

Among the successors, I have a favorite. "The Worker in Sandalwood" was published in Canada in the early twenties by a young English girl named Marjorie Pickthall. It has a familiar background–the unhappy apprentice who is cold and ill-fed on Christmas Eve–but there is an unusually tender note and a spiritual quality in it that is seldom found in any fiction.

Miss Pickthall won a deserved reputation with her verse, but, most unfortunately, she died soon after the appearance of this moving story and did not achieve the place as a writer of prose which she undoubtedly would have won in time.

[illegible] Christmas [illegible] and every [illegible] popular taste, [illegible] 1843. However, the Circle [illegible] by sending [illegible] them [illegible] a circle of authors every Christmas [illegible] to sell under their [illegible] which [illegible]

[illegible] Winter in [illegible] was published [illegible] by [illegible] Margaret Pickard [illegible] the [illegible] Christmas Eve—but there [illegible]

Miss Pickard [illegible] which [illegible] world [illegible]

THE WORKER IN SANDALWOOD

Marjorie Pickthall

I like to think of this as a true story, but you who read may please yourselves, siding either with the curé, who says Hyacinthe dreamed it all, and did the carving himself in his sleep, or with Madame. I am sure that Hyacinthe thinks it true, and so does Madame, but then she has the cabinet, with the little birds and the lilies carved at the corners. Monsieur le curé shrugs his patient shoulders; but then he is tainted with the infidelities of cities, good man, having been three times to Montreal, and once, in an electric car, to Saint Anne. He and Madame still talk it over whenever they meet, though it happened so many years ago, and each leaves the other forever unconvinced. Meanwhile the dust gathers in the infinite fine lines of the little birds' feathers, and softens the lily stamens where Madame's duster may not go; and the wood, ageing, takes on a golden gleam as of immemorial sunsets: that pale red wood, heavy with the scent of the ancient East; the wood that Hyacinthe loved.

It was the only wood of that kind which had ever been seen in Terminaison. Pierre L'Oreillard brought it into the workshop one morning; a small heavy bundle wrapped in sacking, and then in burlap, and then in fine soft cloths. He laid it on a pile of shavings, and unwrapped it carefully and a dim sweetness filled the dark shed and hung heavily in the thin winter sunbeams.

Pierre L'Oreillard rubbed the wood respectfully with his knobby fingers. "It is sandalwood," he explained to Hyacinthe, pride of knowledge making him expansive; "a most precious wood that grows in warm countries, thou great goblin. Smell it, *imbécile*. It is sweeter than cedar. It is to make a cabinet for the old Madame at the big house. Thy great hands shall smooth the wood, *nigaud,* and I—I, Pierre the cabinet-maker, shall render it beautiful." Then he went out, locking the door behind him.

When he was gone, Hyacinthe laid down his plane, blew on his stiff fingers, and shambled slowly over to the wood. He was a great clumsy boy of fourteen, dark-faced, very slow of speech, dull-eyed and uncared for. He was clumsy because it is impossible to move gracefully when you are growing very big and fast on quite insufficient food. He was dull-eyed because all eyes met his unlovingly; uncared for, because none knew the beauty of his soul. But his heavy young hands could carve simple things, like flowers and birds and beasts, to perfection, as the curé pointed out. Simon has a tobacco-jar, carved with pine-cones and squirrels, and the curé has a pipe whose bowl is the bloom of a moccasin-flower, that I have seen. But it is all very long ago. And facts, in these lonely villages, easily become transfigured, touched upon their gray with a golden gleam.

"Thy hands shall smooth the wood, *nigaud,* and I shall render it beautiful," said Pierre L'Oreillard, and went off to drink brandy at the Cinq Chateaux.

Hyacinthe knew that the making of the cabinet would fall to him, as most of the other work did. He also touched the strange sweet wood, and at last laid his cheek against it, while the fragrance caught his breath. "How it is beautiful," said Hyacinthe, and for a moment his eyes glowed and he was happy. Then the light passed, and with bent head he shuffled back to his bench through a foam of white shavings curling almost to his knees.

"Madame perhaps will want the cabinet next week, for that is Christmas," said Hyacinthe, and fell to work harder than ever, though it was so cold in the shed that his breath hung like a little silver cloud and the steel stung his hands. There was a tiny window to his right, through which, when it was clear of frost, one looked on Terminaison, and that was cheerful and made one whistle. But to the left, through the chink of the ill-fitting door, there was nothing but the forest and the road dying away in it, and the trees moving heavily under the snow. Yet, from there came all Hyacinthe's dumb dreams and slow reluctant fancies, which he sometimes found himself able to tell—in wood, not in words.

Brandy was good at the Cinq Chateaux, and Pierre L'Oreillard gave Hyacinthe plenty of directions, but no further help with the cabinet.

"That is to be finished for Madame on the festival, *gros escargot!*" said he, cuffing Hyacinthe's ears furiously, "finished, and with a prettiness about the corners, hearest thou, *ourson?* I suffer from a delicacy of the constitution and a little feebleness in the legs on these days, so that I cannot handle the tools. I must leave this work to thee, *gacheur*. See it is done properly, and stand up and touch a hand to thy cap when I address thee, *orvet,* great slow-worm."

"Yes, monsieur," said Hyacinthe, wearily.

It is hard, when you do all the work, to be cuffed into the bargain, and fourteen is not very old. He went to work on the cabinet with slow, exquisite skill, but on the eve of Noel, he was still at work, and the cabinet unfinished. It meant a thrashing from Pierre if the morrow came and found it still unfinished, and Pierre's thrashings were cruel. But it was growing into a thing of perfection under his slow hands, and Hyacinthe would not hurry over it.

"Then work on it all night, and show it to me all completed in the morning, or thy bones shall mourn thy idleness," said Pierre with a flicker of his little eyes. And he shut Hyacinthe into the workshop with a smoky lamp, his tools, and the sandalwood cabinet.

It was nothing unusual. The boy had often been left before to finish a piece of work overnight while Pierre went off to his brandies. But this was Christmas Eve, and he was very tired. The cold crept into the shed until the scent of the sandalwood could not make him dream himself warm, and the roof cracked sullenly in the forest. There came upon Hyacinthe one of those awful, hopeless despairs that children know. It seemed to be a living presence that caught up his soul and crushed it in black hands. "In all the world, nothing!" said he, staring at the dull flame; "no place, no heart, no love! O kind God, is there a place, a love for me in another world?"

I cannot endure to think of Hyacinthe, poor lad, shut up despairing in the workshop with his loneliness, his cold, and his hunger, on the eve of Christmas. He was but an overgrown, unhappy child, and for unhappy children no aid, at this season, seems too divine for faith. So madame says, and she is very old and very wise. Hyacinthe even looked at the chisel in his hand, and thought that by a touch of that he might lose it all, all, and be at peace, somewhere not far from God; only it was forbidden. Then came the tears, and great sobs that sickened and deafened him, so that he scarcely heard the gentle rattling of the latch.

At least, I suppose it came then, but it may have been later. The story is all so vague here, so confused with fancies that have spoiled the first simplicity. I think that Hyacinthe must have gone to the door, opening it upon the still woods and the frosty stars, and the lad who stood outside must have said: "I see you are working late, comrade. May I come in?" or something like it.

Hyacinthe brushed his ragged sleeve across his eyes, and opened the door wider with a little nod to the other to enter. Those little lonely villages strung along the great river see strange wayfarers adrift inland from the sea. Hyacinthe said to himself that surely here was such a one.

Afterwards he told the curé that for a moment he had been bewildered. Dully blinking into the stranger's eyes, he lost for a flash the first impression of youth and received one of some incredible age or sadness.

But this also passed and he knew that the wanderer's eyes were only quiet, very quiet, like the little pools in the wood where the wild does went to drink. As he turned within the door, smiling at Hyacinthe and shaking some snow from his fur cap, he did not seem more than sixteen or so.

"It is very cold outside," he said. "There is a big oak tree on the edge of the fields that has split in the frost and frightened all the little squirrels asleep there. Next year it will make an even better home for them. And see what I found close by!" He opened his fingers, and showed Hyacinthe a little sparrow lying unruffled in his palm.

"Pauvrette!" said the dull Hyacinthe.

"Pauvrette! Is it then dead?" He touched it with a gentle forefinger.

"No," answered the strange boy, "it is not dead. We'll put it here among the shavings, not far from the lamp, and it will be well by morning."

He smiled at Hyacinthe again, and the shambling lad felt dimly as if the scent of sandalwood had deepened, and the lamp-flame burned clearer. But the stranger's eyes were only quiet, quiet.

"Have you come far?" asked Hyacinthe. "It is a bad season for travelling, and the wolves are out in the woods."

"A long way," said the other; "a long, long way. I heard a child cry. . . ."

"There is no child here," answered Hyacinthe, shaking his head. "Monsieur L'Oreillard is not fond of children, he says they cost too much money. But if you have come far, you must be cold and hungry, and I have no food or fire. At the Cinq Chateaux you will find both!"

The stranger looked at him again with those quiet eyes, and Hyacinthe fancied his face was familiar. "I will stay here," he said, "you are very late at work and you are unhappy."

"Why, as to that," answered Hyacinthe, rubbing again at his cheeks and ashamed of his tears, "most of us are sad at one time or another, the good God knows. Stay here and welcome if it pleases you, and you may take a share of my bed, though it is no more than a pile of balsam boughs and an old blanket, in the loft. But I must work at this cabinet, for the drawer must be finished and the handles put on and these corners carved, all by the holy morning; or my wages will be paid with a stick."

"You have a hard master," put in the other boy, "if he would pay you with blows upon the feast of Noel."

"He is hard enough," said Hyacinthe; "but once he gave me a dinner of sausages and white wine, and once, in the summer, melons. If my eyes will stay open, I will finish this by morning, but indeed I am sleepy. Stay with me an hour or so, comrade, and talk to me of your wanderings, so that the time may pass more quickly."

"I will tell you of the country where I was a child," answered the stranger.

And while Hyacinthe worked, he told–of sunshine and dust; of the shadows of vine-leaves on the flat white walls of a house; of rosy doves on the flat roof; of the flowers that come in the spring, crimson and blue, and the white cyclamen in the shadow of the rocks; of the olive, the myrtle and almond; until Hyacinthe's slow fingers ceased working, and his sleepy eyes blinked wonderingly.

"See what you have done, comrade," he said at last; "you have told of such pretty things that I have done no work for an hour. And now the cabinet will never be finished, and I shall be beaten."

"Let me help you," smiled the other; "I also was bred a carpenter."

At first Hyacinthe would not, fearing to trust the sweet wood out of his own hands, but at length he allowed the stranger to fit in one of the little drawers, and so deftly was the work done, that Hyacinthe pounded his fists on the bench in admiration. "You have a pretty knack," he cried; "it seemed as if you did but hold the drawer in your hands a moment, and hey! ho! it jumped into its place!"

"Let me fit in the other little drawers, while you go and rest a while," said the wanderer. So Hyacinthe curled up among the shavings, and the stranger fell to work upon the little cabinet of sandalwood.

Here begins what the curé will have it is a dream within a dream. Sweetest of dreams was ever dreamed, if that is so. Sometimes I am forced to think with him, but again I see as clearly as with old Madame's eyes, that have not seen the earthly light for twenty years, and with her and Hyacinthe, I say "Credo."

Hyacinthe said that he lay upon the shavings in the sweetness of the sandalwood, and was very tired. He thought of the country where the stranger had been a boy; of the flowers on the hills; of the laughing leaves of aspen, and poplar; of the golden flowering anise and the golden sun upon the dusty roads, until he was warm. All the time through these pictures, as through a painted veil, he was aware of that other boy with the quiet eyes, at work upon the cabinet, smoothing, fitting, polishing. "He does better work than I," thought Hyacinthe, but he was not jealous. And again he thought, "It is growing towards morning. In a little while I will get up and help him." But he did not, for the dream of warmth and the smell of the sandalwood held him in a sweet drowse. Also he said that he thought the stranger was singing as he worked, for there seemed to be a sense of some music in the shed, though he could not tell whether it came from the other boy's lips, or from the shabby old tools as he used them, or from the stars. "The stars are much paler," thought Hyacinthe, "and soon it will be morning, and the corners are not carved yet. I must get up and help this kind one in a little moment. Only I am so tired, and the music and the sweetness seem to wrap me and fold me close, so that I may not move."

He lay without moving, and behind the forest there shone a pale glow of some indescribable colour that was neither green nor blue, while in Terminaison the church bells began to ring. "Day will soon be here!" thought Hyacinthe, immovable in that deep dream of his, "and with day will come Monsieur L'Oreillard and his stick. I must get up and help, for even yet the corners are not carved."

But he did not get up. Instead, he saw the stranger look at him again, smiling as if he loved him, and lay his brown finger lightly upon the four empty corners of the cabinet. And Hyacinthe saw the little squares of reddish wood ripple and heave and break, as little clouds when the wind goes through the sky. And out of them thrust forth little birds, and after them the lilies, for a moment living, but even while Hyacinthe looked, growing hard and reddish-brown and settling back into the sweet wood. Then the stranger smiled again, and laid all the tools neatly in order, and, opening the door quietly, went away into the woods.

Hyacinthe lay still among the shavings for a long time, and then he crept slowly to the door. The sun, not yet risen, set its first beams upon the delicate mist of frost afloat beneath the trees, and so all the world was aflame with splendid gold. Far away down the road a dim figure seemed to move amid the glory, but the glow and the splendour were such that Hyacinthe was blinded. His breath came sharply as the glow beat in great waves on the wretched shed; on the foam of shavings; on the cabinet with the little birds and the lilies carved at the corners.

He was too pure of heart to feel afraid. But, "Blessed be the Lord," whispered Hyacinthe, clasping his slow hands, "for He hath visited and redeemed His people. But who will believe?"

Then the sun of Christ's day rose gloriously, and the little sparrow came from his nest among the shavings and shook his wings to the light.

They Trample on Your Heart **Katherine Anne Porter**

Katherine Anne Porter has written so many remarkable short stories that it should be difficult to select any on the list as her best. But I do not find it at all hard to name my own preference; it is for these stories of Grandmother and old Nannie and Uncle Jimbilly, and the members of the family which Grandmother trained and managed and led out of the wilderness of a war-torn South into the Land of Promise which was called Texas. These are beautiful stories, depicting the backgrounds and the characters with crystal fidelity. It may be that other stories have been written about the South which are just as good but, if there are such, I have been unfortunate enough to miss them.

Two episodes in the series have not been included because they are not directly concerned with the main characters.

THEY TRAMPLE ON YOUR HEART

Katherine Anne Porter

I

Once a year, in early summer, after school was closed and the children were to be sent to the farm, the Grandmother began to long for the country. With an air of tenderness, as if she enquired after a favorite child, she would ask questions about the crops, wonder what kind of gardens the Negroes were making, how the animals were faring. She would remark now and then, "I begin to feel the need of a little change and relaxation, too," in a vague tone of reassurance, as if to say this did not mean that she intended for a moment really to relax her firm hold on family affairs. It was her favorite theory that change of occupation was one way, probably the best way, of resting. The three grandchildren would begin to feel the faint sure stirrings of departure in the house; her son, their father, would assume the air of careful patience which imperfectly masked his annoyance at the coming upsets and inconveniences to be endured at the farm. "Now, Harry, now, Harry!" his mother would warn him, for she was never deceived by his manner; indeed, he never meant her to be; and she would begin trying to placate him by wondering falsely if she could possibly get away, after all, with so much yet to be done where she was. She looked forward with pleasure to a breath of country air. She always imagined herself as walking at leisure in the shade of the orchards watching the peaches ripen; she spoke with longing of clipping the rosebushes, or of tying up the trellised honeysuckle with her own hands. She would pack up her summer-weight black skirts, her thin black-and-white basques, and would get out a broad-brimmed, rather battered straw shepherdess hat she had woven for herself just after the War. Trying it on, turning her head critically this way and that before the mirror, she would decide that it might do nicely for the sun and she always took it along, but never wore it. She wore instead a stiffly starched white chambray bonnet, with a round crown buttoned on a narrow brim; it sat pertly on the top of her head with a fly-away look, the long strings hanging stiffly. Underneath this headdress, her pale, tightly drawn, very old face looked out with stately calm.

In the early spring, when the Indian cling peach tree against the wall of the town house began to bloom, she would say, "I have planted five orchards in three States, and now I see only one tree in bloom." A soft, enjoyable melancholy would come over her; she would stand quite still for a moment looking at the single tree, representing all her beloved trees still blooming, flourishing, and preparing to bring forth fruit in their separate places.

Leaving Aunt Nannie, who had been nurse to her children, in charge of the town house, she set out on her journey.

If departure was a delightful adventure for the children, arriving at the farm was an event for Grandmother. Hinry came running to open the gate, his coal-black face burst into a grin, his voice flying before him: "Howdy-do, Miss Sophia Jane!", simply not noticing that the carry-all was spilling over with other members of the family. The horses jogged in, their bellies jolting and churning, and Grandmother, calling out greetings in her feast-day voice, alighted, surrounded by her people, with the same flurry of travel that marked her journeys by train; but now with an indefinable sense of homecoming, not to the house but to the black, rich soft land and the human beings living on it. Without removing her long veiled widow's bonnet, she would walk straight through the house, observing instantly that everything was out of order; pass out into the yards and gardens, silently glancing, making instant plans for changes; down the narrow path past the barns, with a glance into and around them as she went, a glance of firm and purposeful censure; and on past the canebrake to the left, the hayfields to the right, until she arrived at the row of Negro huts that ran along the bois d'arc hedge.

Stepping up with a pleasant greeting to all, which in no way promised exemption from the wrath to come, she went into their kitchens, glanced into their meal barrels, their ovens, their cupboard shelves, into every smallest crevice and corner, with Littie and Dicey and Hinry and Bumper and Keg following, trying to explain that things was just a little out of shape right now because they'd had so much outside work they hadn't just been able to straighten out the way they meant to; but they were going to get at it right away.

Indeed they were, as Grandmother well knew. Within an hour someone would have driven away in the buckboard with an order for such lime for whitewash, so many gallons of kerosene oil, and so much carbolic acid and insect powder. Home-made lye soap would be produced from the washhouse, and the frenzy would begin. Every mattress cover was emptied of its corn husks and boiled, every little Negro on the place was set to work picking a fresh supply of husks, every hut was thickly white-washed, bins and cupboards were scrubbed, every chair and bedstead was varnished, every filthy quilt was brought to light, boiled in a great iron washpot and stretched in the sun; and the uproar had all the special character of any annual occasion. The Negro women were put at making a fresh supply of shirts for the men and children, cotton dresses and aprons for themselves. Whoever wished to complain now seized his opportunity. Mister Harry had clean forgot to buy shoes for Hinry, look at Hinry: Hinry had been just like that, barefooted the livelong winter. Mister Miller (a red-whiskered man who occupied a dubious situation somewhere between overseer when Mister Harry was absent, and plain hired hand when he was present) had skimped them last winter on everything you could think of—not enough cornmeal, not half enough bacon, not enough wood, not enough of anything. Littie had needed a little sugar for her cawfy and do you think Mister Miller would let her have it? No. Mister Miller had said nobody needed sugar in their cawfy. Hinry said Mister Miller didn't even take sugar in his own cawfy because he was just too stingy. Boosker, the three-year-old baby, had earache in January and Miz Carleton had come down and put lodnum in it and Boosker was acting like she was deef ever since. The black horse Mister Harry bought last fall had gone clean wild and jumped a barbed wire fence and tore his chest almost off and hadn't been any good from that time on.

All these annoyances and dozens like them had to be soothed at once, then Grandmother's attention was turned to the main house, which must be overhauled completely. The big secretaries were opened and shabby old sets of Dickens, Scott, Thackeray, Dr. Johnson's dictionary, the volumes of Pope and Milton and Dante and Shakespeare were dusted off and closed up carefully again. Curtains came down in dingy heaps and went up again stiff and sweet-smelling; rugs were heaved forth in dusty confusion and returned flat and gay with flowers once more; the kitchen was no longer dingy and desolate but a place of heavenly order where it was tempting to linger.

Next the barns and smokehouses and the potato cellar, the gardens and every tree or vine or bush must have that restoring touch upon it. For two weeks this would go on, with the Grandmother a tireless, just and efficient slave driver of every creature on the place. The children ran wild outside, but not as they did when she was not there. The hour came in each day when they were rounded up, captured, washed, dressed properly, made to eat what was set before them without giving battle, put to bed when the time came and no nonsense . . . They loved their Grandmother; she was the only reality to them in a world that seemed otherwise without fixed authority or refuge, since their mother had died so early that only the eldest girl remembered her vaguely; just the same they felt that Grandmother was tyrant, and they wished to be free of her; so they were always pleased when, on a certain day, as a sign that her visit was drawing to an end, she would go out to the pasture and call her old saddle horse, Fiddler.

He had been a fine, thorough-paced horse once, but he was now a weary, disheartened old hero, gray-haired on his jaw and chin, who spent his life nuzzling with pendulous lips for tender bits of grass or accepting sugar cautiously between his shaken teeth. He paid no attention to anyone but the Grandmother. Every summer when she went to his field and called him, he came doddering up with almost a gleam in his filmy eyes. The two old creatures would greet each other fondly. The Grandmother always treated her animal friends as if they were human beings temporarily metamorphosed, but not by this accident dispensed from those duties suitable to their condition. She would have Fiddler brought around under her old side-saddle—her little granddaughters rode astride and she saw no harm in it, for them—and mount with her foot in Uncle Jimbilly's curved hand. Fiddler would remember his youth and break into a stiff-legged gallop, and off she would go with her crepe bands and her old-fashioned riding skirt flying. They always returned at a walk, the Grandmother sitting straight as a sword, smiling, triumphant. Dismounting at the horse-block by herself, she would stroke Fiddler on the neck before turning him over to Uncle Jimbilly, and walk away carrying her train grandly over her arm.

This yearly gallop with Fiddler was important to her; it proved her strength, her unabated energy. Any time now Fiddler might drop in his tracks, but she would not. She would say, "He's getting stiff in the knees," or "He's pretty short-winded this year," but she herself walked lightly and breathed as easily as ever, or so she chose to believe.

That same afternoon or the next day, she would take her long-promised easy stroll in the orchards with nothing to do, her Grandchildren running before her and running back to her side: with nothing at all to do, her hands folded, her skirts trailing and picking up twigs, turning over little stones, sweeping a faint path behind her, her white bonnet askew over one eye, an absorbed fixed smile on her lips, her eyes missing nothing. This walk would usually end with Hinry or Jimbilly being dispatched to the orchards at once to make some trifling but indispensable improvement.

It would then come over her powerfully that she was staying on idling when there was so much to be done at home . . . There would be a last look at everything, instructions, advices, good-bys, blessings. She would set out with that strange look of leaving forever, and arrive at the place in town with the same air of homecoming she had worn on her arrival in the country, in a gentle flurry of greeting and felicitations, as if she had been gone for half a year. At once she set to work restoring to order the place which no doubt had gone somewhat astray in her absence.

II

Uncle Jimbilly was so old and had spent so many years bowed over things, putting them together and taking them apart, making them over and making them do, he was bent almost double. His hands were closed and stiff from gripping objects tightly, while he worked at them, and they could not open altogether even if a child took the thick black fingers and tried to turn them back. He hobbled on a stick; his purplish skull showed through patches in his wool, which had turned greenish gray and looked as if the moths had got at it.

He mended harness and put half soles on the other Negroes' shoes, he built fences and chicken coops and barn doors; he stretched wires and put in new window panes and fixed sagging hinges and patched up roofs; he repaired carriage tops and cranky plows. Also he had a gift for carving miniature tombstones out of blocks of wood; give him almost any kind of piece of wood and he could turn out a tombstone, shaped very like the real ones, with carving, and a name and date on it if they were needed. They were often needed, for some small beast or bird was always dying and having to be buried with proper ceremonies: the cart draped as a hearse, a shoe-box coffin with a pall over it, a profuse floral outlay and, of course, a tombstone. As he worked, turning the long blade of his bowie knife deftly in circles to cut a flower, whittling and smoothing the back and sides, stopping now and then to hold it at arm's length and examine it with one eye closed, Uncle Jimbilly would talk in a low, broken, abstracted murmur, as if to himself; but he was really saying something he meant one to hear. Sometimes it would be an incomprehensible ghost story; listen ever so carefully, at the end it was impossible to decide whether Uncle Jimbilly himself had seen the ghost, whether it was a real ghost at all, or only another man dressed like one; and he dwelt much on the horrors of slave times.

"Dey used to take 'em out and tie 'em down and whup 'em," he muttered, "wid gret big leather strops inch thick long as yo' ahm, wid round holes bored in 'em so's evey time dey hit 'em de hide and de meat done come off dey bones in little round chunks. And wen dey had whupped 'em wid de strop till dey backs was all raw and bloody, dey spread dry cawnshucks on dey backs and set 'em afire and pahched 'em, and den dey poured vinega all ovah 'em . . . Yassuh. And den, the ve'y nex day dey'd got to git back to work in the fiels or dey'd do the same thing right ovah agin. Yassah. Dat was it. If dey didn't git back to work dey got it all right ovah agin."

The children–three of them: a serious, prissy older girl of ten, a thoughtful sad looking boy of eight, and a quick flighty little girl of six –sat disposed around Uncle Jimbilly and listened with faint tinglings of embarrassment. They knew, of course, that once upon a time Negroes had been slaves; but they had all been freed long ago and were now only servants. It was hard to realize that Uncle Jimbilly had been born in slavery, as the Negroes were always saying. The children thought that Uncle Jimbilly had got over his slavery very well. Since they had known him, he had never done a single thing that anyone told him to do. He did his work just as he pleased and when he pleased. If you wanted a tombstone, you had to be very careful about the way you asked for it. Nothing could have been more impersonal and faraway than his tone and manner of talking about slavery, but they wriggled a little and felt guilty. Paul would have changed the subject, but Miranda, the little quick one, wanted to know the worst. "Did they act like that to you, Uncle Jimbilly?" she asked.

"No, *mam,*" said Uncle Jimbilly. "Now whut name you want on dis one? Dey nevah did. Dey done 'em dat way in the rice swamps. I always worked right here close to the house or in town with Miss Sophia. Down in the swamps . . ."

"Didn't they ever die, Uncle Jimbilly?" asked Paul.

"Cose dey died," said Uncle Jimbilly, "cose dey died–dey died," he went on, pursing his mouth gloomily, "by de thousands and tens upon thousands."

"Can you carve 'Safe in Heaven' on that, Uncle Jimbilly?" asked Maria in her pleasant, mincing voice.

"To put over a tame jackrabbit, Missy?" asked Uncle Jimbilly indignantly. He was very religious. "A heathen like dat? No, *mam.* In de swamps dey used to stake 'em out all day and all night, and all day and all night and all day wid dey hans and feet tied so dey couldn't scretch and let de muskeeters eat 'em alive. De muskeeters 'ud bite 'em tell dey was all swole up like a balloon all over, and you could heah 'em howlin and prayin all ovah the swamp. Yassuh. Dat was it. And nary a drop of watah noh a mouful of braid . . . Yassuh, dat's it. Lawd, dey done it. Hosanna! Now take dis yere tombstone and don' bother me no more . . . or I'll . . ."

Uncle Jimbilly was apt to be suddenly annoyed and you never knew why. He was easily put out about things, but his threats were always so exorbitant that not even the most credulous child could be terrified by them. He was always going to do something quite horrible to somebody and then he was going to dispose of the remains in a revolting manner. He was going to skin somebody alive and nail the hide on the barn door, or he was just getting ready to cut off somebody's ears with a hatchet and pin them on Bongo, the crop-eared brindle dog. He was often all prepared in his mind to pull somebody's teeth and make a set of false teeth for Ole Man Ronk . . . Ole Man Ronk was a tramp who had been living all summer in the little cabin behind the smokehouse. He got his rations along with the Negroes and sat all day mumbling his naked gums. He had skimpy black whiskers which appeared to be set in wax, and angry red eyelids. He took morphine, it was said; but what morphine might be, or how he took it, or why, no one seemed to know . . . Nothing could have been more unpleasant than the notion that one's teeth might be given to Ole Man Ronk.

The reason why Uncle Jimbilly never did any of these things he threatened was, he said, because he never could get round to them. He always had so much other work on hand he never seemed to get caught up on it. But some day, somebody was going to get a mighty big surprise, and meanwhile everybody had better look out.

III

In their later years, the Grandmother and old Nannie used to sit together for some hours every day over their sewing. They shared a passion for cutting scraps of the family finery, hoarded for fifty years, into strips and triangles, and fitting them together again in a carefully disordered patchwork, outlining each bit of velvet or satin or taffeta with a running briar stitch in clear lemon-colored silk floss. They had contrived enough bed and couch covers, table spreads, dressing table scarfs, to have furnished forth several households. Each piece as it was finished was lined with yellow silk, folded, and laid away in a chest, never again to see the light of day. The Grandmother was the great-granddaughter of Kentucky's most famous pioneer: he had, while he was surveying Kentucky, hewed out rather competently a rolling pin for his wife. This rolling pin was the Grandmother's irreplaceable treasure. She covered it with an extraordinarily complicated bit of patchwork, added golden tassels to the handles, and hung it in a conspicuous place in her room. She was the daughter of a notably heroic captain in the War of 1812. She had his razors in a shagreen case and a particularly severe-looking daguerreotype taken in his old age, with his chin in a tall stock and his black satin waistcoat smoothed over a still-handsome military chest. So she fitted a patchwork case over the shagreen and made a sort of envelope of cut velvet and violet satin, held together with briar stitching, to contain the portrait. The rest of her handiwork she put away, to the relief of her grandchildren, who had arrived at the awkward age when Grandmother's quaint old-fashioned ways caused them acute discomfort.

In the summer the women sat under the mingled trees of the side garden, which commanded a view of the east wing, the front and back porches, a good part of the front garden and a corner of the small fig grove. Their choice of this location was a part of their domestic strategy. Very little escaped them: a glance now and then would serve to keep them fairly well informed as to what was going on in the whole place. It is true they had not seen Miranda the day she pulled up the whole mint bed to give to a pleasant strange young woman who stopped and asked her for a sprig of fresh mint. They had never found out who stole the giant pomegranates growing too near the fence: they had not been in time to stop Paul from setting himself on fire while experimenting with a miniature blowtorch, but they had been on the scene to extinguish him with rugs, to pour oil on him, and lecture him. They never saw Maria climbing trees, a mania she had to indulge or pine away, for she chose tall ones on the opposite side of the house. But such casualties were so minor a part of the perpetual round of events that they did not feel defeated nor that their strategy was a failure. Summer, in many ways so desirable a season, had its drawbacks. The children were everywhere at once and the Negroes loved lying under the hackberry grove back of the barn playing seven-up, and eating watermelons. The summer house was in a small town a few miles from the farm, a compromise between the rigorously ordered house in the city and the sprawling old farmhouse which Grandmother had built with such pride and pains. It had, she often said, none of the advantages of either country or city, and all the discomforts of both. But the children loved it.

During the winters in the city, they sat in Grandmother's room, a large squarish place with a small coal grate. All the sounds of life in the household seemed to converge there, echo, retreat, and return. Grandmother and Aunt Nannie knew the whole complicated code of sounds, could interpret and comment on them by an exchange of glances, a lifted eyebrow, or a tiny pause in their talk.

They talked about the past, really—always about the past. Even the future seemed like something gone and done with when they spoke of it. It did not seem an extension of their past, but a repetition of it. They would agree that nothing remained of life as they had known it, the world was changing swiftly, but by the mysterious logic of hope they insisted that each change was probably the last; or if not, a series of changes might bring them, blessedly, back full-circle to the old ways they had known. Who knows why they loved their past? It had been bitter for them both, they had questioned the burdensome rule they lived by every day of their lives, but without rebellion and without expecting an answer. This unbroken thread of inquiry in their minds contained no doubt as to the utter rightness and justice of the basic laws of human existence, founded as they were on God's plan; but they wondered perpetually, with only a hint now and then to each other of the uneasiness of their hearts, how so much suffering and confusion could have been built up and maintained on such a foundation. The Grandmother's rôle was authority, she knew that; it was her duty to portion out activities, to urge or restrain where necessary, to teach morals, manners, and religion, to punish and reward her own household according to a fixed code. Her own doubts and hesitations she concealed, also, she reminded herself, as a matter of duty. Old Nannie had no ideas at all as to her place in the world. It had been assigned to her before birth, and for her daily rule she had all her life obeyed the authority nearest to her.

So they talked about God, about heaven, about planting a new hedge of rosebushes, about the new ways of preserving fruit and vegetables, about eternity and their mutual hope that they might pass it happily together, and often a scrap of silk under their hands would start them on long trains of family reminiscences. They were always amused to notice again how the working of their memories differed in such important ways. Nannie could recall names to perfection; she could always say what the weather had been like on all important occasions, what certain ladies had worn, how handsome certain gentlemen had been, what there had been to eat and drink. Grandmother had masses of dates in her mind, and no memories attached to them: her memories of events seemed detached and floating beyond time. For example, the 26th of August, 1871, had been some sort of red-letter day for her. She had said to herself then that never would she forget that date; and indeed, she remembered it well, but she no longer had the faintest notion what had happened to stamp it on her memory. Nannie was no help in the matter; she had nothing to do with dates. She did not know the year of her birth, and would never have had a birthday to celebrate if Grandmother had not, when she was still Miss Sophia Jane, aged ten, opened a calendar at random, closed her eyes, and marked a date unseen with a pen. So it turned out that Nannie's birthday thereafter fell on June 11, and the year, Miss Sophia Jane decided, should be 1827, her own birth-year, making Nannie just three months younger than her mistress. Sophia Jane then made an entry of Nannie's birth-date in the family Bible, inserting it just below her own. "Nannie Gay," she wrote, in stiff careful letters, "(black)," and though there was some uproar when this was discovered, the ink was long since sunk deeply into the paper, and besides no one was really upset enough to have it scratched out. There it remained, one of their pleasantest points of reference.

They talked about religion, and the slack way the world was going nowadays, the decay of behavior, and about the younger children, whom these topics always brought at once to mind. On these subjects they were firm, critical, and unbewildered. They had received educations which furnished them an assured habit of mind about all the important appearances of life, and especially about the rearing of young. They relied with perfect acquiescence on the dogma that children were conceived in sin and brought forth in iniquity. Childhood was a long state of instruction and probation for adult life, which was in turn a long, severe, undeviating devotion to duty, the largest part of which consisted in bringing up children. The young were difficult, disobedient, and tireless in wrongdoing, apt to turn unkind and undutiful when they grew up, in spite of all one had done for them, or had tried to do: for small painful doubts rose in them now and again when they looked at their completed works. Nannie couldn't abide her new-fangled grandchildren. "Wuthless, shiftless lot, jes plain scum, Miss Sophia Jane; I cain't undahstand it aftah all the raisin' dey had."

The Grandmother defended them, and dispraised her own second generation–heartily, too, for she sincerely found grave faults in them–which Nannie defended in turn. "When they are little, they trample on your feet, and when they grow up they trample on your heart." This was about all there was to say about children in any generation, but the fascination of the theme was endless. They said it thoroughly over and over with thousands of small variations, with always an example among their own friends or family connections to prove it. They had enough material of their own. Grandmother had borne eleven children, Nannie thirteen. They boasted of it. Grandmother would say, "I am the mother of eleven children," in a faintly amazed tone, as if she hardly expected to be believed, or could even quite believe it herself. But she could still point to nine of them. Nannie had lost ten of hers. They were all buried in Kentucky. Nannie never doubted or expected anyone else to doubt she had children. Her boasting was of another order. "Thirteen of 'em," she would say, in an appalled voice, "yas, my Lawd and my Redeemah, thirteen!"

The friendship between the two old women had begun in early childhood, and was based on what seemed even to them almost mythical events. Miss Sophia Jane, a prissy, spoiled five-year-old, with tight black ringlets which were curled every day on a stick, with her stiffly pleated lawn pantalettes and tight bodice, had run to meet her returning father, who had been away buying horses and Negroes. Sitting on his arm, clasping him around the neck, she had watched the wagons filing past on the way to the barns and quarters. On the floor of the first wagon sat two blacks, male and female, holding between them a scrawny, half-naked black child, with a round nubbly head and fixed bright monkey eyes. The baby Negro had a potbelly and her arms were like sticks from wrist to shoulder. She clung with narrow, withered, black leather fingers to her parents, a hand on each.

"I want the little monkey," said Sophia Jane to her father, nuzzling his cheek and pointing. "I want that one to play with."

Behind each wagon came two horses in lead, but in the second wagon there was a small shaggy pony with a thatch of mane over his eyes, a long tail like a brush, a round, hard barrel of a body. He was standing in straw to the knees, braced firmly in a padded stall with a Negro holding his bridle. "Do you see that?" asked her father. "That's for you. High time you learned to ride."

Sophia Jane almost leaped from his arm for joy. She hardly recognized her pony or her monkey the next day, the one clipped and sleek, the other clean in new blue cotton. For a while she could not decide which she loved more, Nannie or Fiddler. But Fiddler did not wear well. She outgrew him in a year, saw him pass without regret to a small brother, though she refused to allow him to be called Fiddler any longer. That name she reserved for a long series of saddle horses. She had named the first in honor of Fiddler Gay, an old Negro who made the music for dances and parties. There was only one Nannie and she outwore Sophia Jane. During all their lives together it was not so much a question of affection between them as a simple matter of being unable to imagine getting on without each other.

Nannie remembered well being on a shallow platform out in front of a great building in a large busy place, the first town she had ever seen. Her father and mother were with her, and there was a thick crowd around them. There were several other small groups of Negroes huddled together with white men bustling them about now and then. She had never seen any of these faces before, and she never saw but one of them again. She remembered it must have been summer, because she was not shivering with cold in her cotton shift. For one thing, her bottom was still burning from a spanking someone (it might have been her mother) had given her just before they got on the platform, to remind her to keep still. Her mother and father were field hands, and had never lived in white folks' houses. A tall gentleman with a long narrow face and very high curved nose, wearing a great-collared blue coat and immensely long light-colored trousers (Nannie could close her eyes and see him again, clearly, as he looked that day) stepped up near them suddenly, while a great hubbub rose. The red-faced man standing on a stump beside them shouted and droned, waving his arms and pointing at Nannie's father and mother. Now and then the tall gentleman raised a finger, without looking at the black people on the platform. Suddenly the shouting died down, the tall gentleman walked over and said to Nannie's father and mother, "Well, Eph! Well, Steeny! Mister Jimmerson comin' to get you in a minute." He poked Nannie in the stomach with a thickly gloved forefinger. "Regular crowbait," he said to the auctioneer. "I should have had lagniappe with this one."

"A pretty worthless article right now, sir, I agree with you," said the auctioneer, "but it'll grow out of it. As for the team, you won't find a better, I swear."

"I've had an eye on 'em for years," said the tall gentleman, and walked away, motioning as he went to a fat man sitting on a wagon tongue, spitting quantities of tobacco juice. The fat man rose and came over to Nannie and her parents.

Nannie had been sold for twenty dollars: a gift, you might say, hardly sold at all. She learned that a really choice slave sometimes cost more than a thousand dollars. She lived to hear slaves brag about how much they had cost. She had not known how little she fetched on the block until her own mother taunted her with it. This was after Nannie had gone to live for good at the big house, and her mother and father were still in the fields. They lived and worked and died there. A good worming had cured Nannie's potbelly, she thrived on plentiful food and a species of kindness not so indulgent, maybe, as that given to the puppies; still it more than fulfilled her notions of good fortune.

The old women often talked about how strangely things come out in this life. The first owner of Nannie and her parents had gone, Sophia Jane's father said, hog-wild about Texas. It was a new Land of Promise, in 1832. He had sold out his farm and four slaves in Kentucky to raise the money to take a great twenty-mile stretch of land in southwest Texas. He had taken his wife and two young children and set out, and there had been no more news of him for many years. When Grandmother arrived in Texas forty years later, she found him a prosperous ranchman and district judge. Much later, her youngest son met his granddaughter, fell in love with her, and married her—all in three months.

The judge, by then eighty-five years old, was uproarious and festive at the wedding. He reeked of corn liquor, swore by God every other breath, and was rearing to talk about the good old times in Kentucky. The Grandmother showed Nannie to him. "Would you recognize her?"

"For God Almighty's sake!" bawled the judge, "is that the strip of crow-bait I sold to your father for twenty dollars? Twenty dollars seemed like a fortune to me in those days!"

While they were jolting home down the steep rocky road on the long journey from San Marcos to Austin, Nannie finally spoke out about her grievance. "Look lak a jedge might had better raisin'," she said, gloomily, "look lak he didn't keer how much he hurt a body's feelins."

The Grandmother, muffled down in the back seat in the corner of the old carryall, in her worn sealskin pelisse, showing coffee-brown at the edges, her eyes closed, her hands wrung together, had been occupied once more in reconciling herself to losing a son, and, as ever, to a girl and a family of which she could not altogether approve. It was not that there was anything seriously damaging to be said against any of them; only—well, she wondered at her sons' tastes. What had each of them in turn found in the wife he had chosen? The Grandmother had always had in mind the kind of wife each of her sons needed; she had tried to bring about better marriages for them than they had made for themselves. They had merely resented her interference in what they considered strictly their personal affairs. She did not realize that she had spoiled and pampered her youngest son until he was in all probability unfit to be any kind of a husband, much less a good one. And there was something about her new daughter-in-law, a tall, handsome, firm-looking young woman, with a direct way of speaking, walking, talking, that seemed to promise that the spoiled Baby's days of clover were ended. The Grandmother was annoyed deeply at seeing how self-possessed the bride had been, how she had had her way about the wedding arrangements down to the last detail, how she glanced now and then at her new husband with calm, humorous, level eyes, as if she had already got him sized up. She had even suggested at the wedding dinner that her idea of a honeymoon would be to follow the chuck-wagon on the round-up, and help in the cattle-branding on her father's ranch. Of course she may have been joking. But she was altogether too Western, too modern, something like the "new" woman who was beginning to run wild, asking for the vote, leaving her home and going out in the world to earn her own living . . .

The Grandmother's narrow body shuddered to the bone at the thought of women so unsexing themselves; she emerged with a start from the dark reverie of foreboding thoughts which left a bitter taste in her throat. "Never mind, Nannie. The judge just wasn't thinking. He's very fond of his good cheer."

Nannie had slept in a bed and had been playmate and work-fellow with her mistress; they fought on almost equal terms, Sophia Jane defending Nannie fiercely against any discipline but her own. When they were both seventeen years old, Miss Sophia Jane was married off in a very gay wedding. The house was jammed to the roof and everybody present was at least fourth cousin to everybody else. There were forty carriages and more than two hundred horses to look after for two days. When the last wheel disappeared down the lane (a number of the guests lingered on for two weeks), the larders and bins were half empty and the place looked as if a troop of cavalry had been over it. A few days later Nannie was married off to a boy she had known ever since she came to the family, and they were given as a wedding present to Miss Sophia Jane.

Miss Sophia Jane and Nannie had then started their grim and terrible race of procreation, a child every sixteen months or so, with Nannie nursing both, and Sophia Jane, in dreadful discomfort, suppressing her milk with bandages and spirits of wine. When they each had produced their fourth child, Nannie almost died of puerperal fever. Sophia Jane nursed both children. She named the black baby Charlie, and her own child Stephen, and she fed them justly turn about, not favoring the white over the black, as Nannie felt obliged to do. Her husband was shocked, tried to forbid her; her mother came to see her and reasoned with her. They found her very difficult and quite stubborn. She had already begun to develop her implicit character, which was altogether just, humane, proud, and simple. She had many small vanities and weaknesses on the surface: a love of luxury and a tendency to resent criticism. This tendency was based on her feeling of superiority in judgment and sensibility to almost everyone around her. It made her very hard to manage. She had a quiet way of holding her ground which convinced her antagonist that she would really die, not just threaten to, rather than give way. She had learned now that she was badly cheated in giving her children to another woman to feed; she resolved never again to be cheated in just that way. She sat nursing her child and her foster child, with a sensual warm pleasure she had not dreamed of, translating her natural physical relief into something holy, God-sent, amends from heaven for what she had suffered in childbed. Yes, and for what she missed in the marriage bed, for there also something had failed. She said to Nannie quite calmly, "From now on, you will nurse your children and I will nurse mine," and it was so. Charlie remained her special favorite among the Negro children. "I understand now," she said to her older sister Keziah, "why the black mammies love their foster children. I love mine." So Charlie was brought up in the house as playmate for her son Stephen, and exempted from hard work all his life.

Sophia Jane had been wooed at arm's length by a mysteriously attractive young man whom she remembered well as rather a snubby little boy with curls like her own, but shorter, a frilled white blouse and kilts of the Macdonald tartan. He was her second cousin and resembled her so closely they had been mistaken for brother and sister. Their grandparents had been first cousins, and sometimes Sophia Jane saw in him, years after they were married, all the faults she had most abhorred in her elder brother: lack of aim, failure to act at crises, a philosophic detachment from practical affairs, a tendency to set projects on foot and then leave them to perish or to be finished by someone else; and a profound conviction that everyone around him should be happy to wait upon him hand and foot. She had fought these fatal tendencies in her brother, within the bounds of wifely prudence she fought them in her husband, she was long after to fight them again in two of her sons and in several of her grandchildren. She gained no victory in any case, the selfish, careless, unloving creatures lived and ended as they had begun. But the Grandmother developed a character truly portentous under the discipline of trying to change the characters of others. Her husband shared with her the family sharpness of eye. He disliked and feared her deadly willfullness, her certainty that her ways were not only right but beyond criticism, that her feelings were important, even in the lightest matter, and must not be tampered with or treated casually. He had disappeared at the critical moment when they were growing up, had gone to college and then for travel; she forgot him for a long time, and when she saw him again forgot him as he had been once for all. She was gay and sweet and decorous, full of vanity and incredibly exalted daydreams which threatened now and again to cast her over the edge of some mysterious forbidden frenzy. She dreamed recurrently that she had lost her virginity (her virtue, she called it), her sole claim to regard, consideration, even to existence, and after frightful moral suffering which masked altogether her physical experience she would wake in a cold sweat, disordered and terrified. She had heard that her cousin Stephen was a little "wild," but that was to be expected. He was leading, no doubt, a dashing life full of manly indulgences, the sweet dark life of the knowledge of evil which caused her hair to crinkle on her scalp when she thought of it. Ah, the delicious, the free, the wonderful, the mysterious and terrible life of men! She thought about it a great deal. "Little daydreamer," her mother or father would say to her, surprising her in a brown study, eyes moist, lips smiling vaguely over her embroidery or her book, or with hands fallen on her lap, her face turned away to a blank wall. She memorized and saved for these moments scraps of high-minded poetry, which she instantly quoted at them when they offered her a penny for her thoughts; or she broke into a melancholy little song of some kind, a song she knew they liked. She would run to the piano and tinkle the tune out with one hand, saying, "I love this part best," leaving no doubt in their minds as to what her own had been occupied with. She lived her whole youth so, without once giving herself away; not until she was in middle age, her husband dead, her property dispersed, and she found herself with a houseful of children, making a new life for them in another place, with all the responsibilities of a man but with none of the privileges, did she finally emerge into something like an honest life: and yet, she was passionately honest. She had never been anything else.

Sitting under the trees with Nannie, both of them old and their long battle with life almost finished, she said, fingering a scrap of satin, "It was not fair that Sister Keziah should have had this ivory brocade for her wedding dress, and I had only dotted swiss . . ."

"Times was harder when you got married, Missy," said Nannie. "Dat was de yeah all de crops failed."

"And they failed ever afterward, it seems to me," said Grandmother.

"Seems to me like," said Nannie, "dotted swiss was all the style when you got married."

"I never cared for it," said Grandmother.

Nannie, born in slavery, was pleased to think she would not die in it. She was wounded not so much by her state of being as by the word describing it. Emancipation was a sweet word to her. It had not changed her way of living in a single particular, but she was proud of having been able to say to her mistress, "I aim to stay wid you as long as you'll have me." Still, Emancipation had seemed to set right a wrong that stuck in her heart like a thorn. She could not understand why God, Whom she loved, had seen fit to be so hard on a whole race because they had got a certain kind of skin. She talked it over with Miss Sophia Jane. Many times. Miss Sophia Jane was always brisk and opinionated about it: "Nonsense! I tell you, God does not know whether a skin is black or white. He sees only souls. Don't be getting notions, Nannie–of course you're going to Heaven."

Nannie showed the rudiments of logic in a mind altogether untutored. She wondered, simply and without resentment, whether God, Who had been so cruel to black people on earth, might not continue His severity in the next world. Miss Sophia Jane took pleasure in reassuring her; as if she, who had been responsible for Nannie, body and soul in this life, might also be her sponsor before the judgment seat.

Miss Sophia Jane had taken upon herself all the responsibilities of her tangled world, half white, half black, mingling steadily and the confusion growing ever deeper. There were so many young men about the place, always, younger brothers-in-law, first cousins, second cousins, nephews. They came visiting and they stayed, and there was no accounting for them nor any way of controlling their quietly headstrong habits. She learned early to keep silent and give no sign of uneasiness, but whenever a child was born in the Negro quarters, pink, worm-like, she held her breath for three days, she told her eldest granddaughter, years later, to see whether the newly born would turn black after the proper interval . . . It was a strain that told on her, and ended by giving her a deeply grounded contempt for men. She could not help it, she despised men. She despised them and was ruled by them. Her husband threw away her dowry and her property in wild investments in strange territories: Louisiana, Texas; and without protest she watched him play away her substance like a gambler. She felt that she could have managed her affairs profitably. But her natural activities lay elsewhere, it was the business of a man to make all decisions and dispose of all financial matters. Yet when she got the reins in her hands, her sons could persuade her to this and that enterprise or investment; against her will and judgment she accepted their advice, and among them they managed to break up once more the stronghold she had built for the future of her family. They got from her their own start in life, came back for fresh help when they needed it, and were divided against each other. She saw it as her natural duty to provide for her household, after her husband had fought stubbornly through the War, along with every other man of military age in the connection; had been wounded, had lingered helpless, and had died of his wound long after the great fervor and excitement had faded in hopeless defeat, when to be a man wounded and ruined in the War was merely to have proved oneself, perhaps, more heroic than wise. Left so, she drew her family together and set out for Louisiana, where her husband, with her money, had bought a sugar refinery. There was going to be a fortune in sugar, he said; not in raising the raw material, but in manufacturing it. He had schemes in his head for operating cotton gins, flour mills, refineries. Had he lived . . . but he did not live, and Sophia Jane had hardly repaired the house she bought and got the orchard planted when she saw that, in her hands, the sugar refinery was going to be a failure.

She sold out at a loss, and went on to Texas, where her husband had bought cheaply, some years before, a large tract of fertile black land in an almost unsettled part of the country. She had with her nine children, the youngest about two, the eldest about seventeen years old; Nannie and her three sons, Uncle Jimbilly, and two other Negroes, all in good health, full of hope and greatly desiring to live. Her husband's ghost persisted in her, she was bitterly outraged by his death almost as if he had willfully deserted her. She mourned for him at first with dry eyes, angrily. Twenty years later, seeing after a long absence the eldest son of her favorite daughter, who had died early, she recognized the very features and look of the husband of her youth, and she wept.

During the terrible second year in Texas, two of her younger sons, Harry and Robert, suddenly ran away. They chose good weather for it, in mid-May, and they were almost seven miles from home when a neighboring farmer saw them, wondered and asked questions, and ended by persuading them into his gig, and so brought them back.

Miss Sophia Jane went through the dreary ritual of discipline she thought appropriate to the occasion. She whipped them with her riding whip. Then she made them kneel down with her while she prayed for them, asking God to help them mend their ways and not be undutiful to their mother; her duty performed, she broke down and wept with her arms around them. They had endured their punishment stoically, because it would have been disgraceful to cry when a woman hit them, and besides, she did not hit very hard; they had knelt with her in a shamefaced gloom, because religious feeling was a female mystery which embarrassed them, but when they saw her tears they burst into loud bellows of repentance. They were only nine and eleven years old. She said in a voice of mourning, so despairing it frightened them: "Why did you run away from me? What do you think I brought you here for?" as if they were grown men who could realize how terrible the situation was. All the answer they could make, as they wept too, was that they had wanted to go back to Louisiana to eat sugar cane. They had been thinking about sugar cane all winter . . . Their mother was stunned. She had built a house large enough to shelter them all, of hand-sawed lumber dragged by ox-cart for forty miles, she had got the fields fenced in and the crops planted, she had, she believed, fed and clothed her children; and now she realized they were hungry. These two had worked like men; she felt their growing bones through their thin flesh, and remembered how mercilessly she had driven them, as she had driven herself, as she had driven the Negroes and the horses, because there was no choice in the matter. They must labor beyond their strength or perish. Sitting there with her arms around them, she felt her heart break in her breast. She had thought it was a silly phrase. It happened to her. It was not that she was incapable of feeling afterward, for in a way she was more emotional, more quick, but griefs never again lasted with her so long as they had before. This day was the beginning of her spoiling her children and being afraid of them. She said to them after a long dazed silence, when they began to grow restless under her arms: "We'll grow fine ribbon cane here. The soil is perfect for it. We'll have all the sugar we want. But we must be patient."

By the time her children began to marry, she was able to give them each a good strip of land and a little money, she was able to help them buy more land in places they preferred by selling her own, tract by tract, and she saw them all begin well, though not all of them ended so. They went about their own affairs, scattering out and seeming to lose all that sense of family unity so precious to the Grandmother. They bore with her infrequent visits and her advice and her tremendous rightness, and they were impatient of her tenderness. When Harry's wife died—she had never approved of Harry's wife, who was delicate and hopelessly inadequate at housekeeping, and who could not ever bear children successfully, since she died when her third was born—the Grandmother took the children and began life again, with almost the same zest, and with more indulgence. She had just got them brought up to the point where she felt she could begin to work the faults out of them—faults inherited, she admitted fairly, from both sides of the house—when she died. It happened quite suddenly one afternoon in early October, after a day spent in helping the Mexican gardener of her third daughter-in-law to put the garden to rights. She was on a visit in far western Texas and enjoying it. The daughter-in-law was exasperated but apparently so docile, the Grandmother, who looked upon her as a child, did not notice her little moods at all. The son had long ago learned not to oppose his mother. She wore him down with patient, just, and reasonable argument. She was careful never to venture to command him in anything. He consoled his wife by saying that everything Mother was doing could be changed back after she was gone. As this change included moving a fifty-foot adobe wall, the wife was not much consoled. The Grandmother came into the house quite flushed and exhilarated, saying how well she felt in the bracing mountain air—and dropped dead over the doorsill.

IV

Old Nannie sat hunched upon herself expecting her own death momentarily. The Grandmother had said to her at parting, with the easy prophecy of the aged, that this might be their last farewell on earth; they embraced and kissed each other on the cheeks, and once more promised to meet each other in heaven. Nannie was prepared to start her journey at once. The children gathered around her: "Aunt Nannie, never you mind! We love you!" She paid no attention; she did not care whether they loved her or not. Years afterward, Maria, the elder girl, thought with a pang, they had not really been so very nice to Aunt Nannie. They went on depending upon her as they always had, letting her assume more burdens and more, allowing her to work harder than she should have. The old woman grew silent, hunched over more deeply—she was thin and tall also, with a nobly modeled Negro face, worn to the bone and a thick fine sooty black, no mixed blood in Nannie—and her spine seemed suddenly to have given way. They could hear her groaning at night on her knees beside her bed, asking God to let her rest.

When a black family moved out of a little cabin across the narrow creek, the first cabin empty for years, Nannie went down to look at it. She came back and asked Mister Harry, "Whut you aim to do wid dat cabin?" Mister Harry said, "Nothing," he supposed; and Nannie asked for it. She wanted a house of her own, she said; in her whole life she never had a place of her very own. Mister Harry said, of course she could have it. But the whole family was surprised, a little wounded. "Lemme go there and pass my last days in peace, chil'ren," she said. They had the place scrubbed and whitewashed, shelves put in and the chimney cleaned, they fixed Nannie up with a good bed and a fairly good carpet and allowed her to take all sorts of odds and ends from the house. It was astonishing to discover that Nannie had always liked and hoped to own certain things, she had seemed so contented and wantless. She moved away, and as the children said afterwards to each other, it was almost funny and certainly very sweet to see how she tried not to be too happy the day she left, but they felt rather put upon, just the same.

Thereafter she sat in the serene idleness of making patchwork and braiding woolen rugs. Her grandchildren and her white family visited her, and all kinds of white persons who had never owned a soul related to Nannie, went to see her, to buy her rugs or leave little presents with her.

She had always worn black wool dresses, or black and white figured calico with starchy white aprons and a white ruffled mobcap, or a black taffety cap for Sundays. She had been finicking precise and neat in her ways, and she still was. But she was no more the faithful old servant Nannie, a freed slave: she was an aged Bantu woman of independent means, sitting on the steps, breathing the free air. She began wearing a blue bandanna wrapped around her head, and at the age of eighty-five she took to smoking a corncob pipe. The black iris of the deep, withdrawn old eyes turned a chocolate brown and seemed to spread over the whole surface of the eyeball. As her sight failed, the eyelids crinkled and drew in, so that her face was like an eyeless mask.

The children, brought up in an out-of-date sentimental way of thinking, had always complacently believed that Nannie was a real member of the family, perfectly happy with them, and this rebuke, so quietly and firmly administered, chastened them somewhat. The lesson sank in as the years went on and Nannie continued to sit on the doorstep of her cabin. They were growing up, times were changing, the old world was sliding from under their feet, they had not yet laid hold of the new one. They missed Nannie every day. As their fortunes went down, and they had very few servants, they needed her terribly. They realized how much the old woman had done for them, simply by seeing how, almost immediately after she went, everything slackened, lost tone, went off edge. Work did not accomplish itself as it once had. They had not learned how to work for themselves, they were all lazy and incapable of sustained effort or planning. They had not been taught and they had not yet educated themselves. Now and then Nannie would come back up the hill for a visit. She worked then almost as she had before, with a kind of satisfaction in proving to them that she had been almost indispensable. They would miss her more than ever when she went away. To show their gratitude, and their hope that she would come again, they would heap upon her baskets and bales of the precious rubbish she loved, and one of her great grandsons Skid or Hasty would push them away beside her on a wheelbarrow. She would again for a moment be the amiable, dependent, like-one-of-the-family old servant: "I know my chil'ren won't let me go away empty-handed."

Uncle Jimbilly still pottered around, mending harness, currying horses, patching fences, now and then setting out a few plants or loosening the earth around shrubs in the spring. He muttered perpetually to himself, his blue mouth always moving in an endless disjointed comment on things past and present, and even to come, no doubt, though there was nothing about him that suggested any connection with even the nearest future . . . Maria had not realized until after her grandmother's death that Uncle Jimbilly and Aunt Nannie were husband and wife . . . That marriage of convenience, in which they had been mated with truly royal policy, with an eye to the blood and family stability, had dissolved of itself between them when the reasons for its being had likewise dissolved . . . They took no notice whatever of each other's existence, they seemed to forget they had children together (each spoke of "my children"), they had stored up no common memories that either wished to keep. Aunt Nannie moved away into her own house without even a glance or thought for Uncle Jimbilly, and he did not seem to notice that she was gone . . . He slept in a little attic over the smoke-house, and ate in the kitchen at odd hours, and did as he pleased, lonely as a wandering spirit and almost as invisible . . . But one day he passed by the little house and saw Aunt Nannie sitting on her steps with her pipe.

He sat down awhile, groaning a little as he bent himself into angles, and sunned himself like a weary old dog. He would have stayed on from that minute, but Nannie would not have him. "Whut you doin with all this big house to yoself?" he wanted to know. " 'Tain't no more than just enough fo' me," she told him pointedly; "I don' aim to pass my las' days waitin on no man," she added. "I've served my time, I've done my do, and dat's all." So Uncle Jimbilly crept back up the hill and into his smoke-house attic, and never went near her again . . .

On summer evenings she sat by herself long after dark, smoking to keep away the mosquitoes, until she was ready to sleep. She said she wasn't afraid of anything: never had been, never expected to be. She had long ago got in the way of thinking that night was a blessing, it brought the time when she didn't have to work any more until tomorrow. Even after she stopped working for good and all, she still looked forward with longing to the night, as if all the accumulated fatigues of her life, lying now embedded in her bones, still begged for easement. But when night came, she remembered that she didn't have to get up in the morning until she was ready. So she would sit in the luxury of having at her disposal all of God's good time there was in this world.

When Mister Harry, in the old days, had stood out against her word in some petty dispute, she could always get the better of him by slapping her slatty old chest with the flat of her long hand and crying out: "Why, Mister Harry, you, ain't you shamed to talk lak dat to me? I nuhsed you at dis bosom!"

Harry knew this was not literally true. She had nursed three of his elder brothers; but he always said at once, "All right, Mammy, all right, for God's sake!"–precisely as he said it to his own mother, exploding in his natural irascibility as if he hoped to clear the air somewhat of the smothering matriarchal tyranny to which he had been delivered by the death of his father. Still he submitted, being of that latest generation of sons who acknowledged, however reluctantly, however bitterly, their mystical never to be forgiven debt to the womb that bore them, and the breast that suckled them.

The Other Place **J. B. Priestley**

There is an experience that everyone has had at some time or other; the conviction that they have visited before a place which obviously they are seeing for the first time, or of hearing someone say things they have heard before, although where or when or how they have no way of telling. I think these tricks of memory or psychological quirks of the mind are confined largely to the years of youth. Certainly, when I was a small boy, my mind seemed filled with such vagaries, but for a very long time now they have ceased to visit me.

"The Other Place" offers an explanation. Mr. Priestley tells of being permitted to visit a wonderful land of light and harmony and happiness where he meets people he has known always, seemingly, although they have no place in the life he is living on earth.

THE OTHER PLACE

J. B. Priestley

A short walk beyond Buckden, in Upper Wharfedale, is Hubberholme, one of the smallest and pleasantest places in the world. It consists of an old church, a pub, and a bridge, set in a dale among high moors. In summer, long after the snows have melted, there is rarely much water in the river, so that it glitters and winks; and a man who has been walking for an hour or two can loiter on that bridge for quite a time, waiting for the pub to open and staring at the river. He was already there when I arrived—a big-boned dark fellow about forty—and he was looking down at the water in a glum fashion, without troubling to re-light the cigar he was chewing. Something had disappointed him, and I found it hard to believe Hubberholme had not come up to his expectations; so I spoke to him.

We agreed that it was a fine day, that this was good country; after which I thought I might try to satisfy my curiosity. So I told him how fond I was of Hubberholme, and how I rarely let a couple of years pass without taking another look at it. He said I was quite right, that he could easily imagine himself feeling the same way about it.

"But if you don't mind my saying so," I said, "you looked as if you'd found this place disappointing."

"Well, I guess I did," he said slowly. He had a deep voice and an accent that might have been American or Canadian. "But not in the way you mean, sir. Nothing wrong with this at all. Couldn't be better. But from the way a fellow described it to me, I thought it might be a place I've been trying to find. And it isn't, that's all." And now, perhaps because he did not want to say any more, he did re-light his cigar. But to show me that he was not unfriendly, he asked me where I was staying.

We discovered then that we were both spending the night in the admirable village of Kettlewell, further down the Dale, but had booked ourselves at different inns. After some further chat we agreed not only to walk back to Kettlewell together but to dine too; and after pointing out that I was the older man and this was my country and not his, I made him agree to be my guest. On our walk back I learnt that his name was Harvey Lindfield, that he was an engineer from Toronto, that he had been married but was now divorced and had a small daughter at present living with his sister. He talked readily enough, and was clearly glad of company, but somewhere behind his talk there was a cloud, a shadow, which might be disappointment or bewilderment. It was not, however, until after dinner, when we lit our cigars in the little sitting-room we had to ourselves and drank the excellent rye whisky that he had brought over as his contribution to the evening's hospitality, that I ventured to suggest that something was troubling him. And I admitted that I was curious.

"You'll remember," I told him, "you said that Hubberholme might be a place you were trying to find." I left it at that, but looked at him expectantly.

"It's the damnedest thing," he confessed, staring at the frilled paper in the fire grate. "I can hardly believe it myself, so why should you? I tried telling it once and got stuck about halfway through. If you weren't a writer, I wouldn't risk it now. But you get around, you talk to people, you must know a lot of things happen that can't be explained. Okay—this is one of 'em. The damnedest thing ever. And don't think I could make it up," he continued, regarding me earnestly. "I wouldn't know where to start. Now if you were telling it to me, that 'ud be different. I wouldn't believe you. But I'm no writer, just a plain engineer, and you've got to believe me. I'll just freshen these drinks, then I'll tell it to you the best way I can." And this was the story he told me.

My company (Lindfield began) had ordered a machine from a firm in Blackley, and I was sent over to make sure this machine was what we wanted. Well, it wasn't. Do you want to know about this machine? No, I thought not. The point is—there wasn't a hell of a lot wrong with it, but just enough to keep me there in Blackley making sure they put it right. So there I was, stuck with the Blackley Electrical Engineering Company, and with Blackley. I forgot to say, this was last November.

Do you know Blackley? Yes—well, going through it is about as much as anybody'd want of Blackley. Especially last November, when it rained and rained and rained and if the sun ever rose and shone, I missed it. When they built that place, they must have wanted to punish themselves. It didn't matter how dark and wet a November might be, Blackley was ready to meet it halfway. It was still dark when I got up in the morning, and by four o'clock it was dark again, and in between it rained. Even when you went inside somewhere, pulled down the blinds and turned on the lights, you didn't feel you'd got any illumination. I thought at first my eyesight was going.

I stayed at the Railway Hotel, next to the station and with a nice view of the tracks and sidings. It was darkish and wettish in there too. I changed my room three times, thinking I'd get something better, but I never did. We ate in the Coffee Room, which had sideboards and dish covers and cruets and knives and forks big enough for a roasted ox, only we never had the roasted ox, just a few sad bits of meat and a lot of drowned vegetables. There was an old waiter, blue in the face from heart disease, and two sour-faced waitresses, one long and thin and the other short and thick, and both of 'em dead against us. The only time they looked pleased was when they could tell you something was 'off' or you were too late to have anything. The other fellows there were travelling salesmen, all oldish and defeated, not smart enough to use a car so that they wouldn't have to spend the night in the Railway Hotel, Blackley. After supper they used to sit in a gloomy little hole called the Residents' Lounge, writing long reports explaining why they hadn't taken any orders. It wasn't much better downstairs in the bar. All the customers down there were either earnestly whispering or just sitting staring at nothing. They made you feel somebody important had just died.

I'm not saying the whole town was really like that, but it did seem like that to me. Dark, wet, and dismal. Nothing to do, nowhere to go. It's not that I expected two miles of neon lighting every night and a Big City atmosphere. I've lived in small towns before, and anyhow Blackley wasn't that small–about seventy-five thousand people, I guess. But it hadn't anything for me that I wanted, except that machine I stared at every day, up at the Blackley Electrical Engineering works. On the inside, for somebody who'd properly settled there, the place might have been all right, but on the outside, where I was, it was a living death. If any people there were having a good time, they were doing it behind locked doors. Oh–there were amusements of a sort–a crummy little vaudeville theatre, three or four movie houses, a café where a lot of kids sat about with steaming clothes, and one gaudy big pub where a lot of middle-aged dough-faced whores waited for custom and listened to a blind pianist. I went home with one of 'em one night, but even with the load of gin and whisky I was carrying I couldn't make it, and had to tell her I was meeting a late train. What I did meet–and it took some facing–was that bedroom, cold as organised charity, in the Railway Hotel. I'd have met anybody, getting off any train, just for a change. It was bad enough during the week but Sunday was worse. If I'm ever sent to Hell, it won't be all flames and sulphur and roaring devils; it'll be the Railway Hotel, Blackley, on a wet November Sunday that lasts for ever.

I know what you're thinking–that I didn't give the place a chance, never tried to make the best of it. But I did. Yet somehow I'd no luck. The fellows up at the works were friendly enough–after all, I represented a big order they wanted badly–but even when we all tried, we never got going. The two I saw most of, on the job, Butterworth and Dawson, nice fellows about my own age, took me home and gave me dinner or supper, introduced me to some neighbours, made me talk about Canada, turned on their TV or arranged some bridge. They did their best and so did their wives, but it didn't really work out, perhaps because by that time I felt so dam' lonely and lost I wanted more than I'd a right to expect. I still felt way off on the outside, and couldn't break through. If I tried, got a bit personal, I felt they drew back. It was like calling somewhere when all the people in the house are worried about something, an illness they don't want you to know about or a daughter who's got herself engaged to the wrong man, and they're polite and doing their best but can't really attend to you with most of their minds. So I'd leave 'em feeling more out of it than when I went. Yet I had the notion even then–and you'll understand soon why I say *even then*–that fellows like Butterworth and Dawson might have been real friends if we could only have got rid of the glass wall between us.

I'm no chaser–and as I told you this afternoon I'd had one marriage I was glad to get out of–but it's only natural, especially when a man feels so lonely and out of it, to see if there isn't a woman who might help. And that doesn't just mean a package of sex, as too many people seem to think. There's more in being with a woman than that, though it has to find its place of course. Well, I got to know a woman–she was personnel manager at another works and happened to step across to the Blackley Electrical Engineering place when I was there. Her name was Mavis Gilbert and she was in her early thirties, tallish, dark, good profile, with something pleasant and sensible about her. I took her to the movies once or twice or we met for a drink, and one night she gave me supper where she lived. But that didn't work out either. In fact it made things worse, not better. There was some fellow she couldn't forget, and when she'd had a couple of drinks or had been softened up by a sentimental movie, she didn't even try to forget him. Round about ten-thirty a little lost puppy would come and look out of her eyes. I dare say she'd have let me make love to her, if I'd made an issue out of it; but I knew there wouldn't have been anything gay about it, just awkwardness and apologies and then some quiet sobbing after I'd gone; so I didn't press her, which must have been a relief to her but didn't do me much good. In fact, just because she was a nice girl who ought to have been fairly happy and wasn't, who could feel herself getting drearier and couldn't stop it, she made me feel worse; and by the third week I wasn't seeing her any more but killing the nights with a mixture of hard liquor and fairly soft reading matter. And it still rained, and, as far as I could tell, the sun went out altogether. Sometimes I wondered if I was dead.

Then, just when I'd decided nothing could ever happen again, something happened. One afternoon about five, on my way back from the works, I was crossing the square in front of the railway station, to reach the hotel, when I saw a little old fellow slip and fall with a truck almost on top of him. If he'd been fifty pounds heavier I couldn't have done it, but he couldn't have weighed more than a hundred and twenty; and I jerked him out of the way just in time. I took him into the hotel, made them give him some brandy, and helped to clean the mud off him. He told me he was Sir Alaric Foden; and he was a baronet, though he didn't look like my idea of a baronet. He'd spent most of his life, before he came into the title and the family property, out in India and the Far East; and I'd say that either his mother or one of his grandmothers had been a native of those parts, because his eyes were like black beads floating in yellow oil and looked about as English as the Taj Mahal. His wispy hair and little beard were white, and his face might have been a withered leaf. He always spoke very slowly and with an effort, as if his talking mechanism had got rusted up, and while he kept you waiting for the next word he fixed his black little eyes on you, with hardly a blink, until you began to feel you were already in India or China or somewhere. He was obviously grateful and made a fuss about what I'd done, yet at the same time he didn't give me the impression of being really friendly, though perhaps by then Blackley had made me morbid on the subject. When he found out I wasn't doing anything the next night–and that didn't take long–he asked me to go out to his house and dine with him. He lived about ten miles out, but there was a bus service within a few minutes' walk. I would have to leave about nine-forty-five to get the bus back, but he thought that would give me long enough with him. And so did I.

From now on it's a peculiar story, and I'll have to slow up a bit and take it steady. As I said earlier, I've never told it yet all the way through. I can't decide yet whether I ought to rattle off everything I can remember or sort it out and just give you the high spots. Yes, being a writer you must understand the kind of difficulty, so you won't mind if I stop now and again to see where I'm going and whether I'm putting too much in or leaving too much out. And help yourself to a drink, won't you? Yes, I might as well. Thanks.

Well, sir, the next night I went out by bus and found my way to the country mansion of Sir Alaric Foden, Bart. If I was making this up I'd tell you now what a wonderful place it was and what a fine reception I had, with footmen waiting on us and caviare and champagne cooling nicely in buckets. But it wasn't like that. Oh–it was a mansion all right, though I never saw most of it, and I doubt if Sir Alaric had for some time. But what I did see was damp, chilly and shabby, and you couldn't have paid me to live there. No footmen, not even a butler, only a wheezy old woman to wait on us. And the dinner might have been sent out from the Railway Hotel, all except the wine, which Sir Alaric said was one of his best clarets. He took only about half a glass and made me finish the rest, which I did, not in the dining-room, all cold and cheerless, but upstairs in the library, where there was a fire. It was a big room, and must have had thousands of books in it as well as enough Oriental stuff to stock a curio shop. All through dinner and just afterwards up there he told me very little about himself, but made me talk, chiefly by asking me what I thought about Blackley and how I was doing there. I'm not going to tell you what I said because you've heard most of it already.

"So, Mr. Lindfield," he said when I had talked myself out, "you are–unhappy–in Blackley. Or–at least–bored–depressed–lonely. You would like–to visit–some other place–humph?"

I said I would, but pointed out that just then I hadn't the time or opportunity, having to keep an eye on that machine.

"The time–that is nothing," he said; and he waved a claw at a lacquered grandfather clock as if to abolish it and time. "The opportunity–might be here. Yes–in this room. That is–if you are ready–to take the risk–of visiting–not *some* other place–but *the* Other Place."

"I don't follow you, Sir Alaric." And I wondered if I ought to clear out, although it was only just after nine. But I had to say something. "What's the difference between *some* other place and *the* other place?"

He giggled. I know that sounds all wrong for a little old fellow who must have been at least seventy-five; but you couldn't call it a laugh, and it wasn't hard enough for a cackle, and if it wasn't a giggle then I haven't a word for it. He got up now, and as he talked he began rummaging in a chest of drawers just behind his chair. "The Other Place–is round–a different kind of corner, Mr. Lindfield. You turn a corner–you didn't know was there. Something of a risk. But if you should decide–to pay it a visit–I'll be delighted–to oblige you." Evidently he'd found what he wanted, for now he turned quite sharply. There above the top of his chair were those ebony eyes, with no meaning in them that I could read, staring at me. "I will make it–simple for you–Mr. Lindfield. Yes–a door. You will go–to the Other Place–merely by opening a door. And there–you see, set in the bookshelves–is the door–you will use. Yes–that is the door. You still wish–to visit–the Other Place?"

"Why not?" I said, to humour him. I'd known one man who had a lavatory in his library, behind a door covered with false book backs, and he had worked various gags with it. "What do I do?"

Now he showed me what he had taken out of the drawer. It was a shiny black piece of stone, rather like a large pebble. He sat down, leant forward, resting his elbows on his knees, and held out the stone. "It is simple. Look at this stone–stare into it–while you count–a hundred–quite slowly."

I stared at it and into it, and began counting. I could feel myself starting to squint. After I had counted twenty or so the surface of the stone turned into a hollow darkness that spread and spread as I kept on counting. I heard the grandfather clock chime quarter-past nine, but it seemed a long way off. By the time I had reached eighty my eyes ached and soon after that I began to feel dizzy.

"A hundred," I heard myself say out loud.

"Now, Mr. Lindfield," said Sir Alaric, who might have been telephoning from New Zealand, "get up–go straight to that door–open it–go through."

I felt cock-eyed as I marched towards the bookshelves, but I spotted the door at once and I'd sense enough left to realise it was similar to the one I'd seen before, covered with false book backs. As I opened it I thought I heard Sir Alaric telling me to enjoy my visit. Then I went through and closed the door behind me. I was in a narrow dark place, like a passage, lit at the end by three or four bars of gold. When I moved forward, I saw that these were bright streaks of sunlight coming through a rough broken sort of door on the right. I opened this door–and even now I can remember exactly how it creaked–and then I was staring, dazzled after the long gloom of Blackley, at a garden in full sunlight, in a high summer that looked as if it might go on for ever.

Now let's get one thing straight. It wasn't like a dream. All the dreams I've had have been patchy, with one sketchy sort of scene turning into another, as if there wasn't enough stuff around to make up even one solid background. And in a dream, I've found, you only notice what you want to notice, so to speak, and if a thing isn't in the centre of your focus then it just isn't there at all; there aren't a lot of things, as there are in real life, waiting to be properly noticed all round the edge of your consciousness. This garden wasn't like that at all. It was solidly there, with nothing unfinished and patchy about it. You knew it couldn't begin melting away, change into a room or a ship or a workshop. In fact, it seemed to have an extra solidity, as if it had stayed longer exactly like that than any ordinary garden could do.

A stone-flagged path went through a sort of tunnel of old-fashioned climbing roses. At the other end was a small lawn, bright in the sun, and beyond that some flower beds, burning with colour, set against a rough stone wall. When I reached the lawn I could just see the far bank of a river, not unlike the river at Hubberholme but broader and deeper. Beyond were fields rising sharply, then hanging woods and scree and rocks, and above them the hazy summits of high hills. It was a beautiful place, and you knew at once it was a long way from any trouble. And there was another thing, hard to describe. Have you ever known a room where there was a busy little clock, ticking your life away? And have you ever gone into that room when the clock wasn't there or had stopped, so that your life wasn't being ticked away? Well, arriving at this place was like that, only more so. The busy little clock inside you had stopped or wasn't there any more. The old *tick-tock-tick-tock-hurry-up-must-go* had gone. Nothing was wasting away, running down, draining out. I felt this at once, and it seemed to make everything sharper, more distinct, more itself and waiting to be noticed, whether it was the flame of the flowers or the blue of the sky.

I'd got some bearings now. The rough broken door I'd opened to let myself into this garden belonged to some sort of woodshed at the back of an inn. As I walked down the lawn I was coming round to the front of the inn, which was a longish low building with smooth walls washed in a faded pink. The lawn curved round there, losing its trim look, and became an outside drinking place. There were stout wooden tables and seats. A path led up to the open door of the inn. But I turned my back on that door and went to look over the bottom wall at the river. The nearer bank was quite close, with only a narrow strip of meadow, thick with buttercups and daisies, between it and the wall. A young man was fishing down there, and lying by his side, her head resting against him, was a dark young woman in a green dress. She caught sight of me, and as people do when they're feeling relaxed and happy, she gave me a smile and a wave of the arm that didn't mean anything in particular. And then I saw it was Mavis Gilbert.

Well, that didn't make any particular sense, but there was nothing wrong with it; and I was glad to see her there, looking so happy, complete–and that stuck out a mile–with the fellow she'd always been thinking about when I'd been with her. Good luck to them! I waved back; and then she made her chap turn round, and he waved too and made drinking motions before watching his rod again.

"It's about time too, Lindfield," somebody said, punching me in the back. That was Butterworth. Dawson was just coming out of the inn, carrying a tray with pots of beer on it. He gave a shout when he saw me; you'd have thought the two of them were the oldest friends I had, and had been waiting for me. They were dressed in old shirts and pants, and as brown and merry as sailors home from the sea. We drank the beer and then went loafing on the river bank, smoking and telling tales and watching the water slide by. No glass wall between us now–not on your life!

Their wives were around somewhere and afterwards I met them, all relaxed and friendly, not looking as if they were thinking about something else when they were talking to you. There were other people, of course, and some I'd met at Blackley, only they were quite different now, and others I hadn't, though I can't be sure. You said anything that came into your head, because anything that came into your head there was all right and not likely to hurt anybody; and so did the other people. It was a long day, not because it was dull but because there seemed time for everything, like summer days when you're a kid. And everybody there seemed a bit larger than life, not smaller as they do in places like Blackley. But I can't give you a proper idea of it. Don't think it was paradise or fairyland or anything fancy like that; it wasn't. But don't go too far the other way and think I was having something like a nice fine day at a holiday camp. It was out of this world all right, but it oughtn't to have been, if you see what I mean.

It wasn't until evening that I met her. She was the daughter of the genial fat old boy who kept the inn, and she'd been away from it all day. Her name was Paula, and she showed me the room I had to sleep in, at the end of the landing at the back. My bag was there too, though how it had got there God only knows. And I didn't care, all I cared about was Paula. She looked about thirty, and she was fairly tall for a woman but not scraggy, but broad and firmly set, and she'd a rather broad calm face, with darkish brown hair and grey eyes; and as soon as I saw her I knew I'd been looking for her all my life. There wasn't much light up in that bedroom then, for it was just after sunset and the hills overshadowed the back of the inn, and the room was settling into a green dusk that seemed to put us at the bottom of the sea. But there was light enough for me to see the look on her face, when she waited a moment after showing me the room. I guessed then she knew I felt as if I'd been looking for her all my life. You know that look of tender amusement women have when they're fond of you and sure of you too.

"All day I've been missing you," I said, though I couldn't have explained why I said it. "Everything's been grand, wonderful, just what I needed—except I've been missing you. Now you're here, Paula."

"Yes, Harvey," she said, as if she'd been giving me my first name for the last ten years. "Here I am."

I don't know whether she made a move or I did or we both moved together, but then I had my arms round her—all so snug and easy that I might have done it ten thousand times before—and we kissed. And not one of those fighting, let's-get-on-with-it kisses neither; but one of the other sort you only find when everything else is dead right.

"And now I can't let you go," I told her.

But she pulled away gently, smiling at me. "You know you must. I'll be busy now until half-past ten. Come to me then—to my little sitting-room, through the green door at the far end of the kitchen—you remember? But not before half-past ten. You won't forget that, will you, Harvey?" And she looked at me anxiously, the only time she ever gave me that particular look.

I promised, and off she went then, a busy woman. Well, for the next hour or two, during supper and afterwards, when now and again she and I would exchange a look that was like a clasp of hands, everything was wonderful. It would have been good anyhow—the food and drink with friends so easy and happy, the jokes, the yarns, the songs and dancing after supper—but the idea of having her to myself later on raised everything another two thousand feet into the air. You know how you feel at those times, and this was a whole lot of those times rolled into one.

How long I'd have been there if I hadn't got impatient and turned nasty, I don't know; perhaps for ever. What got into me, what did the dirty on me, beats me, and you might say it's been beating me ever since. But when people began to move off, mostly two by two, and I didn't see her around inside, and the night outside, with no moon but a glitter of stars, was too big and lonely for me, I got impatient and didn't want to join in anything or talk to anybody, except to her of course, while the minutes went by like sick elephants. And I worked up some anger too, the way you do when you must have trouble. To hell with it! Why should she fix a time like that, as if everything had to be done her way? If I was good enough for her to see at half-past ten, I was good enough for quarter-past—what was the difference? I stuck it out a few minutes more, but all the time stoking my impatience like a furnace, and then made a dash for that green door at the far end of the kitchen, daring anybody to try and stop me.

Nobody did, of course; they never do when you're so hell-bent on trouble. There was the kitchen, empty and washed and swept out but still warm and heavy with the smell of food, and only a little lamp burning; but enough light to show me the green door at the opposite end. And now for Paula, who, if she didn't like it, because there were still ten minutes to go before the half-hour, could lump it—after all she belonged to me, and she knew it and knew I knew it. The green door opened easily—they always do, those doors—and there I was.

But not in any little sitting-room with Paula, of course. I was back in Sir Alaric's library, with my heart a lump of lead. I didn't even try to turn back, because I knew I hadn't a hope in hell. And I hated Sir Alaric and his library, which looked like a crummy old junk shop, and I hated myself.

I didn't want to look at Sir Alaric, so I looked at the grandfather clock. The time was nine-twenty; which meant that my day there had lasted about three minutes in here.

"Can I get back there?" I asked him.

"Not tonight, Mr. Lindfield." He seemed amused, and that didn't make me like him any better.

"Why not? I've only been out of this room for three minutes. And I didn't intend to come back so soon. That was a mistake."

"It always is. Perhaps—I ought—to have warned you. But I did—tell you—there was some risk——"

More in despair than hoping for anything, I went to that door and tore it open. There were shelves of odds and ends and a wash-hand basin in the cupboard. I thought I could hear Sir Alaric having a soft giggle. I felt like throwing the big paste-pot at him.

"I take it—Mr. Lindfield—that our little experiment—was successful. You arrived—at the Other Place—humph?"

"I arrived where I'd still like to be," I told him sourly.

"Then—clearly—it was the Other Place." He waited a moment. "You met—friends—there—humph?"

I made my reply a nod. Though he was responsible for getting me there, I didn't want to talk about it to him. But there was something else I had to talk about. "What's that black stone you asked me to stare at, Sir Alaric? And how does it do the trick?"

"It would be—just as sensible—to ask me—how the door—did the trick," he said reproachfully.

"Okay then, how did *you* do the trick?"

I don't know whether he was sleepy or just bored with me, but after he had shaken his head, to show me there was no reply coming, he began to yawn.

But I had to know *something*. "You said it was just a matter of getting round a corner, though of course a different kind of corner. More dimensions or something. Now–look, Sir Alaric, I don't want to keep bothering you, so tell me–could I do it for myself, sit in my hotel bedroom and get round that corner somehow?"

"You–could try, Mr. Lindfield." He sounded very cagey.

I couldn't leave it at that. "I suppose any door would do, wouldn't it, Sir Alaric?"

"Certainly. Any door."

"And that black polished stone was only something to stare at and concentrate on, wasn't it?"

"You–must have something–Mr. Lindfield–to stare at–certainly." Still cagey. And now he got up, and I knew the evening was over, even though it was only about half-past nine. Somehow my going to the Other Place–and I'd decided I might as well call it that–had finished things between us. Perhaps he felt that now he didn't owe me anything for saving him from that truck; we were quits. Perhaps he just didn't like me. I'd decided I didn't take to him, so all was fair and square between us.

"I seemed to be there about ten hours at least," I said, just to keep the conversation going. "But actually I was spending three minutes in that cupboard. That happens in dreams, of course. Yet this didn't seem like a dream."

"It wasn't."

"What was it then?"

He gave me another yawn. "Forgive me–Mr. Lindfield–sometimes I cannot sleep–but tonight–as you see––" In other words, Clear out, Lindfield.

There was more fog than rain that night, and the journey back to Blackley in the bus seemed very long and quite hopeless. At the end of it the Railway Hotel was waiting for me and was ready to do all it could to prove it was very different from the inn in the Other Place. I was in bed by about ten-forty-five and then spent the next four hours hearing railway waggons bumped and banged among the sidings. The following morning, Blackley looked darker and wetter and more dismal than ever.

Up at the Electrical Engineering Works that day I lost my temper because they hadn't yet completed a new bearing they'd promised me, and finally Butterworth was sent for, to explain the delay.

"And that's how it is, old man," he said, at the end of a long explanation, bristling with ministries and permits. "We keep asking them to get cracking, but if they won't move, there isn't a thing we can do. What's the matter? Don't you believe me?"

"Yes," I said, and then, taking a chance, went on: "But I was wondering what happened the other night—or was it last night?—after I left you and Dawson to go and see Paula."

"The other night? Paula?" Obviously he hadn't a clue.

There was no point in going on with it, but I had one more shot. "It was the same day you and I and Dawson drank beer in front of the inn and then went down to the river."

Butterworth had his share of brains but he was one of those Englishmen who never look as if they have any sense at all. He had a big moon-face made of underdone sirloin with some indeterminate features clustering together in the middle of it. And it looked so blank at that moment, I wanted to slug him. "I'm sorry, Lindfield old man," he said, "but there's some mistake."

"Yes, there is," I told him. "So please forget it. I was thinking of some other fellows. But do get that bearing in as soon as you can."

"We will, we will," he said, relieved to discover I'd returned to sanity. "Hate to keep you hanging about like this. Look here, old man, come out and dine with us tomorrow. There'll be eight of us—two tables of bridge."

Well, I went, and Dawson and his wife were there, and Mavis Gilbert; and even the other two, a couple called Jennings, I remembered having seen in the Other Place. So there we were, eight of us, and we'd all been in the Other Place, some of us spending hours together, living the life of Reilly. And although I hadn't much hope even then, I had to try them out. I started first with Mrs. Butterworth, who'd put me next to her at dinner. Did she, I asked, know a delightful little spot with an inn among the hills near a river; and I described the Other Place in some detail. I didn't even feel she was listening properly, because she was one of those anxious hostesses with half their minds in the kitchen; but when I'd finished and had felt a droning bore, she surprised me by saying: "No, I don't know that place. Where is it? Oh—you don't know." And then her eyes widened, and instead of being merely colourless, screwed-up and anxious they were blue, young and alive. "Mr. Lindfield, let's go and find it, shall we?" she whispered; and for a second she was almost the woman I had seen in the Other Place.

During a break in the bridge I was playing with them, I tried the Dawsons and Mrs. Jennings, concentrating on the inn this time, and telling them I had stayed there years ago and had now forgotten where it was. Dawson said it was in North Devon, his wife was sure that it was in Gloucestershire and had been pulled down, and Mrs. Jennings told us she knew a much nicer little pub in Dorset; and I knew that I had drawn a blank from the three of them. There wasn't a peep out of them to suggest they'd ever been near the Other Place. And what made it ten times worse was that I could still remember them there, which made this social evening of ours look as if we were playing charades about zombies.

We finished fairly early, so Mavis Gilbert, who was running me down town in her little car, suggested we stop at her flat for a drink. When we'd tasted it and were feeling easy, she said: "Something's happened to you. I noticed it, and so did Mrs. Butterworth. What is it–or can't you tell?"

"I can tell some of it," I said, "but you won't know what I'm talking about. I saw you by a river–it was a bright warm morning–and you were wearing a green dress."

"Did I look nice?" she asked, smiling to show me she knew I was talking about a dream.

"You looked fine. Very happy too. You were with a fellow–I think I can describe him——"

"Go on. You must."

"He was a stiffish gingerish fellow with the greeny eyes his sort always have–and a scar on the left side of his face——"

"Rodney!" Then she was staring at me, white and angry. "I don't think that's funny. Somebody's been gossiping to you–and now you think this is an amusing way of telling me you know about Rodney and me. Well, I don't think it is."

"Look, Mavis, you've got it all wrong." I took her hand and wouldn't let her snatch it away. "I haven't been discussing you. I never heard of Rodney until now. I simply described the fellow I saw you with, when you were wearing a green dress, down by the river."

"What river?"

"I don't know what river. I wish I did," I told her. "There were lots of people there, the Butterworths and Dawsons included, and you were there with this fellow. There was also a girl called Paula–her father kept the inn where we were all staying." And I described Paula, trying to remember every detail of her appearance. "Do you know anybody like that?"

"She sounds rather like a girl I used to know called Norma Blake," said Mavis. "But she'd nothing to do with an inn. She went in for occupational therapy. It can't be the same girl. I can see this Paula was very special. But where was all this happening?"

So then I had to describe the inn and the river and the hills, and I gave her a sketch of what happened there. But I didn't explain about Sir Alaric and the black stone and the door.

"I don't know any place quite like that," she said slowly, looking rather foggy-eyed. "I was never anywhere like that with Rodney–worse luck! But do you mean to say you dreamt it all?" That's one thing about women, they take this sort of thing seriously, none of your "Come off it, old man" stuff about them.

But, even so, I didn't feel like telling her the whole story. "I can't explain," I said, "but I don't think I did dream it. Somehow I went there–I met all you people, happy as kings–I found Paula–and then, because I was in a hurry, I lost her. And all you people who were there don't seem to know what I'm talking about, which means either that you weren't there and I was making it all up or that you go there and then forget——"

"Oh–I can't bear that," she cried. "I wish you hadn't told me now. It's the sort of thing I've imagined–being somewhere like that with Rodney–yes, night after night, here in this room, I've imagined it. And now you say you saw me there. You're making me feel miserable."

"I've made myself feel miserable. Let's change the subject."

"No," she said, "I must tell you about Rodney now."

And of course she did, with intervals for laughing and crying, and to her it was a wonderful heartbreaking story, enough to keep anybody on the edge of his seat, but to me, though I liked her and didn't mind what I'd seen of Rodney, it was nothing but two hours of trying to keep awake. I got back to the Railway Hotel, which didn't want to let me in, feeling rather worse than when I'd left it to enjoy this night out.

Well, the next few days were like walking across a wet ploughed field wearing lead boots. I tried hard not to be sorry for myself–and about time, you'll say, and I agree; but when you're such a long way from home it's not so easy–and I went to the Reference Library to see if I could get a line on Sir Alaric's magic, and couldn't, and I also made some enquiries about Sir Alaric himself. But the people I asked either had never heard of him or knew he existed but weren't interested. Come to think of it, people in Blackley last winter didn't seem to be much interested in anything. They just went on living for something but didn't quite know what. Sometimes I felt they'd have been better off in the long run if they'd set fire to the place and then started all over again.

Then one night–as a matter of fact it was a Monday, and I think living through another Blackley Sunday might have had something to do with what happened–I had a few slugs of gin, because the whisky had given out, and told myself it was time for action. After all, Sir Alaric had shot me into the Other Place, and now he could shoot me there again, if only to stop me wandering round this grimy dump like a lost soul. He wasn't on the telephone, so I took a chance on his being in and caught a bus out there. It must have been one of the last, because it was late then for Blackley, round about ten o'clock. How I was to get back didn't worry me at all, not in the state of mind I was in then. And if Sir

Alaric had gone to bed, I was ready to make such a commotion that he'd have to get up and let me in. I don't say I was plastered but I wasn't exactly sober.

But he hadn't gone to bed and he invited me in politely enough, though I didn't feel he was pleased to see me. He took me up to his library, where he'd been drowsing over the fire, and then he asked me, with no old-world courtesy at all, what I wanted. And obviously it was no use my pretending I'd gone there to enquire about his health, he'd spotted the mood I was in at once, so there was no point in trying to fool him.

"I want to get back to the Other Place," I told him. "And don't tell me to go away and try to go there on my own, because I've already tried and it doesn't work. Apart from that, I'm having a bad time. I've talked to the people I met there—all except the most important one—and they don't know what I'm talking about. I've even tried putting the place out of my mind, but it won't stay out more than a few minutes. So now, Sir Alaric, with your help, I'm going back."

"Mr. Lindfield—you take—too much—for granted."

"That's because I'm a desperate man, Sir Alaric."

"Desperate men—Mr. Lindfield—should not attempt—to go anywhere. They should—stay at home—and begin to lose—their desperation."

"You're probably right, and we won't argue about it. In fact, we won't argue about anything. I'm going back there, Sir Alaric, and don't try to stop me. Where's that black stone?" And I got up and stood over him. I'm not proud of all this but I might as well tell you everything.

But if I thought I could frighten him, I was a mile out. All he did was to shake his head at me, as if I was ten years old. "You are behaving—very stupidly—Mr. Lindfield. You come here—uninvited—half drunk, I suspect——"

"About that, I'd say," I told him. "And you're quite right, I'm behaving badly. I've a lot of excuses but I won't bore you with them. Just bring out that black stone, Sir Alaric, and I'll do the rest. *Come on,"* I shouted, when he hadn't made a move.

We stared at one another for what seemed quite a long time—and I thought I saw a flicker of flame in those black beady eyes of his—then he went to the chest of drawers and brought out the stone. This time he handed it to me instead of keeping it himself. "Do as you did before," he said coldly. "But be careful—to put down—the stone—before you go—to the door. If you will take—my advice—you will not—attempt this."

"I'm not taking your advice." And I began staring at the stone and counting up to a hundred. Everything happened just as it did the first time—the squinting, the hollow darkness that spread and spread, the dizziness. I put the stone down on the rug and went slowly over to the door in the bookshelves. I opened the door very carefully, as if something might break, probably because I was afraid the magic wouldn't have worked and that all I would see behind the door was the cupboard of odds and ends and its wash-hand basin. But no, I was back all right. There I was in that narrow dark passage with the streaks of sunlight at the end, coming through the rough broken door. Down I went, banged open the door, and hurried out into the garden, where I waited a moment, by the edge of the stone-flagged path among the roses, just to catch my breath.

I don't think I'm cheating when I tell you that even then, right at the start, I guessed something was wrong. But I'll admit I'm not sure what gave me the idea. Let me try and sort it out while you give yourself some more whisky. Okay, thanks, I'll join you. That's fine–thanks. Well, to begin with, everything I could see–and that wasn't much, remember–seemed narrower, not quite the right shape. And the sunshine had a kind of sting to it, wasn't mellow like the other sunshine I remembered. And then the time trick wasn't working right. I felt time had stopped, as it had done before, but it had stopped *in the wrong way*. Don't ask me just what I mean by that, because I'll be damned if I know. But it seemed to have stopped in a sinister way. Anyhow that's as near as I can get to what I felt.

I went through the tunnel of climbing roses and came out on to the lawn, and of course now I knew what to expect–the river, the hills, the drinking place in front of the inn itself. At a first glance, nothing had changed, except that I had an idea the colours were sharper and the shapes not quite the same, a bit meaner somehow. Like a copy of a picture that just missed it, if you see what I mean. And I didn't feel happy, not a bit.

Then it really got to work on me. That river, for instance. When I saw it out of the corner of my eye, not really paying attention to it, it looked just as it had done before, a full smooth stream. But as soon as I really looked at it, to take some pleasure in it, then it shrank to a mere trickle among cracked cakes of brown mud. So I'd look away, and at once I'd know it was an easy broad stretch of water again. Another proper look, and it had dwindled again.

But the people were worse. As I stood there on the lawn, playing hide-and-seek with the river, I knew that where the tables and seats were, in front of the inn, to my left, people were drinking and talking and laughing, just as they'd done before. But when I turned that way, to shout "Hello!" and let them know I was there, they all froze up and were still as waxworks. And what put the finishing touch on it and gave me the creeps was that they were all looking at me, not with any particular expression on their faces but just looking, like dummies. I went towards them, half angry, half terrified. Not a sound. Not a move. Waxworks under an angry sun. I stopped, turned towards the river, and there it was, a miserable trickle again, while at the corner of my eye I could just catch a glimpse of the people coming to life again and could hear them talking and laughing. I whirled round on them, frantic now, and there they were, frozen, staring at me, silent as death.

"What the hell do you think you're playing at?" I shouted at them. Not a sound, not a quiver. And every goddam thing was wrong–the blue of the sky, the feel of the sun, the flowers that withered at a look. I felt I was outside time again, but out now on the wrong side. I had to make something happen in that place even if it meant being flattened by some giant dead hand that would drop from the sky.

I went charging through the gap in the stone wall to the staring dummies in the drinking place. The first one I reached was standing up and I saw that it was Jennings, who'd been dining with me at the Butterworths'.

"Now look, Jennings," I cried, putting a hand on his shoulder, "you know me–Lindfield." And now that I'd concentrated upon him the rest of them were all lively again, and Jennings was the only staring dummy there, unless you count me. "What's the idea? What's the matter with you people?"

He didn't say a thing, never gave so much as a twitch, and I felt that if I didn't take my hand off his shoulder I might push him over. So I took it away, but the next moment, in a blind fury because I couldn't get any response from him, I gave him a sharp slap across the cheek. And the next moment after that–and how it happened I can't tell you–I was down on the grass, out for the count, having taken the hardest punch I'd known since I'd boxed as a light-heavy for the University of Toronto. And while I was down there, waiting for the counting and the bell, I could hear, as if from far away, all those people talking and laughing over their drinks. Harvey Lindfield couldn't pay attention, so off they were again, enjoying themselves.

After a few minutes, feeling dazed and rather sick, I got on to my feet again and looked round. This time they weren't all completely frozen. They moved a little, like weeds under water, and they made some noise –but it wasn't a noise I was glad to hear, for they were laughing in a slow dim under-water fashion, and laughing at me. And then I wondered why I'd wasted any time on these people, if you could still call them people, when I didn't really care about them and had come back to find only one person—Paula. And I knew she wasn't out here. My only chance of finding her was somewhere inside the inn.

She was there, standing alone in the long room that was now as quiet and nearly as dark as a vault. She was no staring dummy but it might have been better if she had been, because the very sight of her standing there turned my heart into ice water. As I went up to her I saw that she was slowly shaking her head and that her cheeks were wet with tears. Everything that's ever been wrong between men and women, all the old long heartbreak, was there between us.

"Paula," I said, "I know it was my fault last time, but now I'm back and I came back, forced my way here, just because of you." I'd have gone on but I knew she wasn't going to talk to me, that she'd do nothing but shake her head and cry, the way they do when at last they feel it's hopeless.

Finally she moved away, and I followed her, wanting to say something but not knowing what to say. There was nobody else about; the place was empty, silent, a mile deep in misery. She went into the kitchen, which was cold and hadn't an appetising smell left, and she walked the length of it until she came to that green door. There she stopped long enough to give me a look and what might have been the shadow of a smile. The door was slowly closing behind her when I arrived—the big masterful type, God help me! I flung open that door and marched through like Alexander the Great.

But of course Sir Alaric wasn't impressed, and I don't blame him. I'd only been away a minute and a half this time, and he didn't care if I came out of his cupboard marching like Alexander the Great or crawling like the Hunchback of Notre Dame. All he cared about was getting me out of his house before I turned ugly and began kicking things around. So he told me in a hurry that a man who lived quarter of a mile down the road would run me into Blackley for about a pound. As a matter of fact he needn't have worried, because this last visit to the Other Place—if it was the Other Place—had taken all the fight out of me.

Once he had got me as far as his front door, Sir Alaric felt he could relax. "It was not—so pleasant—this time, Mr. Lindfield—humph?"

"It was very unpleasant," I told him grumpily. "But it probably serves me right for insisting upon going again. I've not behaved very well. But, come to that, neither have you."

"No, Mr. Lindfield," he said earnestly—and I can see him now, a little white-and-brown wisp of an old fellow, very English up to a point but with India or China looking out of his eyes, "you wrong me—as well as yourself. You have been—to the Other Place. Forget—this last visit—remember the first one. Now—of course—you are dissatisfied. But you have something—I imagine—to be dissatisfied about—now."

"I had before," I grumbled. "We all have. They're almost dying of it in Blackley. All you've done for me, in return for not leaving you in front of that truck, is to add to my dissatisfaction."

"No," he said softly, "there is no addition. Not in—the long run—I think. No—a subtraction. You will see."

Well, I don't know that I have seen, though now and again I think I know what he meant. No, I never saw him again. I called at his house again, a few nights later, but it was all shut up and dark and then I was told he'd gone away, perhaps to stand on his head in Bombay or turn a prayer wheel in Tibet. I took that fellow Jennings out to lunch, just to see how he'd react when I told him that a few nights before, in a place where people turned into staring dummies when you looked hard at them, he'd knocked me cold with a right hook I never even saw. And of course he didn't react at all, just told me he'd stopped dreaming now that he didn't eat cheese in the evening and went on to say that British boxing or any other sport wasn't what it had been.

I had a night out with Mavis Gilbert before I left Blackley, and she told me more about Rodney and made me describe Paula, though I left out the Other Place; and we got rather tight and sentimental and tried to console one another with some messy half-hearted love-making and were about as clever at it as a couple of short-sighted bears. In fact the night ended just as I'd imagined it would when I'd tried to avoid it.

Then the Blackley Electrical Engineering Company completed the machine to our specification, and after having it run and testing it for a couple of days, I watched them take it down and crate it and send it to Liverpool, ready for the next boat. By this time my company was screaming for me, so I booked a passage by plane, and on one of those muffled sad winter afternoons I found myself at London Airport. I mention this because it was there I saw Paula.

You know the way they shepherd you around in airports, as if an idiot school was having a day's outing. Well, my lot was being herded out to the plane just as another lot was being herded in from one, so that a string of us passed each other. And there was Paula—no question about it, I'd doubt my own name sooner.

"Paula!" I shouted, and hurried across to her.

She stopped but looked surprised, and not pleasantly surprised either. "There's some mistake," she said. "I'm Mrs. Endersly—and my name's not Paula and I don't know you."

"What's this?" And the big fellow behind her frowned at me. He owned her. He owned nearly everything. He was one of those men.

"Just a mistake, darling," she said to him, and then she gave me an apologetic little smile, probably because I was looking like a lost dog.

I don't know what I stammered at them, because what I'd suddenly seen in her eyes, like a sort of signal from miles away in their grey depths, had turned me upside down and inside out. And what it had seemed to say was something like this: *Yes, I was Paula when I was there, and now I remember you too, Harvey Lindfield, but where we were and what we can do about it, God knows!* And the next minute I was straggling along with the rest of the sheep, going towards the plane.

So here I am, back again at the first chance I had, but of course taking a holiday this time, with no more Blackley in the rain and the Railway Hotel. And I keep on describing the Other Place to people, and when they tell me they know something like it I go and have a look, which takes me to some of your nicest places, like this Hubberholme where we met this afternoon. Cornwall, Devon, Dorset, Cotswolds, Lake District –I've been all over. Oh–yes–I tried Sir Alaric again, but he died last February–somewhere abroad. Yes–and I asked about that black stone, but everything he had has been sold or given away, and nobody seems to know anything about it. I know–I might try to track it down, I've thought of that.

There's just one other thing worries me from time to time. You must have noticed this yourself. Now and again you meet people who look at you eagerly and cry "Haven't we met before somewhere?" And when you tell 'em you haven't, you see a light go out of their faces. Well, what worries me now about those people is that they may have been to some Other Place of their own and met me there, the way I did with those Blackley people–and of course with Paula. It's the damnedest thing, you know, if we all keep meeting in some Other Place and then can't make other people understand. My God!–look at the time. And I'm running up to Northumberland in the morning, because I've heard of a place there that might possibly be It–you never know, do you?

Johnny One-Eye **Damon Runyon**

To all lovers of pets it must be evident that animals choose their people as often as they are chosen. The two small girls in our family found a black and white kitten in a shoe box, which had been left in an empty lot, and brought him home. We had two other cats at the time and did not need a third but this great little fellow decided he liked the look of things and proceeded to take charge. We named him Luke McGluke and his greatest exploit with us was walking into a dog fight when a big strange animal picked on our small Irish terrier. It is equally hard to believe that one bitterly cold morning we found a rabbit crouched miserably against the house and that he willingly went inside with us. He stayed there all winter, sleeping in a box in the kitchen and begging every morning for a saucer of hot coffee with his breakfast. The long saga of our pets is full of such incidents.

Poor little Johnny One-Eye was badly in need of a home and a protector and he picked out a gangster named Rudolph, which led to tragic adventures.

JOHNNY ONE-EYE

Damon Runyon

This cat I am going to tell you about is a very small cat, and in fact it is only a few weeks old, consequently it is really nothing but an infant cat. To tell the truth, it is just a kitten.

It is gray and white and very dirty and its fur is all frowzled up, so it is a very miserable-looking little kitten to be sure the day it crawls through a broken basement window into an old house in East Fifty-third Street over near Third Avenue in the city of New York and goes from room to room saying merouw, merouw in a low, weak voice until it comes to a room at the head of the stairs on the second story where a guy by the name of Rudolph is sitting on the floor thinking of not much.

One reason Rudolph is sitting on the floor is because there is nothing else to sit on as this is an empty house that is all boarded up for years and there is no furniture whatever in it, and another reason is that Rudolph has a .38 slug in his side and really does not feel like doing much of anything but sitting. He is wearing a derby hat and his overcoat as it is in the wintertime and very cold and he has an automatic Betsy on the floor beside him and naturally he is surprised quite some when the little kitten comes merouwing into the room and he picks up the Betsy and points it at the door in case anyone he does not wish to see is with the kitten. But when he observes that it is all alone, Rudolph puts the Betsy down again and speaks to the kitten as follows:

"Hello, cat," he says.

Of course the kitten does not say anything in reply except merouw but it walks right up to Rudolph and climbs on his lap, although the chances are if it knows who Rudolph is it will hightail it out of there quicker than anybody can say scat. There is enough daylight coming through the chinks in the boards over the windows for Rudolph to see that the kitten's right eye is in bad shape, and in fact it is bulged half out of its head in a most distressing manner and it is plain to be seen that the sight is gone from this eye. It is also plain to be seen that the injury happens recently and Rudolph gazes at the kitten a while and starts to laugh and says like this:

"Well, cat," he says, "you seem to be scuffed up almost as much as I am. We make a fine pair of invalids here together. What is your name, cat?"

Naturally the kitten does not state its name but only goes merouw and Rudolph says, "All right, I will call you Johnny. Yes," he says, "your tag is now Johnny One-Eye."

Then he puts the kitten in under his overcoat and pretty soon it gets warm and starts to purr and Rudolph says:

"Johnny," he says, "I will say one thing for you and that is you are plenty game to be able to sing when you are hurt as bad as you are. It is more than I can do."

But Johnny only goes merouw again and keeps on purring and by and by it falls sound asleep under Rudolph's coat and Rudolph is wishing the pain in his side will let up long enough for him to do the same.

Well, I suppose you are saying to yourself, what is this Rudolph doing in an old empty house with a slug in his side, so I will explain that the district attorney is responsible for this situation. It seems that the D.A. appears before the grand jury and tells it that Rudolph is an extortion guy and a killer and I do not know what all else, though some of these statements are without doubt a great injustice to Rudolph as, up to the time the D.A. makes them, Rudolph does not kill anybody of any consequence in years.

It is true that at one period of his life he is considered a little wild but this is in the 1920's when everybody else is, too, and for seven or eight years he is all settled down and is engaged in business organization work, which is very respectable work, indeed. He organizes quite a number of businesses on a large scale and is doing very good for himself. He is living quietly in a big hotel all alone, as Rudolph is by no means a family guy, and he is highly spoken of by one and all when the D.A. starts poking his nose into his affairs, claiming that Rudolph has no right to be making money out of the businesses, even though Rudolph gives these businesses plenty of first-class protection.

In fact, the D.A. claims that Rudolph is nothing but a racket guy and a great knock to the community, and all this upsets Rudolph no little when it comes to his ears in a roundabout way. So he calls up his lawbooks and requests legal advice on the subject and lawbooks says the best thing he can think of for Rudolph to do is to become as inconspicuous as possible right away but to please not mention to anyone that he gives this advice.

Lawbooks says he understands the D.A. is requesting indictments and is likely to get them and furthermore that he is rounding up certain parties that Rudolph is once associated with and trying to get them to remember incidents in Rudolph's early career that may not be entirely to his credit. Lawbooks says he hears that one of these parties is a guy by the name of Cute Freddy and that Freddy makes a deal with the D.A. to lay off of him if he tells everything he knows about Rudolph, so under the circumstances a long journey by Rudolph will be in the interest of everybody concerned.

So Rudolph decides to go on a journey but then he gets to thinking that maybe Freddy will remember a little matter that Rudolph long since dismisses from his mind and does not wish to have recalled again, which is the time he and Freddy do a job on a guy by the name of The Icelander in Troy years ago and he drops around to Freddy's house to remind him to be sure not to remember this.

But it seems that Freddy, who is an important guy in business organization work himself, though in a different part of the city than Rudolph, mistakes the purpose of Rudolph's visit and starts to out with his rooty-toot-toot and in order to protect himself it is necessary for Rudolph to take his Betsy and give Freddy a little tattooing. In fact, Rudolph practically crochets his monogram on Freddy's chest and leaves him exceptionally deceased.

But as Rudolph is departing from the neighborhood, who bobs up but a young guy by the name of Buttsy Fagan, who works for Freddy as a chauffeur and one thing and another, and who is also said to be able to put a slug through a keyhole at forty paces without touching the sides though I suppose it will have to be a pretty good-sized keyhole. Anyway, he takes a long-distance crack at Rudolph as Rudolph is rounding a corner but all Buttsy can see of Rudolph at the moment is a little piece of his left side and this is what Buttsy hits, although no one knows it at the time, except of course Rudolph, who just keeps on departing.

Now this incident causes quite a stir in police circles, and the D.A. is very indignant over losing a valuable witness and when they are unable to locate Rudolph at once, a reward of five thousand dollars is offered for information leading to his capture alive or dead and some think they really mean dead. Indeed, it is publicly stated that it is not a good idea for anyone to take any chances with Rudolph as he is known to be armed and is such a character as will be sure to resent being captured, but they do not explain that this is only because Rudolph knows the D.A. wishes to place him in the old rocking chair at Sing Sing and that Rudolph is quite allergic to the idea.

Anyway, the cops go looking for Rudolph in Hot Springs and Miami and every other place except where he is, which is right in New York wandering around town with the slug in his side, knocking at the doors of old friends requesting assistance. But all the old friends do for him is to slam the doors in his face and forget they ever see him, as the D.A. is very tough on parties who assist guys he is looking for, claiming that this is something most illegal called harboring fugitives. Besides Rudolph is never any too popular at best with his old friends as he always plays pretty much of a lone duke and takes the big end of everything for his.

He cannot even consult a doctor about the slug in his side as he knows that nowadays the first thing a doctor will do about a guy with a gunshot wound is to report him to the cops, although Rudolph can remember when there is always a sure-footed doctor around who will consider it a privilege and a pleasure to treat him and keep his trap closed about it. But of course this is in the good old days and Rudolph can see they are gone forever. So he just does the best he can about the slug and goes on wandering here and there and around and about and the blats keep printing his picture and saying, where is Rudolph?

Where he is some of the time is in Central Park trying to get some sleep, but of course even the blats will consider it foolish to go looking for Rudolph there in such cold weather, as he is known as a guy who enjoys his comfort at all times. In fact, it is comfort that Rudolph misses more than anything as the slug is commencing to cause him great pain and naturally the pain turns Rudolph's thoughts to the author of same and he remembers that he once hears somebody say that Buttsy lives over in East Fifty-third Street.

So one night Rudolph decides to look Buttsy up and cause him a little pain in return and he is moseying through Fifty-third when he gets so weak he falls down on the sidewalk in front of the old house and rolls down a short flight of steps that lead from the street level to a little railed-in areaway and ground floor or basement door and before he stops rolling he brings up against the door itself and it creaks open inward as he bumps it. After he lays there a while Rudolph can see that the house is empty and he crawls on inside.

Then when he feels stronger, Rudolph makes his way upstairs because the basement is damp and mice keep trotting back and forth over him and eventually he winds up in the room where Johnny One-Eye finds him the following afternoon and the reason Rudolph settles down in this room is because it commands the stairs. Naturally, this is important to a guy in Rudolph's situation, though after he is sitting there for about fourteen hours before Johnny comes along he can see that he is not going to be much disturbed by traffic. But he considers it a very fine place, indeed, to remain planted until he is able to resume his search for Buttsy.

Well, after a while Johnny One-Eye wakes up and comes from under the coat and looks at Rudolph out of his good eye and Rudolph waggles his fingers and Johnny plays with them, catching one finger in his front paws and biting it gently and this pleases Rudolph no little as he never before has any personal experience with a kitten. However, he remembers observing one when he is a boy down in Houston Street, so he takes a piece of paper out of his pocket and makes a little ball of it and rolls it along the floor and Johnny bounces after it very lively indeed. But Rudolph can see that the bad eye is getting worse and finally he says to Johnny like this:

"Johnny," he says, "I guess you must be suffering more than I am. I remember there are some pet shops over on Lexington Avenue not far from here and when it gets good and dark I am going to take you out and see if we can find a cat croaker to do something about your eye. Yes, Johnny," Rudolph says, "I will also get you something to eat. You must be starved."

Johnny One-Eye says merouw to this and keeps on playing with the paper ball but soon it comes on dark outside and inside, too, and in fact, it is so dark inside that Rudolph cannot see his hand before him. Then he puts his Betsy in a side pocket of his overcoat and picks up Johnny and goes downstairs, feeling his way in the dark and easing along a step at a time until he gets to the basement door. Naturally, Rudolph does not wish to strike any matches because he is afraid someone outside may see the light and get nosey.

By moving very slowly, Rudolph finally gets to Lexington Avenue and while he is going along he remembers the time he walks from 125th Street in Harlem down to 110th with six slugs in him and never feels as bad as he does now. He gets to thinking that maybe he is not the guy he used to be, which of course is very true as Rudolph is now forty-odd years of age and is fat around the middle and getting bald, and he also does some thinking about what a pleasure it will be to him to find this Buttsy and cause him the pain he is personally suffering.

There are not many people in the streets and those that are go hurrying along because it is so cold and none of them pay any attention to Rudolph or Johnny One-Eye either, even though Rudolph staggers a little now and then like a guy who is rummed up, although of course it is only weakness. The chances are he is also getting a little feverish and lightheaded because finally he stops a cop who is going along swinging his arms to keep warm and asks him if he knows where there is a pet shop and it is really most indiscreet of such a guy as Rudolph to be interviewing cops. But the cop just points up the street and goes on without looking twice at Rudolph and Rudolph laughs and pokes Johnny with a finger and says:

"No, Johnny One-Eye," he says, "the cop is not a dope for not recognizing Rudolph. Who can figure the hottest guy in forty-eight states to be going along a street with a little cat in his arms? Can you, Johnny?"

Johnny says merouw and pretty soon Rudolph comes to the pet shop the cop points out. Rudolph goes inside and says to the guy like this:

"Are you a cat croaker?" Rudolph says. "Do you know what to do about a little cat that has a hurt eye?"

"I am a kind of a vet," the guy says.

"Then take a glaum at Johnny One-Eye here and see what you can do for him," Rudolph says.

Then he hands Johnny over to the guy and the guy looks at Johnny a while and says:

"Mister," he says, "the best thing I can do for this cat is to put it out of its misery. You better let me give it something right now. It will just go to sleep and never know what happens."

Well, at this, Rudolph grabs Johnny One-Eye out of the guy's hands and puts him under his coat and drops a duke on the Betsy in his pocket as if he is afraid the guy will take Johnny away from him again and he says to the guy like this:

"No, no, no," Rudolph says. "I cannot bear to think of such a thing. What about some kind of an operation? I remember they take a bum lamp out of Joe the Goat at Bellevue one time and he is okay now."

"Nothing will do your cat any good," the guy says. "It is a goner. It will start having fits pretty soon and die sure. What is the idea of trying to save such a cat as this? It is no kind of a cat to begin with. It is just a cat. You can get a million like it for a nickel."

"No," Rudolph says, "this is not just a cat. This is Johnny One-Eye. He is my only friend in the world. He is the only living thing that ever comes pushing up against me warm and friendly and trusts me in my whole life. I feel sorry for him."

"I feel sorry for him, too," the guy says. "I always feel sorry for animals that get hurt and for people."

"I do not feel sorry for people," Rudolph says. "I only feel sorry for Johnny One-Eye. Give me some kind of stuff that Johnny will eat."

"Your cat wants milk," the guy says. "You can get some at the delicatessen store down at the corner. Mister," he says, "you look sick yourself. Can I do anything for you?"

But Rudolph only shakes his head and goes on out and down to the delicatessen joint where he buys a bottle of milk and this transaction reminds him that he is very short in the moo department. In fact, he can find only a five-dollar note in his pockets and he remembers that he has no way of getting any more when this runs out, which is a very sad predicament indeed for a guy who is accustomed to plenty of moo at all times.

Then Rudolph returns to the old house and sits down on the floor again and gives Johnny One-Eye some of the milk in his derby hat as he neglects buying something for Johnny to drink out of. But Johnny offers no complaint. He laps up the milk and curls himself into a wad in Rudolph's lap and purrs.

Rudolph takes a swig of the milk himself but it makes him sick for by this time Rudolph is really far from being in the pink of condition. He not only has the pain in his side but he has a heavy cold which he probably catches from lying on the basement floor or maybe sleeping in the park and he is wheezing no little. He commences to worry that he may get too ill to continue looking for Buttsy, as he can see that if it is not for Buttsy he will not be in this situation, suffering the way he is, but on a long journey to some place.

He takes to going off into long stretches of a kind of stupor and every time he comes out of one of these stupors the first thing he does is to look around for Johnny One-Eye and Johnny is always right there either playing with the paper ball or purring in Rudolph's lap. He is a great comfort to Rudolph but after a while Rudolph notices that Johnny seems to be running out of zip and he also notices that he is running out of zip himself especially when he discovers that he is no longer able to get to his feet.

It is along in the late afternoon of the day following the night Rudolph goes out of the house that he hears someone coming up the stairs and naturally he picks up his Betsy and gets ready for action when he also hears a very small voice calling kitty, kitty, kitty, and he realizes that the party that is coming can be nobody but a child. In fact, a minute later a little pretty of maybe six years of age comes into the room all out of breath and says to Rudolph like this:

"How do you do?" she says. "Have you seen my kitty?"

Then she spots Johnny One-Eye in Rudolph's lap and runs over and sits down beside Rudolph and takes Johnny in her arms and at first Rudolph is inclined to resent this and has a notion to give her a good boffing but he is too weak to exert himself in such a manner.

"Who are you?" Rudolph says to the little pretty, "and," he says, "where do you live and how do you get in this house?"

"Why," she says, "I am Elsie, and I live down the street and I am looking everywhere for my kitty for three days and the door is open downstairs and I know kitty likes to go in doors that are open so I came to find her and here she is."

"I guess I forgot to close it last night," Rudolph says. "I seem to be very forgetful lately."

"What is your name?" Elsie asks, "and why are you sitting on the floor in the cold and where are all your chairs? Do you have any little girls like me and do you love them dearly?"

"No," Rudolph says. "By no means and not at all."

"Well," Elsie says, "I think you are a nice man for taking care of my kitty. Do you love kitty?"

"Look," Rudolph says, "his name is not kitty. His name is Johnny One-Eye, because he has only one eye."

"I call her kitty," Elsie says. "But," she says, "Johnny One-Eye is a nice name too and if you like it best I will call her Johnny and I will leave her here with you to take care of always and I will come to see her every day. You see," she says, "if I take Johnny home Buttsy will only kick her again."

"Buttsy?" Rudolph says. "Do I hear you say Buttsy? Is his other name Fagan?"

"Why, yes," Elsie says. "Do you know him?"

"No," Rudolph says, "but I hear of him. What is he to you?"

"He is my new daddy," Elsie says. "My other one and my best one is dead and so my mamma makes Buttsy my new one. My mamma says Buttsy is her mistake. He is very mean. He kicks Johnny and hurts her eye and makes her run away. He kicks my mamma too. Buttsy kicks everybody and everything when he is mad and he is always mad."

"He is a louse to kick a little cat," Rudolph says.

"Yes," Elsie says, "that is what Mr. O'Toole says he is for kicking my mamma but my mamma says it is not a nice word and I am never to say it out loud."

"Who is Mr. O'Toole?" Rudolph says.

"He is the policeman," Elsie says. "He lives across the street from us and he is very nice to me. He says Buttsy is the word you say just now, not only for kicking my mamma but for taking her money when she brings it home from work and spending it so she cannot buy me nice things to wear. But do you know what?" Elsie says. "My mamma says some day Buttsy is going far away and then she will buy me lots of things and send me to school and make me a lady."

Then Elsie begins skipping around the room with Johnny One-Eye in her arms and singing I am going to be a lady, I am going to be a lady, until Rudolph has to tell her to pipe down because he is afraid somebody may hear her. And all the time Rudolph is thinking of Buttsy and regretting that he is unable to get on his pins and go out of the house.

"Now I must go home," Elsie says, "because this is a night Buttsy comes in for his supper and I have to be in bed before he gets there so I will not bother him. Buttsy does not like little girls. Buttsy does not like little kittens. Buttsy does not like little anythings. My mamma is afraid of Buttsy and so am I. But," she says, "I will leave Johnny here with you and come back tomorrow to see her."

"Listen, Elsie," Rudolph says, "does Mr. O'Toole come home to-night to his house for his supper, too?"

"Oh, yes," Elsie says. "He comes home every night. Sometimes when there is a night Buttsy is not coming in for his supper my mamma lets me go over to Mr. O'Toole's and I play with his dog Charley but you must never tell Buttsy this because he does not like O'Toole either. But this is a night Buttsy is coming and that is why my mamma tells me to get in early."

Now Rudolph takes an old letter out of his inside pocket and a pencil out of another pocket and he scribbles a few lines on the envelope and stretches himself out on the floor and begins groaning oh, oh, oh, and then he says to Elsie like this:

"Look, Elsie," he says, "you are a smart little kid and you pay strict attention to what I am going to say to you. Do not go to bed tonight until Buttsy gets in. Then," Rudolph says, "you tell him you come in this old house looking for your cat and that you hear somebody groaning like I do just now in the room at the head of the stairs and that you find a guy who says his name is Rudolph lying on the floor so sick he cannot move. Tell him the front door of the basement is open. But," Rudolph says, "you must not tell him that Rudolph tells you to say these things. Do you understand?"

"Oh," Elsie says, "do you want him to come here? He will kick Johnny again if he does."

"He will come here, but he will not kick Johnny," Rudolph says. "He will come here, or I am the worst guesser in the world. Tell him what I look like, Elsie. Maybe he will ask you if you see a gun. Tell him you do not see one. You do not see a gun, do you, Elsie?"

"No," Elsie says, "only the one in your hand when I come in but you put it under your coat. Buttsy has a gun and Mr. O'Toole has a gun but Buttsy says I am never, never to tell anybody about this or he will kick me the way he does my mamma."

"Well," Rudolph says, "you must not remember seeing mine, either. It is a secret between you and me and Johnny One-Eye. Now," he says, "if Buttsy leaves the house to come and see me, as I am pretty sure he will, you run over to Mr. O'Toole's house and give him this note, but do not tell Buttsy or your mamma either about the note. If Buttsy does not leave, it is my hard luck but you give the note to Mr. O'Toole anyway.

Now tell me what you are to do, Elsie," Rudolph says, "so I can see if you have got everything correct."

"I am to go on home and wait for Buttsy," she says, "and I am to tell him Rudolph is lying on the floor of this dirty old house with a fat stomach and a big nose making noises and that he is very sick and the basement door is open and there is no gun if he asks me, and when Buttsy comes to see you I am to take this note to Mr. O'Toole but Buttsy and my mamma are not to know I have the note and if Buttsy does not leave I am to give it to Mr. O'Toole anyway and you are to stay here and take care of Johnny my kitten."

"That is swell," Rudolph says. "Now you run along."

So Elsie leaves and Rudolph sits up again against the wall because his side feels easier this way and Johnny One-Eye is in his lap purring very low and the dark comes on until it is blacker inside the room than in the middle of a tunnel and Rudolph feels that he is going into another stupor and he has a tough time fighting it off.

Afterward some of the neighbors claim they remember hearing a shot inside the house and then two more in quick succession and then all is quiet until a little later when Officer O'Toole and half a dozen other cops and an ambulance with a doctor come busting into the street and swarm into the joint with their guns out and their flashlights going. The first thing they find is Buttsy at the foot of the stairs with two bullet wounds close together in his throat, and naturally he is real dead.

Rudolph is still sitting against the wall with what seems to be a small bundle of bloody fur in his lap but which turns out to be what is left of this little cat I am telling you about, although nobody pays any attention to it at first. They are more interested in getting the come-alongs on Rudolph's wrists but before they move him he pulls his clothes aside and shows the doctor where the slug is in his side and the doctor takes one glaum and shakes his head and says:

"Gangrene," he says. "I think you have pneumonia, too, from the way you are blowing."

"I know," Rudolph says. "I know this morning. Not much chance, hey, croaker?"

"Not much," the doctor says.

"Well, cops," Rudolph says, "load me in. I do not suppose you want Johnny, seeing that he is dead."

"Johnny who?" one of the cops says.

"Johnny One-Eye," Rudolph says. "This little cat here in my lap. Buttsy shoots Johnny's only good eye out and takes most of his noodle with it. I never see a more wonderful shot. Well, Johnny is better off but I feel sorry about him as he is my best friend down to the last."

Then he begins to laugh and the cop asks him what tickles him so much and Rudolph says:

"Oh," he says, "I am thinking of the joke on Buttsy. I am positive he will come looking for me, all right, not only because of the little altercation between Cute Freddy and me but because the chances are Buttsy is greatly embarrassed by not tilting me over the first time, as of course he never knows he wings me. Furthermore," Rudolph says, "and this is the best reason of all, Buttsy will realize that if I am in his neighborhood it is by no means a good sign for him, even if he hears I am sick.

"Well," Rudolph says, "I figure that with any kind of a square rattle I will have a better chance of nailing him than he has of nailing me, but that even if he happens to nail me, O'Toole will get my note in time to arrive here and nab Buttsy on the spot with his gun on him. And," Rudolph says, "I know it will be a great pleasure to the D.A. to settle Buttsy for having a gun on him.

"But," Rudolph says, "as soon as I hear Buttsy coming on the sneaksby up the stairs, I can see I am taking all the worst of it because I am now wheezing like a busted valve and you can hear me a block away except when I hold my breath, which is very difficult indeed, considering the way I am already greatly tuckered out. No," Rudolph says, "it does not look any too good for me as Buttsy keeps coming up the stairs, as I can tell he is doing by a little faint creak in the boards now and then. I am in no shape to maneuver around the room and pretty soon he will be on the landing and then all he will have to do is to wait there until he hears me which he is bound to do unless I stop breathing altogether. Naturally," Rudolph says, "I do not care to risk a blast in the dark without knowing where he is as something tells me Buttsy is not a guy you can miss in safety.

"Well," Rudolph says, "I notice several times before this that in the dark Johnny One-Eye's good glim shines like a big spark, so when I feel Buttsy is about to hit the landing, although of course I cannot see him, I flip Johnny's ball of paper across the room to the wall just opposite the door and tough as he must be feeling Johnny chases after it when he hears it light. I figure Buttsy will hear Johnny playing with the paper and see his eye shining and think it is me and take a pop at it and that his gun flash will give me a crack at him.

"It all works out just like I dope it," Rudolph says, "but," he says, "I never give Buttsy credit for being such a marksman as to be able to hit a cat's eye in the dark. If I know this, maybe I will never stick Johnny out in front the way I do. It is a good thing I never give Buttsy a second shot. He is a lily. Yes," Rudolph says, "I can remember when I can use a guy like him."

"Buttsy is no account," the cop says. "He is a good riddance. He is the makings of a worse guy than you."

"Well," Rudolph says, "it is a good lesson to him for kicking a little cat."

Then they take Rudolph to a hospital and this is where I see him and piece out this story of Johnny One-Eye, and Officer O'Toole is at Rudolph's bedside keeping guard over him, and I remember that not long before Rudolph chalks out he looks at O'Toole and says to him like this:

"Copper," he says, "there is no chance of them out-juggling the kid on the reward moo, is there?"

"No," O'Toole says, "no chance. I keep the note you send me by Elsie saying she will tell me where you are. It is information leading to your capture just as the reward offer states. Rudolph," he says, "it is a nice thing you do for Elsie and her mother, although," he says, "it is not nearly as nice as icing Buttsy for them."

"By the way, copper," Rudolph says, "there is the remainders of a pound note in my pants pocket when I am brought here. I want you to do me a favor. Get it from the desk and buy Elsie another cat and name it Johnny, will you?"

"Sure," O'Toole says. "Anything else?"

"Yes," Rudolph says, "be sure it has two good eyes."

The Proud Old Name **C. E. Scoggins**

A few years ago, forty to be exact, I visited the offices of the literary agents Brandt and Brandt on one of my weekly visits to New York as story scout for *The Saturday Evening Post*. One of the brothers–I am not sure if it happened to be Carl or Erd–met me with a manuscript in his hand. "Scog has done it!" he exclaimed. "He's written a novelette this time, and it's packed full of romance."

I read it on the train going back to Philadelphia and found it to be everything Brandt had said. When it was published our readers were extremely enthusiastic, and it proved to be the real beginning of the career of Charles Elbert Scoggins, who later produced a dozen fine novels.

The story was published in 1923 and, as might be expected, the slang which crept in here and there was characteristic of the period. But the story doesn't appear dated in any respect. The struggle between the pretty American girl and the languorous Mexican heiress could have happened yesterday.

THE PROUD OLD NAME

C. E. Scoggins

I

Yes, this is the trail to Hosto. See that little flock of white specks yonder? No, not down in the basin; that's old man Moreno's hacienda; farther on, up under that peak with the streak of fog across it. If I was you, though, I would wait till morning. You have to go right by Moreno's and it will be dark pretty soon; and there is no sense getting yourself shot before they can see you are a white man and a stranger. Huh? Yes, there has been a little trouble. That is where I got this. No, nothing serious; it glanced off my skull. It is what comes of getting old and careless and forgetting that a man can climb a tree.

Sure I can put you up. Pablo! Take the gentleman's horse to the corral. I will be glad to have you. I am celebrating my partner's wedding and I was right lonesome until you came along.

Drink hearty! What is your views on matrimony, anyway? Just a minute. That was my wife, and she understands more English than you would think. You can not get her to talk it because she is afraid you would laugh, but you never know how much she gets. I never know, and I've been married twenty years.

No, there is not much trouble around here as a rule. They do not care who is president and half the time they do not know. Of course you get robbed now and then, but if you know your business it is not much worse than taxes. You let them find a little money, not too much, and give them a drink and keep your gun in sight, and they will not go too far. It is right pitiful when you come to think of it. Once these Indians owned all the land from the Isthmus clear to the Mississippi, and had caves full of gold; but now a hundred dollars looks like all the money in the world to them.

No, they are not against Americans if you treat them right. It is the Spaniards that have held their face in the dirt four hundred years.

I sure am glad to see you. I could tell you was a white man five miles off by the way you sat your horse. I was sitting here celebrating my partner's– Huh? Day before yesterday. I thought I had talked him out of it, but he is a headstrong young fellow and you can not tell him anything.

I remember how I came to take a fancy to him. I had just located this claim, I remember, and I rode up to Siete Minas–that's the biggest outfit in this district, thirty miles north–with some samples to be assayed, and I stayed over that night to take a hand in a poker game. Jimmy had just come down from the States to work there, and he sure was ignorant. He was just out of mining school and that was all he knew about poker.

Yes, what those hardshells ran over him was plenty. A nice young fellow too; he had a soft voice and a bashful grin like he did not want to hurt anybody's feelings, and you could not tell by looking at him that he was losing. That is the way I like to see a man. And one Swede, named Oscar something, him and another fellow took to whipsawing the kid; cross-raising him, you know, which will beat any man because it gives two chances to one.

It was none of my business, but he was a nice young fellow and I kind of hated it. Once or twice I caught me a hand and horned in between them and ran them out on a limb and sawed it off; and I joshed them about playing partners, trying to put the kid wise. Oscar, he did not like it, but he did not feel like starting anything. You know how it is in a poker game: if you start talking and get called, you have got to start shooting or eat plenty of crow.

It was jackpots and no limit, which is no game for young fellows because they have not got the patience. Pretty soon the kid throws in his last greenback for a showdown with this Swede, and he was even too innocent to make the Swede show first.

"What you got?" says Oscar, hurrying him.

"Three queens," says Jimmy, trustful.

" 'Tain't enough," says the Swede. "A flush here."

And he flashes his cards, all red, and throws them face down in the discard. But the kid did not have his eyes shut. He reaches out and turns over this flush and it is four hearts and a diamond.

"This isn't a flush," says he, puzzled.

"That ain't my hand," says the Swede, careless, and pushes the cards to me, which it was my next deal.

"It's what you threw down," says Jimmy.

"That's what you say," says the Swede. "I say it ain't."

And he has raked in the money, and what are you going to do about it? Shoot or shut up; you know how it is in a poker game. It was raw work. Nobody else was in the pot and it was none of our business. The

Swede had all the edge; all he had to do was sit and wait for the kid to make a move. But I could see the kid had never run into anything like that before. I see him getting white over the cheek bones and gathering his feet under him, and he did not have a gun—though of course Oscar would claim he did not know.

"So that's the kind of game you play!" says the kid.

I like a man that talks quiet when he is mad.

But there was no use letting him get shot over a little pot like that. I reached over and kicked him on the shin, friendly.

"Sit down, son," I says. "Mistakes will happen. Don't never fly off in the heat of the day without a blanket."

And I pushed some money over to him and started dealing real quick, because I do not like trouble. But he just sat there kind of dazed, rubbing his shin and passing the cards along. He did not know what to make of it at all. He could see I was friendly, but I reckon he had never sat in a game where you want to watch the deal and look out for cutting into crimps.

Pretty soon Oscar opens a nice pot for the size of it and everybody passes around to me. I give him a little raise and he comes back at me with a big one, talking loud and bold like he was making a bluff, but I could read him like a book because he was mad. He was laying for me, account of my taking up for Jimmy, and this time he had them.

"It looks like I am hooked," I says, regretful. "If I had any sense I would lay down; but not so, Bolivia! I never did have any sense and I am too old to learn. I have got to draw my card and see what happens."

So I drew one card, and he stood pat and bet the limit. I raised, and he raised, and we went at it. He would have kept raising till the last dog was hung; but finally I called.

"What you got?" says he, like he did to Jimmy.

"That ain't the question—yet," I says. "I'm calling you."

He had them, all right. He slams down a big straight flush, jack high, and reaches for the money; but I laughed in his face.

" 'Tain't enough," I says. "Not so, Bolivia! Read these and bust out crying."

And I tossed him my hand, face down, and raked in the money myself. Well, sir, it was ridiculous. He could not get it through his head.

"What's this?" says he, going glassy in the eye.

"That," I says, "is a straight flush, queen high. Or so I say. Read them real careful and tell us what you think."

It was no such thing. There was not a thing in that hand, hardly two cards of the same suit. It was his own medicine; and this time it was me that had the money and him that had to start shooting or shut up.

"And don't say that ain't my hand," I says, "because I just now handed it to you, myself. How do you like it?"

And I sat back and waited for him to make a move. The boys saw something was up; they edged away from us and waited, but a minute went by and I knew he did not have the nerve. The longer you think about it the harder it is to reach for a gun when a man is watching you.

"How about it?" I says.

He croaks, "You win," and snatches up what was left of his money and starts for the door; but I stopped him.

"Whoa!" I says. "You forgot to tell the boys what was in that hand. Do you want them to think I am a crook like you?"

He could have walked out on me; you can not shoot a man in the back; but it takes nerve to turn your back, and he did not have it.

"Straight flush, queen high," he says, husky.

"Much obliged," I says. "Good-by to you!"

And I turned the cards face up on the table. The boys all whooped and yelled, but he never cracked a smile; you take a cheap crook and he can not see a joke if it is on him. He was so rattled he bumped into the door going out, and I reckon he is going yet. He was ashamed to look that kid in the eye again.

"Here you are, kid," I says. "Here is your money back, all peaceable. You see there is no use having any trouble."

But the kid only looked more miserable and pushed it back.

"No, sir," he says, "I didn't have that much. Anyway I–I don't want it. I couldn't take it. Thanks just the same."

I thought he was mad because I was babying him before the boys. So after a while I catch him in his room; but do you think I could make him take it? Not so, Bolivia! He got plumb red in the face trying to explain without hurting my feelings, but finally it dawns on me. He didn't think I had got it honest; but wasn't it the same way the Swede got it? I ask you.

I swear to you I liked it. When you get old you do not feel so sure about what is straight and what is crooked, and it makes you feel good to see a young fellow act so–so young. I made out like I was insulted, but finally I had to laugh; and Jimmy, he can always see a joke. We got to liking each other. When Siete Minas finally shut down on account of bandits, I got him to come in here with me. I needed a man with his education and he was the kind of a damn fool that I liked.

Drink hearty! Well, I was going to ask you–how do you feel about a young fellow getting married?

II

This is a lonesome country for a kid. I remember when I first came down here, just about his age, I pretty near went crazy sometimes. Prospectors do get kind of cracked from being by themselves; maybe you know. The hills hanging over you at night, so many stars and all so big and still that you can not seem to stay inside yourself, and nobody to talk to but the mules. The sun coming up and something driving you on again; pulling you on, over this hill and down that barranca; something that never lets you rest. Hunting for gold! Yes, but it is something else besides. When you do make a strike you feel lost. There is nothing to hunt for after you have found it.

Something that gets into you because you are young and husky, and keeps on driving you when you are old. Concha, she never cared. That is one thing about Indians—money and comfort is nothing much to them.

But Jimmy and me, we hit it off fine. He took to calling me Uncle Lew. He used to josh Concha—that's my wife—as solemn as an owl. He called her Doña Escopeta from the way she blew up like a shotgun when she was mad. She seldom knew what he was talking about, because the things that strike a white man funny are not always funny to them, but she thought he was a great boy to be paying that much attention to her. He had a good head for mining and he was more company than a boat could haul.

Then this last revolution came along and the trains was cut off from Orendain, which is our shipping point; so we shut down all but a little development work, and it left too much time on Jimmy's hands. He took to riding out—prospecting, I thought; but I might have known. Old folks are not much company for a kid.

One day I rode over to see Moreno about some beef; and Moreno was tickled about something, which he is a proud man but jolly when he feels that way. We had two-three drinks, and he takes me by the elbow and leads me out to the main patio of his house; and what do you think?

That is Moreno's hacienda you see down there in the basin. It is quite a place; white buildings, very old, and shady arches around patios with flowers and fountains and cedars trimmed into the shape of fighting cocks; green farms and cattle ranges stretching off to these blue hills, like the world with a fence around it. There was a fountain, I remember, singing a soft and lazy tune that never changed, and lazy sunshine and a warm sweet feeling that got into you. I don't know why it made me feel so cross and old.

There was Jimmy picking flowers with Moreno's daughter, and not even a servant for a chaperon!

Elena, she knew it was queer. Her face was all flushed up; why are girls prettier when they are shy? She was using a fan like these girls do, graceful, half hiding her face and laughing with those big brown eyes of hers; these girls can just make their eyes talk to a man. That poor kid did not know which end he was standing on.

Elena, she knew she had no business to be there with a young fellow by herself. She ducked her head and flew; but Jimmy, he comes up grinning. He had been having the time of his young life. Moreno gives him a dig in the ribs and chuckles to me, "What do you think of my young namesake, eh?"

"Namesake?" I says. I reckon I was kind of sour about it.

But it was so. Santiago is Mexican for James. Yes, and Moreno means dark colored; it is the same as Brown. Funny what a difference it makes! Santiago Moreno is a grandee, mostly Spanish and very proud; but Jimmy Brown is a plain name and a plain gringo kid.

"Don Santiago and I have decided," says the kid in Spanish, "that we are kin–somewhere this side of Adam."

But I would not talk Spanish to him.

"I see you are kin to Adam all right!" I says, sarcastic.

"Oh," he says, "you mean my Spanish lesson."

"Come off!" I says, snorting. "That excuse is all wore out. A walking dictionary! Why don't you think up something new?"

You can not faze that boy. He acts so innocent he is plumb impudent; solemn, you know, but his eyes just twinkles at me.

"You seem to think I am hiding something," says he.

"Not so you could notice it!" I says.

But I had to grin. You can not be sour with that boy, and how are you going to keep a young fellow from falling in love with a pretty girl? Especially if he is lonesome. I can remember when Concha looked mighty sweet to me, and she is more Indian than Elena ever thought of being. Elena is nearly white.

I can't explain. It kind of tickled me, at that–this fool kid walking right through a cast-iron custom and hardly knowing it was there; making up to a rich man's daughter right under her father's nose, when any other young buck would have thought he was lucky to slip a smile and a flower to her going by in her carriage! He was not trained to playing bear, which is standing on your hind legs under a girl's window and whispering for fear the old man will find it out. The only way he knew to pay attention was to march up and do it.

Riding home I tried to talk to him.

"Don't you know," I says, "they don't think it's decent for a young fellow and a girl to be together by themselves?"

"I guess," he says, cheerful, "Don Santiago knows I'm decent. At least he seems willing to take a chance."

He did not see any reason to be afraid of a girl's father. I reckon that was how he got away with it; Moreno had never seen a young fellow act so frank and ignorant, and it tickled him. He seemed to think Jimmy was quite a boy. They was all the time calling each other *tocayo,* namesake, you know, as chummy as a pair of drillers–though Moreno is one of the richest men around here.

Well, you can bust into a custom when you are ignorant, but it will sure close up on you if you stay there long enough. Once or twice I tried to talk to him.

"Son," I says, "people will say you ought to marry that girl."

"I wish they would speak to her about it!" says he, which it seems he had asked her fifteen or sixteen times already. I did not think she would do it. But that is the way these girls are; they think they have to hold off or a man will think they are cheap; but if they like him they sure know how to keep him trying.

And for a while it seemed to do him good. Even after we started shipping ore again I could not think up jobs enough to hold him; and he would come back on a high horse, joshing everybody and working like a house afire. I reckon he was used to girls, back home, and missed them.

People did talk, of course. You can not bust through cast-iron customs without making noise. Nobody said anything to me; they knew better; but Concha was all steamed up about the women talking. And one Sunday over in Hosto, this young Felipe Cuervo, that was sweet on Elena himself, he challenged Jimmy to a duel. The first I knew about it was when the kid came home with a nick shot out of his ear. These people always shoot at your head; but Jimmy, he had shot low, like I always told him, and bust Felipe's hip for him.

I begged the kid to have some sense, but he just laughed. He was a scamp, that boy. He could be impudent in a bashful way that women like, and old folks too; he could make you laugh when you felt like kicking him in the pants. Excuse me if I talk too proud of him. He was the nearest to a son I ever had.

Drink hearty! Do you think a young fellow ought to stay away from women until he is old enough to have some sense?

Well, it would save a lot of trouble. Many a man would be alive and well that is not.

Sometimes I think the Lord never made this country for white men anyway. It is too raw. Beautiful, yes; but violent. The hills are too big and the stars come down too close. The sun is hot and the nights are cold, and when it rains it rains like hell bust loose; and something gets into you. More violent; I can't explain. You get so you do not care. You think you can take it easy, because there is plenty of time and a man lives only once.

But finally it comes to you that there will be nothing but time as long as you live; and it seems long enough, God knows.

It is all right for Indians. They do not have to think. The sun is their friend and the hills are like people to them. Time does not worry them. Take this old fellow that calls himself Guatamo—this cripple that claims to be their king. What do you think of a man with patience enough to catch a thousand humming birds?

They are not like our Indians in the United States. They are older. You would not think it to look at them, but once they had kings just like white people, and cities as big as any in the world. They built roads and bridges and pyramids, and knew things no white man knows to-day. The Spaniards never could have licked them, only they thought Spaniards was gods because they was white and had horses and guns, and they treated them friendly and let them into their cities. But the Spaniards was human, all right, and started paying attention to their women, and the trouble started—like it always does.

This old Guatamo here, he claims to be the great-great-something grandson of Guatamotzin, the prince that killed Moctezuma—or Montezuma, I expect you call him; their king, you know—to keep him from giving in to the Spaniards. And Moctezuma was his uncle, and forgave him and gave the kingdom to him when he was dying. That makes Guatamo king if it is so. He claims to know where the gold is buried, and he is crippled because he has been punished to make him tell. He has got plenty of gold, that is a sure——

Huh? Maybe he did tell them. But they never came back with any of it. They never came back at all. He is a bad man to monkey with, because the Indians think he is kind of sacred.

He does not look much like a king. Old, that is how he looks; you can not tell how old; you could believe he was Guatamotzin himself, alive —hating the Spaniards and waiting for the stars to tell him when to kill all the white men and bring back the day of the Nahuatlecas—all these four hundred years.

But he is just an Indian to Moreno. I was going to tell you.

Along in this last rainy season Jimmy took to going around solemn and absent-minded, and not eating much, and after a while he tells me it is all fixed. He is going to marry Elena.

III

I told him *felicidades,* happiness, you know, and he said thanks. It was none of my business; he was free, white and twenty-one. He didn't have much to say about it, and I didn't.

But all of a sudden I noticed we had said it in Spanish. It seemed natural. His Spanish had got better—better than any gringo had a right to talk; his manners was better too, and it made you feel more offish and polite with him. He was not quite the same.

"Well," I says, "when does the wedding come off?"

He answers kind of vague. He says they are waiting for the legal formalities. I thought he meant the banns; I did not have any idea what that kid had went and done.

But I could see he did not feel so good. I tried to get him to take a trip to the States, which it would be too late after he was married; Elena, she has never been any farther than Guadalajara, and the States would scare her to death. I took to talking about the machinery we ought to buy, but he argues, listless, that we did not have the money to risk buying it just yet. I reckon he was not much interested in mining any more. Why should he be? Moreno owns most of this basin that is any good for farming, and he never had but this one daughter to leave it to.

Once or twice I tried to talk to him. Once I asked if him and Elena was good friends, and he thought I was joking.

"We are not getting married because we hate each other," he says, "that is a sure thing."

"I know what you are getting married for," I says. "I am not so old but what I can remember."

He was sitting just where you are sitting now, gazing out over this blue-rimmed basin that will be all his some day; and the dark was coming fast, like it is now. And by his voice I know the money and position does not mean a thing to him. He is just aching for a girl out there where little lights begin to shine, and all this lonesome twilight closing in.

This is the time when you can talk, if ever. You can not see each other's face so plain, and you forget to wonder what a man will think. The sky fading off and off, the sun just gone but burning a little while like the door of heaven that men dream about, and night and quiet spreading on the hills. You try to talk; you try to say things you can never say—like feeling in the dark to touch somebody you can hear but can not see.

He thinks it is wonderful that a girl could love him enough to marry him. A jack-leg engineer, he calls himself. He has not got any idea what a fine, upstanding, warmhearted young hellion he is.

"Son," I says, "I understand all that. I was a young buck myself once, little as you would think it, and thought women was not human too. I know these girls are good at loving; it is all they know. But are you friends with her? How do you get along with her, talking, and so forth? I mean—does she laugh at what you think is funny?"

I reckon I did not say it right. It kind of shut him up. By his voice I know he is just humoring me; he thinks I do not know how a young fellow feels.

Yes, him and Elena, they laugh plenty when they are together, it seems.

But I had seen them laughing, and I knew. It was not because anything was funny. It was because they were a handsome young fellow and a pretty girl.

"I mean," I says, "you will both live a long time, at least I hope so, and you will be young and high-spirited only a little while. How will you get along when you are old folks, unless you are friends and like the same kind of jokes?"

No young fellow knows how lonesome it is to be married and not understand each other's jokes. I know it does not sound like much. I tried to tell him. I could not say it any plainer than I did; but it did not sound like anything to him. He just humored me because I am an old fellow and he is young and husky. I could tell by his voice that he was just humoring me, and it made me mad because I could not make him see that being married was no joke.

After that I let him alone. It was the rainy season too, and if you are mad at anybody it is no pleasure to be cooped up with him by rain.

It was a miserable way to be. He did not half listen to anything you said, and he was all the time too polite—like a native; like Santiago Moreno, Junior. He was even polite to Concha, and she thought he was mad at her and I could not tell her different. She would fuss around doing little things for him, and she would cut her old eyes at him and wait for him to make fun of her; but he never did. It made me feel worse than if he had been downright mean to her.

Well, one night I was sitting here, the rain coming down like a wall at the edge of the porch, and all of a sudden I hear horses. These days you never know what is coming; tell you the truth, I half hoped it would be trouble. I was feeling pretty sour because me and Jimmy could not get along.

So I felt to see if my gun was loose, and give them a whoop for fear they would miss the camp. You would not want even a bandit to be lost in these hills when it is raining.

But it was two white men and a *remudero* from Orendain—I bet he made them pay in advance and left the money at home—leading a pack mule loaded with suit-cases. They sure was dressy; tapered pants, and belts around their coats, and shiny boots and little silver spurs; you know, like yours; the regular tenderfoot get-up. Why do tenderfeet always wear corduroy? It is hot and it soaks up water like a sponge.

One was a man about forty-five, half-drowned and completely peevish; he falls off his horse and stomps in like he is blaming me for the rain. But the other one–just a kid, fourteen or fifteen, he looks to be–acts like it is all a joke. He prances in and flops into a chair and sticks his legs up to let the water run out of his boots, grinning and wrinkling up his nose kind of cute.

"Pfuff!" says he. "I do believe it's going to rain!"

And he hops up and swings the water off his hat, and he looks younger; there is a sort of baby look about him, his black hair bushed up every way. Well, I was herding them inside when we run into Jimmy and Concha coming out to see what the commotion was; and for a minute I thought Jimmy had gone crazy. He claps his hands to his head and staggers up against the wall.

"I am seeing things!" he moans. "I've got 'em again! A flapper–a real live flapper or my name is not Francis X. Bushman!"

"Why, Francis," says this wet kid, giggling, "how you have changed!"

And it was not a boy at all; it was a girl, for all her hair-cut and her pants like papa's. That was the only time I ever heard Concha laugh out loud.

IV

How do you feel about a woman wearing pants? It sure does not seem right. She was around here all next day, because it kept on raining, and I could not get over being embarrassed about her legs. I could not stand to look at her hair, whacked off that way.

In this country that is what they do to a girl when she goes wrong.

But Concha, she thinks all Americans are crazy anyway, and it tickles her. She cackles right out. And Gene–that is her name, Eugenia Ward, only Gene fits her better, account of her looking and acting so much like a boy–she looks at Concha and laughs, which she seems to think Concha is funny too. She gets on some dry pants and follows Concha into the kitchen and Concha does not run her out. I hear the women just chattering in there, and I go to see if they are plaguing the girl; but it is Jimmy that is plaguing Concha and trying to make her talk English for Gene. Concha is flapping her hands and making out like she is mad, but you can tell she is tickled. It seems like old times to have Jimmy making fun of her again.

Yes, for a while he was more like himself. Him and Gene was all the time joshing each other. They seem to be talking English, but it did not make much sense. It was a circus to watch them.

"Hi, flapper!" says Jimmy, coming in from the mine.

"Don't be quaint," says Gene. "If you call me a flapper I will call you a cake eater or a drug-store cowboy. They went out years and years ago—two years at least."

Then Jimmy begins to limp, hitching one leg like it is wooden, and lets his hands shake and strokes where his beard could be if he had one.

"Marooned," says he in a trembly voice. "Aye, lass, well you may snicker. Poor old Ben Gunn, the world has passed him by. Go, child, and leave me with my memories!"

"Such as?" says Gene.

"You are too young to know," says he. "I can remember when they only showed them to the knee."

"Old stuff," says Gene. "Positively mid-Victorian!"

"How far is it now? But stop! I shudder to think," says Jimmy, shuddering.

"They are not showing them at all," says Gene.

"Eh, well! Old ways are best," says Jimmy, very sad.

What do they care if it rains? He wraps a slicker around her and takes her over to the mine, and she takes it off and the drillers can not work for staring at her pants.

He takes Ward over, and they argue by the hour about our operations, which Ward thinks is plenty crude. Ward is a stockholder in Siete Minas, it seems; that is a big low-grade operation thirty miles north of here; they are shut down because they ship bullion instead of ore and it is just pie for the bandits. But the Siete Minas folks back in the States has got suspicious about getting nothing but assessments out of the mine, and sent Ward down here to investigate. Ward does not tell me this; he has got a jaw like a steel trap and all he asks is questions; but Gene, she tells Jimmy. Women have simply got to talk, and sooner or later they are bound to tell all they know.

That is the way with tenderfeet. They hear the revolution is over, and trains running again, and no Americans killed lately, and they expect profits to pick up and be as usual. They do not understand what the old-timers mean when they say a district is peaceable.

I told Ward he was a fool to go packing that girl around, and he was right upset about it.

"They told me in Guadalajara," he says, "there was no trouble in this district now."

"Depends on what you mean by trouble," I says. "If you ride by daylight, and mind your own business and give up your money peaceable if they get the drop on you, you are not likely to get shot. But a woman is different," I says. "If a daughter of mine got caught out on the trail," I says, "I would sure call it trouble."

The chances were that nothing would happen, but if a woman did run into trouble, out there in the hills, it would be too late to be sorry you had took the chance. Too many men have found out, the last ten-twelve years, that a man with a gun can make his own laws; and some of them are all right, but a good many of them are human.

So he asked me could she stay here till he got back, and I said we would be glad to have her. Yes, sir; they do say hell is full of good intentions. Ward, he did not have a bit of trouble, going or coming; but I let that girl walk right into the middle of the worst mess that has happened around here.

Gene, she was satisfied to stay. It was early one morning when her papa rode off with this fellow from Orendain that brought him. The sun was just coming up behind the ranges; the air fresh and keen, the wet rock sparkling like a million little diamonds, the basin fading off into blue haze and all the peaks like something painted grand against the sky. A clear morning in this altitude can make you kind of drunk.

She stood here watching till they made the dip in the trail, and all of a sudden she draws a deep breath and stretches up her arms.

"Oh, all my life," she says, "I have been hungry for the hills!"

And I remember yet her gray eyes shining. That was the first time that she looked just right to me. That was the first time that I noticed freckles on her nose, and they belonged there, though her hair was nearly black.

I can't explain. She looked like something, standing there–this short-haired slim kid in her neat boots and pants, her head up and a look in her gray eyes, watching the sunrise pour across the world. Like part of it; I can't explain. Like what men think of when they hunt for gold. Boyish and brave and gay and everlasting, like what gets into men to go adventuring. It had you feeling tired and old, remembering. It had you thinking where you missed the trail when you was young.

"What is that little white place yonder?" she wants to know.

"Moreno's hacienda," says Jimmy, speaking short.

But she has read about haciendas, it seems, and she wants to know. A plantation or a ranch or something, is it? She has heard they are like ancient Spain; few–yes, feudal; that is the word she says. Barons, and so forth. Well, I have never been to Spain, but I reckon they do not have Indians for servants over there.

"Old and romantic, is it?" she wants to know.

"Old," says Jimmy, "yes. As to the romance, I am prejudiced. I am going to marry the owner's daughter."

Smiling he says it, but very sharp and clear. Gene turns to look at him and laughs. "Hot dog!" she says. "A real Spanish señorita?"

"Mexican," says Jimmy, but does not explain the difference.

"Tell me about her! Black-eyed and beautiful?"

"Brown-eyed and beautiful," says Jimmy.

"Does she speak English?"

"No."

"I should say it is romantic! Do you sing softly at midnight under her window, and did you have to fight her father and her brothers and her other lovers, like they do in books?"

She was half curious and half making fun; I reckon she did not more than half believe him; but Jimmy, he has lost his taste for joshing completely. He looks at her like he can be pushed just so far.

"Sorry to disappoint you," he says very dry and quiet; "I do not sing, softly or otherwise, at midnight or any other time. She has no brothers and her father is a very good friend of mine. I am going to take his name."

"Take his–oh!" says Gene, looking queer. "You mean–turn Mexican? I don't believe you!"

"Son," I says, "say that over again–slow!"

But he has turned his back and marched off to the mine. By the time I caught up with him he was sitting on a wheelbarrow watching the drillers in Number 3 Drift. I kind of put my hand on his shoulder, but he looked up at me so savage I thought he did not like it.

"Son," I says, "did you say you was going to change your name?"

"I did," says he, like he is not interested.

I could not get it through my head. Oh, it has been done; more than one man has took his wife's name when she is rich and his folks are nobody much. Natives, I mean; they set great store by family and name. And one way of looking at it, I reckon a girl has got as much right to her name as a man has. And yet–a man is a man. A white man is a white man, and you can not get around it.

"Why not?" says he, listless. "Moreno is a good name. It was a proud old name in Spain before Mexico was heard of–before there was any United States. It has been a great name here for a hundred years, and Don Santiago has no son to carry it on. I know how they feel about it."

But I remember how he sat there staring at that gang of drillers. They could have stood on their heads and he would not have noticed. I remember how his hands kept opening and shutting, hard, like he was feeling whether they belonged to him or Santiago Moreno, Junior. He had a fine pair of hands, husky and lean and kind of freckled on the back.

"Yes, but son," I says– "how about the way you feel?"

He makes a motion with his hands, listless; like letting go; like the natives when they mean it makes no difference.

"What is the difference?" he says. "A name–what is a name? A habit. I feel like Jim Brown; well, I shall learn to feel like Santiago Moreno."

"A habit," I says, "that you got from your pa and your grandpa and his father before him."

"It didn't mean much to them," he says, listless. "A family named Brown. Which Brown? Nobody knows."

And he tells me a little about his folks. There was not much to tell. And when you come to think of it, that is the way with most of us. Do you know who your grandpa was? Well, then, your great-grandpa? We do not bank so much on family; with us a man is more himself; and we seldom live in one place a hundred years, because we light out hunting our chance to get ahead.

Jimmy's folks had not got ahead much. His pa sold groceries and died when Jimmy was knee high to a duck, and his ma had to make dresses for a living, and she died just when he was getting big enough to be some help to her. He worked his way through school by waiting table and gathering up laundry, which it seems is no disgrace in mining school; but it is sure nothing to boast of to the Morenos.

He did not know of any near kinfolks but his grandpa, and not much about him.

"He was a carpenter," says the kid–like that.

"An honest trade enough," I says, "for Jesus Christ."

"Oh," he says, "honest," and makes that motion with his hands again, like the natives when they mean it does not amount to much. I don't know why it made me kind of mad.

"Ashamed of him, are you," I says– "Santiago?"

But it was me that was ashamed. He just looked at me.

"You asked me," he says, "and I am telling you. Elena's name means something to her; mine–is a way to know when I am spoken to."

I reckon they had been talking ancestors at him; he kept coming back to his grandpa–the only one of his he knew about.

"I don't even know what his first name was," he says. "Nobody thought it was important, not even he. A humble man; no education, never at ease in his own house; I remember he always went outdoors to smoke when my mother was there. I think he was afraid of her because she had been a school-teacher. A tired, stoop-shouldered old man with rusty shoes and a pipe, named–grandpa."

That is not much in the way of ancestors, is it? Not much to stack up against a proud old family and a girl that is in your blood like liquor. I was not blaming him; a young fellow can not think straight when he is lonesome. And yet–what if your grandpa did not get ahead? How do you know what held him back? You still have got a right to make a start and be somebody's grandpa to be proud of. You still have got a right to be yourself.

We are not proud, but we are sure as good as any Spaniard.

"Son," I says, "look here! How far has this thing gone?"

"How do you mean," he says, "how far? I have given my word. The legal end of it takes time, that's all. Time," he says, "my God! You'd think a man was going to live forever!"

And he makes a motion like throwing something away and goes charging out and gets on his horse and pours the quirt to him. That is what gets you. Time. You see it coming on, day after day and every day the same, and you feel like you could not stand it. And you let yourself go to keep from thinking; do something–do anything to keep from thinking. You can do it–for a while. But you can not keep time from coming on. You get old before you learn it is no use; before you learn to sit and let the days go by. A young fellow can just eat his heart out, thinking.

I knew where he had gone. I could have guessed it, anyway, by the look in his eyes when he came in that night. Like walking in a trance; he did not even think to take his spurs off, but came in dragging them. He stops by Gene's chair–we was just eating supper–and makes her a little bow, polite and absent-minded.

"You were interested in haciendas," he says. "Don Santiago asks me to say he will be honored to have you visit his."

And he makes another little bow to Concha and says, "With permission," like a native, and sits down to eat; but he was not paying attention to anything; he was remembering. Gene, she had never seen him act like that before. You could just see her gray eyes cooling off.

"Thank you," she says, "but I'm not so interested as I was."

"As you wish," says Jimmy, too polite and vague for any use.

He did not say a word about any trouble at Moreno's. Maybe he did not know; I never got a chance to ask him, afterward. Maybe he did not talk to anybody but the family, and they are too polite to talk about the servants stealing and getting shot for it.

He just ate and went into his room and shut the door. Gene sat out here with me a while, but it was lonesome for her. I remember she tried to talk about how peaceable it was. Peaceable! Look at this basin now. These million stars that keep on shining whether you live or die; these hills that look so soft and purple-dark–they looked that way when the first Toltecs came from God knows where. They looked that way when the last Toltec died on a Nahuatl altar, God knows how long ago. They looked that way when Aztec kings ruled over the empire of the Nahuatlecas; greater than Spain it was; and they looked that way when a hundred thousand Nahuatl fighting men went up against the Spaniards' guns and died. Peaceable, yes. What difference does it make to them?

I did not blame her when she went to bed. I sure was not fit company for her—old as I am and sour as I felt. What is the matter with young fellows when they get women on the brain?

V

That very day Moreno had an Indian shot for stealing corn. Oh, nothing new about it; he has shot plenty of them in his time. No, he is not any kind of an officer. He does not need to be. He owns most of the land around here.

That is what all the trouble is about to-day. It is not revolution exactly; revolutions come and go, but this thing gets more so all the time. More like it is in Russia. Yes, bolshevism; that is the word I mean. Francisco Madero, he started it here with his talk about giving the land back to the Indians. That was how he won the first revolution against Diaz. And that was what finished him, too, when the Indians found out he could not do what he said.

It has been more or less the same with every revolution since, the Indians getting bolder and bolder against the rich folks. Time was when the inside walk around the plaza at Hosto was left open for a dozen fine families, but now the big hats and sandal feet and dirty blankets have crowded them out completely. They do not even dare get out of their carriages at the Sunday night concerts; they just drive around a few laps listening to the band and looking rich and proud, and then drive home complaining how the lower classes have gone crazy.

I do not know what it is coming to. It does not look possible to put things back where they was four hundred years ago. For one thing, where are you going to draw the line, when half of them have got some Spanish blood?

They have scared out a good many fine families, that is a sure thing; murdered them or run them back to Spain or to some city for protection. Moreno, though, he did not scare worth a cent. He just got prouder and prouder. He went ahead and had this Indian shot for stealing corn, and the very next day he had a woman——

Huh? Well, not exactly. They just catch a man stealing and start off to jail with him and shoot him trying to escape—you know. The law of flight, they call it. I am not saying it is wrong. A rich man has to protect his property, and he can not be riding around to trials all the time. It sounds kind of rough, but it does discourage stealing, that is a sure thing.

Anyway, it is the way this country has been run four hundred years. But the rich men are mostly Spanish and the thieves are mostly Indian, and you can not blame the Indians for getting tired of it.

We did not know a thing about it here. I was sitting here next morning when Jimmy came out, and I reckon he did not sleep much; his eyes looked like burnt holes in a blanket, and he did not say good morning or be durned to you; he just sat down. Then Gene came out and he got up stiff as a ramrod.

Gene, she went right up to him and put her hand on his arm.

"Jimmy," she says, "I didn't mean to be impertinent. I guess it didn't seem quite real to me. It's–it's all so wide and new," she says, "out here, I don't feel so darned real myself."

"It's quite all right," says Jimmy–polite if it kills him.

"It's not all right," says Gene. "I mean well, but there's simply nobody home. I feel like an oil can," she says, "making wise cracks about things I don't know anything about. Broad A me," she says. "It's just what I deserve."

I know it does not make sense. But it would take a wooden man to be mad at her when she looks like that, her gray eyes looking up at him so honest–sober and sorry, like a kid. Jimmy, he kind of gulps and pats her hand.

"You're all right," he says. "I'm the oil can. Go on," he says, "ask me. Ask me anything; ask me about any of the fourteen men I have killed –or is it sixteen?" And he hauls his gun out of the holster and pretends to be counting the notches in the butt, which there is not any. "Seventeen," he tells her, solemn.

"That is the boy!" says Gene, and I will be eternally dad-gummed if she did not stand up on her tiptoes and offer to kiss him. I never saw such a girl.

Jimmy, he did not do it. He was so embarrassed he turned kind of pale, which he did not feel good that morning anyway.

"Get away from me, woman! You are shocking the assembled multitude," he says, which I did feel kind of like a multitude, at that–kissing and going on; though you could tell she did not mean a bit of harm. "Necking and hitting in the clinches is barred," he says, whatever that means; I never did find out, because Concha came and said breakfast was ready.

But it was more cheerful to see them joshing each other. It was a real pretty morning, and first thing I knew they were talking about riding over to Moreno's after all.

Well, sir, I did not have the heart to interfere. I did not think they would run into any trouble; it's only nine kilometers and the trail is wide open all the way.

But I knew what they wanted with her over there. They would not be easy till they got a look at her. These women think every woman in the world is trying to steal their man.

Well, it would not hurt them to be shocked a little, and Gene was plumb tickled about going exploring. Jimmy, he tells her about their medieval hospitality.

"The man at the gate will kiss your hand," he says; "ancient-retainer stuff, you know; and Don Santiago will tell you his house is yours, and make you believe it too."

"Hot dog!" says Gene. "I'm crazy about ancient retainers. We had a butler once that stayed with us six months."

That is the way she talks. Hot dog or the bee's hips or the snake's elbows means she is tickled. When she says she is crazy she does not mean she is crazy, she means she likes a thing.

"I can rake up a side-saddle," says Jimmy. "Our storekeeper's wife has got one somewhere. Have you got a female skirt?"

"Of course," says Gene, "but what's the big idea? I can't ride side-saddle. I saw a picture of one once; prehistoric, you know. Everybody rides cross-saddle now."

"Not here!" says Jimmy, very dry and final.

Short hair was scandalous enough, without bringing in a woman in pants and straddle of a horse. The Morenos would have fell dead.

I knew what they would think, anyway, about a girl riding nine kilometers with a young fellow, and nobody else along. They would think it was not decent. Besides, I felt responsible for Gene. Not that Jimmy couldn't take care of her; he is a nervy kid and handy with a gun; but there is no use talking, two men is twice as good as one in case of trouble.

So I said I was about due to ride over and see Moreno myself. Gene came dancing out with a dress on, pretty but not a riding habit by any means, and a blue hat like something wrapped around her head. Well, sir, you would be surprised. She looked real grown up. But she sure did not act it. She was like a monkey about that side-saddle, which she had on silk stockings and her dress was pretty but not long.

Dresses do make a woman look different and you can not get around it. More precious somehow. I remember thinking I could not stand to look her papa in the eye if anything was to happen to that girl.

It felt peaceable enough—a pretty morning, the basin spread out like a bright green checkerboard, the horses clipping along and these two kids joshing each other. Jimmy, he was lying when he told her he did not sing. He can sing fine. You can hear him half a mile when he feels good. Riding along, he busts out, and pretty soon Gene joins in. It did not make much sense—about yes, we have not got any bananas, and throwing the dishes away instead of washing them; but it made you feel right gay, at that.

Gene, she could sing rings around him. Her voice goes weaving in and out through his; not like the *segundo* that the native women sing; *se-*

gundo sounds wild and sad, but this was more like joking with the tune.

"Hot dog!" says Jimmy. "The barber-shop kid!"

Gene, she just laughed. She was not a bit touchy about her hair being cut.

They get to singing softer and slower, riding along. Jimmy rides up close and puts his head down by hers, and sings with his eyes half shut like he was listening; and it was worth listening to. It kind of gave you a feeling up the back, the way her voice slid over his like a bow on soft deep fiddle strings.

"That is the boy!" says Jimmy, and he turns around and asks me, "How's that for close harmony, huh?"

"It's right harmonious," I says, "but maybe you could get closer if you was to climb on to the same horse," I says, sarcastic, which Gene did not look much like a boy that day—her face pink with the wind, and this blue hat kind of cute around it, and her eyes bright with singing. I remember how pretty her mouth looked, changing to let her voice float high and clear or settle to a whisper like the far-off hum of bees.

"Here's an old one," she says, and croons a piece of a tune to him and asks him if he knows it, "but full of dirty swipes."

That was what she said—dirty swipes; but there was nothing dirty about it. It is a real sweet song. I have heard Jimmy sing it many a time.

Oh, come, my love, and walk with me—

That is the way it starts, all on one note, only her voice chimes different on every word. Then it drifts into singing gentle and slow. I edged my horse off on to the grass to keep his hoofs from rattling. Their voices melting in together; gentle and sad and sweet, like a slow wind and rain on the roof and thinking of old times when you lie awake at night. I don't remember all of it, only at the end it is something about

——sever,
Say you will leave me never,
Say you'll be mine—forever,
For I ——

I can't explain. I used to sing pretty good, but it has been a long time since I tried it. His voice goes fading up and fading down and hers comes melting into it, golden-soft.

"I love . . . but you."

I did not know the boy could sing so sweet. But I reckon he noticed he was riding too close to her and felt kind of embarrassed about it. He let go her arm and rode along not saying anything. He hardly said another word all the way to the hacienda.

Maybe you noticed before it got dark, there is a kind of a crack out there across the basin? It does not look like much from here, but it is deep and there is quite a river in it. The ford is just outside the hacienda. Riding down to it I see four-five old men sitting there; not doing anything; just sitting there. Yes, everything seemed to be quiet. Too quiet; I can see it now. I remember my left elbow kind of aching where I was shot once, and I thought it was going to rain. But I reckon it was the feel of trouble in my bones.

And I remember how quick old Tolo jumped up from his chair by the big gate where he has been sitting thirty or forty years. Like he was looking for somebody or something; I did not think of it at the time. It looked peaceable enough, the dogs running out to bark and the little naked kids sidling up to stare at Gene, which they had never seen a woman with a hat on.

Tolo unbuckles our spurs and says we are welcome to our house; that is the custom; it does not mean a thing.

"Ancient retainer?" says Gene.

"As advertised," says Jimmy, speaking short. It does beat all how a young fellow can go from sour to gay and back again.

Of course Tolo is not a butler or anything; just a *portero,* a wrinkled old peon with dusty sandals and baggy cotton clothes; but he is plenty ancient. And there is something about a place like that. There is a feeling, and you can not get around it. Out there in the middle of the basin, green fields and cattle ranges stretching off to these blue hills; these long white walls from the days when every hacienda was a fort; these cobbled courtyards worn by horses riding in and out a hundred years—you can not realize that it will ever change. It feels solid, settled, the stones and the houses and the people; and what they do seems right because they have been doing it so long. You could see how it had crept into Jimmy. You could see it creeping into Gene. Tolo bows down and kisses the back of her riding glove, and she was all fixed to laugh, but all of a sudden a queer look comes in her eyes.

"Quick, Jimmy," she whispers, "tell me what I do! I thought it would be funny, but it isn't. It's—dignified!"

Yes, it is kind of touching—these faithful old servants being so humble to you, and all. But it is no more natural for them to be servants than it is for you or me. Once they was proud, too, and made slaves out of people they had beat in fighting.

No, sir, white men do not know it all. Concha can tell you things that happened when the white race was a pup. She did not read it in a book;

the Nahuatlecas do not have books nowadays; the Spaniards burned them all. But you can not keep people from telling their children. It is like looking down a long, dim, splendid hall into the centuries. You get a hazy glimpse of what they used to be–what they are yet, inside, and always will be. Splendid and pitiful; I can't explain. Patient and pitiful, waiting for the stars to tell them when their day will come again.

Maybe it will. Who knows? They are sure getting bolder. It seems Guatamo had sent word to Moreno about mistreating Indians, but you can imagine how much attention Moreno paid to it.

Guatamo is the one that claims to be their king. Myself, I always thought he was just a yarn the mothers told their children. Concha got it from her mother when she was a baby, and she is forty or fifty now. Huh? Yes, I know she looks older than that. These women are grown at fourteen and start getting old at twenty-five.

That was why Elena is kind of touchy about her age; I was going to tell you. Elena is nineteen, which is pretty old not to be married yet.

Guatamo, he claims to be descended from Guatamotzin–the *tzin* Guatamo, that killed his own uncle Moctezuma, because the Spaniards was getting him all fuddled with Christianity. It may be so; I do not claim to know. I reckon he is kind of cracked. He can sit still so long you would not swear he is alive, only his eyes–black and alive with hate that never changes. Pitiful too. He does not understand the white man's world. Gold is no good to him. Time does not mean a thing to him. How long do you think it takes to catch a thousand humming birds? Not just the common gray ones, either; the colored ones, like little jewels dancing in air; *huitzin,* they call them, because they are sacred to their god Huitzil'. Many a Spaniard has been sacri—

Eh?

Oh! *Eres tu,* Concha?

'Sta bien. Ahorita vamos. She says our chocolate is ready.

I wonder how long she has been listening there. Did I say anything about Jimmy's grandpa? It is a kind of a joke, but you could never make her see it. I will have to tell you afterward. You can not get her to talk English, but she listens and you never know how much she gets.

VI

You noticed, Concha would not sit down with us at supper? She is afraid you would not think she is good enough. That is the way the Spaniards have made them feel. Lower classes, that is what they call the Indians. *Pelados;* peeled ones; that is why upperclass Mexicans wear all the whiskers they can raise, to prove they have not got much Indian blood. Moreno, he is as proud of his beard as he is of his old Spanish name. He is high class; I was going to tell you. He knows better than to get haughty with me, but he would think Concha was a servant even if she had a million dollars.

Where did I leave off? Oh, yes; about Guatamo–this crippled old Aztec that claims to be their king.

Well, while Jimmy was having this quarrel with Moreno I hear people running in the patio, and I—— Huh? I thought I told you. It was about this servant spilling a plate of *mole* in Gene's lap. Huh? Why, *mole* is turkey cooked in a black gravy of ground-up peppers. It is real tasty, but nothing for a tenderfoot to tackle. It will knock your head off if you are not used to it.

Where did I leave off anyway?

No, sir, Gene did not feel like laughing any more. There is no use talking, there is something about a place where the same people have lived for generations. These echoing courtyards and these solemn brown women peeping out of doors, quiet–I remember how loud a *vaquero's* spurs sounded leading our horses away. The dark *zaguán* of Moreno's house, the iron-barred *cancel* grinding open to let us into the patio–quiet; so quiet that it scared up the pigeons around the fountain. And the servant says will we have the goodness to be seated while he tells the master, and Gene sat there looking at these thick old arches and the heavy purple clouds of bougainvillea and the cedars all trimmed into shapes. Lost, that was how she looked; little and quiet and young.

Moreno, he did not make her feel at home. He looks kind of fierce when he is not jolly. He is real dark-complected and his eyes make her nervous about her legs, which her dress was modest enough when you got used to it, but certainly not long. Oh, he was polite; they always are; he smiles–that is, he shows his teeth through his beard–and bows very low; too low; there was something sarcastic about it–and says he is her servant; just introducing himself; not that Santiago Moreno is anybody's servant. Not so, Bolivia!

Why are customs stricter about women? When Jimmy used to be ignorant he could just laugh it off; but they sure did not make any allowances for Gene. They looked cross-eyed about her hat until she got nervous about it and took it off to see what was the matter with it, and you ought to have seen them lift their eyebrows about her hair being cut. In this country it means a girl has been disgraced.

Moreno takes us into the *sala,* stiff like a funeral with heavy curtains and pictures of saints and ancestors and about twenty chairs set straight around the wall, and there we sat. Myself, I do not like to sit in *salas.* Out in the *corredor* is good enough for me, where you can get some air and watch the pigeons in the patio. But Gene was a stranger and they had to treat her dignified. Polite, that is the way they are; even if they feel like poisoning you.

It got on Gene's nerves too. She jumped when Moreno clapped his hands to tell a servant to bring wine.

Jimmy, he was no help to her. He translates what she says, polite—like a native; like Santiago Moreno, Junior. I could not help thinking how he had changed since the first time I saw him in this house. He was not jolly with Moreno any more; he was respectful; that is the way native young bucks are raised to treat their father, like he was the Almighty or something. It made you kind of sick. Of course it was none of my business. I was only his partner and he was going to be Moreno's son.

You ought to have seen Gene's face when they hugged each other. Myself, I never give the *abrazo* if I can help it. I can not see any sense to hugging a full-grown man.

Well, old lady Moreno comes in—she is short and fat and powdered heavy because they like to look as white as they can—and she does not talk because she does not know anything to say. She just sits. And Gene gets more nervous trying not to notice the powder and perfume, and the señora is plumb flabbergasted about Gene's hat and legs. These women do not wear hats; they will wear a mantilla worth five hundred dollars, but they think hats are sinful vanity. You never see them outside of cities. And you would think they did not have any legs, they wear so many petticoats. They think legs are not modest.

Elena sails in, and she sure had her war paint on. I do not mean paint or powder; she did not need much because she is fairly white anyway, and mad. She floats up to Gene and bows and says, "Elena Moreno, your servant, Señorita," very polite, but her big brown eyes look more like "What is this the cat dragged in?"

Gene did not know enough to say her own name; Jimmy had to do it for her. She was so flustered that she stood up to shake hands, and it makes Elena madder because it means Gene is younger.

I reckon women are natural enemies about men. They do not trust any man with any woman under forty; they seem to think a man is plumb helpless if a woman gets after him. Yes, sir, Elena was going to show Jimmy that no shameless American girl could be prettier than she was. She sits down by her mama and folds her hands and lets her pretty head droop graceful and sorrowful, and starts talking to him out of the corner of her eyes; and I have got to admit that she did throw Gene in the shade. Elena is sure a pretty girl—these silk skirts sweeping out from her little waist, and this high graceful comb in her hair, her pretty mouth peeping out from behind her fan and her shoulders so round and smooth; they think it is all right to show the upper part of them.

Gene does not talk with her eyes; they are too straight and honest. They only show how she feels, which is that she has lost her taste for haciendas. She leans over and asks me if it is about time to beat it—meaning go home. That is the way she talks.

But of course we could not do that. You can not ride in and out of an hacienda after riding nine kilometers to get there. They would have thought we was *informal,* which is a whole lot worse than informal in English. In Spanish it means you do not care for anybody's feelings, or keep your word, or know how to act proper.

"Gene," I says, "you play the piano, don't you? Anybody that can sing like you can must play the piano. Play us a piece."

"Piano?" she says, looking around for it. She did not know it was a piano, which it is an old one, little and squarish. She got real excited about it, asking how old it was and cooing to it and touching the keys like she was afraid it would fall to pieces.

But they did not know how old it was. I reckon it had always belonged to the Morenos.

"The señorita likes it?" says Moreno, and Jimmy translates.

"I'm crazy about it!" says Gene.

"She likes it very much," says Jimmy.

"Then it is hers," says Moreno.

Polite, that is the way they are; they will offer you anything you admire; and they may think you are crazy, but they will not back out if you have got the nerve to take it. Gene, she joked a little about carrying it home under her arm, but Jimmy did not think it was funny to make fun of customs. No, sir, he was a different boy.

It had a queer tone, thin but fairly sweet. She played something real soft and solemn, like being respectful to it; and the Morenos clapped their hands, polite.

Jimmy, he did not hardly hear it. Elena, she was sure talking with her eyes. These girls can talk to a man by the hour and never say a word; yes, sir, I am not so old but what I can remember. It is enough to make a young fellow dizzy.

But all of a sudden he looks round at Gene. She was playing something different; I bet that old piano never made a noise like that before. Not loud, but kind of sly and cute; it tickled you; I can't explain. It kind of made your feet jiggle. Jimmy, he fidgets for a minute and then goes over by her and starts singing to himself.

"I'll be round to get you in the taxes, honey——"

Something like that; whatever it means, getting you in the taxes. And about dancing the two-step, and something about jolly roll blues. I ask you now!

Well, that was all right, though the Morenos did not like him to be singing English, because they do not know what it is about. But all of a sudden he kind of holds out his elbows and wiggles his shoulders–you know. I pretty near fell dead. It is a motion you can not make before a lady, let alone three of them.

"Santiago!" says Moreno, roaring at him. "Hast thou no shame?"

Gene was so surprised she stopped playing. She was not shocked or anything; I reckon she did not see him do it.

"What's all the shootin' for?" she says. "Are we in wrong?"

She did not mean shooting; at least I did not hear any. Not then.

"I pulled a little shimmy," says the kid, sheepish.

"Why not?" says Gene.

I ask you now! Of course he had not pulled anybody's shimmy; but it is not even polite to talk about. She looks around, innocent, and she sees the way the Morenos are looking. Well, sir, I did not know what to do. I was not brought up in a parlor with three ladies, all mad.

"Don Santiago," I says, "the señorita has never seen an hacienda. Have you the goodness to escort her that she may view the gardens and the stables?"

That is the way with Spanish; you talk polite, no matter how sour you feel. It would have been ridiculous if it had not been so miserable–this fool kid acting polite half the time and natural the other half. It was no pleasure being there. But they have got certain ways of doing, and that is all there is to it. They would have thought we was rude to go home before dinner. They got into the habit of feeding visitors in the days when settlements was few and far between, and they will do it yet or die.

I did not see any sign of trouble. Maybe the peons and *vaqueros* was extra quiet when we came around; I was feeling pretty sour and I did not notice. Maybe Moreno was extra proud with them; he would be; that is the way he is. You can not scare him. He has been a big man here too long.

Nobody told us about this peon being shot the day before for stealing corn. I would not have thought a thing about it anyway. You have to have servants to work a place like that, and you have to be boss or get out. I am not blaming Moreno; he treated them the only way he knew. That is the way the Spaniards have always treated them, making them build churches and be Christians, and flogging them for the good of their souls. Nobody told us about him being warned.

Gene, she thought the gardens were beautiful, which they are, and she liked the horses, which Moreno has certainly got some fine ones. She talked baby talk to Moreno's prize bull for being so old and fat and sulky; she wanted to go in his stall and pet him. She would not believe us when we told her that bull had killed four men. She thought we was joshing her, like Jimmy did about the notches in his gun. That is the way with girls; they are raised peaceable and they do not realize. The wonder is that they are so spunky when hell begins to pop.

VII

Well, sir, I know it is not polite to talk English and then laugh; but what is the use of being miserable when you can find some little thing that is funny? I am not blaming Elena for being mad. It must have been a strain to sit by Gene and be polite to her when she felt like choking her; high-strung, that is the way she is; and Jimmy, he hardly noticed Elena all during dinner. Him and me got tickled about Gene.

Gene, she did not know the name of anything she ate, but she was going to be polite or bust. She was a wonder, that kid. She is not very big and you know how native dinners are; thin soup and then thick soup and then *fideos;* venison and then beef and then turkey *mole,* all with more vegetables than you can shake a stick at, topped off with beans and dessert and coffee and wine. And every time she stops eating, Moreno, he says, polite, that he is afraid she does not like it, and Jimmy translates and she eats it to be polite.

She did not know you are supposed to say it is delicious but you have not got any appetite. And we did not tell her. It was a low-down trick; but we got tickled, watching her.

"Five dollars she makes it and lives!" I says to Jimmy, nudging him in the ribs and whispering, which of course we was sitting on one side of the table and the girls on the other.

He took the bet. I admit it did not look possible, but I still believe I would have won if it had not been for the turkey *mole*. She took a good big bite of it to get it over with, which very likely she could not taste anything by that time anyway. But *mole* is something else again for a tenderfoot. It is not just peppery; it is like eating dynamite if you are not used to it.

"I am afraid the señorita does not like the *mole,"* says Moreno, being polite, and Jimmy kicks my shin and translates as solemn as a judge. Not that he is cruel by nature; he was more used to pepper and he did not realize.

"Tell him I'm crazy about it," says Gene, gasping for breath and drinking water and clapping her napkin to her mouth and trying manful not to cry. "Tell him anything, but give me air!"

"Don't you eat it, kid!" I says. "You have made a good game try and it is worth the money."

But Jimmy, he sees the tears running down her face and feels like a low-down pup because he has let her suffer.

"I ought to be hung!" he says, and starts to explain it to Moreno. "She is crazy–that is, she loves–that is, I mean——"

You can not think in English and talk Spanish. It does not come out right. He used the wrong word for loves; he even used the wrong word for hot; he meant peppery, *picante;* but he was so sorry for Gene that he did not hardly know what he was saying.

"I mean," he says, stuttering, "she is not crazy, she only says she is crazy–I mean she says she is not crazy——"

I reckon the Morenos thought we was all crazy. The *mole* did not taste hot to them.

"Papa," says Elena, "with permission–I can not——"

She was plumb white and her voice was trembling. She makes a motion with both hands and jumps up to leave the table, and she bumped right into the servant just as the woman was reaching for Gene's plate; and flop goes turkey and black gravy and all into Gene's lap.

That finished Gene. Elena, she was plumb paralyzed. A thing like that is just terrible to a native; they are so proud, they know how mortified they would feel if it was to happen to them when they was company, and they are just speechless to have such a thing happen in their house. But Gene, she had been polite all she could stand. She went limp in her chair and fairly whooped and laughed.

"Tell them it doesn't matter," she gasps, waving her hands like she could not get her breath. "Tell them it's all right. I'm all right. Everything's all right. Jimmy, for the love of Mike, get me out of here before I go into hysterics!"

But she was already in them. It sure did not help matters any. The Morenos, they do not laugh when they are mortified; all they could figure was that she was laughing at them or their dinner or their servant being clumsy. No, sir, it was not dignified–Jimmy running around and shaking her and begging her is she burnt or anything, and Moreno and his wife standing up to apologize, and the servant down on her knees trying to scrape the stuff out of Gene's lap. Poor Gene just laughed harder than ever.

No, sir, they do not laugh things off. They just get fighting mad; and all they know to do is blame the servant. Of course the woman was scared to talk back. She just stood and took it all like a dumb animal caught out in a storm.

So I touched Elena on the shoulder and told her to tell them it was her fault, bumping into the woman that way. Well, sir, she whirled on me like a tiger.

"You!" she says. "Who are you that you should come into this house and laugh? Who are you that you should accuse me in defense of a miserable *india?* You–the husband of one! But naturally!"

She read my funeral proper. I am not blaming her; high-strung, that is the way she is; and she was upset plenty, Jimmy paying attention to another girl and petting her and trying to make her stop laughing. Besides, what is the use of getting mad at a woman? All you can do is talk, and they can outtalk you every time. And it is so that Concha is an Indian. What is the use of getting mad about it?

"Gene," I says, "if you think you can walk now, let's be going. I reckon our company can be spared."

But Jimmy, he turns around and catches Elena by the arm.

"Be quiet!" he says, speaking quiet himself.

She tries to jerk loose, but is not strong enough. And you can tell she is glad she is not. It is a relief to her to turn loose and fight; she is Indian enough herself to want to be treated rough.

"You!" she screams at him–not calling him thou. "Who are you to reproach me? You, who have brought this shameless woman into my house!"

But of course fighting is not dignified. Jimmy, he was not hurting her; only trying to make her listen to him; but Moreno bawls at him.

"Santiago! Blockhead boy! Art thou crazy?"

Then Jimmy forgot himself. He give that girl a shake she would remember. Her head pretty near bobbed off and her comb went spinning across the floor. It was the surprise of her young life. He turned her loose and she stood there like a lamb.

"Almost!" he says, breathing hard but speaking quiet. "Am I to tolerate that my friends shall be insulted in this house? You knew the señorita was a foreigner when you asked me to bring her here, yet you have dared to look her from above to below because her customs are not the customs of the country. You dare——"

"Silence!" bawls Moreno. I reckon he could not believe his ears. "Is it thus that a son shall address a father? Is it that I shall teach thee?"

There was a minute when he looked like murder. By gum, I wish you had been there. This half-freckled, blue-eyed young son-of-a-gun standing up to Santiago Moreno and calling him down in his own house; speaking quiet but looking that fellow square in the eye.

"I am not your son," he says. "I keep my word; but I was born a foreigner and I can not remake myself in a day. I am not a child that you should humiliate me. Lay hand on me and you will see. I keep my word," he says, "but I do not tolerate that my friends shall be treated so. Elena has dared to reproach Don Luis with his wife that is an Indian. Is it that she feels shame for the Indian blood in her own veins?"

"And who are you," Elena blazes at him, "that you should dare to tell me what I dare?"

She was just aching to be treated rough—her eyes just blazing at him, daring him, her head up and her hair half down; right wild and beautiful; I can't explain. But Jimmy, he did not touch her. There was a minute when you could hear them breathing. That was when I heard people running in the patio. I remembered it afterward; I remember kind of wondering what their hurry was.

Jimmy, he makes a motion with his hands like letting go.

"Say I am nobody," he says, quiet. "Call it that. Nevertheless he is my friend. You shall unblame yourself to him."

"And if I do not?" says Elena, panting.

"I go," he says, "with God."

That is a way of saying go and not come back—never, *jamás,* not any more forever! I grabbed him by the arm.

"Well, come on, son!" I says. "Let's go!"

But you do not know that kid. Not so, Bolivia! He had give his word and he was giving them a chance to hold him to it if they wanted.

A mule is wishy-washy compared to him when he gets it into his head a thing is right. And I won't deny there had been talk about him courting Elena right in the house that way—going to see her, American fashion. She would have a hard time finding another husband around here.

I am not saying Moreno thought of that. Maybe he did; or maybe it hit his Spanish pride just right.

"Eso!" he roars. "That is the way, my Santiaguito! Thou art indeed my son! A Moreno is loyal. A Moreno does not tolerate!"

And he throws his arms around the kid, patting him on the back and calling him his little Santiago and making a fuss over him. It was enough to make you sick, which Jimmy is as big as Moreno ever thought of being. And he roars to Elena, jovial, that she has got to apologize to me and Gene, and she does it. That is, she says she is sorry and I said it was all right; not that she cared; she did not hardly look at me; she was looking at Jimmy. That is the way with proud folks, they get tame awful quick if you are prouder.

"Thou are not angry with me any more?" she whispers to him.

And he smiles to her; but he was kind of quiet and pale; listless; I can't explain.

"No," he says, "I am not angry with thee, Elena. I know it was because thou didst not understand."

Nor never would. I did not have the heart to hang around any more, and Gene's dress being ruined was a good excuse. I says with permission I will take her home. Jimmy, he says with permission he will accompany us, and the señora says we have permission, and we shook hands all round and said much pleasure, all very quiet and polite. And Moreno clapped his hands to tell the servant to tell the *corralero* to have our horses saddled.

The servant did not come. Nobody came. Moreno steps out into the patio and roars for somebody to send somebody quick. The pigeons flew up and settled down and that was all. The house was silent as the grave.

That was when I remembered people running in the patio. I says maybe something has happened; but we went outside and could not see a soul. We got clear round the chapel before we see the *administrador* coming from the outer gate. He looks at Moreno and jerks a thumb over his shoulder, half sarcastic and half joshing and half upset about it too.

"Our friend the king," he says, "in his own person."

Moreno swears and grabs a machete off a saddled horse and goes stomping out the gate. King or no king, he would not stand for any foolishness from any Indian.

VIII

This was the only time I ever saw Guatamo. Mighty few white men have. He does not get around much; he can not walk much and he will not ride a horse because the Spaniards brought them. That was what those old men had been doing down there by the ford all morning–waiting for him. Don't ask me how they knew that he was coming. How do Indians know anything? Don't ask me what he thought he was going to do about Moreno treating peons the way he did. I reckon the poor old gump did not have any more idea than a goat. Myself, I think he is kind of cracked; but it is bad business fooling with anything that a million mothers tell their children.

Myself, I do not swear he is a king. He has got gold ornaments that was never made in these days–plenty of them; they say it is the gold of Moctezuma; but he may be just a crazy old fellow that has stumbled on it and has fooled himself into believing he is descended from Guatamotzin by thinking about it fifty or a hundred years. That is how he got crippled, trying to make him tell where the gold is. The fellows that done it, they never lived to brag about it, though. These Indians are used to being kicked around themselves, but Guatamo is like Jesus Christ to them.

I would not let Jimmy and Gene go down. It was none of our business to be mixing in.

Outside the gate the ground falls away sharp down to the river. It was like a high seat at a bull ring—looking down on this crowd of peons and women and children, the big straw hats of *vaqueros* tossing here and there like chips on a pond—surging back out of Moreno's way. No, sir, Moreno was not afraid of any quantity of Indians. I remember the dust spurting under his feet, tramping down solid and savage. I remember the whacks he gave them with the flat of the machete when they did not move fast enough.

"Like slaves!" says Jimmy, breathing through his nose.

They are not slaves, of course. They are supposed to get wages; the way it works, though, is that they get credit for clothes and food, and so forth, and the master takes it out of the wages and the wages never catch up and so they can not quit. That is the old system; they are trying to do away with it, but as long as there is rich men in this country there will be peonage. They get along pretty good, at that. Only when something like this comes up you feel right sorry for them.

There was twenty or thirty little naked kids down there on their little naked knees getting Guatamo's blessing. You ought to have heard them yell when Moreno whacked their little naked behinds. Likely it was the first time he had ever noticed them, and it scared them half to death.

One of the old men holds up his right hand, solemn, and says something. It was too far to hear; but I heard Moreno bellowing all right.

"What king nor what nothing! *Hola!* Sebastian! Gonzalo! Pepe! Drive me these cattle to their stalls! I finish with this foolishness. I show them that in this *barrio* there is no king but me."

Roaring to his *sobrestantes,* his overseers, you know; proud men themselves and used to making peons step.

"Oh! Oh!" says Gene. "What is the matter? What are they fighting for?"

You could not call it fighting. Cattle he called them, and cattle they acted like. That is the difference between hacienda peons and drillers or muckers in a mine. They are not free labor, used to going where they can get the best wages. They was born working for Moreno; it is a habit with them to be afraid of him and the *sobrestantes*. When they are hit they move; the *sobrestantes* yelling and kicking them right and left, Moreno roaring and laying on with the machete. I reckon he did not care much whether he hit them with the flat or the edge. Some of them was bleeding pretty bad, stampeding past us up the hill. Naked kids crying and stumbling around like scared rabbits, and scared mothers screaming at them to run faster.

It was not pretty to watch; but we did not run. There was nowhere to run to but where the stampede was going. I just pulled Gene to one side out of the dust and waited.

Moreno comes up to us, puffing and blowing but very polite.

"Señorita," he says, "most deeply I regret if this impertinence has distressed your grace. Forgive one more moment of delay and I send your horses to you."

Then he grins and points with the machete.

"Behold," he says, "the king and all his court!"

He had not hit Guatamo or the old men; maybe it came to him that he had better not. Guatamo sitting down there by the river, only these three or four worn-out old peons left to do him honor. Only these two ignorant, half-naked young hill Indians squatting there like statues with their paddles in their hands; only the water rippling past his painted canoe like it has rippled for ten thousand years, not caring. Gene had to go down and get a look at him. But he did not give any sign of seeing us—this poor old king of slaves; this shriveled relic of a forgotten empire, sitting there, so still you could not swear he was alive, his crazy black eyes staring straight at Gene Ward and never flickering. Maybe he did not see. Maybe the white man's world goes on around him like a dream.

"Oh, lovely! Lovely!" says Gene. "But what is it? Velvet?"

She meant the cape that covered his old bones. Color—a million colors melted into one; color that shimmered and flowed when you moved, like silk that changes every way you look at it. But not glossy like silk; soft, just drinking in light and giving it back to you melted into color. I had heard of that cape but I had never seen it. I reckon it is the only one in the world to-day. Made of the skins of humming birds—the tiny jeweled ones; thousands and thousands of them; they are no bigger than the tip end of your little finger. *Huitzin* they call them because they are sacred to their god Huitzilopochtli. It means you belong to the family of the king.

But even the *huitzin* cape, even the gold could not make him look like anything but a poor old mummy; not much bigger than a ten-year-old boy, all shriveled down to nothing. Old, old as the hills he looked—the hills out yonder, never caring, as blue for white men as they had ever been for Aztec kings.

I told Gene what little I knew about him, and her eyes got very big and solemn.

"Oh!" she says, whispering. "Is this the vale of Anahuac?"

I was surprised. But it seems she had only read about it in a book—about Moctezuma—Montezuma she calls him—and Guatamotzin and the *noche triste;* the sad night, the Spaniards call it, when Cortez thought the Nahuatlecas was going to run them out in spite of all they could do.

"No," I says. "The valley of Anahuac is near a thousand miles from here. But even a cripple could travel that far in four hundred years."

That is the feeling that you get–like it was old Guatamotzin himself, alive. We kind of talked in whispers, watching him. Then our horses came. The peon that brought them sort of looks at Jimmy like he wanted to say something, but instead of saying it he goes over and kneels down in front of Guatamo. One of the old men translates what he says, and he talks loud because Guatamo is kind of deaf, it seems. And Guatamo moved for the first time since we had been watching him. He raised his head and looked up the hill with those hot, crazy black eyes of his, and made like he was going to stand up. Then he let his head drop and pulled the *huitzin* cape across his face.

"What is it?" says Jimmy, asking me.

"I don't know," I says, lying to him, which I do understand a few words of Nahua from Concha. No, she is not an Aztec; she is a Chichimec; but all the main tribes of the Nahuatlecas used to talk the same. That is what Nahuatleca means–talkers of Nahua. But they have mostly forgotten it. That is why this poor old Guatamo had to have an interpreter to talk to his own people.

"I don't know," I says, lying to the kid. "Come on," I says, "let's go!"

But he called the peon and asked him.

"Excuse, Excellency," says the man, "excuse that she spoke of you–but the *mesera*–she who had the misfortune to spill the *mole* on the dress of the señorita–she was telling us how valiantly your grace defied Don Santiago in the dining-room. And Don Santiago came upon us and heard, and he is going to have that rash woman flogged."

"Come on, kid," I says. "There ain't a thing you can do about it."

That was the difference between me and him. I hated it as much as he did, but I knew it was no use interfering and he did not care whether it was any use or not. He just showed his teeth and whirled his horse and went back up that hill like a bat out of thunder.

Well, sir, I did not know what to do. Like as not that fool kid would go bulging in there and get himself shot, the humor Moreno was in; yet here I had Gene on my hands. I looked at her. I thought she would be kind of scared and sick, but she was plain mad at me.

"Well?" she says. "Aren't you going to help him?"

"Come on!" I says. "We might as well get hung for a sheep as a lamb."

We could not go as fast as Jimmy did, because Gene would have fell off. Come to think of it, a side-saddle is a fool thing anyway. What is the sense of pretending that women have not got legs? What did the good Lord give them legs for if not to use?

I took her by Moreno's house and yelled to her to go in there and stay there. Did you ever see a human whipped? I hope you never do. It is no way to treat a dumb brute, let alone a man or a woman born to walk upright on two legs. They do not do it much these days; only when they want to put the fear of God into them. I reckon Moreno was just crazy mad that day.

I did not see the start of it. I see this crowd of peons in this corral, and this woman with her hands tied up to a post, and Jimmy's horse dancing loose and Jimmy and this *sobrestante* rolling on the ground. I lit running with my gun in my hand. I was not going to interfere if the fight was fair, but these people do not know how to fight fair. A knife or a gun is all they know.

Wham! goes Jimmy's fist on the *sobrestante's* jaw. The rest of it happened quick as a gun flash; quicker than that, because I did not have time to shoot. Moreno and three or four *sobrestantes* was standing there with guns to keep the peons in order while they got their lesson. But one of the *sobrestantes* whirls to take a crack at Jimmy's head with his gun barrel. A man jumps between us and then there is men all over them.

I kept yanking men by the back of the neck, hauling them off and yelling to Jimmy to come out of that mess. I see a knife sticking out of the back of a khaki coat, and I felt pretty sick because I thought it was him; but it was only the *sobrestante.* Then I hear the kid yelling somewhere.

"Gene! Gene! For God's sake, beat it out of here!"

I might have known that girl would not stay put. She was right there, hopping up and down and shaking Jimmy by the arm.

"Are you hurt? Jimmy! Are you hurt? Are you hurt?"

"Not yet!" says Jimmy, and fairly snatched her feet off the ground.

Moreno went by us; I did not have any idea that fellow could run so fast; but that corral was no place for bosses now. He had nothing to depend on but his *sobrestantes,* and he was losing them rapid. The air was full of machetes, which a machete is something you can lay your hand on any time around an hacienda; it is a tool and a first-class thing to fight with, heavy and sharp and long.

It was no place for me either. My skin is fairly white and they are not taking time to ask me was my grandpa American or Spanish. I know I did not ask who it was when a machete knocked my hat off; I just turned around and shot him and kept going. I remember the whow! whow! of two shots echoing hollow in the *zaguán* of Moreno's house, and Jimmy shoving out a fellow that toppled right on my heels. Then the big wooden doors boomed shut and we were inside, Jimmy and Gene and me and Moreno coughing with powder smoke and asking each other if we were hurt or anything; Elena and the *administrador* and old lady Moreno screeching at us through the bars of the *cancel.*

"Santiago! Santiaguito! *Por dios,* what happens?"

IX

Reach me that bottle over there, will you? I have not talked so much since old Heck was a pup. Usually there is some white man by here every day or so; but it is just my luck that nobody has happened along since this thing broke; and it is pretty lonesome sitting here by myself and thinking. And it is no use talking about it to Concha. All she sees is that Jimmy is gone, and the Morenos are gone, and she can not see anything funny about getting shot behind the ear. She thinks I am drunk because I keep feeling the place and grinning to myself; but I am just thinking how those Indians could not have got in the house if they had not plugged me. I am not kicking. It serves me right for getting old and careless and forgetting that a man can climb a tree.

Drink hearty! Where did I leave off?

Well, there we were. They could not burn the house down because it was adobe. They could have busted the outer *zaguán* doors with a log or something, but the inner door would stop them and we could shoot them through the bars. They could not pull the bars off the windows without getting in front of them. They did try to come at us over the roof–you know how these houses are, a hollow square around the patio–but we heard the ladder going up and me and Jimmy climbed up on the roof and shot the first head that showed, and reached over and threw the ladder down, and got nothing but a few chips of tile in our faces. They are not very good at shooting quick.

But there we were. They could not get in and we could not get out.

"We must get word to the *rurales,*" says Moreno, down in the patio watching for somebody to try to bust in a window or a door.

I had to laugh. Up there on the roof I could see the basin spread out empty to the rim of hills; only a few trails of dust where the *vaqueros* had galloped in to help smoke us out, and a few specks of peons hoofing it home; it was as good as a holiday to them.

The nearest *rurales* was at Hosto, fifteen kilometers the other side of there. And their *comandante* was no mind reader. Not so, Bolivia! He is a fat fellow named Nuñez, and all he thinks about is eating and politics, which he had got his job out of the last revolution.

All we could hope for was that word of the trouble would reach Hosto somehow. All we could do was hold out as long as we could. By daylight it was easy; or ought to have been. All we had to do was keep them from climbing on to the roof or sniping us from other roofs; they tried that, but we discouraged them. The other roofs was lower and we could see them easier than they could see us.

But it got awful dull. You can talk about your terrible fixes, but a thing like that is tedious. I reckon it was duller down in the patio. First thing I knew, Gene came scrambling up the vine trellis like a monkey, and I did not have the heart to send her down.

"How come you are not scared?" I says to her.

"I am," says she.

"You sure don't look it," I says, which she has lost her hat, and her short hair is flying up cute, and her gray eyes steady, and her face—I can't explain. Young. That is it. She sits there on the coping and looks a long time off to the hills before she answers.

"I am afraid," she says. "Men—the hates of men——" And she looks at me. "But there is something," she says, "out here. Maybe it is the hills. I'm city bred. I never felt the earth so wide. So big and strong and real. Eternal and infinitely calm. It—it makes panic—an impertinence. It makes a life seem little, and life seem infinitely more. Does that mean anything to you?"

You think it over. She could talk sense as plain as anybody when she tried.

Well, I got careless, sitting there talking, and listening to her and Jimmy. I kept an eye on the roofs, of course; but nothing happened, only the sun went down; and I got careless. I never thought about that big bushy tree sticking up behind the stables, not fifty yards away. And finally a man crawls up into it with a rifle that must have been made in the spring of 'seventy-three, and gets a good rest and takes his time and spatters about half a pound of lead on my thick skull.

It seems I rolled off into the patio and fell on the *administrador* and pretty near broke his back. Gene, she comes flying down to see if I am killed or anything, and Jimmy lies down on the roof and starts shooting up that tree; but a young fellow can not think of two things at once. They got a ladder up and jumped on him from behind. They could have knifed him right then; but Indians have got their own way of figuring.

Well, sir, Moreno and the *administrador* gave up. I am not blaming them; they was caught. They would only have got themselves killed fighting, and the women too. They thought I was dead. I thought so, too, till finally my head started to ache something terrible.

The patio was full of Indians. I thought I had gone half blind; I did not realize that I had been unconscious and it was nearly dark. I hear old Guatamo talking, his voice thin and slow, and I see him perched on the edge of the fountain, a few pigeons flapping around and scolding him. King or no king, they did not like him to be sitting there. I did not know enough Nahua to follow what he said; but pretty soon one of the old men starts translating. He was reading Moreno's funeral all the way from Cortez clear down to Porfirio Diaz, blaming him for all that the Spaniards have ever done to them.

I could not see very well for legs and the dusk and my head aching, and I thought I had better keep still till I could figure what to do. This old man is standing right by me. Then I see Moreno all trussed up like a turkey to be roasted, but I could not see Jimmy or Gene anywhere. And I felt pretty sick. I could not help thinking what on earth would I tell Gene's papa when he got back.

"Make ready!" says the old man, solemn.

And they lay Moreno back over a stone bench and tear his shirt open; you know, to cut his heart out. Well, sir, the white man does not live that can stand it. I reached out and grabbed that old hellion's legs from under him. At the same time I hear Jimmy yelling; and I am telling you they could not hold me down. I hit the floor all right, but I came bucking up with Indians all over me. I did not know there was that many Indians in the world.

"How are you getting along?" I yells. "Where's Gene?"

"Right here!" yells Jimmy, bumping up and down like me. But they did not seem to want to knife us. I wondered why.

And then somebody roars, "Hands up!" and there is a commotion right.

The *rurales* had came at last. This fellow Nuñez–this fat *comandante* –his voice is kind of rough and loud, but it was not half rough enough or loud enough to suit me.

I yells, "Hands up! The *rurales!* The *rurales!*" for fear they might not notice it. And I put my hands up, and the Indians that was wrastling with me put theirs up, and pretty soon everybody had them up but Moreno and Jimmy and the ladies, which theirs was tied behind them. Yes, sir, it looked like we was saved. Moreno rolls off the bench and gets up and hops–did you ever see a man try to walk with his feet tied?–and falls down and puts his face on the *comandante's* foot, half crying, he was so grateful.

Nuñez, he just looked down at him and laughed. These *rurales* are a tough bunch and trouble is what they live on. They are good fighters, but it is sure no use expecting them to be sorry for anybody.

"Hoh-hoh-ho!" he roars. "The fine Señor Don Santiago Moreno, he has changed from what his custom is. He does not seem so *orgulloso,* so proud as I have seen him other times. How does it seem to you, boys?" he says, and the *rurales* crowded around and laughed at Moreno squirming on the floor.

But I was busy untying Jimmy and did not pay much attention till I heard Nuñez roar out an order, very military.

"Stand him up! Santiago Moreno," he says, trying to make it sound legal, "in the name of the revolution and the President of the Republic of Mexico I confiscate your estates! Squad Number One! Bring lanterns, torches, anything. Squad Number Two! Take me this *científico* out and shoot him!"

Científicos, that is what they call the men that sided with Porfirio Diaz in the old days–mostly rich men and mostly Spanish. Most of them are dead or chased out of the country now–like the Terrazas family that used to own pretty near the whole state of Chihuahua; young Terrazas murdered and old Terrazas in Spain and the politicians dividing up his land. But this is an out-of-the-way place. The big politicians never paid much attention to it and the little politicians had never had the nerve to tackle Santiago Moreno.

It hits this Nuñez like an inspiration. Nuñez, he is not a Spaniard and he is not an Indian; he is a revolutionary and a politician, and all he thinks about is eating and playing both ends against the middle. He does not care a thing about Guatamo or the Nahuatlecas, but he is right tickled to realize that they have got Moreno treed for him. It comes to him that he is a made man.

X

It hits Moreno different. I felt right sorry for him; I turned around and grabbed Nuñez by the arm.

"Captain," I says, "don't shoot him. Tell him he has got to get out of the country or something. He has had enough trouble without getting shot."

"Squad Number Three!" says Nuñez. "Shoot this gringo too!"

Well, sir, you can not realize that you are going to be shot. Some other fellow, yes; you have seen other fellows dead; but you have always been alive, far as you know, and you have not got much to go by. But I did not make a fuss because I did not want Jimmy and Gene to get messed up in it. I started to walk out; but Jimmy had heard. He could not believe it any more than I did.

"*Señor comandante!*" he says. "Are you crazy? You can't do this!"

"Who says I can't?" says Nuñez, haughty.

"I do!" says Jimmy. What else could he say? "Don Luis is an American!"

"I have shot a hundred Americans," says Nuñez. "Who are you that I should hesitate to shoot you too?"

That is not so, of course. There has not been much more than two hundred Americans killed altogether, and of course he did not kill half of them himself. But there has been plenty of them killed, and durn little ever done about it. Jimmy and me and Gene would only be two or three more.

"Who, me?" says Jimmy. That was not bluff; he was surprised.

"You," says Nuñez. "And why not? Who are you?"

Jimmy, he looks at him a minute. By gum, I wish you could have seen that boy! Smiling and yet not smiling; proud; I can't explain. He was plumb tired of being asked who he was in that tone of voice.

"If you must know," he says, "I am the grandson of old man Brown."

"Brah-oon?" says Nuñez.

"Himself," says Jimmy.

"Exactly!" I answers. "That's who he is. The grandson of old man Brown himself. You mean to tell me you did not know?"

Well, sir, this Nuñez scratched his head. In this country you do not brag about your grandpa unless he is somebody. In Spanish the same as in English, "old man" can mean old man or it can mean the boss. Far as he knew, old man Brown could be the President of the United States; or the Secretary of War; or anybody. And he did not like the quiet way the kid said it, like it was a joke on somebody; Nuñez sure did not want it to be on him.

"Who is the old man Brah-oon?"

"Why," says Jimmy, "my grandfather."

"And Don Santiago is to be the young Señor Brown's father-in-law!" I says. "You had better order him brought back here quick. Do you want the responsibility of shooting the father-in-law of the grandson of old man Brown?"

I wish you had been there. Jimmy, he sees he has got Nuñez going; he just looks him in the eye

"Quick!" I says. "The young señor does not care about the estate; you can have it. If you wish, he will engage that Don Santiago shall leave the country. But his execution is a thing he will not forgive."

"Quick!" says Jimmy.

Nuñez did not know what to do. Exile sounds pretty legal to him, and shooting is a thing he knows all about. But when a man is dead and you wish he was not, there is mighty little you can do about it.

"Can your grace promise that he will go?"

"Bring him here," says Jimmy, "and you will see."

Quiet and confident he says it, looking that fellow in the eye. That is a thing the natives never will understand about a bluff. They know the word from the boys playing poker around here, but they never will know what it means. They think it is just a smart trick; just wind. No, sir, a good bluff is more than just fooling the other fellow about the cards in your hand. It is playing what is in you against what is in him.

If Jimmy had not felt the way he did he could not have made it stick. He was the grandson of old man Brown and he was not ashamed of it if he was going to be shot the next minute. And when he saw he had this *comandante* going, he had the nerve to play the hand out without batting an eye.

Drink hearty! The way I look at it, if the stuff is in you, it does not matter where you got it. If not, all the grandpas in the world will not make you different. How do you feel about it?

Huh? Did Moreno promise? You try it some time. Stand up against a wall and look a few rifles in the eye and listen for the word to fire. You will be in the humor to promise anything.

It did not strike me so funny at the time, but riding home that night I had to laugh. The *rurales* camped right there in the patio, which they was not going to let Moreno out of their sight until he was gone; and we went into the *comedor* for a cup of chocolate, because we needed a little something to calm us down. And you ought to have seen them act respectful to that kid.

"Where do you go?" I says, polite. "To Spain?"

"Say yes, papa!" Elena begs him. "To Spain, papa! To Spain!"

She has been raised to think it is the greatest country in the world. Well, maybe it is—for them. Their kinfolks live there. A good many of their friends have been chased there. And in Spain you can find proud names behind every bush.

"Perhaps," says Moreno, and speaks to Jimmy in a low voice for fear the *rurales* will hear. "Why hast thou not told us, Santiago, that thy grandfather is of importance in the United States?"

Jimmy was looking kind of listless and worn out. "He was not of importance," he says, quiet. "He was a carpenter."

"A—carpenter!" says old lady Moreno. "An architect, perhaps?"

"A carpenter. A worker with his hands. Nor more nor less."

"But thou hast said to this creature Nuñez——"

"That he was my grandfather."

"But the manner of thy saying it!" says Elena. "So *orgulloso!* Proud!"

"A joke," says Jimmy. "A jest."

But it was no joke to them. They was plumb cross-eyed for fear the *rurales* would find it out; and how could the grandson of a carpenter protect them?

Jimmy, he sits and looks at them. All of a sudden he kind of kicks me under the table. There is a kind of a look in his face; solemn; I can't explain.

"I am ashamed that I have not told you all," he says. "It is your right to know. My grandfather was a carpenter; my father was a vender of groceries—"

"Groceries!" says Elena, which in this country a grocer is not much.

"—and I myself have served at menial tasks. I have served table, I have been an assistant to a laundry—"

I could have yelled out loud. That durn kid looking down like he was ashamed!

"And my mother," he says, "was a sewing woman. My fortunes go with yours if it is your wish–even to Spain; even to the ends of the—"

"Your fortunes!" says Moreno. "It is perhaps your fortune that you seek! Bloff," he says, which bluff is a word they know– "you *Yanquis* and your bloff! Very nearly it has obtained you fortune and an honorable name!"

"But I confess it now," says Jimmy, humble. "And in Spain there would be few to know, to cast dishonor on your name; only the chance that some man whom I served–it shall be for Elena to say."

"You forget," says Moreno, "that it is I who order in this house!"

He was afraid to trust Elena; but he need not have been. Gene, she could not figure what was happening until then. She looks at me, and I had to look away for fear I would laugh out loud.

"The gate, Jimmy?" she says.

"The air," says Jimmy. "Through with your chocolate? Let's go."

"Amen!" says she. That was the way they talked–no sense to it; but they both seemed to know what they meant.

I kept my face straight until I got outside; but riding home I had to laugh. I laughed so loud that Jimmy and Gene thought I was getting feverish with my head. But not so, Bolivia! I was just thinking. Spaniards and Americans and Indians and Chinamen–every one of them thinks he is better than the others; but the fact is, they are just different. Not only their skins but clear to the backbone. You can change your habits and you can change your name, but you can not change what is in you. What is the use of arguing which is better?

Yes, Jimmy, he was right worried about my head. Next day Ward came back from Siete Minas, and Jimmy asked me, anxious, if I could get along all right while he took Ward and Gene to the railroad at Orendain. And then I reckon he decided the railroad was dangerous, too, because a couple of days after that a fellow rode over with a telegram Jimmy had sent from Guadalajara, asking me if my head was all right and saying he was going to run up to the States to buy that machinery I had been trying to get him to buy. But he did not tell me where I could send him a telegram not to go.

That was two-three weeks ago. Then to-day I get another telegram. Wait till I strike a match. I have pretty near wore it out reading it.

"Have been too busy to buy machinery. Married to-day. Will buy machinery on wedding trip. Prepare to extend operations. Ward financing purchase of machinery for one-third interest. Wire your approval care of Hotel Windsor, New York. Look for us home when you see us coming. Grade place for building house. Gene says tell Concha she is a sweet old thing. Love to you both from Mr. and Mrs. James T. Brown."

I do not care what he does with the mine; he can give it to Ward if he wants to; all I want is to hear him joshing people around here. It is pretty lonesome when you get used to having a young fellow around. And if he has simply got to get married it might as well be Gene. She is not much like a woman anyway. There is some sense to a girl like that. She has got backbone. And the biggest thing is something I bet you will think is a little thing. They like the same kind of jokes. They will not get lonesome because they are good friends with each other. Jimmy, he will not have to be telling her she is more beautiful than the stars in the heavens, and she will not have to be telling him he is the bravest, handsomest man in the world. Not so, Bolivia! He will just say to her, "You are the barber-shop kid," and she will say to him, "That is the boy!" And when they have troubles they can josh each other out of them. Yes, and their kids will be husky young gringos and have blue eyes and more freckles than a guinea egg, and they will call me grandpa or I will tan their bright young hides for them. It is as good a name as any man could want.

That telegram was a day and a half getting here. So to-day I have been trying to make up for lost time, celebrating. But it is kind of lonesome celebrating by yourself; I am sure glad you came along. Drink hearty to the grandson and granddaughter-in-law of old man Brown!

Huh? Oh, Concha feels good about it all right. I showed her the words where Gene said she was a sweet old thing, and she was so tickled she bust right out crying. But it is no use explaining to her about Jimmy's grandpa. She would say that Jimmy is all right even if his grandpa was a carpenter, and I am afraid to try to explain that it is a joke. I am afraid that she might think it is on her.

The Pieces of a Fan **Vincent Sheean**

Vincent Sheean has devoted himself in recent years to biographical work and has won himself wide acclaim. Among his best-known books are *A Life of Gandhi* and, more recently, *Dorothy and Red,* the story of Dorothy Thompson and Sinclair Lewis. They were both close friends of his, so that he has told their story, in and out of matrimony, with warmth and affection as well as candor and a faithful adherence to the truth.

But it should not be forgotten that he began his literary career as a writer of short stories. One of his best stories has been selected for this book because it has an historical background and adds to the variety so essential in any collection of this kind. It deals with a day in French history when the storm clouds, presaging the coming of the revolution and the Terror, were visible to discerning eyes—but not to those of the King or his charming companion, Madame Pompadour.

THE PIECES OF A FAN

Vincent Sheean

The whole fan was made of ivory, the fan part containing about three times as many leaves of the delicately carved stuff as the seven sticks at the base. It was this that made the thing so impossible to repair. Once broken, it had to remain broken, although its loveliness, even in fragments, made it worth preserving. Consequently they laid the pieces together closely, in the shape the fan originally wore, and when it was spread like that on a smooth piece of blue velvet it took a keen eye to detect the lines that shattered it. There was a neat and usual glass case over it, of course, in the lower left-hand corner of which was stuck a label reading:

> FAN. *Probably by Welkoeckt or Saumier, about 1753. Was the property of the Marquise de Pompadour and was kept by her until her death in this broken state. When she broke it and why she kept it are not known. Observe the lacelike fragility of the carving between the sticks.*

The room in which this case stood was given over to pictures, furniture and curiosities of the same period—several portraits, works by Nattier and Boucher, miniatures, *tabatières* and whole showcases full of the little jeweled toys of Versailles. In one corner, in an oblong case, lay the crumbling frills of a parasol, with a barometer in its ivory handle. This, too, had belonged to the Marquise de Pompadour and represented the lady in her more rustic moods, when she had taken the air on the terraces of Bellevue. In the middle of the wall, over the fan, were a pair of crossed rapiers, as elegant and improbable as the fan itself. The whole house was musty and dim, filled with the still, shrouded air of an unfrequented museum, and in fact it was too far off the tourist's usual lines to be much visited, even if it had not cost ten francs for the ticket of admission. These ten francs, in the view of the custodian, were responsible for the failure of the museum as a museum; at some lower tariff, such as two francs fifty or even four francs, crowds of visitors would have paid to see the fans and snuffboxes of the red-heeled gentry who had preceded them to dust.

This was possible. At any rate, on the day when Norton went to see the place there was nobody else there—nobody, that is, but the plaintive custodian, who talked too much and had to be tipped heavily to be still. Norton's imagination did not people the house with ghosts, for he was not excessively familiar with eighteenth-century gewgaws or the events they hung upon. He is a banker with an orderly mind, and was conscious chiefly of a feeling of wonder at the extraordinary useless expenditure represented by these fragile splendors. Still, the broken fan fascinated him. He lingered over it for a long time, trying to follow the lines of its breakage and wondering how it had been possible in the first place to work a material—even ivory—into such an intricate cobweb. He was good at sketching, and the whim seized him to make a little drawing of the thing on one leaf of his pocket notebook. He tried to indicate in this sketch how the fan had been broken originally, and succeeded to his own satisfaction, although even so he could not for the life of him imagine how the break had occurred. It was not broken but shattered, and had been put together again with astonishing skill and patience. It was shattered as if it had been thrown with violence against a stone; deliberately, that is, and with intent to shatter it.

When Norton got back to his hotel in Paris he had a dream about that fan. It was a remarkable dream in that nothing whatever happened in it. He simply saw the fan come together, all of its pieces, rise fan-shaped in the air against some kind of grayish background and grow. That was all, but that was enough, for it grew and grew and grew until it seemed to fill every inch of space in the world, and whole armies could have passed between its sticks. The design of the ivory lacework came out with terrible enormity, and the whole thing grew so fast that he could see its smallest details actually enlarging. It was still growing—against the flat impossibility of growing any more, since there was no more space—when he woke up, shaking with terror. It had the effect on him of the most gruesome nightmare.

He held off for two or three days, but at last he returned to the old house out at Marly and made another sketch. He was at a loss to explain the fascination of the fan, but there seemed to him something that demanded an answer in it. A fan was only a fan, and this one had been broken into bits a hundred and seventy-five years or so ago. Why, then, did its mere appearance in a dream—growing, to be sure, but only growing—have such a disastrous effect upon his nerves and imagination?

He would not have been so exercised over the matter if he had had other things to occupy his time and mind, but he happened to be alone in Paris for six weeks, and he was past the age for easy amusements; the shattered fan in the old house at Marly spread itself across a providential emptiness. He did not have the same dream again, exactly, but twice the fan figured vaguely in his sleeping hallucinations–so vaguely that he could not remember just how when he woke up. But each time, although the dream was not to be recalled, the effects were the same as before: he was shaking with the most unreasonable terror. The whole thing was so absurd that he could have shaken it off with a laugh if he had been at home, at work, engaged in the ordinary routine of a very ordinary life. Here, in enforced idleness and deliberate solitude, it came to be a preoccupation. He got a number of books on the period of that fan and began to read about it, not lightly, not for amusement or learning, but as busily as a dog digging for a bone, a detective burrowing for a clue. The figures of the age began to exist for him and move incongruously about the corridors of his modern, comfortable hotel: the cold, haughty, hypocritical Choiseul, the Duc de Richelieu, red heeled and scented, and the gruff old Maréchal de Noailles; the soft little Abbé de Bernis, kind and fearful; Luynes, forever washing his hands of the sins of the world; and centrally, the very heart of Versailles, Mme de Pompadour, to whom the fan had once belonged, and who had kept it, for unknown reasons, after it had been broken to bits. These, and the fat, secretive, treacherous king, a sheaf of letters and a regiment of court ladies, the fierce Archbishop of Paris in his unceasing wrath, the Jesuits coming and going, the angry and conspiratorial Parlement of lawyers, associated into a world that became more real for him, after two or three weeks, than the desultory, half-noticed meals and walks which constituted his own existence just then.

One day when he had been walking for a little longer than usual he came back to his hotel quite tired and sat down to have a drink in the deserted bar. It was not the right hour for drinking–it was too early, or too late, for the hordes that frequented the place–but there was a barman on duty to give Norton a double whisky and soda. The little room was only half lighted; the barman down at the end was seated on a stool, working a crossword puzzle; the chairs and tables were undisturbed by human beings. There, in that half-light, the whisky combined with fatigue to send Norton into a half sleep. He says he was at no time fully asleep, or so he believes. But in that state, whatever it was, and in that silent, dim, stale-smelling place, he saw the fan for the last time, saw it whole and saw it broken, and–this is the wonder–neither feared nor forgot what he had seen, but remembered and no longer cared.

It rose before him exactly as it had done when he had first dreamed of it. In the beginning it was lying flat in its glass case; then there was no glass case there, and the fan rose of itself on its base and grew, spread, enlarged. Norton could see each turn and twist of its exquisite carving grow huge and heavy as it grew; it assumed a marmoreal, architectural heaviness; the sticks were pillars and the ivory lacework of the fan part hung like great marble chains. It grew until there was nothing to be seen anywhere but the fan. But this time there came a moment at which it stopped growing: it was arrested for one monstrously beautiful moment in the air, and then quivered and was rent and whipped apart into nothing. It did not dissolve or vanish in any appropriately gentle fashion, Norton says—it was mightily racked and slashed apart into a million pieces which hurled themselves into farthest space and were seen no more. What Norton now looked at was a small room with woodwork and chairs and tables of a style he had learned to recognize. There was a fire sputtering away cheerfully in the elaborate little fireplace and a woman writing at the desk beside it. Without the slightest difficulty he could read what she was writing. Odder still, although she wrote it in French he could read it in English. He knew the room and its occupant. It was the red lacquer cabinet of Mme de Pompadour.

Jeannette Poisson, Marquise de Pompadour, 1753.

According to the best authorities this lady, although as individual a phenomenon as the age displayed, was a social phenomenon as well. As De Nolhac says, if she had not existed somebody else very much like her would have taken her place. In an age of rapid social disintegration the caste framework of Versailles had grown too brittle to resist; women of the Paris bourgeoisie were a rising tide to be succeeded, in their turn, by women of a still lower order; Jeannette Poisson, invading Versailles with a mask on her pretty, acquisitive face, was a kind of drum major, and, not in her origins or her morals, but in her mere progression from the town to the palace, constituted an attack upon the fortress of the past.

Jeannette Poisson, Marquise de Pompadour, 1753.

The room was silent except for the crackling of the fire and the pen. The lady was dressed in pale blue silk brocade, which deepened the blue of her eyes and enhanced the delicacy of her lovely, enameled face. She was now thirty-two, and marked her sense of increased age and dignity (for she had an official position, now, too, and could hand a towel to the queen on Holy Thursday, as well as sitting down on a tabouret at evening courts, like the duchesses) by greater decorum in dress: the blue brocade went almost to the neck, where it was lost in a confusion of lace like the lace which fell over her forearm. She wrote fluently, without pausing for words; hers was an educated mind, and she had much frequented the company of the philosophers. She was writing to Choiseul, her ambassador–the king's ambassador, but in fact her own–to the Pope. She was in fact rapping the Pope over the knuckles, and not too gently, for his reluctance to do as she wished in matters concerning the Jesuits and the Parlement.

"If the Holy Father has forgotten his history," she wrote, "remind him of the Thirty Years' War."

She pursued this letter, one of her best efforts, to its spirited termination, and then rang a bell on the desk.

"Let them come in now," she said without looking up. She was ranging the letters on her desk–this for the ordinary post, that for the diplomatic courier–when the door in the red lacquer wall opened to admit the Abbé de Bernis.

He was a small, soft, anxious man with a deprecating, thoughtful way about him, and the marquise gave him her hand to kiss almost without attention. Bernis had ceased to command her attention a long time ago; she had learned what he had to teach her and treated him carelessly now, with none of the mixed deference and coquetry she habitually used in her talk with other ministers. He had no sense of power except through her, and it was his anxious consciousness of her will that made him hesitate to make any statement definite.

At present he was faced with a difficulty more obscure and incomprehensible than even the difficulties of war and peace, the question of the Jesuits or the alliance with Austria. All of those could be treated by Bernis and his marquise with a certain amount of frankness, but there was one point upon which no frankness was possible. The calamities of the French arms in Canada, in India, in Germany, the loss of the greater part of the navy, the crumbling of what had been a world empire–all of which Norton knew about in a static, coexistent way, as we know events of the past in their totality without respect to the order of their occurrence–were referred to in this conversation under their most immediate aspects: a British flotilla had captured a French fort, a French general had been beaten and died. Norton never could remember exactly what was said on these points. The whole thing had the imprecise but positive effect of a scene played out in a dream; it happened as a whole, but it was impossible to tell what its details were; no doubt some of the events to which reference seemed to be made had not yet occurred, and others, no doubt, had occurred too long ago to be rationally the subject of talk between the marquise and the foreign minister. This telescopic and anachronistic quality, tissuelike but vague, gave the thing its essential unreality and thus enabled Norton to contend, as he did afterwards contend when he told me about it, that he was constantly aware of the barman invisibly working out crossword puzzles behind the appearance of the red lacquer cabinet. The red lacquer cabinet was superimposed upon present realities and made them invisible, but did not in consequence acquire the space-and-time solidity of actual chronological events. Thus the marquise spoke of the fall of Louisburg as if it had just occurred, whereas even Norton was aware, having been informed by the fan of the date, that it had not yet taken place. The marquise was tearful over Canada, agitated over Germany, and trembled with indignation against the States of Holland. At one point she rose and went to the map unrolled on a table in the middle of the room. From her writing desk she took a small gilt box containing tiny black patches for the face—*mouches de toilette*. She stuck these onto the map at strategic points, as a general sticks flags, to impress upon Bernis the military necessities of the situation.

"These," she said, "we cannot afford to lose."

When the talk turned upon the threatened provinces in the east of France she took her fan from a chair beside her and gesticulated at Bernis with it. Here it was that Norton saw the fan, in its ordinary shape and size, intact, for the first time.

"If that wretch Richelieu keeps on retreating," said the marquise, "we shall lose Alsace and Lorraine and the Franche-Comté."

She counted the provinces on the sticks of her fan, pointing a long, exquisite finger at each stick and frowning with concentration.

"It is possible," Bernis said, "that the marshal has no choice. His army is without food, ammunition or shoes."

"Nonsense," said the marquise, snapping her fan together with decision. "It is impossible. Send for Paris-Duverney. Send for his brother. It is their business to see that the army is supplied."

Bernis coughed deferentially. He knew (and Norton knew much better, having read the works of authors on the subject, whereas Bernis only knew the facts) that the Paris brothers supplied their own necessities first and those of the marquise, the requirements of the army coming far behind. But any protest more violent than a cough was beyond the abbé's powers. Even the cough was interpreted amiss by the lady, and she shook her ivory fan at him fiercely.

"Richelieu," she said, "is a scoundrel and our enemy. You know this as well as I do. If his army were the best equipped on earth he would still say that it had no means of fighting—this to excuse his own incompetence. I would give a great deal to get rid of Richelieu."

For a moment, as she shook her fan, Norton seemed to see, against the elaborate fireplace, the elaborately laced, painted and brocaded person of the Duc de Richelieu, snuffbox in hand, sneering in a manner worthy of his quarterings. And as this figure dissolved against the carved marble its place was taken–so rapidly that it was almost simultaneous, the impression of a moment–by men in numbers, large numbers, crawling over a hillside under a lurid illumination, their white uniforms gray with dirt and tattered into rags, their hungry faces smeared with blood. The shocking intrusion was gone in a flash, and the red lacquer cabinet was as it had been before; Norton alone had seen it; the marquise and Bernis were as intent as ever upon their high subjects of converse. It was the marquise, of course, who introduced the one subject upon which frankness between them was impossible. Bernis had thought of nothing else since the beginning, but had dutifully and fearfully waited for her to speak.

"Now," she said, tapping the fan upon one pale blue brocaded knee, "I want to know what you have done about the disgraceful pamphlets, the work of that monster in Prussia."

Bernis coughed again. From the portfolio which had rested at his feet throughout the conversation he took out a number of papers.

"I do not see how we can prevent them from appearing, madame," he said humbly. "They are printed at the Hague. We have evidence that they are written by the King of Prussia himself–in fact there is no doubt in the matter. I have brought the latest of them with me to show you if you like."

"I do not wish to see them," said the marquise grandly. She had already perused them all in secret–as Norton, of course, knew, but Bernis did not. "What I wish to know is how they are permitted to enter France, to circulate, as I hear, very freely, and to cause me to be laughed at and vilified from one end of the country to the other."

She caught her breath and added:

"And what is worse, they are said to attack the majesty of the king."

"I think not, madame," said Bernis mildly, "or at any rate only indirectly. The chief of them are concerned only with you. The King of Prussia is a vile monster and seems to have a special hatred for your youth and beauty, madame. Such things are not in nature, and we cannot fight against them."

"Let him distil his poison," said the marquise, mounting the highest of her high horses. "Let him do it at Potsdam, where they are used to it and it does not matter. But in sweet France, where hatred is unknown, such villainous rubbish should not be allowed to circulate. What are the police for? What are the frontier guards doing? The people are already deceived enough, and led away from their proper loyalties, by all these difficulties–the price of bread, the troublemaking lawyers in their infernal Parlement, the eternal archbishop–without the poison of that disgusting Frederick. When I think how he sent his stupid old ambassador here day after day to flatter me . . . Fortunately, I am immune to flattery. I knew what he was about from the beginning."

"Beauty," said the abbé mechanically, "needs no flattery."

"The man is an enemy to all humanity," said the marquise, continuing her tirade. "For two sous I would send down to Switzerland for that ape, M. de Voltaire, and see if he could not invent some calumny that would attack the Prussian as he attacks me. Except, of course, that M. de Voltaire is perhaps even worse. Disloyal and selfish—disloyalty everywhere. What are we to do, Abbé, against this universal disloyalty? Everything has changed."

She went on in this vein for some time, indulging her helpless hatred of the Prussian Frederick and his busy pamphleteering. Norton could have told her that it was no use, but his was, of course, superior knowledge. He watched her narrowly, hardly listening to what she said. He knew, as a matter of fact, that such moods were not frequent with her, for except when she was viciously attacked by the ridicule of the Potsdam inkwells, she was eminently good natured; Frederick had learned the way to upset her even temper.

Bernis intervened at last, and the marquise sat down again, her face tinged with natural color underneath its paint.

"We are taking every precaution we can possibly take, madame," he said. "The frontier guards are receiving new instructions today, and the Paris booksellers and suchlike wretches are to be visited by the police very thoroughly. If this produces no relief we shall arrest a number of responsible officials at the frontiers and in Paris, and see what discipline will do."

"Nothing unjust," said the marquise virtuously, "should be done. This is the king's constant wish. But if a little visit to the Bastille would make some of these police officers more attentive to their duty, perhaps it would be advisable. One thing is sure: the poison from Prussia must be stopped. It is responsible for half the filthy songs they sing in the streets about us. And besides, I cannot bear to think of that wizened little simulacrum of a man cackling in his lair over these wretched inventions. It is too much. It is——"

The red lacquer wall suddenly gave vent to an opening door, which had been an ordinary panel before. Norton knew that this was the door to the private staircase which led to the king's apartments, and he recognized, in the fat, magnificent figure in the door, the king himself, Louis XV. The marquise and Bernis turned towards that figure and saluted it appropriately, the marquise in a *révérence* to the floor and

Bernis with a court bow. The king raised the lady and kissed her hand without taking notice of Bernis.

"You are busy, Marquise," he said, "with affairs of state?"

His voice had that warning note of irony and contempt which nobody, throughout his life, was to hear without terror. Norton, who knew him well by now, was conscious of a slight twinge of anxiety himself, in spite of the hundred and eighty years between them.

"Indeed, no, sire," said the lady. "We were talking of the topics of the day. Your Majesty did not hunt today?"

"I have not been well," said Louis without looking at her. His fat and melancholy face was clouded over with suspicion, the secretive, discontented look that was native to it. Norton's pulse quickened with fear for the marquise (he liked the marquise, for she was very lovely) and even a little for poor Bernis.

The king did not sit down, but stood by the fireplace, fiddling with the lace of his gold-encrusted coat. The coat was green and the breeches white; over his increasing paunch there was a glittering waistcoat of yellow and gold thread. He had been dressed and scented with great care, and his face was garishly painted. His eyes refused to contemplate either of the two before him. Bernis, pretending to see in a slight movement of the royal right hand the signal of dismissal, advanced to take his leave.

"Stay here," the king told him indifferently. "I am leaving in a moment."

He paused to let this statement be well understood. Norton was conscious of an almost breathless suspense. There was no way of telling what time of day it was, but at any hour it would have been unusual for the king to descend to the red lacquer cabinet for only a moment. The marquise had lost color, and her patches of paint glistened red on her cheeks. The abbé looked at the carpet.

"I was thinking," said the king coldly, reflectively, as if on a subject of no immediate interest to anybody present, "about that staircase. It might be walled up. Yes, I think it might be walled up. I am making some changes in the apartments upstairs. The other door may well serve–ah–in future."

For a space the silence was as still and hostile as a whirr of swords. The marquise was very pale now, but she held her head very straight. It cost her an effort to speak.

"We shall meet at supper, sire, as arranged?" she asked.

The question betrayed such a consciousness of calamity that even Louis was unnerved for a moment. His frown deepened, and he twitched at his laces irritably.

"There will be no supper tonight, madame," he said. "I am not well."

He stood there for a moment, a heavy, glittering, mysterious and secretive agglomeration of humanity and upholstery, his boredom and his anger at war on his flushed face. Then he walked across to the panel again and swung it open.

"You may resume your discussion of the topics of the day," he said, and closed the door behind him.

The marquise rose from her deep courtesy and sat down at her desk with her back to Bernis. She shaded her face with her hand.

"Do you want me to go, madame?" Bernis asked. His voice was as solicitous as ever.

"Who is it, Bernis?" she asked without turning round. "Have you heard?"

Bernis pretended not to understand.

"I do not know what you mean, madame. Who . . . ?"

"Oh, there must be a girl," she said. "There must be. There have been before, I know. But it was never like this. Tell me——"

She turned round and faced him. Her courage in disaster made her eyes flash and her throat beat with pulses.

"I don't know," he said humbly. "I should tell you if I knew."

"It would be worse, Bernis, far worse, if there were no girl at all," she said. "If it were only boredom. Do you understand that, Bernis? It would be worse if it were only boredom. That is why I must know. I know about the girls. Two of them were introduced by agents of that Prussian monster. But I have heard of no woman lately. Tell me, old friend, we can speak frankly, can't we? Do you know nothing at all?"

"Nothing, madame," he said. "I do not often hear these things. You might better ask Lebel."

"I saw him today," she said, "and he mentioned nothing of the kind. I always question him particularly. I am afraid, Bernis. This–this has never happened before. This may be–the end."

"The king has no friend more devoted than you," said Bernis, "and he knows it. Even if there were, as you say, a lady, that still would make no difference to–to the friendship that–ah–unites you."

She rose and came towards him.

"Thank you, Bernis," she said, taking his hand. "Go away now. I must have time to think. This is awful. This is something that has never happened before. This hurts–here."

She indicated the position of her heart with the tip of the ivory fan. Her eyes were sparkling with tears. Bernis kissed her hand and turned to go.

"Take the papers, take the maps, take all that," she said a little wildly. "I do not want all that."

"Very well, madame," he said submissively, gathering up some of the papers. She turned her back on him and looked at the fire. He stopped, just before he left the little room, and deposited all the papers on the table again. Norton was glad to see him do this, as of course she would have more need of them than ever in the future. It was exactly what Norton would have advised him to do, but it was rather remarkable that Bernis himself had known this without being told.

The marquise was tapping her fan on her blue brocaded skirt. The tears had fallen now and were streaking her exquisite face with lines of wet black and red. Upon the tessellated marble in front of the fireplace was spread out the pattern of the last eight years for her to gaze down upon. Love, triumph and despair, the year of Fontenoy, her golden year, and the parades at Choisy and the gilded carriages at the hunt in the forest of St Germain, washed across the marble and mixed the years and the days. There was the green bower of Étioles, and there was the face of the king. She looked down through her tears for a long time, while Norton waited, knowing–and he knew exactly now–what she would do. She stared at the floor and shuddered, shuddered and stared. Perhaps she saw the rest of her life there, too, as Norton knew it, a struggle without a moment's relief; perhaps she saw only the procession of ladies at the Parc aux Cerfs and the face of the king. Whatever she saw, she could not bear it. She straightened up sharply and flung her ivory fan with all her force on the marble in front of the fire. It was shattered into bits, and as Norton stared, horrified, the red lacquer cabinet and the weeping lady were there no more, and the fan lay, yellowed and old but still in bits, carefully put together by an antiquarian hand, under the glass case with its label in one corner:

> FAN. *Probably by Welkoeckt or Saumier, about 1753. Was the property of the Marquise de Pompadour and was kept by her until her death in this broken state. When she broke it and why she kept it are not known. Observe the lacelike fragility of the carving between the sticks.*

Norton sat looking across his half-emptied glass at the dim barroom. The barman was still working crossword puzzles in the corner. Somebody turned the lights on presently, and people began to come in for their evening drinks, and Norton paid his bill and went away. He was a little ashamed of himself, and stopped at the porter's desk in the hall to order tickets for a musical comedy that night.

[illegible] of all the [illegible]

[illegible] some of the [illegible] shaped [illegible] the [illegible] the water [illegible] in the future [illegible] up [illegible] being lost [illegible]

The [illegible] her blue [illegible]. The [illegible] with [illegible] weight in [illegible] of the [illegible] down [illegible] for [illegible] the hunt [illegible] marks [illegible]

[illegible] the deck [illegible] and [illegible] now what [illegible] understand [illegible] her [illegible] was shattered [illegible] the [illegible] and the [illegible] and old [illegible]

[illegible]

[illegible]

Dawn **Elie Wiesel**

This is an almost unbearably gripping story, based on a tragic incident during the years when the people of Israel were struggling to establish themselves.

> One morning the official Jerusalem radio announced that David ben Moshe, condemned to death for terroristic activities, would be hanged. The announcement made no mention of John Dawson. But his anguished listeners knew. John Dawson, as well as David ben Moshe, would die. The Movement would keep its word.
> "Who is to kill him?" I asked Gad.
> "You are," he replied.

The story which develops out of this is tense, dramatic, and told with unusual power.

DAWN

Elie Wiesel

Somewhere a child began to cry. In the house across the way an old woman closed the shutters. It was hot with all the heat of an autumn evening in Palestine.

Standing near the window I looked out at the transparent twilight whose descent made the city seem silent, motionless, unreal, and very far away. Tomorrow, I thought for the hundredth time, I shall kill a man, and I wondered if the crying child and the woman across the way knew.

I did not know the man. To my eyes he had no face; he did not even exist, for I knew nothing about him. I did not know whether he scratched his nose when he ate, whether he talked or kept quiet when he was making love, whether he gloried in his hate, whether he betrayed his wife or his God or his own future. All I knew was that he was an Englishman and my enemy. The two terms were synonymous.

"Don't torture yourself," said Gad in a low voice. "This is war."

His words were scarcely audible, and I was tempted to tell him to speak louder, because no one could possibly hear. The child's crying covered all other sounds. But I could not open my mouth, because I was thinking of the man who was doomed to die. Tomorrow, I said to myself, we shall be bound together for all eternity by the tie that binds a victim and his executioner.

"It's getting dark," said Gad. "Shall I put on the light?"

I shook my head. The darkness was not yet complete. As yet there was no face at the window to mark the exact moment when day changed into night.

A beggar had taught me, a long time ago, how to distinguish night from day. I met him one evening in my home town when I was saying my prayers in the overheated synagogue, a gaunt, shadowy fellow, dressed in shabby black clothes, with a look in his eyes that was not of this world. It was at the beginning of the war. I was twelve years old, my parents were still alive, and God still dwelt in our town.

"Are you a stranger?" I asked him.

"I'm not from around here," he said in a voice that seemed to listen rather than speak.

Beggars inspired me with mingled feelings of love and fear. I knew that I ought to be kind to them, for they might not be what they seemed. Hassidic literature tells us that a beggar may be the prophet Elijah in disguise, come to visit the earth and the hearts of men and to offer the reward of eternal life to those that treat him well. Nor is the prophet Elijah the only one to put on the garb of a beggar. The Angel of Death delights in frightening men in the same way. To do him wrong is more dangerous; he may take a man's life or his soul in return.

And so the stranger in the synagogue inspired me with fear. I asked him if he was hungry and he said no. I tried to find out if there was anything he wanted, but without success. I had an urge to do something for him, but did not know what.

The synagogue was empty and the candles had begun to burn low. We were quite alone, and I was overcome by increasing anxiety. I knew that I shouldn't be there with him at midnight, for that is the hour when the dead rise up from their graves and come to say their prayers. Anyone they find in the synagogue risks being carried away, for fear he betray their secret.

"Come to my house," I said to the beggar. "There you can find food to eat and a bed in which to sleep."

"I never sleep," he replied.

I was quite sure then that he was not a real beggar. I told him that I had to go home and he offered to keep me company. As we walked along the snow-covered streets he asked me if I was ever afraid of the dark.

"Yes, I am," I said. I wanted to add that I was afraid of him, too, but I felt he knew that already.

"You mustn't be afraid of the dark," he said, gently grasping my arm and making me shudder. "Night is purer than day; it is better for thinking and loving and dreaming. At night everything is more intense, more true. The echo of words that have been spoken during the day takes on a new and deeper meaning. The tragedy of man is that he doesn't know how to distinguish between day and night. He says things at night that should only be said by day."

He came to a halt in front of my house. I asked him again if he didn't want to come in, but he said no, he must be on his way. That's it, I thought; he's going back to the synagogue to welcome the dead.

"Listen," he said, digging his fingers into my arm. "I'm going to teach you the art of distinguishing between day and night. Always look at a window, and failing that look into the eyes of a man. If you see a face, any face, then you can be sure that night has succeeded day. For, believe me, night has a face."

Then, without giving me time to answer, he said good-by and disappeared into the snow.

Every evening since then I had made a point of standing near a window to witness the arrival of night. And every evening I saw a face outside. It was not always the same face, for no one night was like another. In the beginning I saw the face of the beggar. Then, after my father's death, I saw his face, with the eyes grown large with death and memory. Sometimes total strangers lent the night their tearful face or their forgotten smile. I knew nothing about them except that they were dead.

"Don't torture yourself in the dark," said Gad. "This is war."

I thought of the man I was to kill at dawn, and of the beggar. Suddenly I had an absurd thought: what if the beggar were the man I was to kill?

Outside, the twilight faded abruptly away as it so often does in the Middle East. The child was still crying, it seemed to me more plaintively than before. The city was like a ghost ship, noiselessly swallowed up by the darkness.

I looked out the window, where a shadowy face was taking shape out of the deep of the night. A sharp pain caught my throat. I could not take my eyes off the face. It was my own.

An hour earlier Gad had told me the Old Man's decision. The execution was to take place, as executions always do, at dawn. His message was no surprise; like everyone else I was expecting it. Everyone in Palestine knew that the Movement always kept its word. And the English knew it too.

A month earlier one of our fighters, wounded during a terrorist operation, had been hauled in by the police and weapons had been found on him. A military tribunal had chosen to exact the penalty stipulated by martial law: death by hanging. This was the tenth death sentence the mandatory power in Palestine had imposed upon us. The Old Man decided that things had gone far enough; he was not going to allow the English to transform the Holy Land into a scaffold. And so he announced a new line of action–reprisals.

By means of posters and underground-radio broadcasts he issued a solemn warning: Do not hang David ben Moshe; his death will cost you dear. From now on, for the hanging of every Jewish fighter an English mother will mourn the death of her son. To add weight to his words the Old Man ordered us to take a hostage, preferably an army officer. Fate willed that our victim should be Captain John Dawson. He was out walking alone one night, and this made him an easy prey for our men were on the lookout for English officers who walked alone in the night.

John Dawson's kidnaping plunged the whole country into a state of nervous tension. The English army proclaimed a forty-eight-hour curfew, every house was searched, and hundreds of suspects were arrested. Tanks were stationed at the crossroads, machine guns set up on the rooftops, and barbed-wire barricades erected at the street corners. The whole of Palestine was one great prison, and within it there was another, smaller prison where the hostage was successfully hidden.

In a brief, horrifying proclamation the High Commissioner of Palestine announced that the entire population would be held responsible if His Majesty's Captain John Dawson were to be killed by the terrorists. Fear reigned, and the ugly word *pogrom* was on everyone's lips.

"Do you really think they'd do it?"

"Why not?"

"The English? Could the *English* ever organize a pogrom?"

"Why not?"

"They wouldn't dare."

"Why not?"

"World opinion wouldn't tolerate it."

"Why not? Just remember Hitler; world opinion tolerated him for quite some time."

The situation was grave. The Zionist leaders recommended prudence; they got in touch with the Old Man and begged him, for the sake of the nation, not to go too far: there was talk of vengeance, of a pogrom, and this meant that innocent men and women would have to pay.

The Old Man answered: If David ben Moshe is hanged, John Dawson must die. If the Movement were to give in the English would score a triumph. They would take it for a sign of weakness and impotence on our part, as if we were saying to them: Go ahead and hang all the young Jews who are holding out against you. No, the Movement cannot give in. Violence is the only language the English can understand. Man for man. Death for death.

Soon the whole world was alerted. The major newspapers of London, Paris, and New York headlined the story, with David ben Moshe sharing the honors, and a dozen special correspondents flew into Lydda. Once more Jerusalem was the center of the universe.

In London, John Dawson's mother paid a visit to the Colonial Office and requested a pardon for David ben Moshe, whose life was bound up with that of her son. With a grave smile the Secretary of State for Colonial Affairs told her: Have no fear. The Jews will never do it. You know how they are; they shout and cry and make a big fuss, but they are frightened by the meaning of their own words. Don't worry; your son isn't going to die.

The High Commissioner was less optimistic. He sent a cable to the Colonial Office, recommending clemency. Such a gesture, he said, would dispose world-wide public opinion in England's favor.

The Secretary personally telephoned his reply. The recommendation had been studied at a Cabinet meeting. Two members of the Cabinet had approved it, but the others said no. They alleged not only political reasons but the prestige of the Crown as well. A pardon would be interpreted as a sign of weakness; it might give ideas to young, self-styled idealists in other parts of the Empire. People would say: "In Palestine a group of terrorists has told Great Britain where to get off." And the Secretary added, on his own behalf: "We should be the laughingstock of the world. And think of the repercussions in the House of Commons. The opposition are waiting for just such a chance to sweep us away."

"So the answer is no?" asked the High Commissioner.

"It is."

"And what about John Dawson, sir?"

"They won't go through with it."

"Sir, I beg to disagree."

"You're entitled to your opinion."

A few hours later the official Jerusalem radio announced that David ben Moshe's execution would take place in the prison at Acre at dawn the next day. The condemned man's family had been authorized to pay him a farewell visit and the population was enjoined to remain calm.

After this came the other news of the day. At the United Nations a debate on Palestine was in the offing. In the Mediterranean two ships carrying illegal immigrants had been detained and the passengers taken to internment on Cyprus. An automobile accident at Natanya: one man dead, two injured. The weather forecast for the following day: warm, clear, visibility unlimited. . . . We repeat the first bulletin: David ben Moshe, condemned to death for terroristic activities, will be hanged. . . .

The announcer made no mention of John Dawson. But his anguished listeners knew. John Dawson, as well as David ben Moshe, would die. The Movement would keep its word.

"Who is to kill him?" I asked Gad.

"You are," he replied.

"Me?" I said, unable to believe my own ears.

"You," Gad repeated. "Those are the Old Man's orders."

I felt as if a fist had been thrust into my face. The earth yawned beneath my feet and I seemed to be falling into a bottomless pit, where existence was a nightmare.

"This is war," Gad was saying.

His voice sounded as if it came from very far away; I could barely hear it.

"This is war. Don't torture yourself."

"Tomorrow I shall kill a man," I said to myself, reeling in my fall. "I shall kill a man, tomorrow."

I

Elisha is my name. At the time of this story I was eighteen years old. Gad had recruited me for the Movement and brought me to Palestine. He had made me into a terrorist.

I had met Gad in Paris, where I went, straight from Buchenwald, immediately after the war. When the Americans liberated Buchenwald they offered to send me home, but I rejected the offer. I didn't want to relive my childhood, to see our house in foreign hands. I knew that my parents were dead and my native town was occupied by the Russians. What was the use of going back? "No thanks," I said; "I don't want to go home."

"Then where do you want to go?"

I said I didn't know; it didn't really matter.

After staying on for five weeks in Buchenwald I was put aboard a train for Paris. France had offered me asylum, and as soon as I reached Paris a rescue committee sent me for a month to a youth camp in Normandy.

When I came back from Normandy the same organization got me a furnished room on the rue de Marois and gave me a grant which covered my living expenses and the cost of the French lessons which I took every day of the week except Saturday and Sunday from a gentleman with a mustache whose name I have forgotten. I wanted to master the language sufficiently to sign up for a philosophy course at the Sorbonne.

The study of philosophy attracted me because I wanted to understand the meaning of the events of which I had been the victim. In the concentration camp I had cried out in sorrow and anger against God and also against man, who seemed to have inherited only the cruelty of his creator. I was anxious to re-evaluate my revolt in an atmosphere of detachment, to view it in terms of the present.

So many questions obsessed me. Where is God to be found? In suffering or in rebellion? When is a man most truly a man? When he submits or when he refuses? Where does suffering lead him? To purification or to bestiality? Philosophy, I hoped, would give me an answer. It would free me from my memories, my doubts, my feeling of guilt. It would drive them away or at least bring them out in concrete form into the light of day. My purpose was to enroll at the Sorbonne and devote myself to this endeavor.

But I did nothing of the sort, and Gad was the one who caused me to abandon my original aim. If today I am only a question mark, he is responsible.

One evening there was a knock at my door. I went to open it, wondering who it could be. I had no friends or acquaintances in Paris and spent most of the time in my room, reading a book or sitting with my hand over my eyes, thinking about the past.

"I would like to talk with you."

The man who stood in the doorway was young, tall, and slender. Wearing a raincoat, he had the appearance of a detective or an adventurer.

"Come in," I said after he had already entered.

He didn't take off his coat. Silently he walked over to the table, picked up the few books that were there, riffled their pages, and then put them down. Then he turned to me.

"I know who you are," he said. "I know everything about you."

His face was tanned, expressive. His hair was unruly, one strand perpetually on his forehead. His mouth was hard, almost cruel; thus accentuating the kindness, the intensity, and warm intelligence in his eyes.

"You are more fortunate than I, for I know very little about myself."

A smile came to his lips. "I didn't come to talk about your past."

"The future," I answered, "is of limited interest to me."

He continued to smile.

"The future," he asked, "are you attached to it?"

I felt uneasy. I didn't understand him. The meaning of his questions escaped me. Something in him set me on edge. Perhaps it was the advantage of his superior knowledge, for he knew who I was, although I didn't even know his name. He looked at me with such familiarity, such expectation, that for a moment I thought he had mistaken me for someone else, that it wasn't me he had come to see.

"Who are you?" I asked. "What do you want with me?"

"I am Gad," he said in a resonant voice, as if he were uttering some cabalistic sentence which contained an answer to every question. He said "I am Gad" in the same way that Jehovah said "I am that I am."

"Very good," I said with mingled curiosity and fear. "Your name is Gad. Happy to know you. And now that you've introduced yourself, may I ask the purpose of your call? What do you want of me?"

His piercing eyes seemed to look straight through me. After several moments of this penetrating stare he said in a quite matter-of-fact way:

"I want you to give me your future."

Having been brought up in the Hassidic tradition I had heard strange stories about the Meshulah, the mysterious messenger of fate to whom nothing is impossible. His voice is such as to make a man tremble, for the message it brings is more powerful than either the bearer or the recipient. His every word seems to come from the absolute, the infinite, and its significance is at the same time fearful and fascinating. Gad is a Meshulah, I said to myself. It was not his physical appearance that gave me this impression, but rather what he said and the way he said it.

"Who are you?" I asked again, in terror.

Something told me that at the end of the road we were to travel together I should find another man, very much like myself, whom I should hate.

"I am a messenger," he said.

I felt myself grow pale. My premonition was correct. He was a messenger, a man sent by fate, to whom I could refuse nothing. I must sacrifice everything to him, even hope, if he asked it.

"You want my future?" I asked. "What will you do with it?"

He smiled again, but in a cold, distant manner, as one who possesses a power over men.

"I'll make it into an outcry," he said, and there was a strange light in his dark eyes. "An outcry first of despair and then of hope. And finally a shout of triumph."

I sat down on my bed, offering him the only chair in the room, but he remained standing. In the Hassidic legends the messenger is always portrayed standing, as if his body must at all times serve as a connecting link between heaven and earth. Standing thus, in a trench coat which seemed as if it had never been taken off and were an integral part of his body, with his head inclined toward his right shoulder and a fiery expression in his eyes, he proceeded to tell me about the Movement.

He smoked incessantly. But even when he paused to light a cigarette he continued to stare obliquely at me and never stopped talking. He talked until dawn, and I listened with my eyes and mind wide open. Just so I had listened as a child to the grizzled master who revealed to me the mysterious universe of the Cabala, where every idea is a story and every story, even one concerned with the life of a ghost, is a spark from eternity.

That night Gad told me about Palestine and the age-old Jewish dream of recreating an independent homeland, one where every human act would be free. He told me also of the Movement's desperate struggle with the English.

"The English government has sent a hundred thousand soldiers to maintain so-called order. We of the Movement are no more than a hundred strong, but we strike fear into their hearts. Do you understand what I am saying? We cause the English–yes, the English–to tremble!" The sparks in his dark eyes lit up the fear of a hundred thousand uniformed men.

This was the first story I had ever heard in which the Jews were not the ones to be afraid. Until this moment I had believed that the mission of the Jews was to represent the trembling of history rather than the wind which made it tremble.

"The paratroopers, the police dogs, the tanks, the planes, the tommy guns, the executioners–they are all afraid. The Holy Land has become, for them, a land of fear. They don't dare walk out on the streets at night, or look a young girl in the eye for fear that she may shoot them in the belly, or stroke the head of a child for fear that he may throw a hand grenade in their face. They dare neither to speak nor to be silent. They are afraid."

Hour after hour Gad spoke to me of the blue nights of Palestine, of their calm and serene beauty. You walk out in the evening with a woman, you tell her that she is beautiful and you love her, and twenty centuries hear what you are saying. But for the English the night holds no beauty. For them every night opens and shuts like a tomb. Every night two, three, a dozen soldiers are swallowed up by the darkness and never seen again.

Then Gad told me the part he expected me to play. I was to give up everything and go with him to join the struggle. The Movement needed fresh recruits and reinforcements. It needed young men who were willing to offer it their future. The sum of their futures would be the freedom of Israel, the future of Palestine.

It was the first time that I had heard of any of these things. My parents had not been Zionists. To me Zion was a sacred ideal, a Messianic hope, a prayer, a heartbeat, but not a place on the map or a political slogan, a cause for which men killed and died.

Gad's stories were utterly fascinating. I saw in him a prince of Jewish history, a legendary messenger sent by fate to awaken my imagination, to tell the people whose past was now their religion: Come, come; the future is waiting for you with open arms. From now on you will no longer be humiliated, persecuted, or even pitied. You will not be strangers encamped in an age and a place that are not yours. Come, brothers, come!

Gad stopped talking and went to look out the window at the approaching dawn. The shadows melted away and a pale, prematurely weary light the color of stagnant water invaded my small room.

"I accept your offer," I said.

I said it so softly that Gad seemed not to hear. He remained standing by the window and after a moment of silence turned around to say:

"Here is the dawn. In our land it is very different. Here the dawn is gray; in Palestine it is red like fire."

"I accept, Gad," I repeated.

"I heard you," he said, with a smile the color of the Paris dawn. "You'll be leaving in three weeks."

The autumn breeze blowing in through the window made me shiver. Three weeks, I reflected, before I plunge into the unknown. Perhaps my shiver was caused not so much by the breeze as by this reflection. I believe that even then unconsciously I knew that at the end of the road I was to travel with Gad, a man was waiting, a man who would be called upon to kill another man, myself.

> *Radio Jerusalem*. . . . Last-minute news flashes. David ben Moshe's execution will take place at dawn tomorrow. The High Commissioner has issued an appeal for calm. Curfew at nine o'clock. No one will be allowed on the streets. I repeat, no one will be allowed on the streets. The army has orders to shoot at sight. . . .

The announcer's voice betrayed his emotion. As he said the name David ben Moshe there must have been tears in his eyes.

All over the world the young Jewish fighter was the hero of the day. All the wartime resistance movements of Europe held rallies in front of the British embassies; the chief rabbis of the capital cities sent a joint petition to His Majesty the King. Their telegram–with some thirty signatures at the bottom–ran: "Do not hang a young man whose only crime is fidelity to his ideal." A Jewish delegation was received at the White House and the President promised to intercede. That day the heart of humanity was one with that of David ben Moshe.

It was eight o'clock in the evening and completely dark. Gad switched on the light. Outside the child was still crying.

"The dirty dogs," said Gad; "they're going to hang him."

His face and hands were red and perspiring. He paced up and down the room, lighting one cigarette after another, only to throw each one away.

"They're going to hang him," he repeated. "The bastards!"

The news broadcast came to an end and a program of choral singing followed. I started to turn the radio off but Gad held me back.

"It's a quarter past eight," he said. "See if you can get our station."

I was too nervous to turn the dial.

"I'll find it," said Gad.

The broadcast had just begun. The announcer was a girl with a resonant, grave voice familiar to every one of us. Every evening at this hour men, women, and children paused in their work or play to listen to the vibrant, mysterious voice which always began with the same eight words: *You are listening to the Voice of Freedom. . . .*

The Jews of Palestine loved this girl or young woman without knowing who she was. The English would have given anything to lay hands upon her. In their eyes she was as dangerous as the Old Man; she too was a part of the Legend. Only a very few people, no more than five, knew her identity, and Gad and I were among them. Her name was Ilana; she and Gad were in love and I was a friend to both of them. Their love was an essential part of my life. I needed to know that there was such a thing as love and that it brought smiles and joy in its wake.

You are listening to the Voice of Freedom, Ilana repeated.

Gad's dark face quivered. He was bent almost double over the radio, as if he wanted to touch with his hands and eyes the clear, deeply moving voice of Ilana, which tonight was his voice and mine and that of the whole country.

"Two men are preparing to meet death at dawn tomorrow," said Ilana, as if she were reading a passage from the Bible. "One of them deserves our admiration, the other our pity. Our brother and guide, David ben Moshe, knows why he is dying; John Dawson does not know. Both of them are vigorous and intelligent, on the threshold of life and happiness. They might have been friends, but now this can never be. At dawn tomorrow at the same hour, the same minute, they will die—but not together, for there is an abyss between them. David ben Moshe's death is meaningful; John Dawson's is not. David is a hero, John a victim. . . ."

For twenty minutes Ilana went on talking. The last part of her broadcast was dedicated exclusively to John Dawson, because he had the greater need of comfort and consolation.

I knew neither David nor John, but I felt bound to them and their fates. It flashed across my mind that in speaking of John Dawson's imminent death Ilana was speaking of me also, since I was his killer. Who was to kill David ben Moshe? For a moment I had the impression that I was to kill both of them and all the other Johns and Davids on earth. I was the executioner. And I was eighteen years old. Eighteen years of searching and suffering, of study and rebellion, and they all added up to this. I wanted to understand the pure, unadulterated essence of human nature, the path to the understanding of man. I had sought after the truth, and here I was about to become a killer, a participant in the work of death and God. I went over to the mirror hanging on the wall and looked into my face. I almost cried out, for everywhere I saw my own eyes.

As a child I was afraid of death. I was not afraid to die, but every time I thought of death I shuddered.

"Death," Kalman, the grizzled master, told me, "is a being without arms or legs or mouth or head; it is all eyes. If ever you meet a creature with eyes everywhere, you can be sure that it is death."

Gad was still leaning over the radio.

"Look at me," I said, but he did not hear.

"John Dawson, you have a mother," Ilana was saying. "At this hour she must be crying, or eating her heart out in silent despair. She will not go to bed tonight. She will sit in a chair near the window, watch in hand, waiting for dawn. Her heart will skip a beat when yours stops beating forever. 'They've killed my son,' she will say. 'Those murderers!' But we are not murderers, Mrs. Dawson. . . ."

"Look at me, Gad," I repeated.

He raised his eyes, shot me a glance, shrugged his shoulders, and went back to the voice of Ilana. Gad doesn't know that I am death, I thought to myself. But John Dawson's mother, sitting near the window of her London flat, must surely know. She is gazing out into the night, and the night has a thousand eyes, which are mine.

"No, Mrs. Dawson, we are not murderers. Your Cabinet ministers are murderers; they are responsible for the death of your son. We should have preferred to receive him as a brother, to offer him bread and milk and show him the beauties of our country. But your government made him our enemy and by the same token signed his death warrant. No, we are not murderers."

I buried my head in my hands. The child outside had stopped crying.

II

In all probability I had killed before, but under entirely different circumstances. The act had other dimensions, other witnesses. Since my arrival in Palestine several months before, I had taken part in various tangles with the police, in sabotage operations, in attacks on military convoys making their way across the green fields of Galilee or the white desert. There had been casualties on both sides, but the odds were in our favor because the night was our ally. Under cover of darkness we took the enemy by surprise; we set fire to an army encampment, killed a dozen soldiers, and disappeared without leaving any traces behind us. The Movement's objective was to kill the greatest number of soldiers possible. It was that simple.

Ever since the day of my arrival, my first steps on the soil of Palestine, this idea had been imprinted upon my brain. As I stepped off the ship at Haifa two comrades picked me up in their car and took me to a two-storey house somewhere between Ramat-Gan and Tel Aviv. This house was ostensibly occupied by a professor of languages, to justify the comings and goings of a large number of young people who were actually, like myself, apprentices of a school of terrorist techniques. The cellar served as a dungeon where we kept prisoners, hostages, and those of our comrades who were wanted by the police. Here it was that John Dawson was awaiting execution. The hiding place was absolutely secure. Several times English soldiers had searched the house from top to bottom; their police dogs had come within a few inches of John Dawson, but there was a wall between them.

Gad directed our terrorist instruction. Other masked teachers taught us the use of a revolver, a machine gun, a hand grenade. We learned also to wield a dagger, to strangle a man from behind without making a sound, and to get out of practically any prison. The course lasted for six weeks. For two hours every day Gad indoctrinated us with the Movement's ideology. The goal was simply to get the English out; the method, intimidation, terror, and sudden death.

"On the day when the English understand that their occupation will cost them blood they won't want to stay," Gad told us. "It's cruel–inhuman, if you like. But we have no other choice. For generations we've wanted to be better, more pure in heart than those who persecuted us. You've all seen the result: Hitler and the extermination camps in Germany. We've had enough of trying to be more just than those who claim to speak in the name of justice. When the Nazis killed a third of our people just men found nothing to say. If ever it's a question of killing off Jews, everyone is silent; there are twenty centuries of history to prove it. We can rely only on ourselves. If we must become more unjust and inhuman than those who have been unjust and inhuman to us, then we shall do so. We don't like to be bearers of death; heretofore we've chosen to be victims rather than executioners. The commandment *Thou shalt not kill* was given from the summit of one of the mountains here in Palestine, and we were the only ones to obey it. But that's all over; we must be like everybody else. Murder will be not our profession but our duty. In the days and weeks and months to come you will have only one purpose: to kill those who have made us killers. We shall kill in order that once more we may be men. . . ."

On the last day of the course a masked stranger addressed us. He spoke of what our leaders called the eleventh commandment: *Hate your enemy*. He had a soft, timid, romantic voice, and I think he was the Old Man. I'm not quite sure, but his words fired our enthusiasm and made us tremble with emotion. Long after he had gone away I felt them vibrate within me. Thanks to him I became part of a Messianic world where destiny had the face of a masked beggar, where not a single act was lost or a single glance wasted.

I remembered how the grizzled master had explained the sixth commandment to me. Why has a man no right to commit murder? Because in so doing he takes upon himself the function of God. And this must not be done too easily. Well, I said to myself, if in order to change the course of our history we have to become God, we shall become Him. How easy that is we shall see. No, it was not easy.

The first time I took part in a terrorist operation I had to make a superhuman effort not to be sick at my stomach. I found myself utterly hateful. Seeing myself with the eyes of the past I imagined that I was in the dark gray uniform of an SS officer. The first time . . .

They ran like rabbits, like drunken rabbits, looking for the shelter of a tree. They seemed to have neither heads nor hands, but only legs. And these legs ran like rabbits sotted with wine and sorrow. But we were all around them, forming a circle of fire from which there was no escape. We were there with our tommy guns, and our bullets were a flaming wall on which their lives were shattered to the accompaniment of agonized cries which I shall hear until the last day of my life.

There were six of us. I don't remember the names of the five others, but Gad was not among them. That day he stayed at the school, as if to show that he had complete confidence in us, as if he were saying: "Go to it; you can get along without me." My five comrades and I set out either to kill or to be killed.

"Good luck!" said Gad as he shook hands with us before we went away. "I'll wait here for your return."

This was the first time that I had been assigned to any operation, and I knew that when I came back–if I came back–I should be another man. I should have undergone my baptism of fire, my baptism of blood. I knew that I should feel very differently, but I had no idea that I should be ready to vomit.

Our mission was to attack a military convoy on the road between Haifa and Tel Aviv. The exact spot was the curve near the village of Hedera; the time late afternoon. In the disguise of workmen coming home from their job we arrived at the chosen place thirty minutes before H-hour. If we had come any earlier our presence might have attracted attention. We set mines on either side of the curve and moved into planned positions. A car was waiting fifty yards away to take us to Petach Tivka, where we were to split up and be driven in three other cars back to our base at the school.

The convoy arrived punctually upon the scene: three open trucks carrying about twenty soldiers. The wind ruffled their hair and the sun shone upon their faces. At the curve the first truck was exploded by one of our mines and the others came to an abrupt halt with screeching brakes. The soldiers leaped to the ground and were caught in the cross-fire of our guns. They ran with lowered heads in every direction, but their legs were cut by our bullets, as if by an immense scythe, and they fell shrieking to the ground.

The whole episode lasted no more than a single minute. We withdrew in good order and everything went according to plan. Our mission was accomplished. Gad was waiting at the school and we made our report to him. His face glowed with pride.

"Good work," he said. "The Old Man won't believe it."

It was then that nausea overcame me. I saw the legs running like frightened rabbits and I found myself utterly hateful. I remembered the dreaded SS guards in the Polish ghettos. Day after day, night after night, they slaughtered the Jews in just the same way. Tommy guns were scattered here and there, and an officer, laughing or distractedly eating, barked out the order: *Fire!* Then the scythe went to work. A few Jews tried to break through the circle of fire, but they only rammed their heads against its insurmountable wall. They too ran like rabbits, like rabbits sotted with wine and sorrow, and death mowed them down.

No, it was not easy to play the part of God, especially when it meant putting on the field-gray uniform of the SS. But it was easier than killing a hostage.

In the first operation and those that followed I was not alone. I killed, to be sure, but I was one of a group. With John Dawson I would be on my own. I would look into his face and he would look into mine and see that I was all eyes.

"Don't torture yourself, Elisha," said Gad. He had turned off the radio and was scrutinizing me intently. "This is war."

I wanted to ask him whether God, the God of war, wore a uniform.

But I chose to keep silent. God doesn't wear a uniform, I said to myself. God is a member of the Resistance movement, a terrorist.

Ilana arrived a few minutes before the curfew with her two bodyguards, Gideon and Joab. She was restless and somber, more beautiful than ever. Her delicate features seemed chiseled out of brown marble and there was an expression of heartrending melancholy on her face. She was wearing a gray skirt and a white blouse and her lips were very pale.

"Unforgettable . . . that broadcast of yours," murmured Gad.

"The Old Man wrote it," said Ilana.

"But your voice. . . ."

"That's the Old Man's creation, too," said Ilana, sinking exhausted into a chair. And after a moment of complete silence she added: "Today I saw him crying. I have an idea that he cries more often than we know."

The lucky fellow, I thought to myself. At least he can cry. When a man weeps he knows that one day he will stop.

Joab gave us the latest news of Tel Aviv, of its atmosphere of anxiety and watchful waiting. People were afraid of mass reprisals, and all the newspapers had appealed to the Old Man to call off John Dawson's execution. The name of John Dawson rather than that of David ben Moshe was on everyone's lips.

"That's why the Old Man was crying," said Gad, brushing a stubborn lock of hair back from his forehead. "The Jews are not yet free of their persecution reflex. They haven't the guts to strike back."

"In London the Cabinet is in session," Joab went on. "In New York the Zionists are holding a huge demonstration in Madison Square Garden. The UN is deeply concerned."

"I hope David knows," said Ilana. Her face had paled to a bronze hue.

"No doubt the hangman will tell him," said Gad.

I understood the bitterness in his voice. David was a childhood friend and they had entered the Movement together. Gad had told me this only after David's arrest, for it would have been unsafe before. The less any one of us knew about his comrades the better; this is one of the basic principles of any underground organization.

Gad had been present when David was wounded; in fact, he was in command of the operation. It was supposed to be what we called a "soft job," but the courageous stupidity of a sentry had spoiled it. His was the fault if David was to be hanged on the morrow. Although wounded and in convulsions he had continued to crawl along the ground with a bullet in his belly and even to shoot off his gun. The mischief that a courageous, diehard fool can do!

It was night. An army truck came to a halt at the entrance of the red-capped paratroopers' camp near Gedera, in the south. In it were a major and three soldiers.

"We've come to get some arms," the major said to the sentry. "A terrorist attack is supposed to take place this evening."

"Those goddamned terrorists," the sentry mumbled from under his mustache, handing back the major's identification papers.

"Very good, Major," he said, opening the gate. "You can come in."

"Thanks," said the major. "Where are the stores?"

"Straight ahead and then two left turns."

The car drove through, followed these directions and stopped in front of a stone building.

"Here we are," said the major.

They got out, and a sergeant saluted the major and opened the door. The major returned his salute and handed him an order with a colonel's signature at the bottom, an order to consign to the bearer five tommy guns, twenty rifles, twenty revolvers, and the necessary ammunition.

"We're expecting a terrorist attack," the major explained condescendingly.

"Goddamned terrorists," muttered the sergeant.

"We've no time to lose," the major added. "Can you hurry?"

"Of course, sir," said the sergeant. "I quite understand."

He pointed out the arms and ammunition to the three soldiers, who silently and quickly loaded them onto the truck. In a very few minutes it was all done.

"I'll just keep this order, sir," said the sergeant as the visitors started to go away.

"Right you are, Sergeant," said the major, climbing into the truck.

The sentry was just about to open the gate when in his sentry box the telephone rang. With a hasty apology he went to answer. The major and his men waited impatiently.

"Sorry, sir," said the sentry as he emerged from the box. "The sergeant wants to see you. He says the order you brought him is not satisfactory."

The major got down from the truck.

"I'll clear it up with him on the telephone," he said.

As the sentry turned around to re-enter the box the major brought his fist down on the back of his neck. The sentry fell noiselessly to the ground. Gad went over to the gate, opened it, and signaled to the driver to go through. Just then the sentry came to and started shooting. Dan put a bullet into his belly while Gad jumped onto the truck and called out:

"Let's go! And hurry!"

The wounded sentry continued to shoot and one of his bullets punctured a tire. Gad retained his self-possession and decided that the tire must be changed.

"David and Dan, keep us covered," he said in a quiet, assured voice.

David and Dan grabbed two of the recently received tommy guns and stood by.

By now the whole camp was alerted. Orders rang out and gunfire followed. Every second was precious. Covered by David and Dan, Gad changed the tire. But the paratroopers were drawing near. Gad knew that the important thing was to make off with the weapons.

"David and Dan," he said, "stay where you are. We're leaving. See if you can hold them back for three minutes longer while we get away. After that you can make a dash for it. Try to get to Gedera, where friends will give you shelter. You know where to find them."

"Yes, I know," said David, continuing to shoot. "Go on, and hurry!"

The arms and ammunition were saved, but David and Dan had to pay. Dan was killed and David wounded. All on account of a stubbornly courageous sentry with a bullet in his belly!

"He was a wonderful fellow, David," said Ilana. Already she spoke of him as if he belonged to the past.

"I hope the hangman knows it," retorted Gad.

I understood his bitterness; indeed I envied it. He was losing a friend, and it hurt. But when you lose a friend every day it doesn't hurt so much. And I'd lost plenty of friends in my time; sometimes I thought of myself as a living graveyard. That was the real reason I followed Gad to Palestine and became a terrorist: I had no more friends to lose.

"They say that the hangman always wears a mask," said Joab, who had been standing silently in front of the kitchen door. "I wonder if it's true."

"I think it is," I said. "The hangman wears a mask. You can't see anything but his eyes."

Ilana went over to Gad, stroked his hair, and said in a sad voice: "Don't torture yourself, Gad. This is war."

III

During the hour that followed nobody said a word. They were all thinking of David ben Moshe. David was not alone in his death cell; his friends were with him. All except me. I did not think of David except when they pronounced his name. When they were silent my thoughts went out to someone else, to a man I did not yet know, any more than I knew David, but whom I was fated to know. My David ben Moshe had the name and face of an Englishman, Captain John Dawson.

We sat around the table and Ilana served us some steaming tea. For some time we sipped it without speaking. We looked into the golden liquid in our cups as if we were searching in it for the next step after our silence and the meaning of the events which had brought it about. Then, in order to kill time, we spoke of our memories, of such of them that centered on death.

"Death saved my life," Joab began.

He had a young, innocent, tormented face; dark, confused eyes, and hair as white as that of an old man. He wore a perpetually sleepy expression and yawned from one end of the day to the other.

"A neighbor who was against us because of his pacifist convictions reported me to the police," he went on. "I took shelter in an insane asylum whose superintendent was an old school friend. I stayed there for two weeks, until the police found my traces. 'Is he here?' they asked the superintendent. 'Yes,' he admitted. 'He's here; he's a very sick man.' 'What's the matter with him?' they asked. 'He imagines he's dead,' the superintendent told them. But they insisted on seeing me. I was brought to the superintendent's office, where two police officials assigned to the antiterrorist campaign were waiting. They spoke to me but I did not answer. They asked me questions but I pretended not to hear. Even so, they were not convinced that I was crazy. Overriding the superintendent's protest, they took me away and submitted me to forty-eight hours of interrogation. I played dead, and played it successfully. I refused to eat or drink; when they slapped my hands and face I did not react. Dead men feel no pain and so they do not cry. After forty-eight hours I was taken back to the asylum."

As I listened to Joab various thoughts floated to the surface of my mind. I remembered hearing some of my comrades refer to Joab as the Madman.

"Funny, isn't it?" he said. "Death actually saved my life."

We kept silence for several minutes, as if to pay homage to death for saving his life and giving the name of Madman to a fellow with an innocent, tormented face.

"Several days later, when I left the asylum, I saw that my hair had turned white," Joab concluded.

"That's one of death's little jokes," I put in. "Death loves to change the color of people's hair. Death has no hair; it has only eyes. God, on the other hand, has no eyes at all."

"God saved me from death," said Gideon.

We called Gideon the Saint. First because he *was* a saint, and second because he looked like one. He was a husky, inarticulate fellow some twenty years old, who took pains to make himself inconspicuous and was always mumbling prayers. He wore a beard and side curls, went nowhere without a prayer book in his pocket. His father was a rabbi, and when he learned that his son meant to become a terrorist he gave him his blessing. There are times, his father said, when words and prayers are not enough. The God of grace is also the God of war. And war is not a matter of mere words.

"God saved me from death," Gideon repeated. "His eyes saved me. I too was arrested and tortured. They pulled my beard, lit matches under my fingernails, and spat in my face, all in order to make me confess that I had taken part in an attempt against the life of the High Commissioner. But in spite of the pain I did not talk. More than once I was tempted to cry out, but I kept quiet because I felt that God's eyes were upon me. God is looking at me, I said to myself, and I must not disappoint Him. My torturers never stopped shouting, but I kept my thoughts on God and on His eyes, which are drawn to human pain. For lack of evidence they finally had to set me free. If I had admitted my guilt I should be dead."

"And then," I put in, "God would have closed His eyes."

Ilana refilled our cups.

"What about you, Ilana?" I asked. "What saved your life?"

"A cold in the head," she replied.

I burst out laughing, but no one else joined in. My laugh was raucous and artificial.

"A cold in the head?" I repeated.

"Yes," said Ilana, quite seriously. "The English have no description of me; they know only my voice. One day they hauled in a whole group of women, myself among them. At the police station a sound engineer compared each one of our voices to that of the mysterious announcer of the Voice of Freedom. Thanks to the fact that I had a heavy cold I was quickly eliminated and four other women were detained for further questioning."

Once more I was tempted to laugh, but the others were glum and silent. A cold, I thought to myself. And in this case it turned out to have more practical use than either faith or courage. Next we all looked at Gad, who was almost crushing his teacup between his fingers.

"I owe my life to three Englishmen," he said. With his head almost on his right shoulder and his eyes fixed on the cup, he seemed to be addressing the rapidly cooling tea. "It was very early in the game," he went on. "For reasons that no longer matter the Old Man had ordered three hostages taken. They were all sergeants, and I was assigned to kill one of them, any one; the choice was up to me. I was young then, about the age of Elisha, and suffered great mental agony from having this unwanted role thrust upon me. I was willing to play the executioner, but not the judge. Unfortunately, during the night I lost contact with the Old Man and could not explain my reluctance. The sentence had to be carried out at dawn, and how was I to choose the victim? Finally I had an idea. I went down to the cellar and told the three sergeants that the choice was up to them. If you don't make it, I said, then all three of you will be shot. They decided to draw lots, and when dawn came I put a bullet in the unlucky fellow's neck."

Involuntarily I looked at Gad's hands and face, the familiar hands and face of my friend, who had put a bullet in the neck of a fellow human being and now talked coldly, almost indifferently, about it. Was the sergeant's face gazing up at him from his cup of golden cool tea?

"What if the sergeants had refused to settle it among themselves?" I asked. "What then?"

Gad squeezed the cup harder than ever, almost as if he were trying to break it.

"I think I'd have killed myself instead," he said in a flat voice. And after a moment of heavy silence he added: "I tell you I was young and very weak."

All eyes turned toward me, in expectation of my story. I gulped down a mouthful of bitter tea and wiped the perspiration off my forehead.

"I owe my life to a laugh," I said. "It was during one winter at Buchenwald. We were clothed in rags and hundreds of people died of cold every day. In the morning we had to leave our barracks and wait outside in the snow for as long as two hours until they had been cleaned. One day I felt so sick that I was sure the exposure would kill me, and so I stayed behind, in hiding. Quite naturally I was discovered and the cleaning squad dragged me before one of the many assistant barracks leaders. Without stopping to question me he caught hold of my throat and said dispassionately: 'I'm going to choke you.' His powerful hands closed in on my throat and in my enfeebled condition I did not even try to put up a fight. Very well, I said to myself; it's all over. I felt the blood gather in my head and my head swell to several times its normal size, so that I must have looked like a caricature, a miserable clown. I was sure from one minute to the next that it would burst into a thousand shreds like a child's toy balloon. At this moment the assistant leader took a good look at me and found the sight so comical that he released his grip and burst out laughing. He laughed so long that he forgot his intention to kill. And that's how I got out of it unharmed. It's funny, isn't it, that I should owe my life to an assassin's sense of humor?"

I expected my listeners to scrutinize my head to see if it had really returned to its normal size, but they did nothing of the sort. They continued to stare into their stone-cold tea. In the next few minutes nobody opened his mouth. We had no more desire to call up the past or to listen to our fellows tell their troubled life stories. We sat in restless silence around the table. Every one of us, I am sure, was asking himself to what he *really* owed his life. Gideon was the first to speak.

"We ought to take the Englishman something to eat," he said.

Yes, I said to myself, Gideon is sad, too. He's thinking of John Dawson. He must be; it's inevitable.

"I don't imagine he's hungry," I said aloud. "You can't expect a man condemned to die to have an appetite." And to myself I added: "Or a man condemned to kill, either."

There must have been a strange tone in my voice, for the others raised their heads and I felt the puzzled quality of their penetrating stares.

"No," I said stubbornly; "a man condemned to die can't be hungry."

They did not stir, but sat petrified as the seconds dragged interminably by.

"The condemned man's traditional last meal is a joke," I said loudly, "a joke in the worst possible taste, an insult to the corpse that he is about to be. What does a man care if he dies with an empty stomach?"

The expression of astonishment lingered in Gad's eyes, but Ilana looked at me with compassion and Gideon with friendliness. Joab did not look at me at all. His eyes were lowered, but perhaps that was his way of looking out of them.

"He doesn't know," remarked Gideon.

"He doesn't know what?" I asked, without any conscious reason for raising my voice. Perhaps I wanted to hear myself shout, to arouse my anger and see it reflected in the motionless shadows in the mirror and on the wall. Or perhaps out of sheer weakness. I felt powerless to change anything, least of all myself, in spite of the fact that I wanted to introduce a transformation into the room, to reorder the whole of creation. I would have made the Saint into a Madman, have given John Dawson's name to Gad and his fate to David. But I knew there was nothing I could do. To have such power I should have had to take the place of death, not just of the individual death of John Dawson, the English captain who had no more appetite than I.

"What doesn't he know?" I repeated stridently.

"He doesn't know he's going to die," said Gideon in a sorrowfully dreamy voice.

"His stomach knows," I retorted. "A man about to die listens only to his stomach. He pays no attention to his heart or to his past, or to yours for that matter. He doesn't even hear the voice of the storm. He listens to his stomach and his stomach tells him that he is going to die and that he isn't hungry."

I had talked too fast and too loud and I was left panting. I should have liked to run away, but my friends' stares transfixed me. Death sealed off every exit, and everywhere there were eyes.

"I'm going down to the cellar," said Gideon. "I'll ask him if he wants something to eat."

"Don't ask him anything," I said. "Simply tell him that tomorrow, when the sun rises above the blood-red horizon, he, John Dawson, will say good-by to life, good-by to his stomach. Tell him that he's going to die."

Gideon got up, with his eyes still on me, and started toward the kitchen and the entrance to the cellar. At the door he paused.

"I'll tell him," he said, with a quickly fading smile. Then he turned on his heels and I heard him going down the stairs.

I was grateful for his consent. He and not I would warn John Dawson of his approaching end. I could never have done it. It's easier to kill a man than to break the news that he is going to die.

"Midnight," said Joab.

Midnight, I reflected, the hour when the dead rise out of their graves and come to say their prayers in the synagogue, the hour when God Himself weeps over the destruction of the Temple, the hour when a man should be able to plumb the depths of his being and to discover the Temple in ruins. A God that weeps and dead men that pray.

"Poor boy!" murmured Ilana.

She did not look at me, but her tears scrutinized my face. Her tears rather than her eyes caressed me.

"Don't say that, Ilana. Don't call me 'poor boy.' "

There were tears in her eyes, or rather there were tears in the place of her eyes, tears which with every passing second grew heavier and more opaque and threatened to overflow. . . . I was afraid that suddenly the worst would happen: the dusky Ilana would no longer be there; she would have drowned in her tears. I wanted to touch her arm and say *Don't cry*. Say what you like, but don't cry.

But she wasn't crying. It takes eyes to cry, and she had no eyes, only tears where her eyes should have been.

"Poor boy!" she repeated.

Then what I had foreseen came true. Ilana disappeared, and Catherine was there instead. I wondered why Catherine had come, but her apparition did not particularly surprise me. She liked the opposite sex, and particularly she liked little boys who were thinking of death. She liked to speak of love to little boys, and since men going to their death are little boys she liked to speak to them of love. For this reason her presence in the magical room—magical because it transcended the differences, the boundary lines between the victim and the executioner, between the present and the past—was not surprising.

I had met Catherine in Paris in 1945, when I had just come from Buchenwald, that other magical spot, where the living were transformed into dead and their future into darkness. I was weakened and half starved. One of the many rescue committees sent me to a camp where a hundred boys and girls were spending their summer vacation. The camp was in Normandy, where the early morning breeze rustled the same way it did in Palestine.

Because I knew no French I could not communicate with the other boys and girls. I ate and sunbathed with them, but I had no way of talking. Catherine was the only person who seemed to know any German and occasionally we exchanged a few words. Sometimes she came up to me at the dining-room table and asked me whether I had slept well, enjoyed my meal, or had a good time during the day.

She was twenty-six or -seven years old; small, frail, and almost transparent, with silky blonde, sunlit hair and blue, dreamy eyes which never cried. Her face was thin but saved from being bony by the delicacy of the features. She was the first woman I had seen from nearby. Before this—that is, before the war—I did not look at women. On my way to school or the synagogue I walked close to the walls, with my eyes cast down on the ground. I knew that women existed, and why, but I did not appreciate the fact that they had a body, breasts, legs, hands, and lips whose touch sets a man's heart to beating. Catherine revealed this to me.

The camp was at the edge of a wood, and after supper I went walking there all by myself, talking to the murmuring breeze and watching the sky turn a deeper and deeper blue. I liked to be alone.

One evening Catherine asked if she might go with me, and I was too timid to say anything but yes. For half an hour, an hour, we walked in complete silence. At first I found the silence embarrassing, then to my surprise I began to enjoy it. The silence of two people is deeper than the silence of one. Involuntarily I began to talk.

"Look how the sky is opening up," I said.

She threw back her head and looked above her. Just as I had said, the sky was opening up. Slowly at first, as if swept by an invisible wind, the stars drew away from the zenith, some moving to the right, others to the left, until the center of the sky was an empty space, dazzlingly blue and gradually acquiring depth and outline.

"Look hard," I said. "There's nothing there."

From behind me Catherine looked up and said not a word.

"That's enough," I said; "let's go on walking."

As we walked on I told her the legend of the open sky. When I was a child the old master told me that there were nights when the sky opened up in order to make way for the prayers of unhappy children. On one such night a little boy whose father was dying said to God: "Father, I am too small to know how to pray. But I ask you to heal my sick father." God did what the boy asked, but the boy himself was turned into a prayer and carried up into Heaven. From that day on, the master told me, God has from time to time shown Himself to us in the face of a child.

"That is why I like to look at the sky at this particular moment," I told Catherine. "I hope to see the child. But you are a witness to the truth. There's nothing there. The child is only a story."

It was then for the first time during the evening that Catherine spoke. "Poor boy!" she exclaimed. "Poor boy!"

She's thinking of the boy in the story, I said to myself. And I loved her for her compassion.

After this Catherine often went walking with me. She questioned me about my childhood and my more recent past, but I did not always answer. One evening she asked me why I kept apart from the other boys and girls in the camp.

"Because they speak a language I can't understand," I told her.

"Some of the girls know German," she said.

"But I have nothing to say to them."

"You don't have to say anything," she said slowly, with a smile. "All you have to do is love them."

I didn't see what she was driving at and said so. Her smile widened and she began to speak to me of love. She spoke easily and well. Love is this and love is that; man is born to love; he is only alive when he is in the presence of a woman he loves or should love. I told her that I knew nothing of love, that I didn't know it existed or had a right to exist.

"I'll prove it to you," she said.

The next evening, as she walked at my left side over the leaf-covered path, she took hold of my arm. At first I thought she needed my support, but actually it was because she wanted to make me feel the warmth of her body. Then she claimed to be tired and said it would be pleasant to sit down on the grass under a tree. Once we had sat down she began to stroke my face and hair. Then she kissed me several times; first her lips touched mine and then her tongue burned the inside of my mouth. For several nights running we returned to the same place, and she spoke to me of love and desire and the mysteries of the heart. She took my hand and guided it over her breasts and thighs, and I realized that women had breasts and thighs and hands that could set a man's heart to beating and turn his blood to fire.

Then came the last evening. The month of vacation was over and I was to go back to Paris the next day. As soon as we had finished supper we went to sit for the last time under the tree. I felt sad and lonely, and Catherine held my hand in hers without speaking. The night was fair and calm. At intervals, like a warm breath, the wind played over our faces. It must have been one or two o'clock in the morning when Catherine broke the silence, turned her melancholy face toward me, and said:

"Now we're going to make love."

These words made me tremble. I was going to make love for the first time. Before her there had been no woman upon earth. I didn't know what to say or do; I was afraid of saying the wrong thing or making some inappropriate gesture. Awkwardly I waited for her to take the initiative. With a suddenly serious look on her face she began to get undressed. She took off her blouse and in the starlight I saw her ivory-white breasts. Then she took off the rest of her clothes and was completely naked before me.

"Take off your shirt," she ordered.

I was paralyzed; there was iron in my throat and lead in my veins; my arms and hands would not obey me. I could only look at her from head to foot and follow the rise and fall of her breasts. I was hypnotized by the call of her outstretched, naked body.

"Take off your shirt," she repeated.

Then, as I did not move, she began to undress me. Deliberately she took off my shirt and shorts. Then she lay back on the grass and said:

"Take me."

I got down on my knees. I stared at her for a long time and then I covered her body with kisses. Absently and without saying a word she stroked my hair.

"Catherine," I said, "first there is something I must tell you."

Her face took on a blank and anguished expression, and there was anguish in the rustle of the breeze among the trees.

"No, no!" she cried. "Don't tell me anything. Take me, but don't talk."

Heedless of her objection I went on:

"First, Catherine, I must tell you. . . ."

Her lips twisted with pain, and there was pain in the rustle of the breeze.

"No, no, no!" she implored. "Don't tell me. Be quiet. Take me quickly, but don't talk."

"What I have to tell you is this," I insisted: "You've won the game. I love you, Catherine. . . . I love you."

She burst into sobs and repeated over and over again:

"Poor boy! You poor boy!"

I picked up my shirt and shorts and ran away. Now I understood. She was referring not to the little boy in the sky but to me. She had spoken to me of love because she knew that I was the little boy who had been turned into a prayer and carried up into Heaven. She knew that I had died and come back to earth, dead. This was why she had spoken to me of love and wanted to make love with me. I saw it all quite clearly. She liked making love with little boys who were going to die; she enjoyed the company of those who were obsessed with death. No wonder that her presence this night in Palestine was not surprising.

"Poor boy!" said Ilana, in a very quiet voice, for the last time. And a deep sigh escaped from her breast, which made her tears free to flow, to flow on and on until the end of time.

IV

Suddenly I became aware that the room was stuffy, so stuffy that I was almost stifled.

No wonder. The room was small, far too small to receive so many visitors at one time. Ever since midnight the visitors had been pouring in. Among them were people I had known, people I had hated, admired, forgotten. As I let my eyes wander about the room I realized that all of those who had contributed to my formation, to the formation of my permanent identity, were there. Some of them were familiar, but I could not pin a label upon them; they were names without faces or faces without names. And yet I knew that at some point my life had crossed theirs.

My father was there, of course, and my mother, and the beggar. And the grizzled master. The English soldiers of the convoy we had ambushed at Gedera were there also. And around them friends and brothers and comrades, some of them out of my childhood, others that I had seen live and suffer, hope and curse at Buchenwald and Auschwitz. Alongside my father there was a boy who looked strangely like myself as I had been before the concentration camps, before the war, before everything. My father smiled at him, and the child picked up the smile and sent it to me over the multitude of heads which separated us.

Now I understood why the room was so stuffy. It was too small to hold so many people at a time. I forced a passage through the crowd until I came to the little boy and thanked him for the smile. I wanted to ask him what all these people were doing in the room, but on second thought I saw that this would be discourteous toward my father. Since he was present I should address my question to him.

"Father, why are all these people here?"

My mother stood beside him, looking very pale, and her lips tirelessly murmured: "Poor little boy, poor little boy! . . ."

"Father," I repeated, "answer me. What are you all doing here?"

His large eyes, in which I had so often seen the sky open up, were looking at me, but he did not reply. I turned around and found myself face to face with the rabbi, whose beard was more grizzled than ever.

"Master," I said, "what has brought all these people here tonight?"

Behind me I heard my mother whisper, "Poor little boy, my poor little boy."

"Well, Master," I repeated, "answer me, I implore you."

But he did not answer either; indeed, he seemed not even to have heard my question, and his silence made me afraid. As I had known him before, he was always present in my hour of need. Then his silence had been reassuring. Now I tried to look into his eyes, but they were two globes of fire, two suns that burned my face. I turned away and went from one visitor to another, seeking an answer to my question, but my presence struck them dumb. Finally I came to the beggar, who stood head and shoulders above them all. And he spoke to me, quite spontaneously.

"This is a night of many faces," he said.

I was sad and tired.

"Yes," I said wearily, "this is a night of many faces, and I should like to know the reason why. If you are the one I think you are, enlighten and comfort me. Tell me the meaning of these looks, this muteness, these presences. Tell me, I beseech you, for I can endure them no longer."

He took my arm, gently pressed it, and said:

"Do you see that little boy over there?" and he pointed to the boy who looked like myself as I had been.

"Yes, I see him," I replied.

"He will answer all your questions," said the beggar. "Go talk to him."

Now I was quite sure that he was not a beggar. Once more I elbowed my way through the crowd of ghosts and arrived, panting with exhaustion, at the young boy's side.

"Tell me," I said beseechingly, "what you are doing here? And all the others?"

He opened his eyes wide in astonishment.

"Don't you know?" he asked.

I confessed that I did not know.

"Tomorrow a man is to die, isn't he?"

"Yes," I said, "at dawn tomorrow."

"And you are to kill him, aren't you?"

"Yes, that's true; I have been charged with his execution."

"And you don't understand, do you?"

"No."

"But it's all quite simple," he exclaimed. "We are here to be present at the execution. We want to see you carry it out. We want to see you turn into a murderer. That's natural enough, isn't it?"

"How is it natural? Of what concern is the killing of John Dawson to you?"

"You are the sum total of all that we have been," said the youngster who looked like my former self. "In a way we are the ones to execute John Dawson. Because you can't do it without us. Now, do you see?"

I was beginning to understand. An act so absolute as that of killing involves not only the killer but, as well, those who have formed him. In murdering a man I was making them murderers.

"Well," said the boy, "do you see?"

"Yes, I see," I said.

"Poor boy, poor boy!" murmured my mother, whose lips were now as gray as the old master's hair.

"He's hungry," said Gideon's voice, unexpectedly.

I had not heard him come back up the stairs. Saints have a disconcertingly noiseless way. They walk, laugh, eat, and pray, all without making a sound.

"Impossible," I protested.

He can't be hungry, I was thinking. He's going to die, and a man who's going to die can't be hungry.

"He said so himself," Gideon insisted, with a shade of emotion in his voice.

Everyone was staring at me. Ilana had stopped crying, Joab was no longer examining his nails, and Gad looked weary. All the ghosts, too, seemed to be expecting something of me, a sign perhaps, or a cry.

"Does he know?" I asked Gideon.

"Yes, he knows." And after a moment he added: "I told him."

"How did he react?"

It was important for me to know the man's reaction. Was the news a shock? Had he stayed calm, or protested his innocence?

"He smiled," said Gideon. "He said that he already knew. His stomach had told him."

"And he said he was hungry?"

Gideon hid his twitching hands behind his back.

"Yes, that's what he said. He said he was hungry and he had a right to a good last meal."

Gad laughed, but the tone of his laugh was hollow.

"Typically English," he remarked. "The stiff upper lip."

His remark hung over our heads in midair; no one opened up to receive it. My father shot me a hard glance, as if to say *A man is going to die, and he's hungry*.

"Might as well admit it," said Gad. "The English have iron digestions."

No one paid any attention to this remark either. I felt a sudden stab of pain in my stomach. I had not eaten all day. Ilana got up and went into the kitchen.

"I'll fix him something to eat," she declared.

I heard her moving about, slicing a loaf of bread, opening the icebox, starting to make coffee. In a few minutes she came back with a cup of coffee in one hand and a plate in the other.

"This is all I can find," she said. "A cheese sandwich and some black coffee. There's no sugar. . . . Not much of a meal, but it's the best I can do." And after several seconds of silence she asked: "Who's going to take it down?"

The boy standing beside my father stared hard at me. His stare had a voice, which said:

"Go on. Take him something to eat. He's hungry, you know."

"No," I responded. "Not I. I don't want to see him. Above all, I don't want to see him eat. I want to think of him, later on, as a man who never ate."

I wanted to add that I had cramps in my stomach, but I realized that this was unimportant. Instead I said: "I don't want to be alone with him. Not now."

"We'll go with you," said the little boy. "It's wrong to hold back food from a man who's hungry. You know that."

Yes, I knew. I had always given food to the hungry. You, beggar, you remember. Didn't I offer you bread? But tonight is different. Tonight I can't do it.

"That's true," said the little boy, picking up the train of my reflections. "Tonight is different, and you are different also, or at least you're going to be. But that has nothing to do with the fact that a man's hungry and must have something to eat."

"But he's going to die tomorrow," I protested. "What's it matter whether he dies with a full stomach or an empty one?"

"For the time being he's alive," the child said sententiously. My father nodded in acquiescence, and all the others followed his example. "He's alive and hungry, and you refuse to give him anything to eat?"

All these heads, nodding like the tops of black trees, made me shudder. I wanted to close my eyes but I was ashamed. I couldn't close my eyes in the presence of my father.

"Very well," I said resignedly. "I accept. I'll take him something to eat." As if obeying the baton of an invisible conductor the nodding heads were still. "I'll take him something to eat," I repeated. "But first tell me something, little boy. Are the dead hungry too?"

He looked surprised.

"What–you don't know?" he exclaimed. "Of course they are."

"And should we give them something to eat?"

"How can you ask? Of course you should give them something to eat. Only it's difficult. . . ."

"Difficult . . . difficult . . . difficult . . . ," the ghosts echoed together.

The boy looked at me and smiled.

"I'll tell you a secret," he whispered. "You know that at midnight the dead leave their graves, don't you?"

I told him that I knew; I had been told.

"Have you been told that they go from the graveyard to the synagogue?"

Yes, I had been told that also.

"Well, it's true," said the little boy. Then, after a silence which accentuated what was to follow, he went on in a voice so still that if it had not been inside myself I could never have heard it: "Yes, it's true. They gather every night in the synagogue. But not for the purpose you imagine. They come not to pray but to eat—"

Everything in the room–walls, chairs, heads–began to whirl around me, dancing in a pre-established rhythm, without stirring the air or setting foot on the ground. I was the center of a multitude of circles. I wanted to close my eyes and stop up my ears, but my father was there, and my mother, and the master and the beggar and the boy. With all those who had formed me around me I had no right to stop up my ears and close my eyes.

"Give me those things," I said to Ilana. "I'll take them to him."

The dancers stopped in their tracks, as if I were the conductor and my words his baton. I stepped toward Ilana, still standing at the kitchen door. Suddenly Gad rushed forward and reached her side before me.

"I'll do it," he said.

Almost brutally he snatched the cup and plate from Ilana's hands and went precipitately down the stairs.

Joab looked at his watch. "It's after two."

"Is that all?" asked Ilana. "It's a long night, the longest I've ever lived through."

"Yes, it's long," Joab agreed.

Ilana bit her lips. "There are moments when I think it will never end, that it will last indefinitely. It's like the rain. Here the rain, like everything else, suggests permanence and eternity. I say to myself: It's raining today and it's going to rain tomorrow and the next day, the next week and the next century. Now I say to myself: There's night now and there will be night tomorrow, and the day, the week, the century after."

She paused abruptly, took a handkerchief from the cuff of her blouse and wiped her perspiring forehead.

"I wonder why it's so stuffy in here," she said, "particularly this late at night."

"It will be cooler early tomorrow," promised Joab.

"I hope so," said Ilana. "What time does the sun rise?"

"Around five o'clock."

"And what time is it now?"

"Twenty past two," said Joab, looking again at his watch.

"Aren't you hot, Elisha?" Ilana asked me.

"Yes, I am," I answered.

Ilana went back to her place at the table. I walked over to the window and looked out. The city seemed faraway and unreal. Deep in sleep, it spawned anxious dreams, hopeful dreams, dreams which would proliferate other dreams on the morrow. And these dreams in their turn would engender new heroes, who would live through the night and prepare to die at dawn, to die and to give death.

"Yes, I'm hot, Ilana," I said. "I'm stifling."

I don't know how long I stood, sweating, beside the open window, before a warm, vibrant, reassuring hand was laid on my shoulder. It was Ilana.

"What are you thinking?" she said.

"I'm thinking of the night," I told her. "Always the same thing—"

"And of John Dawson?"

"Yes, of John Dawson."

Somewhere in the city a light shone in a window and then went out. No doubt a man had looked at his watch or a mother had gone to find out whether her child was smiling in his sleep.

"You didn't want to see him, though," said Ilana.

"I don't want to see him."

One day, I was thinking, my son will say: "All of a sudden you look sad. What's wrong?" "It's because in my eyes there is a picture of an English captain called John Dawson, just as he appeared to me at the moment of his death. . . ." Perhaps I ought to put a mask on his face; a mask is more easily killed and forgotten.

"Are you afraid?" asked Ilana.

"Yes."

Being afraid, I ought to have told her, is nothing. Fear is only a color, a backdrop, a landscape. That isn't the problem. The fear of either the victim or the executioner is unimportant. What matters is the fact that each of them is playing a role which has been imposed upon him. The two roles are the extremities of the estate of man. The tragic thing is the imposition.

"You, Elisha, *you* are afraid?"

I knew why she had asked. You, Elisha, who lived through Auschwitz and Buchenwald? You who any number of times saw God die? You are afraid?

"I *am* afraid, though, Ilana," I repeated.

She knew quite well that fear was not in fact the real theme. Like death, it is only a backdrop, a bit of local color.

"What makes you afraid?"

Her warm, living hand was still on my shoulder; her breasts brushed me and I could feel her breath on my neck. Her blouse was wet with perspiration and her face distraught. She doesn't understand, I thought to myself.

"I'm afraid he'll make me laugh," I said. "You see, Ilana, he's quite capable of swelling up his head and letting it burst into a thousand shreds, just in order to make me laugh. That's what makes me afraid."

But still she did not understand. She took the handkerchief from her cuff and wiped my neck and temples. Then she kissed my forehead lightly and said:

"You torture yourself too much, Elisha. Hostages aren't clowns. There's nothing so funny about them."

Poor Ilana! Her voice was as pure as truth, as sad as purity. But she did not understand. She was distracted by the externals and did not see what lay behind them.

"You may be right," I said in resignation. "We make *them* laugh. They laugh when they're dead."

She stroked my face and neck and hair, and I could still feel the pressure of her breasts against my body. Then she began to talk, in a sad but clear voice, as if she were talking to a sick child.

"You torture yourself too much, my dear," she said several times in succession. At least she no longer called me "poor boy," and I was grateful. "You mustn't do it. You're young and intelligent, and you've suffered quite enough already. Soon it will all be over. The English will get out and we shall come back to the surface and lead a simple, normal life. You'll get married and have children. You'll tell them stories and make them laugh. You'll be happy because they're happy, and they *will* be happy, I promise you. How could they be otherwise with a father like you? You'll have forgotten this night, this room, me, and everything else—"

As she said "everything else" she traced a sweeping semicircle with her hand. I was reminded of my mother. She talked in the same moving voice and used almost the same words in the same places. I was very fond of my mother. Every evening, until I was nine or ten years old, she put me to sleep with lullabies or stories. There is a goat beside your bed, she used to tell me, a goat of gold. Everywhere you go in life the goat will guide and protect you. Even when you are grown up and very rich, when you know everything a man can know and possess all that he should possess, the goat will still be near you.

"You talk as if you were my mother, Ilana," I said.

My mother, too, had a harmonious voice, even more harmonious than Ilana's. Like the voice of God it had power to dispel chaos and to impart a vision of the future which might have been mine, with the goat to guide me, the goat I had lost on the way to Buchenwald.

"You're suffering," said Ilana. "That's what it means when a man speaks of his mother."

"No, Ilana," I said. "At this moment she's the one to suffer."

Ilana's caresses became lighter, more remote. She was beginning to understand. A shadow fell across her face. For some time she was silent, then she joined me in looking at the hand night held out to us through the window.

"War is like night," she said. "It covers everything."

Yes, she was beginning to understand. I hardly felt the pressure of her fingers on my neck.

"We say that ours is a holy war," she went on, "that we're struggling against something and for something, against the English and for an independent Palestine. That's what we say. But these are words; as such they serve only to give meaning to our actions. And our actions, seen in their true and primitive light, have the odor and color of blood. This is war, we say; we must kill. There are those, like you, who kill with their hands, and others–like me–who kill with their voices. Each to his own. And what else can we do? War has a code, and if you deny this you deny its whole purpose and hand the enemy victory on a silver platter. That we can't afford. We need victory, victory in war, in order to survive, in order to remain afloat on the surface of time."

She did not raise her voice. It seemed as if she were chanting a lullaby, telling a bedtime story. There was neither passion nor despair nor even concern in her intonation.

All things considered, she was quite right. We were at war; we had an ideal, a purpose–and also an enemy who stood between us and its attainment. The enemy must be eliminated. And how? By any and all means at our command. There were all sorts of means, but they were unimportant and soon forgotten. The purpose, the end, this was all that would last. Ilana was probably correct in saying that one day I should forget this night. But the dead never forget; they would remember. In their eyes I should be forever branded a killer. There are not a thousand ways of being a killer; either a man is one or he isn't. He can't say I'll kill only ten or only twenty-six men; I'll kill for only five minutes or a single day. He who has killed one man alone is a killer for life. He may choose another occupation, hide himself under another identity, but the executioner or at least the executioner's mask will be always with him. There lies the problem: in the influence of the backdrop of the play upon the actor. War had made me an executioner, and an executioner I would remain even after the backdrop had changed, when I was acting in another play upon a different stage.

"I don't want to be a killer," I said, sliding rapidly over the word as I ejected it.

"Who does?" said Ilana.

She was still stroking my neck, but somehow I had the impression that it was not really *my* neck, *my* hair her fingers were caressing. The noblest woman in the world would hesitate to touch the skin of a killer, of a man who would have the label of killer his whole life long.

I cast a rapid glance behind me to see if the others were still there. Gideon and Joab were dozing, with their heads pillowed on their arms, on the table. Gideon seemed, even in his sleep, to be praying. Gad was still in the cellar and I wondered why he had stayed there so long. As for the ghosts, they followed the conversation but, to my surprise, took no part in it. Ilana was silent.

"What are you thinking?" I murmured.

She did not reply and after a few minutes I posed the question again. Still there was no answer. We were both silent. And the crowd behind me, the crowd of petrified silences, whose shadows absorbed the light and turned it into something sad, funereal, hostile, was silent as well. The sum of these silences filled me with fear. Their silences were different from mine; they were hard, cold, immobile, lifeless, incapable of change.

As a child I had been afraid of the dead and of the graveyard, their shadowy kingdom. The silence with which they surrounded themselves provoked my terror. I knew that now, at my back, in serried ranks as if to protect themselves from the cold, they were sitting in judgment upon me. In their frozen world the dead have nothing to do but judge, and because they have no sense of past or future they judge without pity. They condemn not with words or gestures but with their very existence.

At my back they were sitting in judgment upon me; I felt their silences judging mine. I wanted to turn around but the mere idea filled me with fear. Soon Gad will come up from the cellar, I said to myself, and later it will be my turn to go down. Dawn will come, and this crowd will melt into the light of day. For the present I shall stay beside Ilana, at the window, with my back to them.

A minute later I changed my mind. My father and mother, the master and the beggar were all there. I could not insult them indefinitely by turning my back; I must look at them face to face. Cautiously I wheeled around. There were two sorts of light in the room: one white, around the sleeping Gideon and Joab, the other black, enveloping the ghosts.

I left Ilana lost in thought, perhaps in regret, at the window, and began to walk about the room, pausing every now and then before a familiar face, a familiar sorrow. I knew that these faces, these sorrows were sitting in judgment upon me. They were dead and they were hungry. When the dead are hungry they judge the living without pity. They do not wait until an action has been achieved, a crime committed. They judge in advance.

Only when I perceived the silence of the boy, a silence eloquent in his eyes, did I decide to speak. He had a look of anxiety which made him seem older, more mature. I shall speak up, I said to myself. They have no right to condemn the little boy.

As I approached my father I saw the sorrow on his face. My father had stolen away a minute before the Angel of Death came to take him; in cheating the Angel he had taken with him the human sorrow which he endured while he was alive.

"Father," I said, "don't judge me. Judge God. He created the universe and made justice stem from injustices. He brought it about that a people should attain happiness through tears, that the freedom of a nation, like that of a man, should be a monument built upon a pile, a foundation of dead bodies. . . ."

I stood in front of him, not knowing what to do with my head, my eyes, my hands. I wanted to transfer the lifeblood of my body into my voice. At moments I fancied I had done so. I talked for a long time, telling him things that doubtless he already knew, since he had taught them to me. If I repeated them it was only in order to prove to him that I had not forgotten.

"Don't judge me, Father," I implored him, trembling with despair. "You must judge God. He is the first cause, the prime mover; He conceived men and things the way they are. You are dead, Father, and only the dead may judge God."

But he did not react. The sorrow written upon his emaciated, unshaven face became even more human than before. I left him and went over to my mother, who was standing at his right side. But my pain was too great for me to address her. I thought I heard her murmur: "Poor boy, poor boy!" and tears came to my eyes. Finally I said that I wasn't a murderer, that she had not given birth to a murderer but to a soldier, to a fighter for freedom, to an idealist who had sacrificed his peace of mind —a possession more precious than life itself—to his people, to his people's right to the light of day, to joy, to the laughter of children. In a halting, feverishly sobbing voice, this was all that I could find to say.

When she too failed to react I left her and went to my old master, of all those present the least changed by death. Alive, he had been very much the same as now; we used to say that he was not of this world, and now this was literally true.

"I haven't betrayed you," I said, as if the deed were already done. "If I were to refuse to obey orders I should betray my living friends. And the living have more rights over us than the dead. You told me that yourself. *Therefore choose life,* it is written in the Scriptures. I have espoused the cause of the living, and that is no betrayal."

Beside him stood Yerachmiel, my friend and comrade and brother. Yerachmiel was the son of a coachman, with the hands of a laborer and the soul of a saint. We two were the master's favorite pupils; every evening he studied with us the secrets of the Cabala. I did not know that Yerachmiel too was dead. I realized it only at the moment when I saw him in the crowd, at the master's side—or rather a respectful step behind him.

"Yerachmiel my brother," I said, ". . . remember . . . ?"

Together we had spun impossible dreams. According to the Cabala, if a man's soul is sufficiently pure and his love deep enough he can bring the Messiah to earth. Yerachmiel and I decided to try. Of course we were aware of the danger: No one can force God's hand with impunity. Men older, wiser, and more mature than ourselves had tried in vain to wrest the Messiah from the chains of the future; failing in their purpose they had lost their faith, their reason, and even their lives. Yerachmiel and I knew all this, but we were resolved to carry out our plan regardless of the obstacles that lay in wait along the way. We promised to stick to each other, whatever might happen. If one of us were to die, the other would carry on. And so we made preparations for a voyage in depth. We purified our souls and bodies, fasting by day and praying by night. In order to cleanse our mouths and their utterances we spoke as little as possible and on the Sabbath we spoke not at all.

Perhaps our attempt might have been successful. But war broke out and we were driven away from our homes. The last time I had seen

Yerachmiel he was one of a long column of marching Jews deported to Germany. A week later I was sent to Germany myself. Yerachmiel was in one camp, I in another. Often I wondered whether he had continued his efforts alone. Now I knew: he had continued, and he was dead.

"Yerachmiel," I said; "Yerachmiel my brother, remember. . . ."

Something about him had changed: his hands. Now they were the hands of a saint.

"We too," I said, "my comrades in the Movement and I, are trying to force God's hand. You who are dead should help us, not hinder. . . ."

But Yerachmiel and his hands were silent. And somewhere in the universe of time the Messiah was silent as well. I left him and went over to the little boy I used to be.

"Are you too judging me?" I asked. "You of all people have the least right to do that. You're lucky; you died young. If you'd gone on living you'd be in my place."

Then the boy spoke. His voice was filled with echoes of disquiet and longing.

"I'm not judging you," he said. "We're not here to sit in judgment. We're here simply because you're here. We're present wherever you go; we are what you do. When you raise your eyes to Heaven we share in their sight; when you pat the head of a hungry child a thousand hands are laid on his head; when you give bread to a beggar we give him that taste of paradise which only the poor can savor. Why are we silent? Because silence is not only our dwelling-place but our very being as well. We *are* silence. And your silence is us. You carry us with you. Occasionally you may see us, but most of the time we are invisible to you. When you see us you imagine that we are sitting in judgment upon you. You are wrong. Your silence is your judge."

Suddenly the beggar's arm brushed against mine. I turned and saw him behind me. I knew that he was not the Angel of Death but the prophet Elijah.

"I hear Gad's footsteps," he said. "He's coming up the stairs."

"I hear Gad's footsteps," said Ilana, touching my arm. "He's coming up the stairs."

Slowly and with a blank look on his face Gad came into the room. Ilana ran toward him and kissed his lips, but gently he pushed her away.

"You stayed down there so long," she said. "What kept you?"

A cruel, sad smile crossed Gad's face.

"Nothing," he said. "I was watching him eat."

"He ate?" I asked in surprise. "You mean to say he was able to eat?"

"Yes, he ate," said Gad. "And with a good appetite, too."

I could not understand.

"What?" I exclaimed. "You mean to say he was hungry?"

"I didn't say he was hungry," Gad retorted. "I said he ate with a good appetite."

"So he wasn't hungry," I insisted.

Gad's face darkened.

"No, he wasn't hungry."

"Then why did he eat?"

"I don't know," said Gad nervously. "Probably to show me that he can eat even if he's not hungry."

Ilana scrutinized his face. She tried to catch his eye, but Gad was staring into space.

"What did you do after that?" she asked uneasily.

"After what?" said Gad brusquely.

"After he'd finished eating."

Gad shrugged his shoulders.

"Nothing," he said.

"What do you mean, *nothing?*"

"Nothing. He told me stories."

Ilana shook his arm.

"Stories? What kind of stories?"

Gad sighed in resignation.

"Just stories," he repeated, obviously tired of answering questions he considered grotesque.

I wanted to ask if he had laughed, if the hostage had got a laugh out of him. But I refrained. The answer could only have been absurd.

Gad's reappearance had roused Gideon and Joab from their sleep. With haggard faces they looked around the room, as if to assure themselves they weren't dreaming. Stifling a yawn, Joab asked Gad for the time.

"Four o'clock," said Gad, consulting his watch.

"So late? I'd never have thought it."

Gad beckoned to me to come closer.

"Soon it will be day," he observed.

"I know."

"You know what you have to do?"

"Yes, I know."

He took a revolver out of his pocket and handed it to me. I hesitated.

"Take it," said Gad.

The revolver was black and nearly new. I was afraid to even touch it, for in it lay all the whole difference between what I was and what I was going to be.

"What are you waiting for?" asked Gad impatiently. "Take it."

I held out my hand and took it. I examined it for a long time as if I did not know what purpose it could possibly serve. Finally I slipped it into my trouser pocket.

"I'd like to ask you a question," I said to Gad.

"Go ahead."

"Did he make you laugh?"

Gad stared at me coldly, as if he had not understood my question or the necessity for it. His brow was furrowed with preoccupation.

"John Dawson," I said. "Did he make you laugh?"

Gad's eyes stared through me; I felt them going through my head and coming out the other side. He must have been wondering what was going on in my mind, why I harped on this unimportant question, why I didn't seem to be suffering or to be masking my suffering or lack of suffering.

"No," he said at last; "he didn't make me laugh."

His own mask cracked imperceptibly. All his efforts were bent upon controlling the expression of his eyes, but he had neglected his mouth, and it was there that the crack showed. His upper lip betrayed bitterness and anger.

"How did you do it?" I asked in mock admiration. "Weren't his stories funny?"

Gad made a strange noise, not unlike a laugh. The silence that followed accentuated the sadness which an invisible hand had traced upon his lips.

"Oh, they were funny all right, very funny. But they didn't make me laugh."

He took a cigarette out of his shirt pocket, lit it, drew a few puffs and then, without waiting for me to ask anything more, went on:

"I was thinking of David, that's all."

I'll think of David too, I reflected. He'll protect me. John Dawson may try to make me laugh, but I won't do it. David will come to my rescue.

"It's getting late," said Joab, stifling another yawn.

The night was still looking in on us. But quite obviously it was getting ready to go away. I came to a sudden decision.

"I'm going down," I said.

"So soon?" said Gad, in a tone revealing either emotion or mere surprise. "You've got plenty of time. As much as an hour. . . ."

I said that I wanted to go down before the time was up, to see the fellow, and talk, and get to know him. It was cowardly, I said, to kill a complete stranger. It was like war, where you don't shoot at men but into the night, and the wounded night emits cries of pain which are almost human. You shoot into the darkness, and you never know whether any of the enemy was killed, or which one. To execute a stranger would be the same thing. If I were to see him only as he died I should feel as if I had shot at a dead man.

This was the reason I gave for my decision. I'm not sure it was exact. Looking back, it seems to me that I was moved by curiosity. I had never seen a hostage before. I wanted to see a hostage who was doomed to die and who told funny stories. Curiosity or bravado? Perhaps a little of both. . . .

"Do you want me to go with you?" asked Gad. A lock of hair had fallen over his forehead, but he did not push it back.

"No, Gad," I said. "I want to be alone with him."

Gad smiled. He was a commander, proud of his subaltern and expressing his pride in a smile. He laid his hand affectionately on my shoulder.

"Do you want someone to go with you?" asked the beggar.

"No," I repeated. "I'd rather be alone."

His eyes were immeasurably kind.

"You can't do it without them," he said, nodding his head in the direction of the crowd behind us.

"They can come later," I conceded.

The beggar took my head in his hands and looked into my eyes. His look was so powerful that for a moment I doubted my identity. I am that look, I said to myself. What else could I be? The beggar has many looks, and I am one of them. But his expression radiated kindness, and I knew that he could not regard kindly his own look. That was how my identity came back to me.

"Very well," he said; "they'll come later."

Now the boy, looking over the shadowy heads and bodies between us, offered to go with me. "Later," I said. My answer made him sad, but I could only repeat: "Later. I want to be alone with him."

"Good," said the child. "We'll come later."

I let my look wander over the room, hoping to leave it there and pick it up when I returned.

Ilana was talking to Gad, but he did not listen. Joab was yawning. Gideon rubbed his forehead as if he had a headache.

In an hour everything will be different, I reflected. I shan't see it the same way. The table, the chairs, the walls, the window, they will all have changed. Only the dead–my father and mother, the master and Yerachmiel–will be the same, for we all of us change together, in the same way, doing the same things.

I patted my pocket to make sure the revolver was still there. It was; indeed, I had the strange impression that it was alive, that its life was part of mine, that it had the same present and future destiny as myself. I was its destiny and it was mine. In an hour it too will have changed, I reflected.

"It's late," said Joab, stretching.

With my eyes I bade farewell to the room, to Ilana, to Gideon and his prayers, to Joab and his confused expression, to the table, the window, the walls, and the night. Then I went hurriedly into the kitchen as if I were going to my own execution. As I went down the stairs my steps slackened and became heavy.

V

John Dawson was a handsome man. In spite of his unshaven face, tousled hair, and rumpled shirt there was something distinguished about him.

He seemed to be in his forties–a professional soldier, no doubt–with penetrating eyes, a resolute chin, thin lips, a broad forehead, and slender hands.

When I pushed open the door I found him lying on a camp bed, staring up at the ceiling. The bed was the only piece of furniture in the narrow white cell. Thanks to an ingenious system of ventilation we had installed, the windowless cell was less stuffy than the open room above.

When he became aware of my presence John Dawson showed neither surprise nor fear. He did not get up but simply raised himself into a sitting position. He scrutinized me at length without saying a word, as if measuring the density of my silence. His stare enveloped my whole being and I wondered if he saw that I was a mass of eyes.

"What time is it?" he asked abruptly.

In an uncertain voice I answered that it was after four. He frowned, as if in an effort to grasp the hidden meaning of my words.

"When is sunrise?" he said.

"In an hour," I answered. And I added, without knowing why: "Approximately."

We stared at each other for a long interval, and suddenly I realized that time was not moving at its normal, regular pace. In an hour I shall kill him, I thought. And yet I didn't really believe it. This hour which separates me from murder will be longer than a lifetime. It will belong, always, to the distant future; it will never be one with the past.

There was something age-old in our situation. We were alone not only in the cell but in the world as well, he seated, I standing, the victim and the executioner. We were the first–or the last–men of creation; certainly we were alone. And God? He was present, somewhere. Perhaps He was incarnate in the liking with which John Dawson inspired me. The lack of hate between executioner and victim, perhaps this is God.

We were alone in the narrow white cell, he sitting on the bed and I standing before him, staring at each other. I wished I could see myself through his eyes. Perhaps he was wishing he could see himself through mine. I felt neither hate nor anger nor pity; I liked him, that was all. I liked the way he scowled when he was thinking, the way he looked down at his nails when he was trying to formulate his thoughts. Under other circumstances he might have been my friend.

"Are you the one?" he asked abruptly.

How had he guessed it? Perhaps by his sense of smell. Death has an odor and I had brought it in with me. Or perhaps as soon as I came through the door he had seen that I had neither arms nor legs nor shoulders, that I was all eyes.

"Yes," I said.

I felt quite calm. The step before the last is the hard one; the last step brings clearheadedness and assurance.

"What's your name?" he asked.

This question disturbed me. Is every condemned man bound to ask it? Why does he want to know the name of his executioner? In order to take it with him to the next world? For what purpose? Perhaps I shouldn't have told him, but I could refuse nothing to a man condemned to die.

"Elisha," I said.

"Very musical," he observed.

"It's the name of a prophet," I explained. "Elisha was a disciple of Elijah. He restored life to a little boy by lying upon him and breathing into his mouth."

"You're doing the opposite," he said with a smile.

There was no trace of anger or hate in his voice. Probably he too felt clearheaded and assured.

"How old are you?" he asked with aroused interest.

"Eighteen," I told him. For some reason I added: "Nearly nineteen."

He raised his head and there was pity on his thin, suddenly sharpened face. He stared at me for several seconds, then sadly nodded his head.

"I'm sorry for you," he said.

I felt his pity go through me. I knew that it would permeate me completely, that the next day I should be sorry for myself.

"Tell me a story," I said. "A funny one, if you can."

I felt my body grow heavy. The next day it would be heavier still, I reflected. The next day it would be weighed down by my life and his death, "I'm the last man you'll see before you die," I went on. "Try to make him laugh."

Once more I was enveloped by his look of pity. I wondered if everyone condemned to die looked at the last man he saw in the same way, if every victim pitied his executioner.

"I'm sorry for you," John Dawson repeated.

By dint of an enormous effort I managed to smile.

"That's no funny story," I remarked.

He smiled at me in return. Which of our two smiles was the sadder?

"Are you sure it isn't funny?"

No, I wasn't so sure. Perhaps there *was* something funny about it. The seated victim, the standing executioner–smiling, and understanding each other better than if they were childhood friends. Such are the workings of time. The veneer of conventional attitudes was wiped off; every word and look and gesture was naked truth instead of just one of its facets. There was harmony between us; my smile answered his; his pity was mine. No human being would ever understand me as he understood me at this hour. Yet I knew that this was solely on account of the roles that were imposed upon us. This was what made it a funny story.

"Sit down," said John Dawson, making room for me to his left on the bed.

I sat down. Only then did I realize that he was a whole head taller than I. And his legs were longer than mine, which did not even touch the ground.

"I have a son your age," he began, "but he's not at all like you. He's fair-haired, strong, and healthy. He likes to eat, drink, go to the pictures, laugh, sing, and go out with the girls. He has none of your anxiety, your unhappiness."

And he went on to tell me more about this son who was "studying at Cambridge." Every sentence was a tongue of flame which burned my body. With my right hand I patted the revolver in my pocket. The revolver too was incandescent, and burned my fingers.

I mustn't listen to him, I told myself. He's my enemy, and the enemy has no story. I must think of something else. That's why I wanted to see him, in order to think of something else while he was talking. Something else . . . but what? Of Ilana? Of Gad? Yes, I should think of Gad, who was thinking of David. I should think of our hero, David ben Moshe, who. . . .

I shut my eyes to see David better, but to no purpose, because I had never met him. A name isn't enough, I thought. One must have a face, a voice, a body, and pin the name of David ben Moshe upon them. Better think of a face, a voice, a body that I actually knew. Gad? No, it was difficult to imagine Gad as a man condemned to die. Condemned to die . . . that was it. Why hadn't I thought of it before? John Dawson was condemned to die; why shouldn't I baptize him David ben Moshe? For the next five minutes you are David ben Moshe . . . in the raw, cold, white light of the death cell of the prison at Acre. There is a knock at the door, and the rabbi comes in to read the Psalms with you and hear you say the *Vidui,* that terrible confession in which you admit your responsibility not only for the sins you have committed, whether by word, deed, or thought, but also for those you may have caused others to commit. The rabbi gives you the traditional blessing: "The Lord bless you and keep you . . ." and exhorts you to have no fear. You answer that you are unafraid, that if you had a chance you would do the same thing all over. The rabbi smiles and says that everyone on the outside is proud of you. He is so deeply moved that he has to make a visible effort to hold back his tears; finally the effort is too much for him and he sobs aloud. But you, David, do not cry. You have tender feelings for the rabbi because he is the last man (the executioner and his assistants don't count) you will see before you die. Because he is sobbing you try to comfort him. "Don't cry," you say; "I'm not afraid. You don't need to be sorry for me."

"I'm sorry for you," said John Dawson. *"You* worry me, not my son."

He put his feet down on the floor. He was so tall that when he stood up he had to bend over in order not to bump his head against the ceiling. He put his hands in the pockets of his rumpled khaki trousers and began to pace up and down the cell: five steps in one direction, five in the other.

"That I admit is funny," I observed.

He did not seem to hear, but went on pacing from wall to wall. I looked at my watch; it was twenty past four. Suddenly he stopped in front of me and asked for a cigarette. I had a package of Players in my pocket and wanted to give them to him. But he refused to take the whole package, saying quite calmly that obviously he didn't have time to smoke them all.

Then he said with sudden impatience:

"Have you a pencil and paper?"

I tore several pages out of my notebook and handed them to him, with a pencil.

"Just a short note which I'd like to have sent to my son," he declared. "I'll put down the address."

I handed him the notebook to use as a pad. He laid the notebook on the bed and leaned over to write from a standing position. For several minutes the silence was broken only by the sound of the pencil running over the paper.

I looked down in fascination at his smooth-skinned hands with their long, slender, aristocratic fingers. With hands like those, I thought, it's easy to get along. There's no need to bow, smile, talk, pay compliments, or bring flowers. A pair of such hands do the whole job. Rodin would have liked to sculpt them. . . .

The thought of Rodin made me think of Stefan, a German I had known at Buchenwald. He had been a sculptor before the war, but when I met him the Nazis had cut off his right hand.

In Berlin, during the first years after Hitler came to power, Stefan and some of his friends organized an embryonic resistance group which the Gestapo uncovered shortly after its founding. Stefan was arrested, questioned, and subjected to torture. Give us names, they told him, and we will set you free. They beat and starved him, but he would not talk. Day after day and night after night they prevented him from sleeping, but still he did not give in. Finally he was haled before the Berlin chief of the Gestapo, a timid, mild man, who in a soft-spoken, fatherly manner, advised him to stop being foolishly stubborn. The sculptor heard him out in stony silence. "Come on," said the chief. "Give us just one name, as a sign of good will." Still Stefan would not speak. "Too bad," said the chief. "You're obliging me to hurt you."

At a sign from the chief two SS men led the prisoner into what looked like an operating room, with a dentist's chair installed near the window. Beside it, on a table with a white oilcloth cover, was an orderly array of surgical instruments. They shut the window, tied Stefan onto the chair and lit cigarettes. The mild-mannered chief came into the room, wearing a white doctor's jacket.

"Don't be afraid," he said; "I used to be a surgeon."

He puttered around with the instruments and then sat down in front of the prisoner's chair.

"Give me your right hand," he said. Studying it at close range, he added: "I'm told you're a sculptor. You have nothing to say? Well, I know it. I can tell from your hands. A man's hands tell a lot about him. Take mine, for instance. You'd never take them for a surgeon's hands, would you? The truth is that I never wanted to be a doctor. I wanted to be a painter or a musician. I never became one, but I still have the hands of an artist. Look at them."

"I looked at them, with fascination," Stefan told me. "He had the most beautiful, the most angelic hands I have ever seen. You would have sworn that they belonged to a sensitive, unworldly man."

"As a sculptor you need your hands," the Gestapo chief went on. "Unfortunately *we* don't need them," and so saying he cut off a finger.

The next day he cut off a second finger, and the day after that a third. Five days, five fingers. All five fingers of the right hand were gone.

"Don't worry," the chief assured him. "From a medical point of view, everything is in good order. There's no danger of infection."

"I saw him five times," Stefan told me. (For some inexplicable reason he was not killed but simply sent to a concentration camp.) "Every day for five days I saw him from very near by. And every time I could not take my eyes off those hands of his, the most beautifully shaped hands I had ever seen. . . ."

John Dawson finished his note and held it out to me, but I hardly saw it. My attention was taken by his proud smooth-skinned, frail hands.

"Are you an artist?" I asked him.

He shook his head.

"You've never painted or played a musical instrument, or at least wanted to do so?"

He scrutinized me in silence and then said dryly:

"No."

"Then perhaps you studied medicine."

"I never studied medicine," he said, almost angrily.

"Too bad."

"Too bad? Why?"

"Look at your hands. They're the hands of a surgeon. The kind of hands it takes to cut off fingers."

Deliberately he laid the sheets of paper on the bed.

"Is that a funny story?" he asked.

"Yes, very funny. The fellow who told it to me thought so. He used to laugh over it until he cried."

John Dawson shook his head and said in an infinitely sad voice:

"You hate me, don't you?"

I didn't hate him at all, but I wanted to hate him. That would have made it all very easy. Hate—like faith or love or war—justifies everything.

"Elisha, why did you kill John Dawson?"

"He was my enemy."

"John Dawson? Your enemy? You'll have to explain that better."

"Very well. John Dawson was an Englishman. The English were enemies of the Jews in Palestine. So he was my enemy."

"But Elisha, I still don't understand why you killed him. Were you his only enemy?"

"No, but I had orders. You know what that means."

"And did the orders make him your only enemy? Speak up, Elisha. Why did you kill John Dawson?"

If I had alleged hate, all these questions would have been spared me.

Why did I kill John Dawson? Because I hated him, that's all. The absolute quality of hate explains any human action even if it throws something inhuman around it.

I certainly wanted to hate him. That was partly why I had come to engage him in conversation before I killed him. It was absurd reasoning on my part, but the fact is that while we were talking I hoped to find in him, or in myself, something that would give rise to hate.

A man hates his enemy because he hates his own hate. He says to himself: This fellow, my enemy, has made me capable of hate. I hate him not because he's my enemy, not because he hates me, but because he arouses me to hate.

John Dawson has made me a murderer, I said to myself. He has made me the murderer of John Dawson. He deserves my hate. Were it not for him, I might still be a murderer, but I wouldn't be the murderer of John Dawson.

Yes, I had come down to the cellar to feed my hate. It seemed easy enough. Armies and governments the world over have a definite technique for provoking hate. By speeches and films and other kinds of propaganda they create an image of the enemy in which he is the incarnation of evil, the symbol of suffering, the fountainhead of the cruelty and injustice of all times. The technique is infallible, I told myself, and I shall turn it upon my victim.

I did try to draw upon it. All enemies are equal, I said. Each one is responsible for the crimes committed by the others. They have different faces, but they all have the same hands, the hands that cut my friends' tongues and fingers.

As I went down the stairs I was sure that I would meet the man who had condemned David ben Moshe to death, the man who had killed my parents, the man who had come between me and the man I had wanted to become, and who was now ready to kill the man in me. I felt quite certain that I would hate him.

The sight of his uniform added fuel to my flames. There is nothing like a uniform for whipping up hate. When I saw his slender hands I said to myself: Stefan will carve out my hate for them. Again, when he bent his head to write the farewell note to his son, the son "studying at Cambridge," who liked to "laugh and go out with the girls," I thought: David is writing a last letter too, probably to the Old Man, before he puts his head in the hangman's noose. And when he talked, my heart went out to David, who had no one to talk to, except the rabbi. You can't talk to a rabbi, for he is too concerned with relaying your last words to God. You can confess your sins, recite the Psalms or the prayers for the dead, receive his consolation or console him, but you can't talk, not really.

I thought of David whom I had never met and would never know. Because he was not the first of us to be hanged we knew exactly when and how he would die. At about five o'clock in the morning the cell door would open and the prison director would say: Get ready, David ben Moshe; the time has come. "The time has come," this is the ritual phrase, as if this and no other time had any significance. David would cast a look around the cell and the rabbi would say: "Come, my son." They would go out, leaving the cell door open behind them (for some reason no one ever remembers to close it) and start down the long passageway leading to the execution chamber. As the man of the hour, conscious of the fact that the others were there solely on his account, David would walk in the center of the group. He would walk with his head held high—all our heroes held their heads high—and a strange smile on his lips. On either side of the passageway a hundred eyes and ears would wait for him to go by, and the first of the prisoners to perceive his approach would intone the *Hatikva,* the song of hope. As the group advanced the song would grow louder, more human, more powerful, until its sound rivaled that of the footsteps. . . .

When John Dawson spoke of his son I heard David's footsteps and the rising song. With his words John Dawson was trying to cover up the footsteps, to erase the sight of David walking down the passageway and the strange smile on his lips, to drown out the despairing sound of the *Hatikva*, the song of hope.

I wanted to hate him. Hate would have made everything so simple. . . . Why did you kill John Dawson? I killed him because I hated him. I hated him because David ben Moshe hated him, and David ben Moshe hated him because he talked while he David was going down the somber passageway at whose far end he must meet his death.

"You hate me, Elisha, don't you?" John Dawson asked. There was a look of overflowing tenderness in his eyes.

"I'm trying to hate you," I answered.

"Why must you try to hate me, Elisha?"

He spoke in a warm, slightly sad voice, remarkable for the absence of curiosity.

Why? I wondered. What a question! Without hate, everything that my comrades and I were doing would be done in vain. Without hate we could not hope to obtain victory. Why do I try to hate you, John Dawson? Because my people have never known how to hate. Their tragedy, throughout the centuries, has stemmed from their inability to hate those who have humiliated and from time to time exterminated them. Now our only chance lies in hating you, in learning the necessity and the art of hate. Otherwise, John Dawson, our future will only be an extension of the past, and the Messiah will wait indefinitely for his deliverance.

"Why must you try to hate me?" John Dawson asked again.

"In order to give my action a meaning which may somehow transcend it."

Once more he slowly shook his head.

"I'm sorry for you," he repeated.

I looked at my watch. Ten minutes to five. Ten minutes to go. In ten minutes I should commit the most important and conclusive act of my life. I got up from the bed.

"Get ready, John Dawson," I said.

"Has the time come?" he asked.

"Very nearly," I answered.

He rose and leaned his head against the wall, probably in order to collect his thoughts or to pray or something of the kind.

Eight minutes to five. Eight minutes to go. I took the revolver out of my pocket. What should I do if he tried to take it from me? There was no chance of his escaping. The house was well guarded and there was no way of getting out of the cellar except through the kitchen. Gad, Gideon, Joab, and Ilana were on guard upstairs, and John Dawson knew it.

Six minutes to five. Six minutes to go. Suddenly I felt quite clear-headed. There was an unexpected light in the cell; the boundaries were drawn, the roles well defined. The time of doubt and questioning and uncertainty was over. I was a hand holding a revolver; I was the revolver that held my hand.

Five minutes to five. Five minutes to go.

"Have no fear, my son," the rabbi said to David ben Moshe. "God is with you."

"Don't worry, I'm a surgeon," said the mild-mannered Gestapo chief to Stefan.

"The note," John Dawson said, turning around. "You'll send it to my boy, won't you?"

He was standing against the wall; he was the wall. Three minutes to five. Three minutes to go.

"God is with you," said the rabbi. He was crying, but now David did not see him.

"The note. You won't forget, will you?" John Dawson insisted.

"I'll send it," I promised, and for some reason I added: "I'll mail it today."

"Thank you," said John Dawson.

David is entering the chamber from which he will not come out alive.

The hangman is waiting for him. He is all eyes. David mounts the scaffold. The hangman asks him whether he wants his eyes banded. Firmly David answers no. A Jewish fighter dies with his eyes open. He wants to look death in the face.

Two minutes to five. I took a handkerchief out of my pocket, but John Dawson ordered me to put it back. An Englishman dies with his eyes open. He wants to look death in the face.

Sixty seconds before five o'clock. One minute to go.

Noiselessly the cell door opened and the dead trooped in, filling us with their silence. The narrow cell had become almost unbearably stuffy.

The beggar touched my shoulder and said:

"Day is at hand."

And the boy who looked the way I used to look said, with an uneasy expression on his face:

"This is the first time—" His voice trailed off, and then, as if remembering that he had left the sentence suspended he picked it up: "the first time I've seen an execution."

My father and mother were there too, and the grizzled master, and Yerachmiel. Their silence stared at me.

David stiffened and began to sing the *Hatikva.*

John Dawson smiled, with his head against the wall and his body as erect as if he were saluting a general.

"Why are you smiling?" I asked.

"You must never ask a man who is looking at you the reason for his smile," said the beggar.

"I'm smiling," said John Dawson, "because all of a sudden it has occurred to me that I don't know why I am dying." And after a moment of silence he added: "Do you?"

"You see?" said the beggar. "I told you that was no question to ask a man who is about to die."

Twenty seconds. This minute was more than sixty seconds long.

"Don't smile," I said to John Dawson. What I meant was: "I can't shoot a man who is smiling."

Ten seconds.

"I want to tell you a story," he said, "a funny story."

I raised my right arm.

Five seconds.

"Elisha—"

Two seconds. He was still smiling.

"Too bad," said the little boy. "I'd like to have heard his story."

One second.

"Elisha–" said the hostage.

I fired. When he pronounced my name he was already dead; the bullet had gone through his heart. A dead man, whose lips were still warm, had pronounced my name: *Elisha*.

He sank very slowly to the ground, as if he had slipped from the top of the wall. His body remained in a sitting position, with the head bowed down between the knees, as if he were still waiting to be killed. I stayed for a few moments beside him. There was a pain in my head and my body was growing heavy. The shot had left me deaf and dumb. That's it, I said to myself. It's done. I've killed. I've killed Elisha.

The ghosts began to leave the cell, taking John Dawson with them. The little boy walked at his side as if to guide him. I seemed to hear my mother say: "Poor boy! Poor boy!"

Then with heavy footsteps I walked up the stairs leading to the kitchen. I walked into the room, but it was not the same. The ghosts were gone. Joab was no longer yawning. Gideon was looking down at his nails and praying for the repose of the dead. Ilana lifted a sad countenance upon me; Gad lit a cigarette. They were silent, but their silence was different from the silence which all night long had weighed upon mine. On the horizon the sun was rising.

I went to the window. The city was still asleep. Somewhere a child woke up and began to cry. I wished that a dog would bark, but there was no dog anywhere nearby.

The night lifted, leaving behind it a grayish light the color of stagnant water. Soon there was only a tattered fragment of darkness, hanging in midair, the other side of the window. Fear caught my throat. The tattered fragment of darkness had a face. Looking at it, I understood the reason for my fear. The face was my own.

The Clicking of Cuthbert **P. G. Wodehouse**

The author himself describes this story as "the work of a very nearly desperate man, an 18 handicap man, who has got to look pretty slippery if he doesn't want to find himself in the twenties again." The fanaticism of the real golfer shows in every line of this amusing yarn. And then, for good measure, he launches out and takes the hide off two-fisted dowagers who cram culture down the throats of good Americans to whom a proper grip on a short iron is much more important than a proper appreciation of the latest Russian novel.

And finally, on top of everything else, he introduces Adeline into the story, a girl so beautiful that, in the opinion of Cuthbert Banks, the rest of her sex looked like battered repaints.

What more could one ask?

The Clicking of Cuthbert — P. G. Wodehouse

The author himself described this story as "the work of a very nearly desperate man, an 18 handicap man, who has got to look pretty slippy if he doesn't want to find himself in the [illegible] again." The [illegible] of the real golfer shows in every [illegible]. And then, for good measure, he [illegible] out and takes the [illegible] off [illegible] who [illegible] on the [illegible] of good Americans to whom a proper grip on a [illegible] is much more important than a proper appreciation of the Great Russian novel.

And finally, on top of everything else, he introduces [illegible] into the story, a girl so [illegible] that, in the opinion of Cuthbert Banks, the tea [illegible] like [illegible].

What more could one ask?

THE CLICKING OF CUTHBERT

P. G. Wodehouse

The young man came into the smoking-room of the club-house, and flung his bag with a clatter on the floor. He sank moodily into an arm-chair and pressed the bell.

"Waiter!"

"Sir?"

The young man pointed at the bag with every evidence of distaste.

"You may have these clubs," he said. "Take them away. If you don't want them yourself, give them to one of the caddies."

Across the room the Oldest Member gazed at him with a grave sadness through the smoke of his pipe. His eye was deep and dreamy,–the eye of a man who, as the poet says, has seen Golf steadily and seen it whole.

"You are giving up golf?" he said.

He was not altogether unprepared for such an attitude on the young man's part: for from his eyrie on the terrace above the ninth green he had observed him start out on the afternoon's round and had seen him lose a couple of balls in the lake at the second hole after taking seven strokes at the first.

"Yes!" cried the young man fiercely. "For ever, dammit! Footling game! Blanked infernal fat-headed silly ass of a game! Nothing but a waste of time."

The Sage winced.

"Don't say that, my boy."

"But I do say it. What earthly good is golf? Life is stern and life is earnest. We live in a practical age. All round us we see foreign competition making itself unpleasant. And we spend our time playing golf! What do we get out of it? Is golf any *use?* That's what I'm asking you. Can you name me a single case where devotion to this pestilential pastime has done a man any practical good?"

The Sage smiled gently.

"I could name a thousand."

"One will do."

"I will select," said the Sage, "from the innumerable memories that rush to my mind, the story of Cuthbert Banks."

"Never heard of him."

"Be of good cheer," said the Oldest Member. "You are going to hear of him now."

It was in the picturesque little settlement of Wood Hills (said the Oldest Member) that the incidents occurred which I am about to relate. Even if you have never been in Wood Hills, that suburban paradise is probably familiar to you by name. Situated at a convenient distance from the city, it combines in a notable manner the advantages of town life with the pleasant surroundings and healthful air of the country. Its inhabitants live in commodious houses, standing in their own grounds, and enjoy so many luxuries–such as gravel soil, main drainage, electric light, telephone, baths (h. and c.), and company's own water, that you might be pardoned for imagining life to be so ideal for them that no possible improvement could be added to their lot. Mrs. Willoughby Smethurst was under no such delusion. What Wood Hills needed to make it perfect, she realized, was Culture. Material comforts are all very well, but, if the *summum bonum* is to be achieved, the Soul also demands a look in, and it was Mrs. Smethurst's unfaltering resolve that never while she had her strength should the Soul be handed the loser's end. It was her intention to make Wood Hills a centre of all that was most cultivated and refined, and, golly! how she had succeeded. Under her presidency the Wood Hills Literary and Debating Society had tripled its membership.

But there is always a fly in the ointment, a caterpillar in the salad. The local golf club, an institution to which Mrs. Smethurst strongly objected, had also tripled its membership; and the division of the community into two rival camps, the Golfers and the Cultured, had become more marked than ever. This division always acute, had attained now to the dimensions of a Schism. The rival sects treated one another with a cold hostility.

Unfortunate episodes came to widen the breach. Mrs. Smethurst's house adjoined the links, standing to the right of the fourth tee: and, as the Literary Society was in the habit of entertaining visiting lecturers, many a golfer had foozled his drive owing to sudden loud outbursts of applause coinciding with his down-swing. And not long before this story opens a sliced ball, whizzing in at the open window, had come within an ace of incapacitating Raymond Parsloe Devine, the rising young novelist (who rose at that moment a clear foot and a half) from any further exercise of his art. Two inches, indeed, to the right and Raymond must inevitably have handed in his dinner-pail.

To make matters worse, a ring at the front-door bell followed almost immediately, and the maid ushered in a young man of pleasing appearance in a sweater and baggy knickerbockers who apologetically but firmly insisted on playing his ball where it lay, and what with the shock of the lecturer's narrow escape and the spectacle of the intruder standing on the table and working away with a niblick, the afternoon's session had to be classed as a complete frost. Mr. Devine's determination, from which no argument could swerve him, to deliver the rest of his lecture in the coal-cellar gave the meeting a jolt from which it never recovered.

I have dwelt upon this incident, because it was the means of introducing Cuthbert Banks to Mrs. Smethurst's niece, Adeline. As Cuthbert, for it was he who had so nearly reduced the muster-roll of rising novelists by one, hopped down from the table after his stroke, he was suddenly aware that a beautiful girl was looking at him intently. As a matter of fact, everyone in the room was looking at him intently, none more so than Raymond Parsloe Devine, but none of the others were beautiful girls. Long as the members of Wood Hills Literary Society were on brain, they were short on looks, and, to Cuthbert's excited eye, Adeline Smethurst stood out like a jewel in a pile of coke.

He had never seen her before, for she had only arrived at her aunt's house on the previous day, but he was perfectly certain that life, even when lived in the midst of gravel soil, main drainage, and company's own water, was going to be a pretty poor affair if he did not see her again. Yes, Cuthbert was in love: and it is interesting to record, as showing the effect of the tender emotion on a man's game, that twenty minutes after he had met Adeline he did the short eleventh in one, and as near as a toucher got a three on the four-hundred-yard twelfth.

I will skip lightly over the intermediate stages of Cuthbert's courtship and come to the moment when—at the annual ball in aid of the local Cottage Hospital, the only occasion during the year on which the lion, so to speak, lay down with the lamb, and the Golfers and the Cultured met on terms of easy comradeship, their differences temporarily laid aside—he proposed to Adeline and was badly stymied.

That fair, soulful girl could not see him with a spy-glass.

"Mr. Banks," she said, "I will speak frankly."

"Charge right ahead," assented Cuthbert.

"Deeply sensible as I am of—"

"I know. Of the honour and the compliment and all that. But, passing lightly over all that guff, what seems to be the trouble? I love you to distraction——"

"Love is not everything."

"You're wrong," said Cuthbert, earnestly. "You're right off it. Love——" And he was about to dilate on the theme when she interrupted him.

"I am a girl of ambition."

"And very nice, too," said Cuthbert.

"I am a girl of ambition," repeated Adeline, "and I realise that the fulfilment of my ambitions must come through my husband. I am very ordinary myself——"

"What!" cried Cuthbert. "You ordinary? Why, you are a pearl among women, the queen of your sex. You can't have been looking in a glass lately. You stand alone. Simply alone. You make the rest look like battered repaints."

"Well," said Adeline, softening a trifle, "I believe I am fairly good-looking——"

"Anybody who was content to call you fairly good-looking would describe the Taj Mahal as a pretty nifty tomb."

"But that is not the point. What I mean is, if I marry a nonentity I shall be a nonentity myself for ever. And I would sooner die then be a nonentity."

"And, if I follow your reasoning, you think that that lets *me* out?"

"Well, really, Mr. Banks, *have* you done anything, or are you likely ever to do anything worth while?"

Cuthbert hesitated.

"It's true," he said, "I didn't finish in the first ten in the Open, and I was knocked out in the semifinal of the Amateur, but I won the French Open last year."

"The–what?"

"The French Open Championship. Golf, you know."

"Golf! You waste all your time playing golf. I admire a man who is more spiritual, more intellectual."

A pang of jealousy rent Cuthbert's bosom.

"Like What's-his-name Devine?" he said, sullenly.

"Mr. Devine," replied Adeline, blushing faintly, "is going to be a great man. Already he has achieved much. The critics say that he is more Russian than any other young English writer."

"And is that good?"

"Of course it's good."

"I should have thought the wheeze would be to be more English than any other young English writer."

"Nonsense! Who wants an English writer to be English? You've got to be Russian or Spanish or something to be a real success. The mantle of the great Russians has descended on Mr. Devine."

"From what I've heard of Russians, I should hate to have that happen to *me.*"

"There is no danger of that," said Adeline, scornfully.

"Oh! Well, let me tell you that there is a lot more in me than you think."

"That might easily be so."

"You think I'm not spiritual and intellectual," said Cuthbert, deeply moved. "Very well. Tomorrow I join the Literary Society."

Even as he spoke the words his leg was itching to kick himself for being such a chump, but the sudden expression of pleasure on Adeline's face soothed him; and he went home that night with the feeling that he had taken on something rather attractive. It was only in the cold, grey light of the morning that he realised what he had let himself in for.

I do not know if you have had any experience of suburban literary societies, but the one that flourished under the eye of Mrs. Willoughby Smethurst at Wood Hills was rather more so than the average. With my feeble powers of narrative, I cannot hope to make clear to you all that Cuthbert Banks endured in the next few weeks. And, even if I could, I doubt if I should do so. It is all very well to excite pity and terror, as Aristotle recommends, but there are limits. In the ancient Greek tragedies it was an ironclad rule that all the real rough stuff should take place off-stage, and I shall follow this admirable principle. It will suffice if I say merely that J. Cuthbert Banks had a thin time. After attending eleven debates and fourteen lectures on *vers libre* Poetry, the Seventeenth-Century Essayists, the Neo-Scandinavian Movement in Portuguese Literature, and other subjects of a similar nature, he grew so enfeebled that, on the rare occasions when he had time for a visit to the links, he had to take a full iron for his mashie shots.

It was not simply the oppressive nature of the debates and lectures that sapped his vitality. What really got right in amongst him was the torture of seeing Adeline's adoration of Raymond Parsloe Devine. The man seemed to have made the deepest possible impression upon her plastic emotions. When he spoke, she leaned forward with parted lips and looked at him. When he was not speaking—which was seldom—she leaned back and looked at him. And when he happened to take the next seat to her, she leaned sideways and looked at him. One glance at Mr. Devine would have been more than enough for Cuthbert; but Adeline found him a spectacle that never palled. She could not have gazed at him with a more rapturous intensity if she had been a small child and he a saucer of ice-cream. All this Cuthbert had to witness while still endeavouring to retain the possession of his faculties sufficiently to enable him to duck and back away if somebody suddenly asked him what he thought of the sombre realism of Vladimir Brusiloff. It is little wonder that he tossed in bed, picking at the coverlet, through sleepless nights, and had to have all his waistcoats taken in three inches to keep them from sagging.

This Vladimir Brusiloff to whom I have referred was the famous Russian novelist, and, owing to the fact of his being in the country on a lecturing tour at the moment, there had been something of a boom in his works. The Wood Hills Literary Society had been studying them for weeks, and never since his first entrance into intellectual circles had Cuthbert Banks come nearer to throwing in the towel. Vladimir specialized in grey studies of hopeless misery, where nothing happened till page three hundred and eighty, when the moujik decided to commit suicide. It was tough going for a man whose deepest reading hitherto had been Vardon on the Push-Shot, and there can be no greater proof of the magic of love than the fact that Cuthbert stuck it without a cry. But the strain was terrible and I am inclined to think that he must have cracked, had it not been for the daily reports in the papers of the internecine strife which was proceeding so briskly in Russia. Cuthbert was an optimist at heart, and it seemed to him that, at the rate at which the inhabitants of that interesting country were murdering one another, the supply of Russian novelists must eventually give out.

One morning, as he tottered down the road for the short walk which was now almost the only exercise to which he was equal, Cuthbert met Adeline. A spasm of anguish flitted through all his nerve-centres as he saw that she was accompanied by Raymond Parsloe Devine.

"Good morning, Mr. Banks," said Adeline.

"Good morning," said Cuthbert, hollowly.

"Such good news about Vladimir Brusiloff."

"Dead?" said Cuthbert, with a touch of hope.

"Dead? Of course not. Why should he be? No, Aunt Emily met his manager after his lecture at Queen's Hall yesterday, and he has promised that Mr. Brusiloff shall come to her next Wednesday reception."

"Oh, ah!" said Cuthbert, dully.

"I don't know how she managed it. I think she must have told him that Mr. Devine would be there to meet him."

"But you said he was coming," argued Cuthbert.

"I shall be very glad," said Raymond Devine, "of the opportunity of meeting Brusiloff."

"I'm sure," said Adeline, "he will be very glad of the opportunity of meeting you."

"Possibly," said Mr. Devine. "Possibly. Competent critics have said that my work closely resembles that of the great Russian Masters."

"Your psychology is so deep."

"Yes, yes."

"And your atmosphere."

"Quite."

Cuthbert in a perfect agony of spirit prepared to withdraw from this love-feast. The sun was shining brightly, but the world was black to him. Birds sang in the tree-tops, but he did not hear them. He might have been a moujik for all the pleasure he found in life.

"You will be there, Mr. Banks?" said Adeline, as he turned away.

"Oh, all right," said Cuthbert.

When Cuthbert had entered the drawing-room on the following Wednesday and had taken his usual place in a distant corner where, while able to feast his gaze on Adeline, he had a sporting chance of being overlooked or mistaken for a piece of furniture, he perceived the great Russian thinker seated in the midst of a circle of admiring females. Raymond Parsloe Devine had not yet arrived.

His first glance at the novelist surprised Cuthbert. Doubtless with the best motives, Vladimir Brusiloff had permitted his face to become almost entirely concealed behind a dense zareba of hair, but his eyes were visible through the undergrowth, and it seemed to Cuthbert that there was an expression in them not unlike that of a cat in a strange backyard surrounded by small boys. The man looked forlorn and hopeless, and Cuthbert wondered whether he had had bad news from home.

This was not the case. The latest news which Vladimir Brusiloff had had from Russia had been particularly cheering. Three of his principal creditors had perished in the last massacre of the *bourgeoisie,* and a man whom he owed for five years for a samovar and a pair of overshoes had fled the country, and had not been heard of since. It was not bad news from home that was depressing Vladimir. What was wrong with him was the fact that this was the eighty-second suburban literary reception he had been compelled to attend since he had landed in the country on his lecturing tour, and he was sick to death of it. When his agent had first suggested the trip, he had signed on the dotted line without an instant's hesitation. Worked out in roubles, the fees offered had seemed just about right. But now, as he peered through the brushwood at the faces round him, and realised that eight out of ten of those present had manuscripts of some sort concealed on their persons, and were only waiting for an opportunity to whip them out and start reading, he wished that he had stayed at his quiet home in Nijni-Novgorod, where the worst thing that could happen to a fellow was a brace of bombs coming in through the window and mixing themselves up with his breakfast egg.

At this point in his meditations he was aware that his hostess was looming up before him with a pale young man in horn-rimmed spectacles at her side. There was in Mrs. Smethurst's demeanour something of the unction of the master-of-ceremonies at the big fight who introduces the earnest gentleman who wishes to challenge the winner.

"Oh, Mr. Brusiloff," said Mrs. Smethurst, "I do so want you to meet Mr. Raymond Parsloe Devine, whose work I expect you know. He is one of our younger novelists."

The distinguished visitor peered in a wary and defensive manner through the shrubbery, but did not speak. Inwardly he was thinking how exactly like Mr. Devine was to the eighty-one other younger novelists to whom he had been introduced at various hamlets throughout the country. Raymond Parsloe Devine bowed courteously, while Cuthbert, wedged into his corner, glowered at him.

"The critics," said Mr. Devine, "have been kind enough to say that my poor efforts contain a good deal of the Russian spirit. I owe much to the great Russians. I have been greatly influenced by Sovietski."

Down in the forest something stirred. It was Vladimir Brusiloff's mouth opening, as he prepared to speak. He was not a man who prattled readily, especially in a foreign tongue. He gave the impression that each word was excavated from his interior by some up-to-date process of mining. He glared bleakly at Mr. Devine, and allowed three words to drop out of him.

"Sovietski no good!"

He paused for a moment, set the machinery working again, and delivered five more at the pithead.

"I spit me of Sovietski!"

There was a painful sensation. The lot of a popular idol is in many ways an enviable one, but it has the drawback of uncertainty. Here to-day and gone to-morrow. Until this moment Raymond Parsloe Devine's stock had stood at something considerably over par in Wood Hills intellectual circles, but now there was a rapid slump. Hitherto he had been greatly admired for being influenced by Sovietski, but it appeared now that this was not a good thing to be. It was evidently a rotten thing to be. The law could not touch you for being influenced by Sovietski, but there is an ethical as well as a legal code, and this it was obvious that Raymond Parsloe Devine had transgressed. Women drew away from him slightly, holding their skirts. Men looked at him censoriously. Adeline Smethurst started violently, and dropped a tea-cup. And Cuthbert Banks, doing his popular imitation of a sardine in his corner, felt for the first time that life held something of sunshine.

Raymond Parsloe Devine was plainly shaken, but he made an adroit attempt to recover his lost prestige.

"When I say I have been influenced by Sovietski, I mean, of course, that I was once under his spell. A young writer commits many follies. I have long since passed through that phase. The false glamour of Sovietski has ceased to dazzle me. I now belong whole-heartedly to the school of Nastikoff."

There was a reaction. People nodded at one another sympathetically. After all, we cannot expect old heads on young shoulders, and a lapse at the outset of one's career should not be held against one who has eventually seen the light.

"Nastikoff no good," said Vladimir Brusiloff, coldly. He paused, listening to the machinery.

"Nastikoff worse than Sovietski."

He paused again.

"I spit me of Nastikoff!" he said.

This time there was no doubt about it. The bottom had dropped out of the market, and Raymond Parsloe Devine Preferred were down in the cellar with no takers. It was clear to the entire assembled company that they had been all wrong about Raymond Parsloe Devine. They had allowed him to play on their innocence and sell them a pup. They had taken him at his own valuation, and had been cheated into admiring him as a man who amounted to something, and all the while he had belonged to the school of Nastikoff. You never can tell. Mrs. Smethurst's guests were well-bred, and there was consequently no violent demonstration, but you could see by their faces what they felt. Those nearest Raymond Parsloe jostled to get further away. Mrs. Smethurst eyed him stonily through a raised lorgnette. One or two low hisses were heard, and over at the other end of the room somebody opened the window in a marked manner.

Raymond Parsloe Devine hesitated for a moment, then, realising his situation, turned and slunk to the door. There was an audible sigh of relief as it closed behind him.

Vladimir Brusiloff proceeded to sum up.

"No novelists any good except me. Sovietski–yah! Nastikoff–bah! I spit me of zem all. No novelists anywhere any good except me. P. G. Wodehouse and Tolstoi not bad. Not good, but not bad. No novelists any good except me."

And, having uttered this dictum, he removed a slab of cake from a near-by plate, steered it through the jungle, and began to champ.

It is too much to say that there was a dead silence. There could never be that in any room in which Vladimir Brusiloff was eating cake. But certainly what you might call the general chit-chat was pretty well down and out. Nobody liked to be the first to speak. The members of the Wood Hills Literary Society looked at one another timidly. Cuthbert, for his part, gazed at Adeline; and Adeline gazed into space. It was plain that the girl was deeply stirred. Her eyes were opened wide, a faint flush crimsoned her cheeks, and her breath was coming quickly.

Adeline's mind was in a whirl. She felt as if she had been walking gaily along a pleasant path and had stopped suddenly on the very brink of a precipice. It would be idle to deny that Raymond Parsloe Devine had attracted her extraordinarily. She had taken him at his own valuation as an extremely hot potato, and her hero-worship had gradually been turning into love. And now her hero had been shown to have feet of clay. It was hard, I consider, on Raymond Parsloe Devine, but that is how it goes in this world. You get a following as a celebrity, and then you run up against another bigger celebrity and your admirers desert you. One could moralise on this at considerable length, but better not, perhaps. Enough to say that the glamour of Raymond Devine ceased abruptly in that moment for Adeline, and her most coherent thought at this juncture was the resolve, as soon as she got up to her room, to burn the three signed photographs he had sent her and to give the autographed presentation set of his books to the grocer's boy.

Mrs. Smethurst, meanwhile, having rallied somewhat, was endeavouring to set the feast of reason and flow of soul going again.

"And how do you like England, Mr. Brusiloff?" she asked.

The celebrity paused in the act of lowering another segment of cake.

"Dam good," he replied, cordially.

"I suppose you have travelled all over the country by this time?"

"You said it," agreed the Thinker.

"Have you met many of our great public men?"

"Yais–Yais–Quite a few of the nibs–Lloyid Gorge, I meet him. But——" Beneath the matting a discontented expression came into his face, and his voice took on a peevish note. "But I not meet your *real* great men–your Arbmishel, your Arreevadon–I not meet them. That's what gives me the pipovitch. Have *you* ever met Arbmishel and Arreevadon?"

A strained, anguished look came into Mrs. Smethurst's face and was reflected in the faces of the other members of the circle. The eminent Russian had sprung two entirely new ones on them, and they felt that their ignorance was about to be exposed. What would Vladimir Brusiloff think of the Wood Hills Literary Society? The reputation of the Wood

Hills Literary Society was at stake, trembling in the balance, and coming up for the third time. In dumb agony Mrs. Smethurst rolled her eyes about the room searching for someone capable of coming to the rescue. She drew blank.

And then, from a distant corner, there sounded a deprecating cough, and those nearest Cuthbert Banks saw that he had stopped twisting his right foot round his left ankle and his left foot round his right ankle and was sitting up with a light of almost human intelligence in his eyes.

"Er—" said Cuthbert, blushing as every eye in the room seemed to fix itself on him, "I think he means Abe Mitchell and Harry Vardon."

"Abe Mitchell and Harry Vardon?" repeated Mrs. Smethurst, blankly. "I never heard of—"

"Yais! Yais! Most! Very!" shouted Vladimir Brusiloff, enthusiastically. "Arbmishel and Arreevadon. You know them, yes, what, no, perhaps?"

"I've played with Abe Mitchell often, and I was partnered with Harry Vardon in last year's Open."

The great Russian uttered a cry that shook the chandelier.

"You play in ze Open? Why," he demanded reproachfully of Mrs. Smethurst, "was I not been introducted to this young man who play in opens?"

"Well, really," faltered Mrs. Smethurst. "Well, the fact is, Mr. Brusiloff—"

She broke off. She was unequal to the task of explaining, without hurting anyone's feelings, that she had always regarded Cuthbert as a piece of cheese and a blot on the landscape.

"Introduct me!" thundered the Celebrity.

"Why, certainly, certainly, of course. This is Mr. —." She looked appealingly at Cuthbert.

"Banks," prompted Cuthbert.

"Banks!" cried Vladimir Brusiloff. "Not Cootaboot Banks?"

"*Is* your name Cootaboot?" asked Mrs. Smethurst, faintly.

"Well, it's Cuthbert."

"Yais! Yais! Cootaboot!" There was a rush and swirl, as the effervescent Muscovite burst his way through the throng and rushed to where Cuthbert sat. He stood for a moment eyeing him excitedly, then, stooping swiftly, kissed him on both cheeks before Cuthbert could get his guard up. "My dear young man, I saw you win ze French Open. Great! Great! Grand! Superb! Hot stuff, and you can say I said so! Will you permit one who is but eighteen at Nijni-Novgorod to salute you once more?"

And he kissed Cuthbert again. Then, brushing aside one or two intellectuals who were in the way, he dragged up a chair and sat down.

"You are a great man!" he said.

"Oh, no," said Cuthbert modestly.

"Yais! Great. Most! Very! The way you lay your approach-putts dead from anywhere!"

"Oh, I don't know."

Mr. Brusiloff drew his chair closer.

"Let me tell you one vairy funny story about putting. It was one day I play at Nijni-Novgorod with the pro. against Lenin and Trotsky, and Trotsky had a two-inch putt for the hole. But, just as he addresses the ball, someone in the crowd he tries to assassinate Lenin with a rewolwer —you know that is our great national sport, trying to assassinate Lenin with rewolwers—and the bang puts Trotsky off his stroke and he goes five yards past the hole, and then Lenin, who is rather shaken, you understand, he misses again himself, and we win the hole and match and I clean up three hundred and ninety-six thousand roubles, or fifteen shillings in your money. Some gameovitch! And now let me tell you one other vairy funny story——"

Desultory conversation had begun in murmurs over the rest of the room, as the Wood Hills intellectuals politely endeavoured to conceal the fact that they realised that they were about as much out of it at this reunion of twin souls as cats at a dog-show. From time to time they started as Vladimir Brusiloff's laugh boomed out. Perhaps it was a consolation to them to know that he was enjoying himself.

As for Adeline, how shall I describe her emotions? She was stunned. Before her very eyes the stone which the builders had rejected had become the main thing, the hundred-to-one shot had walked away with the race. A rush of tender admiration for Cuthbert Banks flooded her heart. She saw that she had been all wrong. Cuthbert, whom she had always treated with a patronising superiority, was really a man to be looked up to and worshipped. A deep, dreamy sigh shook Adeline's fragile form.

Half an hour later Vladimir and Cuthbert Banks rose.

"Goot-a-bye, Mrs. Smet-thirst," said the Celebrity. "Zank you for a most charming visit. My friend Cootaboot and me we go now to shoot a few holes. You will lend me clobs, friend Cootaboot?"

"Any you want."

"The niblicksky is what I use most. Goot-a-bye, Mrs. Smet-thirst."

They were moving to the door, when Cuthbert felt a light touch on his arm. Adeline was looking up at him tenderly.

"May I come, too, and walk round with you?"

Cuthbert's bosom heaved.

"Oh," he said, with a tremor in his voice, "that you would walk round with me for life!"

Her eyes met his.

"Perhaps," she whispered, softly, "it could be arranged."

"And so," (concluded the Oldest Member), "you see that golf can be of the greatest practical assistance to a man in Life's struggle. Raymond Parsloe Devine, who was no player, had to move out of the neighbourhood immediately, and is now, I believe, writing scenarios out in California for the Flicker Film Company. Adeline is married to Cuthbert, and it was only his earnest pleading which prevented her from having their eldest son christened Abe Mitchell Ribbed-Faced Mashie Banks, for she is now as keen a devotee of the great game as her husband. Those who know them say that theirs is a union so devoted, so——"

The Sage broke off abruptly, for the young man had rushed to the door and out into the passage. Through the open door he could hear him crying passionately to the waiter to bring back his clubs.

The Legacy **Virginia Woolf**

Virginia Woolf, who was a most industrious worker, wrote many stories which she stored away for later use, intending, no doubt, to revise them. When she died, there was a drawer filled with these manuscripts, and her husband decided that it would be unfair to her devoted admirers and to posterity not to issue a book of the unpublished work. The stories which were thus brought to light were widely praised, particularly *A Haunted House,* which is now ranked with her greatest work. Several of the stories were, in the belief of Mr. Woolf, intended for revision before being published, but he felt they should not be withheld on that account. I, for one, am glad he took this course, for one of the unrevised stories, "The Legacy," seems to me an exceptional piece of work and unneedful of further attention.

"The Legacy" has a semi-political background and deals largely with the change in marital relationships which can be brought about by a husband's absorption in his career. A quiet and thoughtful story, it is nevertheless certain to startle readers by the unexpectedness of the final situation.

THE LEGACY

Virginia Woolf

"For Sissy Miller." Gilbert Clandon, taking up the pearl brooch that lay among a litter of rings and brooches on a little table in his wife's drawing-room, read the inscription: "For Sissy Miller, with my love."

It was like Angela to have remembered even Sissy Miller, her secretary. Yet how strange it was, Gilbert Clandon thought once more, that she had left everything in such order–a little gift of some sort for every one of her friends. It was as if she had foreseen her death. Yet she had been in perfect health when she left the house that morning, six weeks ago; when she stepped off the kerb in Piccadilly and the car had killed her.

He was waiting for Sissy Miller. He had asked her to come; he owed her, he felt, after all the years she had been with them, this token of consideration. Yes, he went on, as he sat there waiting, it was strange that Angela had left everything in such order. Every friend had been left some little token of her affection. Every ring, every necklace, every little Chinese box–she had a passion for little boxes–had a name on it. And each had some memory for him. This he had given her; this–the enamel dolphin with the ruby eyes–she had pounced upon one day in a back street in Venice. He could remember her little cry of delight. To him, of course, she had left nothing in particular, unless it were her diary. Fifteen little volumes, bound in green leather, stood behind him on her writing table. Ever since they were married, she had kept a diary. Some of their very few–he could not call them quarrels, say tiffs–had been about that diary. When he came in and found her writing, she always shut it or put her hand over it. "No, no, no," he could hear her say. "After I'm dead–perhaps." So she had left it him, as her legacy. It was the only thing they had not shared when she was alive. But he had always taken it for granted that she would outlive him. If only she had stopped one moment, and had thought what she was doing, she would be alive now. But she had stepped straight off the kerb, the driver of the car had said at the inquest. She had given him no chance to pull up. . . . Here the sound of voices in the hall interrupted him.

"Miss Miller, Sir," said the maid.

She came in. He had never seen her alone in his life, nor, of course, in tears. She was terribly distressed, and no wonder. Angela had been much more to her than an employer. She had been a friend. To himself, he thought, as he pushed a chair for her and asked her to sit down, she was scarcely distinguishable from any other woman of her kind. There were thousands of Sissy Millers–drab little women in black carrying attaché cases. But Angela, with her genius for sympathy, had discovered all sorts of qualities in Sissy Miller. She was the soul of discretion; so silent; so trustworthy, one could tell her anything, and so on.

Miss Miller could not speak at first. She sat there dabbing her eyes with her pocket handkerchief. Then she made an effort.

"Pardon me, Mr. Clandon," she said.

He murmured. Of course he understood. It was only natural. He could guess what his wife had meant to her.

"I've been so happy here," she said, looking round. Her eyes rested on the writing table behind him. It was here they had worked–she and Angela. For Angela had her share of the duties that fall to the lot of a prominent politician's wife. She had been the greatest help to him in his career. He had often seen her and Sissy sitting at that table–Sissy at the typewriter, taking down letters from her dictation. No doubt Miss Miller was thinking of that, too. Now all he had to do was to give her the brooch his wife had left her. A rather incongruous gift it seemed. It might have been better to have left her a sum of money, or even the typewriter. But there it was–"For Sissy Miller, with my love." And, taking the brooch, he gave it her with the little speech that he had prepared. He knew, he said, that she would value it. His wife had often worn it. . . . And she replied, as she took it almost as if she too had prepared a speech, that it would always be a treasured possession. . . . She had, he supposed, other clothes upon which a pearl brooch would not look quite so incongruous. She was wearing the little black coat and skirt that seemed the uniform of her profession. Then he remembered–she was in mourning, of course. She, too, had had her tragedy–a brother, to whom she was devoted, had died only a week or two before Angela. In some accident was it? He could not remember–only Angela telling him. Angela, with her genius for sympathy, had been terribly upset. Meanwhile Sissy Miller had risen. She was putting on her gloves. Evidently she felt that she ought not to intrude. But he could not let her go without saying something about her future. What were her plans? Was there any way in which he could help her?

She was gazing at the table, where she had sat at her typewriter, where the diary lay. And, lost in her memories of Angela, she did not at once answer his suggestion that he should help her. She seemed for a moment not to understand. So he repeated:

"What are your plans, Miss Miller?"

"My plans? Oh, that's all right, Mr. Clandon," she exclaimed. "Please don't bother yourself about me."

He took her to mean that she was in no need of financial assistance. It would be better, he realized, to make any suggestion of that kind in a letter. All he could do now was to say as he pressed her hand, "Remember, Miss Miller, if there's any way in which I can help you, it will be a pleasure. . . ." Then he opened the door. For a moment, on the threshold, as if a sudden thought had struck her, she stopped.

"Mr. Clandon," she said, looking straight at him for the first time, and for the first time he was struck by the expression, sympathetic yet searching, in her eyes. "If at any time," she continued, "there's anything I can do to help you, remember, I shall feel it, for your wife's sake, a pleasure. . . ."

With that she was gone. Her words and the look that went with them were unexpected. It was almost as if she believed, or hoped, that he would need her. A curious, perhaps a fantastic idea occurred to him as he returned to his chair. Could it be, that during all those years when he had scarcely noticed her, she, as the novelists say, had entertained a passion for him? He caught his own reflection in the glass as he passed. He was over fifty; but he could not help admitting that he was still, as the looking-glass showed him, a very distinguished-looking man.

"Poor Sissy Miller!" he said, half laughing. How he would have liked to share that joke with his wife! He turned instinctively to her diary. "Gilbert," he read, opening it at random, "looked so wonderful. . . ." It was as if she had answered his question. Of course, she seemed to say, you're very attractive to women. Of course Sissy Miller felt that too. He read on. "How proud I am to be his wife!" And he had always been very proud to be her husband. How often, when they dined out somewhere, he had looked at her across the table and said to himself, "She is the loveliest woman here!" He read on. That first year he had been standing for Parliament. They had toured his constituency. "When Gilbert sat down the applause was terrific. The whole audience rose and sang: 'For he's a jolly good fellow.' I was quite overcome." He remembered that, too. She had been sitting on the platform beside him. He could still see the glance she cast at him, and how she had tears in her eyes. And then? He turned the pages. They had gone to Venice. He recalled that happy holiday after the election. "We had ices at Florians." He smiled—she was still such a child; she loved ices. "Gilbert gave me a most interesting account of the history of Venice. He told me that the Doges . . ." she had written it all out in her schoolgirl hand. One of the delights of travelling with Angela had been that she was so eager to learn. She was so terribly ignorant, she used to say, as if that were not one of her charms. And then–he opened the next volume–they had come back to London. "I was so anxious to make a good impression. I wore my wedding dress." He could see her now sitting next old Sir Edward; and making a conquest of that formidable old man, his chief. He read on rapidly, filling in scene after scene from her scrappy fragments. "Dined at the House of Commons. . . . To an evening party at the Lovegroves'. Did I realize my responsibility, Lady L. asked me, as Gilbert's wife?" Then, as the years passed–he took another volume from the writing table–he had become more and more absorbed in his work. And she, of course, was more often home. . . . It had been a great grief to her, apparently, that they had had no children. "How I wish," one entry read, "that Gilbert had a son!" Oddly enough he had never much regretted that himself. Life had been so full, so rich as it was. That year he had been given a minor post in the government. A minor post only, but her comment was: "I am quite certain now that he will be Prime Minister!" Well, if things had gone differently, it might have been so. He paused here to speculate upon what might have been. Politics was a gamble, he reflected; but the game wasn't over yet. Not at fifty. He cast his eyes rapidly over more pages, full of the little trifles, the insignificant, happy, daily trifles that had made up her life.

He took up another volume and opened it at random. "What a coward I am! I let the chance slip again. But it seemed selfish to bother him with my own affairs, when he had so much to think about. And we so seldom have an evening alone." What was the meaning of that? Oh, here was the explanation–it referred to her work in the East End. "I plucked up courage and talked to Gilbert at last. He was so kind, so good. He made no objection." He remembered that conversation. She had told him that she felt so idle, so useless. She wished to have some work of her own. She wanted to do something–she had blushed so prettily, he remembered, as she said it, sitting in that very chair–to help others. He had bantered her a little. Hadn't she enough to do looking after him, after her home? Still, if it amused her, of course he had no objection. What was it? Some district? Some committee? Only she must promise not to make herself ill. So it seemed that every Wednesday she went to Whitechapel. He remembered how he hated the clothes she wore on those occasions. But she had taken it very seriously, it seemed. The diary was full of references like this: "Saw Mrs. Jones. . . . She has ten children. . . .

Husband lost his arm in an accident. . . . Did my best to find a job for Lily." He skipped on. His own name occurred less frequently. His interest slackened. Some of the entries conveyed nothing to him. For example: "Had a heated argument about socialism with B. M." Who was B. M.? He could not fill in the initials; some woman, he supposed, that she had met on one of her committees. "B. M. made a violent attack upon the upper classes. . . . I walked back after the meeting with B. M. and tried to convince him. But he is so narrow-minded." So B. M. was a man–no doubt one of those "intellectuals," as they call themselves, who are so violent, as Angela said, and so narrow-minded. She had invited him to come and see her apparently. "B. M. came to dinner. He shook hands with Minnie!" That note of exclamation gave another twist to his mental picture. B. M., it seemed, wasn't used to parlourmaids; he had shaken hands with Minnie. Presumably he was one of those tame working men who air their views in ladies' drawing-rooms. Gilbert knew the type, and had no liking for this particular specimen, whoever B. M. might be. Here he was again. "Went with B. M. to the Tower of London. . . . He said revolution is bound to come. . . . He said we live in a Fool's Paradise." That was just the kind of thing B. M. would say–Gilbert could hear him. He could also see him quite distinctly–a stubby little man, with a rough beard, red tie, dressed as they always did in tweeds, who had never done an honest day's work in his life. Surely Angela had the sense to see through him? He read on. "B. M. said some very disagreeable things about ——." The name was carefully scratched out. "I told him I would not listen to any more abuse of ——" Again the name was obliterated. Could it have been his own name? Was that why Angela covered the page so quickly when he came in? The thought added to his growing dislike of B. M. He had had the impertinence to discuss him in this very room. Why had Angela never told him? It was very unlike her to conceal anything; she had been the soul of candour. He turned the pages, picking out every reference to B. M. "B. M. told me the story of his childhood. His mother went out charring. . . . When I think of it, I can hardly bear to go on living in such luxury. . . . Three guineas for one hat!" If only she had discussed the matter with him, instead of puzzling her poor little head about questions that were much too difficult for her to understand! He had lent her books. *Karl Marx, The Coming Revolution.* The initials B. M., B. M., B. M., recurred repeatedly. But why never the full name? There was an informality, an intimacy in the use of initials that was very unlike Angela. Had she called him B. M. to his face? He read on. "B. M. came unexpectedly after dinner. Luckily, I was alone." That was only a year ago. "Luckily"–why luckily?–"I was alone." Where had he been that night? He checked the date in his engagement book. It had been the night of the Mansion House dinner. And B. M. and Angela had spent the evening alone! He tried to recall that evening. Was she waiting up for him when he came back? Had the room looked just as usual? Were there glasses on the table? Were the chairs drawn close together? He could remember nothing—nothing whatever, nothing except his own speech at the Mansion House dinner. It became more and more inexplicable to him—the whole situation: his wife receiving an unknown man alone. Perhaps the next volume would explain. Hastily he reached for the last of the diaries—the one she had left unfinished when she died. There, on the very first page, was that cursed fellow again. "Dined alone with B. M. . . . He became very agitated. He said it was time we understood each other. . . . I tried to make him listen. But he would not. He threatened that if I did not . . ." the rest of the page was scored over. She had written "Egypt. Egypt. Egypt," over the whole page. He could not make out a single word; but there could be only one interpretation: the scoundrel had asked her to become his mistress. Alone in his room! The blood rushed to Gilbert Clandon's face. He turned the pages rapidly. What had been her answer? Initials had ceased. It was simply "he" now. "He came again. I told him I could not come to any decision. . . . I implored him to leave me." He had forced himself upon her in this very house. But why hadn't she told him? How could she have hesitated for an instant? Then: "I wrote him a letter." Then pages were left blank. Then there was this: "No answer to my letter." Then more blank pages; and then this: "He has done what he threatened." After that—what came after that? He turned page after page. All were blank. But there, on the very day before her death, was this entry: "Have I the courage to do it too?" That was the end.

Gilbert Clandon let the book slide to the floor. He could see her in front of him. She was standing on the kerb in Piccadilly. Her eyes stared; her fists were clenched. Here came the car. . . .

He could not bear it. He must know the truth. He strode to the telephone.

"Miss Miller!" There was silence. Then he heard someone moving in the room.

"Sissy Miller speaking"—her voice at last answered him.

"Who," he thundered, "is B. M.?"

He could hear the cheap clock ticking on her mantelpiece; then a long drawn sigh. Then at last she said:

"He was my brother."

He *was* her brother; her brother who had killed himself. "Is there," he heard Sissy Miller asking, "anything that I can explain?"

"Nothing!" he cried. "Nothing!"

He had received his legacy. She had told him the truth. She had stepped off the kerb to rejoin her lover. She had stepped off the kerb to escape from him.